NATIONAL GALLERY CATALOGUES

THE BRITISH SCHOOL

NATIONAL GALLERY CATALOGUES

THE BRITISH SCHOOL

Judy Egerton

National Gallery Publications, London

Distributed by Yale University Press

To Michael Levey and Martin Wyld
my past and present luminaries in Trafalgar Square

First published in Great Britain in 1998 by
National Gallery Publications Limited
5/6 Pall Mall East, London SW1Y 5BA

ISBN 1 85709 170 1 hardback

525264

British Library Cataloguing-in-Publication Data.
A catalogue record is available from the British Library.

Library of Congress Catalog Card Number: 97-76288

Edited by Diana Davies
Designed by Gillian Greenwood
Typeset by Helen Robertson

Printed and bound in Italy by Grafiche Milani

Frontispiece: J.M.W. Turner, *Rain, Steam, and Speed* (detail)

Contents

Sponsor's Preface

The National Gallery's collection of works by artists of the British School includes some of the greatest achievements of painters whose names are high in the nation's role of honour, including Constable, Gainsborough, Lawrence, Reynolds, Stubbs, Turner and Wright of Derby. The last catalogue of the National Gallery's British School, published in 1959, was not illustrated and has long been out of print. The Gallery has now produced a fully illustrated catalogue of its current representation of the British School.

The British Land Company PLC is sponsoring this new catalogue as part of its long-term support for the work of British artists, and it is a happy coincidence for us that it has been compiled by Judy Egerton, who was responsible for the *Wright of Derby* exhibition of 1990, sponsored by British Land.

British Land is one of the oldest of Britain's property companies, having been founded in 1856. Our sponsorship of National Gallery projects began in 1997, when the Company sponsored the *Young Gainsborough* exhibition. We support the National Gallery's aims of long-term care and custodianship of resources, a discerning policy on new acquisitions, the constant process of restoration and refurbishment, and the desire to make the best use of assets held. In our own sphere our business strives to attain similar objectives.

John Ritblat, CHAIRMAN

Foreword

The first in an entirely new series of detailed and fully illustrated catalogues of the National Gallery's different schools of painting, the British School catalogue is itself a challenge to Roger Fry's assertion, in a famous lecture in 1934, that 'ours is a minor school'. In the context of the National Gallery, the British School is, in numerical terms, smaller than the German or the Early Netherlandish. Yet the quality of the paintings is exceptionally high, and they play in every sense a major part in the story of European painting as it is told in Trafalgar Square. In the present arrangement of the Gallery, for example, the visitor moving from eighteenth- to nineteenth-century France passes the Constables that so marked Delacroix, and the Turners which Monet saw in the National Gallery in 1870 and without which much of his later work would have been unthinkable. The British chapter is clearly an integral part of the European story.

This would surely have surprised the great Victorian scholar of British painting, Richard Redgrave, who was convinced that, whatever its inherent merits, English art could hardly hope to have any impact on artists from other traditions.

Since the opening of the Tate Gallery in 1897, when the bulk of the British pictures was removed to Millbank, works have moved to and fro between the two galleries, making the British presence in Trafalgar Square a fluctuating feast. In the years since the last catalogue (first edition 1946) – in which Holbein still figured as a sort of honorary British national – important works have been transferred and a number of key acquisitions made. A full discussion of the National Gallery's collection with its current cast list, and taking account of the extensive recent scholarship, is therefore doubly welcome.

The 1946 catalogue, compiled by Martin Davies, is part of the series he produced after the Second World War which set new standards of scholarly rigour and scrupulous observation. They form one of the proudest traditions of the National Gallery, a tradition which we believe the present catalogue continues and develops. We are fortunate that Judy Egerton, after retiring from the Tate Gallery, was willing to take on the task and she has accomplished it with verve, style and erudition: this is scholarship to be read, nor merely referred to. We are much in her debt.

We have been able to produce the catalogue in this form thanks to the support of John Ritblat who has, by numerous acts of philanthropy, allowed many people in this country to enjoy their patrimony. We hope this catalogue will do the same and will reach a wide audience. We thank him and The British Land Company for their generosity.

Neil MacGregor, DIRECTOR

Acknowledgements

In the Director's Foreword, Neil MacGregor justly expresses the National Gallery's thanks to John Ritblat and the British Land Company for sponsoring the publication of this catalogue. My own gratitude to John Ritblat is more personal, dating from his sponsorship of my *Wright of Derby* exhibition at the Tate Gallery in 1990; and like many other members of the London Library, I almost daily bless his name for literally casting light (without blazon of logo) on the central area of its indexes and issue desk.

I am grateful to Neil MacGregor for inviting me, on my retirement from the Tate Gallery, to compile this catalogue of the National Gallery's British Collection. In this task, my principal ally has been Martin Wyld, Chief Restorer, with whom I have examined every painting. More indirectly, I owe much to the inspiration of Sir Michael Levey, Director of the National Gallery 1973–86. I did not serve under him; but for me, his various writings (including the occasional piquant postcard) have been truly luminous, in the sense of lighting a way which one might hope to tread. While best known for his publications on Italian artists – above all, for *Tiepolo* (1986) – Levey's sensibilities have never been confined by the boundaries of 'Schools'. In this catalogue, I have drawn deeply on two essays on Gainsborough and Lawrence, each published to accompany National Gallery exhibitions: *The Painter's Daughters chasing a Butterfly* (1975) and *A Royal Subject: Portraits of Queen Charlotte* (1977); but the debt extends to *Sir Thomas Lawrence*, Levey's catalogue of a brilliant exhibition at the National Portrait Gallery, 1980.

Among numerous scholars to whom I am indebted, I am particularly grateful to Graham Reynolds for reading and making helpful comments on all my Constable entries, and to Hugh Belsey for similar help over all the Gainsborough entries; but they are of course not responsible for any vagaries in them.

I am abidingly grateful for being allowed regularly to work in four institutions whose resources are invaluable for the study of British Art: The Paul Mellon Centre for Studies in British Art, under the benign directorship of Brian Allen; the National Portrait Gallery Library and Archives; the Royal Academy Library, where I am particularly indebted to Nick Savage and Helen Valentine; and the Clore Gallery Study Room, Tate Gallery, whose curator David Blayney Brown and his assistants Sarah Taft and Andrew Loukes have been unfailingly helpful.

Many others have kindly helped over specific points: this generous company includes Julian Agnew; Fred Bachrach; Sven Bruntjen; Duncan Bull; Patsy Byrne; Fabia Claris; Stephen Coppel; Tim Clayton; John S. Creasey; Aileen Dawson; William Drummond; Andrew Edmunds; Sir Brinsley Ford; David Fraser; Peter Funnell; Kenneth Garlick; John Gage; Eileen Harris; John Harris; John Hayes; Abigail Holmes; John Ingamells; Raymond Jannetta; Alex Kidson; Richard and Christopher Kingzett, Alastair Laing; David Landau; Adam Lawrence; Deborah Lee; Sir Mark Lennox-Boyd; John Leopold; Jonathan Mason; Christopher Mendez; Frances Mount; Sheila O'Connell; Jeremy Rex-Parkes; Marcia Pointon; Aileen Ribeiro; Michael Rosenthal; Martin Royalton-Kisch; Francis Russell; Edward Saunders; William Schupbach; Jacob Simon; Kim Sloan; Susan Sloman; Robert Snell; John Sunderland; Catherine Whistler; John Human Wilson; Andrew Wilton and Andrew Wyld. Acknowledgment is made throughout the catalogue to many others, including county archivists and keepers of muniments.

Within the National Gallery, it is not the custom to thank individual members of staff for helping in ways which are deemed to be part of their normal duties. I must therefore forgo the pleasure of thanking by name all those, particularly in the Library, the Archives, the Photographic Department and the Registry, who have helped me.

For the preparation of the book for publication, my thanks are offered to Gillian Greenwood, designer of this and forthcoming National Gallery Schools catalogues; Diana Davies, the editor; Sue Curnow, production manager; and Felicity Luard, publisher.

Introduction

In 1824, when the National Gallery opened its doors – a traditional phrase, though in fact all that was opened in 1824 was the single modest front door of John Julius Angerstein's former town house in Pall Mall, depicted on p. 363 – no official statement was made concerning the Gallery's present or future aims; indeed, those aims were not succinctly defined until the National Gallery Report of 1994–5. It was left to popular publications such as *Half Holidays at the National Gallery* (published in 1902 by the *Pall Mall Gazette* as an 'Extra', price sixpence) to sum them up as '(1) to form as complete an historical collection as possible; and (2) to admit none but the best specimens'.

From the start, it was accepted that, ideally, the National Gallery should represent the 'best specimens' of the British School, as well as those of the Italian, French, Flemish, Dutch, Spanish and other continental schools of painting. But in practice, the British collection grew more haphazardly and far more rapidly than those of the foreign schools, with gifts and bequests greatly outnumbering carefully chosen purchases. By 1897 it amounted to over 500 works, or one-third of the National Gallery's entire collection; but by then Providence, in the guise of 'Mr Tate of Streatham', was doing his best to come to the rescue.

The establishment of the Tate Gallery in 1897 as the National Gallery of British Art, under government aegis and with Sir Henry Tate's gift of 67 paintings and three bronzes as its nucleus, enabled the National Gallery to play a large role in building up the new collection by gradually transferring large numbers of British paintings (and almost all its sculpture) from its own overcrowded building in Trafalgar Square to the Tate Gallery's initially more spacious home on Millbank. At first the Tate Gallery was a daughter institution of the National Gallery, ownership of all its pictures being vested in the Trustees of the National Gallery. Not until an Act of 1954 did the Tate Gallery become completely independent of the National Gallery. That Act, paradoxically, came into operation on St Valentine's Day 1955.

The development of the National Gallery as a whole lies beyond the scope of this Introduction. All that will be attempted here is a brief account of some significant stages in the history of its collection of British pictures, geared as much as possible to those 61 British works which today (in 1998) remain in the National Gallery's collection, and which include portraits of men who helped to shape the Gallery's history. In the catalogue entries which follow, these subjects are all dignified by their NG (for National Gallery) inventory numbers; when first mentioned here, they are more simply indicated by an asterisk. Other works mentioned here have of course remained in the national collection (it would need an Act of Parliament to eject them), but are now in the Tate Gallery.

The growth of the collection

The National Gallery's founding collection – 38 paintings purchased by the government from the late *John Julius Angerstein's collection in 1824 – included nine British paintings: William Hogarth's *Self Portrait with a Pug*, his six paintings of **Marriage A-la-Mode*, Reynolds's **Lord Heathfield* and Wilkie's *A Village Holiday* (three large, highly imaginative paintings by Henry Fuseli RA, bought by Angerstein from the artist, were silently ignored). The promised gift of sixteen paintings with which *Sir George Beaumont had spurred the government on to action in 1824 ('Buy Angerstein's pictures, and I will give you mine!') included four British paintings: Richard Wilson's *Distant View of Mæcenas' Villa, Tivoli* and *The Destruction of the Children of Niobe*, Benjamin West's *Pylades and Orestes brought as Victims before Iphigenia* and Wilkie's *The Blind Fiddler*. These duly entered the nation's collection in 1828. In the previous year, *Charles Long, Lord Farnborough, a founder-Trustee, had presented the National Gallery with its first Gainsborough, **The Market Cart*; and in 1830 the Governors of the British Institution presented a second Gainsborough, **The Watering Place*.

Acceptance of such works, by generally acknowledged masters, guaranteed the British School an honourable place in the National Gallery, but inspired little immediate effort to make it more representative. For many years, works by Hogarth, Reynolds, Gainsborough and Wilkie, mostly presented or bequeathed, dominated the collection. Nothing by any of Hogarth's British predecessors was acquired until William Dobson's *Portrait of Endymion Porter* was purchased in 1888. Reynolds, and the Grand Manner of portraiture which he demonstrated (though not imperishably), cast a long and perhaps still lingering shadow over the Gallery's representation of British art. Compared with portraiture, landscape paintings gained ground only slowly. The concerted success of a group of John Constable's friends and admirers in buying **The Cornfield* and presenting it to the National Gallery at the end of 1837 deserves applause; the Gallery acquired nothing by Constable during his lifetime.

No purchases of British pictures were made before 1862. The home-grown product has rarely been the chief preoccupation of any of the National Gallery's Directors or Trustees, and certainly their early energies were concentrated, wisely, on acquiring 'foreign' works. Sir Charles Eastlake, Keeper 1843–7 and Director 1854–65, made conspicuously brilliant purchases of Italian, French, Flemish and Spanish pictures; but although he was himself a 'British artist' (combining the role of Director of the National Gallery with that of President of the Royal Academy), he bought no British pictures for the Gallery until, during his last three years, he purchased six: three portraits (Reynolds's **Captain*

Orme and Gainsborough's **Mrs Siddons* and **Dr Ralph Schomberg*) and three more diverse works: James Ward's large *Landscape with Cattle*, John Crome's *Mousehold Heath, Norwich* and John Singleton Copley's *Death of Major Peirson*. But Eastlake's reluctance to buy British pictures probably chiefly reflects the fact that while he was in office, the National Gallery received a large gift of British works from the collector Robert Vernon, and an even larger number of works from the estate of J.M.W. Turner.

The Vernon Gift in 1847 and the Turner Bequest in 1856 together quadrupled the Gallery's holdings of British pictures within a single decade. Robert Vernon's gift of 157 British paintings and seven sculptures, mostly by living or recently deceased artists, introduced the National Gallery overnight to the work of modern British artists such as Callcott, Egg, Etty, Herring, Landseer, C.R. Leslie and Mulready; and it included two paintings by Eastlake himself: a biblical subject, *Christ lamenting over Jerusalem*, and a romantic history painting, *The Escape of Francesco Novello di Carrara, with his Wife, from the Duke of Milan*.

The Vernon Gift also included the first two paintings by J.M.W. Turner to enter the Gallery. Turner's intention to reserve many of his pictures as a bequest to the nation was fairly well known; perhaps primarily for that reason, the Gallery had made no effort to acquire his works during his lifetime. On his death in December 1851, Turner's will was contested by his relatives, lengthy litigation being finally resolved in 1856 by a decree of the Court of Chancery whereby the nation (in effect the National Gallery) was deemed to be the heir of all paintings and drawings by Turner, whether finished or unfinished, which remained with him at his death. The re-shaping of Turner's will into 'The Turner Bequest' is a complex matter; here it must suffice to say that the result was that approximately 100 'finished pictures', 182 'unfinished pictures' and 19,049 'drawings and sketches in colour and in pencil' formally entered the National Gallery's custodianship in September 1856. But many of Turner's oils remained uninventoried (and therefore uncatalogued and unhung) for decades, either because (like **The Evening Star* and **Margate (?), from the Sea*) they were considered too unfinished for display or because they needed restoration; only 79 of Turner's oils (and none of his drawings and watercolours) were included in the National Gallery's British School catalogue of 1895.

Even before the arrival of the Turner Bequest, the entire National Gallery was short of space. It had moved in 1838 from a town house in Pall Mall into William Wilkins's new building in Trafalgar Square; but half of that building – the east wing – was occupied by the Royal Academy, until its move in 1869 to Burlington House. Confronted with the Vernon Gift and, hard on its heels, the Turner Bequest, the National Gallery had little choice but to resort to ad hoc or out-house solutions. By arrangement with the Treasury (under whose direct control the National Gallery remained until 1965), the Vernon pictures were displayed in Marlborough House, in upstairs rooms which became popularly known as the Vernon Gallery; those of Turner's pictures which were ready for display joined them there. When the Marlborough House rooms were needed again by royalty, the Vernon pictures and the Turners were despatched to the South Kensington Museum, established in 1852 (and later renamed the Victoria and Albert Museum), where, according to *The Times*, they hung 'in long, cheerless corridors'. In September 1861 the National Gallery Trustees belatedly realised that Turner's will stipulated that acceptance of his pictures was conditional on the creation of a gallery for them within ten years of the date of his death; hastily, the Turners were returned to Trafalgar Square, where space designated The Turner Gallery was cleared (but not created) for them.

Although portraiture continued to dominate the Gallery's collection, the Vernon Gift had introduced many other aspects of British art, thus widening the doors to the acceptance (and more occasionally the purchase) of landscapes, history paintings, literary subjects and even animal paintings. Here only a few of the diverse works which once hung in the National Gallery in the company of Reynolds and Gainsborough can be instanced. Frith's *The Derby Day*, the sensation of the Royal Academy exhibition of 1858, was bequeathed by its short-lived purchaser to the Gallery the following year. Joseph Wright of Derby's **Experiment on a Bird in the Air Pump* was accepted as a gift in 1863. *William Boxall RA, Eastlake's successor as Director (1866–74), bought John Martin's spectacular *Destruction of Pompeii and Herculaneum* in 1869 (fifteen years after the artist's death); but it hung only briefly in the National Gallery, before being despatched on long loan to Manchester City Art Gallery (and thence, in due course, to the Tate). Boxall, always sympathetic to 'the work of an original mind', also wanted to buy William Blake's tempera painting *The Spiritual Form of Pitt guiding Behemoth* when the ageing Samuel Palmer offered it to the National Gallery, but was not supported either by his Trustees or by the Treasury (it was eventually acquired, more cheaply, from Palmer's executors in 1882). Henry Fuseli RA, rejected in the Gallery's founding purchase of 1824, made his first appearance in the national collection in 1887, when his eerily erotic *Titania and Bottom* was accepted as a gift. The Gallery's purchase in 1878 of James Ward's *Gordale Scar* concealed some embarrassment, since half a century earlier the Gallery could have had it as a gift. The vast (333 × 422 cm) canvas, painted in 1811 for the 2nd Lord Ribblesdale, proved too large for him to hang at Gisburn Park, and, with Ward's approval, he offered to present it to the projected National Gallery, as soon as it was established and had room for it. Rolled up, it was duly despatched to the British Museum, whose Trustees acted for the National Gallery in its infancy, and whose storerooms served it as a repository. There it remained (to Ward's anguish), in limbo and still rolled up, until 1857, when it was returned to Gisburn Park. When, in 1878, the Trustees wrote to (by now the 4th) *Lord Ribblesdale hoping to take up the offer of *Gordale Scar*, Ribblesdale replied entirely truthfully that he could not afford to present it (see p. 236), but would sell it to the Gallery. Frederic Burton RA, Director from 1874 to 1894, bought (among other things) William Dyce's *Pegwell Bay* and Rossetti's *Ecce Ancilla Domini*, the Gallery's first purchase (in 1886, four years after the artist's death) of any Pre-Raphaelite work.

The Vernon Gift had brought works by contemporaries into the national collection. While not without precedent (Wilkie, after all, was and continued until 1841 to be 'living' when paintings by him were presented to the Gallery in its early years), this seemed from 1847 to open the door to contemporary artists eager for a place in the national Valhalla. Many offered their works; too many of them were chosen. It should be noted here that for most of this period, the National Gallery's entire curatorial staff consisted of the Director and one assistant; it is not surprising that mistakes were occasionally made through insufficient examination of the quality, condition or even title to ownership of pictures presented or bequeathed (for two instances of contretemps over ownership, see Reynolds, **Lady Cockburn and her Three Eldest Sons* and Gainsborough, *Dr Ralph Schomberg*). Without a definition of the ideal scope of the Gallery's British School, it grew incoherently as well as rapidly. It was well into the twentieth century before the cautious (but hardly definitive) phrase 'works which have stood the test of time' was devised as a qualification for the acceptance of unsolicited offers of pictures.

Intermittently, but for over half a century, the lack of adequate space for the display of British art provoked public comment. 'Shall we long continue to brave the contempt of every enlightened foreigner who visits the metropolis, by the indifference England shows in the matter of her works of Art?' Thus the *Art-Journal* rhetorically enquired in 1857, when the first pictures from the nation's 'magnificent heritage' from Turner were displayed in the upper rooms of Marlborough House; and it continued: 'With possessions worthy of a great and enlightened nation, we hide them in holes and corners, not as a miser hoards his gold, to keep it safely, but as if we were half ashamed of what we hold.'

Despite increasing public pressure for a gallery devoted to British art, it had become clear by 1890 that the government was not going to finance such a thing. It was left to a private individual – a business-man who, having made his money out of sugar, chose to spend a great deal of it on works of art by contemporary British artists – to evolve a practical proposition. The name of 'Mr Tate of Streatham' began to appear regularly in the newspapers. In March 1890 Henry Tate offered to present about sixty modern English pictures from his collection to the National Gallery, on condition that they were displayed there in a room bearing his name. The National Gallery declined this offer, but supported a new proposition which Tate made to the Treasury: if it would provide a site for a new gallery for British art, he would finance its construction, as well as presenting it with his pictures. 'Everyone agrees... that we ought to have such a gallery', declared *The Times* on 23 June 1890: not quite true, but complications in the story are omitted here. A site was found on Millbank; building began. The new gallery was formally opened on 21 July 1897 by the Prince of Wales (later King Edward VII), to whom Henry Tate handed the deeds of gift. Thus the new gallery became the property of the nation, while Henry Tate became a baronet (and, in order to represent the Tate Gallery's interests, a Trustee of the National Gallery).

Officially, the new gallery was named the National Gallery of British Art, Millbank, but it soon became known as the Tate Gallery (or, more popularly, as the Tate). Its establishment under the control of the National Gallery's Trustees presented them with the need to make numerous decisions (though, as will be seen, few irreversible ones). The first decision involved the principles on which approximately one hundred paintings should be selected from the collection at Trafalgar Square for immediate transfer to Millbank, there to join the Tate's founding collection of works in Sir Henry Tate's gift (to these were added eighteen paintings by G.F. Watts, presented by the artist, and a group of works purchased under the terms of the Chantrey Bequest, arbitrarily transferred by the Treasury from the Victoria and Albert Museum to Millbank, making a total of 279 works when the Tate Gallery opened).

Recognising 'the great difficulty of making a selection which will be accepted as consistent and logical', the National Gallery's Trustees postulated, in a memorandum of 4 May 1897, three principles to guide the selection of works for transfer:

1. That we should so far as possible avoid denuding the walls of the Trafalgar Square Gallery of the masterpieces which have until now hung there.
2. That only the pictures which belong clearly to the British modern school should be removed.
3. That we should endeavour to avoid a selection, which upon the face of it, bears the appearance of having been dictated by a desire to send only inferior works of art to the new Gallery.

If this can be summed up as a policy of retaining 'masterpieces' in Trafalgar Square, transferring only 'the British modern school' to Millbank and avoiding the appearance of consigning 'inferior works' to the new gallery, then it is a policy whose first point was and continued to be upheld, but whose second and third points were and continued to be interpreted pragmatically.

The 'modern' school was at first deemed to consist of works by artists born after 1790, this date later being brought forward to 1800. The majority of the first 96 pictures to be transferred were by nineteenth-century artists, and had entered the National Gallery as part of the Vernon Gift. In the selection from outside the Vernon Gift, Dyce's *Pegwell Bay*, Rossetti's *Ecce Ancilla Domini* and Frith's *The Derby Day* were among the best things to be sent in 1897 (but *The Derby Day* was recalled to Trafalgar Square in 1919, remaining there until 1951). Breaking its own rule (2, in the statement above), the National Gallery included six paintings by Constable (born in 1776) among its first 96 transfers; but here pragmatism worked to the Tate Gallery's advantage. Thanks to generous gifts and bequests, including those from Constable's daughter Isabel in 1887–8, the National Gallery's collection included sixteen works by Constable by 1897; therefore its

Trustees, 'wishing to assist the Millbank Gallery' and believing that 'the loss of a few of his works would not be felt', concluded that there was 'no reason why it [the Tate] should not be allowed to have a certain number of Constables' (but they retained one of the finest, *The Valley Farm* from the Vernon Gift, until 1919). Thus the Tate's Constable collection, now one of its chief glories, was begun. The Trustees also decided that since they were 'rich in Wilkies', four of these might be added to the first transfer of pictures.

Sooner or later, the remaining Vernon Gift pictures were transferred to the Tate; but given the National Gallery's awareness that certain of its Victorian pictures had become highly popular, some were transferred later than others, Landseer's *Dignity and Impudence* for instance being retained at Trafalgar Square until 1929. The National Gallery chose to retain a representative group of works by Turner, but agreed that all other paintings in the Turner Bequest (and all the watercolours and drawings) should gradually be transferred to the Tate, where Sir Joseph Duveen's donation of a Turner Wing, completed in 1910, had added worthy space; but the transfer of Turner oils necessarily took time, since many still awaited restoration, and about a dozen others (including **The Parting of Hero and Leander*) were on long loan to provincial galleries.

As the Tate's collection grew, its need for adequate representation of other artists 'born before 1790' became evident. So there began a long process by which the national collection of works by such artists as Hogarth, Reynolds, Gainsborough, Constable, Wilson and Zoffany was divided between the two galleries, while the National Gallery's entire holdings of the works of many artists – among them Cotman, Crome, Fuseli, Hoppner, Morland, Opie, Raeburn, Romney, Ward and even Wilkie, the National Gallery's early favourite – left Trafalgar Square, seemingly forever.

From the start, the National Gallery, long hard-pressed for space, was relieved that its ranks of British artists had been decently thinned, declaring in its 1897 Report that the transfer to the Tate now made it possible to hang all its remaining British pictures in Trafalgar Square 'without crowding ... and to better advantage than before'.

The collection in Trafalgar Square decreases in size

In 1911, a committee of the Trustees of the National Gallery under the chairmanship of Lord Curzon endorsed Sir Henry Tate's aim that the Tate Gallery should be 'a National Gallery of British art in all its branches', but got no further to defining the scope of their own British collection than reiterating the point made by their predecessors in 1897 – that great masterpieces should continue to be hung at the National Gallery. In their Report, published in 1915, they made the following prediction:

> A time will gradually come ... when London will be recognized as possessing two National Galleries of the first class, instead of one. In Trafalgar Square will always be visible the supreme glories of British painting, alongside of their fellows, but to Millbank the student will go who desires to follow the history and evolution of indigenous art.

For the National Gallery, transfers to the Tate over the following decades provided what its 1938–45 Report called 'a welcome opportunity to revise the representation of the British School' (though some critics called it weeding). As time went on, both galleries made acquisitions independently of each other; but apart from the notion of retaining 'masterpieces', the National Gallery remained reluctant to define or limit the ideal scope of its own British collection, admitting (in a Memorandum of 1983, referred to later) the 'lack of an entirely consistent attitude to representation of the School'.

To decide that 'the supreme glories of British painting' should always be displayed in Trafalgar Square was, from the date of the Curzon Committee Report of 1915 onwards, a good deal easier than identifying the 'supreme' in a large and miscellaneous collection. It was easier to decide – at least in principle – what should be transferred to the Tate than what should be kept in Trafalgar Square.

Transfers of British pictures to the Tate, begun in 1897, continued, in varying numbers and at a varying pace, for most of this century. There were particularly large transfers in 1919 and 1929, and in 1954, at the time of the Act which separated the two galleries. On the whole, the National Gallery's transfer of works to the Tate was made in the spirit of a kindly parent endowing a daughter with good things, though there was a certain amount of attic-clearing from Trafalgar Square, particularly of large works. James Ward's vast *Gordale Scar* was an early transfer, in 1907, accompanied by his almost equally large *Landscape with Cattle*. John Martin's *Destruction of Pompeii and Herculaneum*, Boxall's purchase in 1869, was transferred in 1918 (but was destroyed in the Thames flood of 1928). Still more illogical (and less creditable) was the National Gallery's transfer to the Tate in 1900 of fifteen or so 'modern foreign' works previously (for 'convenience') attached to its own British collection. This caused a small furore. 'What have Horace Vernet and Ary Scheffer to do in a National Gallery of British Art?' demanded the *Daily Graphic* on 5 September 1903, asking the same question about Bonvin, Costa, Fantin-Latour and Rosa Bonheur. The Tate itself did not want the 'modern foreign' pictures, and in time returned them. From this group, Delaroche's *Execution of Lady Jane Grey*, exhibited at the Royal Academy in 1838, and thought to have been irredeemably ruined in the Thames flood of 1928, made its way back to Trafalgar Square where, fully restored (but now part of the French School), it enjoys immense popularity.

Certain realms of subject matter, especially subjects drawn from history, literature and imagination – Copley's *Death of Major Peirson* and Fuseli's *Titania and Bottom*, for instance, and all works by Blake – were perceived as the province of the Tate rather than the National Gallery. Such transfers, leaving portraiture to predominate in the National Gallery, would not have surprised Fuseli himself. Ruminating on the Englishman's taste in art (after a game of whist at Farington's house, 24 July 1805), he expressed 'little hope of Poetical Painting finding encouragement in England. Portrait with them is everything. Their taste & feelings all go to realities, – The ideal does not operate on their minds. Historical painting, viz: matter of fact, they may encourage.' Today, 'historical painting' can be said to be represented in the National Gallery's British Collection only by Turner, in such works as **Dido building Carthage* and **The Fighting Temeraire*, though these, thankfully, are hardly of a 'matter of fact' nature.

Few discussions over which pictures should be transferred were minuted; but probably some balance between the Tate's needs and the National Gallery's instinct for which pictures were appropriate to Trafalgar Square was kept in mind. The sense in which the word 'transfer' was used was never defined. In practice, 'transferring' did not signify transfer of ownership, but merely the physical to-ing and fro-ing of pictures (in some cases, back and forth several times) between the two galleries. The National Gallery frequently had second thoughts and, as the senior partner in the relationship, generally prevailed. By 1950, for instance, it regretted having transferred (in 1919, from its own founding collection) Hogarth's six paintings of *Marriage A-la-Mode*, and secured their return; but in their place, it sent to the Tate Hogarth's *Self Portrait with a Pug*, followed by *The Heads of Six of Hogarth's Servants*, two 'masterpieces' which remain there. In 1919, the National Gallery had reserved the right to reclaim pictures which had been 'transferred' to the Tate; but any legal right to do so ceased with the 1954 Act which separated the two institutions. The National Gallery's request in 1983 for the return to Trafalgar Square of four highly important paintings – Hogarth's **The Graham Children*, Wright of Derby's *An Experiment on a Bird in the Air Pump*, Gainsborough's *The Market Cart*, and Sargent's **Lord Ribblesdale* – was agreed by the Tate, but reluctantly, since each of the four pictures (hanging in the National Gallery by 1986) was a keenly felt loss to the Tate. At a meeting between the Directors and Chairmen of Trustees of both institutions, the Tate expressed its concern 'that its collection of British paintings should not be periodically denuded'. The National Gallery stated that its request for the four pictures represented 'the present limit of what was wished for from the Tate Gallery for the showing of British pictures at Trafalgar Square'; and in a joint Memorandum of 1983, it was agreed that any future requests for transfers should be referred to both galleries' Liaison Committee. Wisely, no formal statement that transfers should cease has ever been made.

Gradually, the National Gallery evolved a selection of pictures from its own original collection which should hang in Trafalgar Square to represent British art in a European context; and from about 1960, it proceeded to add further works whose only common denominator was that they had attained 'masterpiece' status'. After the 1954 Act, such purchases were deliberately made by the National Gallery for its own collection, irrespective of wishing to 'assist the Millbank gallery'. Some of these drew attention to the National Gallery's collection of British pictures in a manner to which it had not often been accustomed. They included Gainsborough's **Mr and Mrs Andrews* in 1960, Stubbs's **Milbanke and Melbourne Families* in 1975 (after its still surprising rejection by the Tate Gallery as a 'worn' picture) and Wright of Derby's **Mr and Mrs Coltman* in 1984. It is likely that some of these purchases were made in the light of recent scholarship which gave new status to artists hitherto not previously highly regarded in Trafalgar Square. Benedict Nicolson's great work *Wright of Derby: Painter of Light* (1968) may well have reminded the National Gallery that they owned a 'masterpiece' in Wright's *Experiment on a Bird in the Air Pump*, which had not hung in Trafalgar Square for seventy years (presented in 1863, sent on long loan to Derby Art Gallery in 1912 and thence directly to the Tate, it was reclaimed only in 1983). Similarly, Basil Taylor's illuminating study of Stubbs had drawn attention to the artist's many-sided genius. In 1898, the National Gallery had transferred its first example of Stubbs's work (*A Grey Hunter with a Groom and Greyhound*) to the Tate Gallery; it retained **A Gentleman driving a Lady in a Phaeton*, a small panel presented in 1920, but did not acquire another until it purchased (in 1975, four years after Basil Taylor's Stubbs was published) *The Milbanke and Melbourne Families*. This is a fitting point at which to note that the Gallery's latest 'masterpiece' purchase, in December 1997, was Stubbs's **Whistlejacket*, which was not merely purchased (with assistance from the Heritage Lottery Fund) but triumphantly projected by laser-beam on to the National Gallery's façade. But in no sense has the National Gallery attempted to rival the Tate's role as a comprehensive representation of the mainstream of British art, let alone its tributaries.

The National Gallery's 1938–45 Report had envisaged that British paintings in Trafalgar Square should represent 'the classic period of British painting, from Hogarth to Turner and Constable'. Its range today is hardly more than that. The shades of *Dignity and Impudence*, *The Derby Day* or *Titania and Bottom* are no longer even faintly perceptible. Excluding such late works by Turner as **Rain, Steam, and Speed* (1844), the only works in the Gallery's British collection which now represent the long Victorian era (an intensely prolific period in British art, which produced works as different from each other as Landseer's *High Life – Low Life* and Rossetti's *Beata Beatrix*) are a small **Self Portrait* by William Boxall (Director, 1865–74) and a marble bust of *Sir Henry Austen Layard (a Gallery Trustee and benefactor) by John Warrington Wood. Here the National Gallery comes close to self-regard. Sargent's *Lord Ribblesdale* (dated 1902), reclaimed from the Tate in 1983 allegedly to 'bring the collection more up-to-date by representing the 20th century', remains the latest work in it.

Sargent himself, though an American citizen all his life, is included in the National Gallery's British School (as in the Tate's British Collection, where he is more fully represented) because he settled in London in 1885 and was based there until his death forty years later. Since the outright departure to the Tate of such Scottish artists as Raeburn and Wilkie (and the lack from the start of any work by Ramsay), 'British' is indeed a misnomer for the Gallery's collection, consisting as it chiefly does of the work of a small group of Englishmen and two Welshmen (Richard Wilson and Thomas Jones): but regional representation has never been among its aims, and the establishment of the National Gallery of Scotland (in 1859) and the Scottish National Portrait Gallery (in 1882) enabled Scottish art at its finest to be displayed there.

The National Gallery's British collection as it now hangs probably fulfils the Curzon Committee's vision of a collection of 'masterpieces'; but that word has subsequently forfeited meaning by being over-used by almost all galleries seeking funds for acquisitions or publicity for exhibitions. Mercifully, not all the works in the National Gallery's present British collection qualify unreservedly as 'masterpieces', or as the 'supreme glories' which Lord Curzon's 1915 committee envisaged hanging there. As Sir John Rothenstein (Director of the Tate Gallery 1938–64) remarked in 1962: 'A gallery only of established masterpieces ... would be like a city whose every building was an architectural triumph.'

The selection evolved over time, recently supplemented by purchases in which a long purse supported fairly vague strategy, takes some account of the art historians' view of what is important, but does not disregard the public's feeling for what is truly loved. This is not the place for detailed analysis of what was retained, what deliberately purchased, and what transferred; but it is clear that where groups of works by artists remain in the collection, some effort was made to show chronological development. Gainsborough is an instance of this. His **John Plampin*, an endearing work but hardly a 'supreme glory', reveals the young artist earning his living as a portraitist in his native Suffolk, while **Mr and Mrs William Hallett*, a late and seemingly romantic idyll (but see p. 122), dates from the artist's last years. The fact that *Mr and Mrs Andrews*, purchased in 1960, displays Gainsborough's early Suffolk style more amply hardly makes *Plampin*'s departure from the National Gallery necessary: indeed, his very pose seems to urge that a collection of British art, even in Trafalgar Square, should not take itself too seriously. It seems likely that the National Gallery's decision to retain two early, tender double portraits of *Gainsborough's daughters, while sending their portraits as adults to the Tate, took account of public affection for the earlier two: but who can be sure? In the case of Reynolds, of whose works the National Gallery once had large holdings, it seems that anything very large, such as *Lord Ligonier* or *Three Ladies adorning a Term of Hymen*, was sooner or later transferred to the Tate, as well as all 'fancy pictures' (*The Age of Innocence*, *The Infant Samuel*, *The Snake in the Grass*), leaving the National Gallery in 1998 with five portraits deemed to have 'stood the test of time'. Technically, **Lord Heathfield* – already judged because of Reynolds's faulty technique to be in ruinous condition within thirty years of completion – cannot be said to have stood the test of time: yet the National Gallery had the good sense to recognise the portrait of a hero when it had one, however battered.

The present British collection consists almost entirely of 'works which have stood the test of time'. The one exception to such classic status is **A Wall in Naples*, a plein-air study in oil on paper by Thomas Jones, an artist whose work of this kind was unknown until 1956. This tiny but immensely powerful work was purchased in 1993, but acquired primarily for its relevance to the National Gallery's growing collection of oil sketches by artists of all European schools (amidst which it hangs) rather than for its British collection. But it is unquestionably a 'British' picture, and as such is catalogued here.

A once large, heterogeneous British collection has by 1998 become a small, reasonably coherent but hardly representative one. In 1895, on the eve of the foundation of the Tate Gallery, the Gallery's British collection had occupied six of its (then) 22 rooms, plus a seventh reserved as 'The Turner Gallery'. Only the 'Early Italian' School, the Gallery's most important collection since its foundation in 1824, occupied more space (eight rooms) than the British. By 1939 the British School occupied four rooms in the Gallery; by 1954 it occupied two (still more or less its present allocation of space, with three or four full-length portraits usually commanding places of honour in Barry's decorative dome room). While the Gallery's British School has diminished in numbers, its other Schools have grown; the Italian School today includes 972 works, the Dutch 451, the French 365, the Netherlandish 144, the German 84 and the Spanish 52. Once (in 1895) amounting in numbers to almost one-third of the National Gallery's entire collection, the British School today amounts to under one-thirtieth part of the 2278 works at present in the National Gallery's collection.

Arrangement of the Catalogue

This is a catalogue of the 61 works which represent the British School in the National Gallery now, at the beginning of 1998. The first *Descriptive Catalogue of the Pictures in the National Gallery, with Critical Remarks on their Merits*, by W. Young Ottley, was published in 1832 (earlier catalogues were hardly more than hand-lists). The first scholarly catalogue devoted to the Gallery's British pictures – *National Gallery Catalogues: The British School* – was compiled by Martin Davies (Director 1968–73). Its first edition in 1946 included 333 pictures. By 1959, when Davies published a revised edition (following large transfers of pictures upon the Tate's separation in 1954 from the National Gallery in 1954), the number of British pictures in the National Gallery had been reduced to 99.

Martin Davies's British School catalogue still stands as a model of concise record and meticulous (sometimes astringent) footnotes. This catalogue is chattier. I have tried to combine accurate information about the making and subsequent history of the pictures with more concern for their subject matter than Martin Davies allowed himself. Here I share to the full Neil MacGregor's conviction that the public should have as much information as possible about their pictures. In a collection still dominated by portraits, much information about sitters (men, women and, in the largest portrait of all, a horse) is available; some of it may help to assess how far a portraitist has succeeded in reflecting individual character. The background information offered here can, of course, be skipped, leaving the illustrations – or better still, the actual works – to speak for themselves.

All the works have been examined in the company of Martin Wyld, the Gallery's Chief Restorer. He has compiled all the Technical Notes except for those on Hogarth's *Marriage A-la-Mode*, which have been contributed by David Bomford. Many of these Technical Notes incorporate the results of detailed examination by Ashok Roy, Head of the Scientific Department, and by his colleagues Raymond White and Jennie Pilc. The bibliography of published work on the techniques and pigments used by artists during the period covered by this catalogue (pp. 442–4) has been compiled by Jo Kirby of the Gallery's Scientific Department.

The catalogue is arranged in the two parts into which it fairly naturally falls. Part I catalogues the well-known and deservedly popular works which are nearly always on view (except when lent to outside exhibitions). The artists represented in it are Constable, Gainsborough, Hogarth, Thomas Jones, Lawrence, Reynolds, Sargent, Stubbs, Turner, Wilson, Wright of Derby and Zoffany, arranged in alphabetical order, with their works (when more than one) in their known (or likely) chronological sequence. The time-span of works by this small group of twelve artists is hardly more than 150 years, from Hogarth's six paintings of *Marriage A-la-Mode*, of about 1742, to Sargent's *Lord Ribblesdale*, dated 1902. In this part of the catalogue, movements of pictures to and from the Tate are briefly noted (below the heading Exhibited), such information being offered to reassure those who remember seeing, say, Wright of Derby's **An Experiment on a Bird in the Air Pump* in the Tate rather than in the National Gallery (or recalling locations given in past literature) that their recollection was not at fault. Under this heading, movements for short periods usually indicate loans supplied by the Tate to fill gaps on the National Gallery walls when it lent pictures for exhibition elsewhere. 'Tate 1960–1', frequently noted, indicates the period of the Gallery's winter exhibition National Gallery Acquisitions 1953–62; to make room for this exhibition, most of its British School pictures were accommodated and displayed in the Tate Gallery.

Part II catalogues the Gallery's collection of portraits (including four marble busts) of those who played significant parts in the history of the National Gallery itself. Since it is in a sense a narrative (though an incomplete one) of the Gallery's history, Part II is presented chronologically, according to the various sitters' relationships to the National Gallery. Lawrence is the only artist to appear in both parts of this catalogue (his portrait of **Queen Charlotte* appears in Part I, his two portraits of **John Julius Angerstein* in Part II). In this group, Sir George Beaumont (grudgingly sitting to Hoppner, an artist he habitually denigrated) will be a familiar figure in the history of British art. Other Trustees and benefactors – preeminently, perhaps, Layard of Nineveh – will be better known outside the perspectives of the National Gallery, while two of its minor heroes – William Seguier, the Gallery's first Keeper, and William Boxall RA, its second Director – may hardly be known at all.

Few portraits of National Gallery benefactors were ever transferred to the Tate; the only exceptions appear to be the transfer of the first version of Linnell's portrait of **Samuel Rogers* (the National Gallery retaining a second version) and the transfer in 1949 of Hoppner's portrait of *Charles Long, Lord Farnborough*, accepted by the National Gallery as a gift in 1934, but hung for a few months only, before being pronounced by Sir Kenneth Clark (Director, 1933–45) 'not worth a place'. The National Gallery retains a finer image of Long in the form of Chantrey's marble bust. Most of the works in Part II are hung in the Reception Area or the Reserve Collection.

All but one of the benefactors who figure in Part II have one thing in common: they bought pictures, but begat no heirs, and therefore chose to give or bequeath paintings to the National Gallery. The exception is the actor-manager Thomas Denison Lewis, who in 1849 bequeathed not only **Mr Lewis as The Marquis in the Midnight Hour* (Shee's portrait of his famous actor-father), but also £10,000 for future Gallery purchases. Prudently invested, the Lewis Fund enabled the purchase of many National Gallery pictures of all schools, including two much-loved British pictures: the *Heads of Six of Hogarth's Servants* and Gainsborough's **Cornard Wood*. The Hogarth was transferred to the Tate in 1960: thus, unknowingly, Lewis became a benefactor to both institutions.

An Appendix includes provisional catalogue entries for *Portrait of a Lady*, painted by Cornelius Johnson (or Jonson van Ceulen) after his return to Holland, and *On the Delaware*, by the wholly American painter George Inness. Both were included in Martin Davies's *British School* catalogue, but since they do not properly belong to the British School, they will eventually be included in more appropriate Schools catalogues.

For details of the National Gallery's British collection just before the establishment of the Tate Gallery, see *A Descriptive and Historical Catalogue of the Pictures in the National Gallery*, London 1895. The early history of the Tate Gallery and its relationship with the National Gallery is most knowledgeably recounted in John Rothenstein, *The Tate Gallery*, London 1962. For the list of the first 96 pictures to be transferred from the National Gallery to the Tate, see the *National Gallery Report*, London 1897, pp. 8–10. In recent editions of *The Tate Gallery Collections: Concise Catalogue* (latest edn. 1991), the prefix N before an inventory number signifies initial ownership by the National Gallery. Mary Chamot, *The Tate Gallery British School: A Concise Catalogue*, London 1953, records dates of the latest (but not of intermediate) transfers of pictures up to 1953. *The National Gallery Report 1938–45* gives (under 'Exchanges with the Tate Gallery', pp. 29–32) some account of transfers, chiefly from the perspective of Trafalgar Square. Quotations from National Gallery Trustees' decisions are from their Board Minutes; these, and the 'Memorandum on Representation of British Painting at the National Gallery and Tate Gallery' agreed by the Chairmen of the Trustees and Directors of both institutions in May 1983, are unpublished (National Gallery Archives).

Sources most frequently cited, usually in abbreviated form

ALLEN 1987
Brian Allen, *Francis Hayman*, exh. cat. Kenwood, London 1987; includes 'Checklist of paintings, drawings, book illustrations and prints', pp. 171–93, New Haven and London 1987

ARMSTRONG 1898, 1904
(Sir) Walter T. Armstrong, *Gainsborough and his Place in English Art*, London 1898, rev. edn 1904

BARRELL 1980
John Barrell, *The Dark Side of the Landscape*, Cambridge 1980

BARRY 1809
James Barry, *Works*, 2 vols, London 1809

BELSEY 1988
Hugh Belsey, *Gainsborough's Family*, exh. cat., Gainsborough's House, Sudbury 1988

BERMINGHAM 1987
Ann Bermingham, *Landscape and Ideology: The English Rustic Tradition, 1740–1867* (USA 1986), London 1987

BINDMAN 1981
David Bindman, *Hogarth*, London 1981, reprinted 1994

BOASE
Frederic Boase, *Modern English Biography*, 6 vols (3 vols A–Z, 1892–1901 and Supplement, 3 vols A–Z, 1908–21), Truro 1892–1921

BROWN 1991
see National Gallery Catalogues

BROWN 1996–7
Christopher Brown, *Rubens's Landscapes*, exh. cat., London, National Gallery, 1996–7, London 1997

BURKE 1955
ed. Joseph Burke, *William Hogarth: The Analysis of Beauty, with the Rejected Passages from the Manuscript Notes and Autobiographical Notes*, Oxford 1955

BUTLIN AND JOLL 1984
Martin Butlin and Evelyn Joll, *The Paintings of J.M.W. Turner*, 2 vols, New Haven and London 1977, rev. edn 1984

CHALONER SMITH
J. Chaloner Smith, *British Mezzotinto Portraits*, 4 vols, London 1883

CORMACK 1970
'The Ledgers of Sir Joshua Reynolds', transcribed by Malcolm Cormack, *Walpole Society 1968–1970*, Vol XLII, London 1970, pp. 105–69.

DAVIES 1946/1959
see National Gallery Catalogues

EGERTON 1984
Judy Egerton, *George Stubbs*, exh. cat. (including essays by or contributions from Robert Shepherd, Ian McClure and Rupert Featherstone and Lynn Koehnline) of an exhibition shown London, Tate Gallery, and New Haven, Yale Center for British Art, London 1984

EGERTON 1990
Judy Egerton, *Wright of Derby*, exh. cat. (including a catalogue of prints after Wright by Tim Clayton and essays by David Fraser, Rica Jones and Paul Mitchell), London, Tate Gallery, Paris, Grand Palais and New York, Metropolitan Museum of Art, London 1990

EINBERG 1987
Elizabeth Einberg, *Manners and Morals: Hogarth and British Painting 1700–1760*, exh. cat., Tate Gallery, London 1987

EINBERG AND EGERTON
Elizabeth Einberg and Judy Egerton, *The Age of Hogarth: British Painters born 1675–1709*, London 1988

FDC
ed. Leslie Parris, Conal Shields and Ian Fleming-Williams, *John Constable: Further Documents and Correspondence* [i.e. further to JCC, q.v.], Suffolk Records Society, London and Ipswich 1975

FARINGTON, DIARY
The Diary of Joseph Farington, 16 vols (Vols I–VI ed. Kenneth Garlick and Angus Macintyre; Vols VII–XVI ed. Kathryn Cave), New Haven and London 1978–84 (Index ed. Evelyn Newby forthcoming, 1998)

FINBERG 1961
A.J. Finberg, *The Life of J.M.W.Turner R.A.*, 1939, 2nd edn revised by Hilda F. Finberg, 1961

FLEMING-WILLIAMS AND PARRIS 1984
Ian Fleming-Williams and Leslie Paris, *The Discovery of Constable*, London 1984

FRY 1951
Roger Fry, *Reflections on British Painting* (1934), London 1951

FULCHER 1856
George Williams Fulcher, *Life of Thomas Gainsborough, R.A.*, London 1856, 2nd (rev.) edn also dated 1856

GEC *Complete Baronetage*
G[eorge] E[dward] C[okayne], *The Complete Baronetage*, 5 vols, London 1900–6

GEC *Complete Peerage*
G[eorge] E[dward] C[okayne], *The Complete Peerage*, new edn, revised and enlarged, ed. The Hon Vicary Gibbs et al., 13 vols, London 1910–40

GAGE 1969
John Gage, *Colour in Turner: Poetry and Truth*, London 1969

GAGE, *Correspondence*, 1980
ed. John Gage, *Collected Correspondence of J.M.W. Turner*, Oxford 1980

GAGE 1987
John Gage, *J.M.W. Turner: 'A Wonderful Range of Mind'*, Oxford 1987

GARLICK 1989
Kenneth Garlick, *Sir Thomas Lawrence*, Oxford 1989

GETTY PROVENANCE INDEX
ed. Burton B. Fredericksen et al., *The Index of Paintings sold in the British Isles during the Nineteenth Century*: I, 1801–5, Santa Barbara 1988; II, 1806–10, Santa Barbara 1990; III, 1811–15, Munich 1993; IV, 1816–20, Munich 1996

GORDON 1986
Dillian Gordon, *The National Gallery Schools of Painting: British Paintings*, London 1986

GRAVES 1907
ed. Algernon Graves, *The Society of Artists of Great Britain 1760–1791; The Free Society of Artists 1761–1783, A Complete Dictionary of Contributors*, London 1907, facsimile reprint, Bath, 1969

GRAVES, DICTIONARY, 1905–6
ed. Algernon Graves, *The Royal Academy of Arts: A Complete Dictionary of Contributors 1769–1904*, 8 vols, London 1905–6

GRAVES, BI
Algernon Graves, *The British Institution, 1806–1867*, London 1908

GRAVES, LOANS
Algernon Graves, *A Century of Loan Exhibitions, 1813–1912*, 5 vols, London 1913–15

GRAVES AND CRONIN 1889–1901
Algernon Graves and William Vine Cronin, *A History of the Works of Sir Joshua Reynolds P.R.A.*, 4 vols, London 1899–1901

GUNNIS 1951
Rupert Gunnis, *Dictionary of British Sculptors 1660–1851*, rev. edn [1951]

HAMERTON 1879
P.G. Hamerton, *The Life of J.M.W. Turner, R.A.*, London 1879

HAMILTON 1874
Edward Hamilton, *The Engraved Works of Sir Joshua Reynolds*, London 1874

HASKELL AND PENNY 1981
Francis Haskell and Nicholas Penny, *Taste and the Antique: The Lure of Classical Sculpture 1500–1900*, New Haven and London 1981

HAYDON, DIARY
ed. Willard Bissell Pope, *The Diary of Benjamin Robert Haydon*, 5 vols, Cambridge, Mass., 1960–3

HAYES 1970
John Hayes, *The Drawings of Thomas Gainsborough*, 2 vols, London 1970

HAYES 1971
John Hayes, *Gainsborough as Printmaker*, London 1971

HAYES 1975
John Hayes, *Gainsborough*, London 1975

HAYES 1982
John Hayes, *The Landscape Paintings of Thomas Gainsborough*, 2 vols (I: Critical Text; II: Catalogue Raisonné), London 1982

HERRMANN 1990
Luke Herrmann, *Turner Prints: The Engraved Work of J.M.W. Turner*, Oxford 1990

HIGHFILL et al.
Philip H. Highfill, Kalman A. Burnim and Edward A. Langhans, *A Biographical Dictionary of Actors, Actresses, Musicians, Dancers, Managers & other Stage Personnel in London, 1600–1800*, 16 vols, Carbondale, Southern Illinois, 1968–93

HOLLSTEIN: see under individual engravers' names in
(1) F.W. Hollstein, *Dutch and Flemish Etchings Engravings and Woodcuts ca. 1400–1700*, 46 vols, Amsterdam, 1949–95; continues as *The New Hollstein* ....
(2) F.W. Hollstein, continued by other compilers, *German Engravings, Etchings and Woodcuts*, 43 vols to date, Amsterdam and Rotterdam 1954–

INGAMELLS 1997
A Dictionary of British and Irish Travellers in Italy 1701–1800, compiled from the Brinsley Ford Archive by John Ingamells, New Haven and London 1997

IVY 1991
Judy Crosby Ivy, *Constable and the Critics, 1802–1837*, Woodbridge 1991

KERSLAKE 1977
John Kerslake, *Early Georgian Portraits: National Portrait Gallery*, 2 vols, London 1977

JCC
ed. R.B. Beckett, *John Constable's Correspondence*, 6 vols, Suffolk Records Society, Ipswich 1962–8

LAING 1995
Alastair Laing, *In Trust for the Nation: Paintings from National Trust Houses*, exh. cat., National Gallery, London 1995

LEVEY 1971
see National Gallery Catalogues

LINDSAY 1966
Jack Lindsay, *Turner: His Life and Work*, London 1966, reprinted 1973

MANNERS AND MORALS, *see* EINBERG 1987

MILLAR 1969
Oliver Millar, *The Later Georgian Pictures in the Collection of Her Majesty the Queen*, 2 vols, London 1969

NAMIER AND BROOKE 1964
ed. Sir Lewis Namier and John Brooke, *The History of Parliament: The House of Commons 1754–1790*, 3 vols, London 1964

NATIONAL GALLERY CATALOGUES
Christopher Brown, *The Dutch School 1600–1900* (rev. edn of Neil MacLaren's catalogue of 1960), London 1991
Martin Davies, *The British School*, London 1946, rev. edn 1959
Martin Davies, *The Earlier Italian Schools*, London 1951, rev. edn 1961
Michael Levey, *The Seventeenth and Eighteenth Century Italian Schools*, London 1971

NICHOLS AND STEEVENS
John Nichols and George Steevens, *The Genuine Works of William Hogarth; with Biographical Anecdotes*, 3 vols, London 1806–17

NICHOLSON 1990
Kathleen Nicholson, *Turner's Classical Landscapes: Myth and Meaning*, Princeton 1990

NICOLSON 1968
Benedict Nicolson, *Joseph Wright of Derby, Painter of Light*, 2 vols, London 1968

*NMM 1988
ed. *Concise Catalogue of Oil Paintings in the National Maritime Museum*, London 1988

NPG DICTIONARY
ed. Richard Ormond and Malcolm Rogers, *Dictionary of British Portraiture: National Portrait Gallery*, 4 vols, London 1979–81

O'DONOGHUE AND HAKE
Catalogue of Engraved British Portraits preserved in the Department of Prints and Drawings in the British Museum, Freeman O'Donoghue (I–IV), with Henry M. Hake (V), Supplement and Indexes by Henry M. Hake (VI), 6 vols, London 1908–25

ORMOND 1973
Richard Ormond, *Early Victorian Portraits: National Portrait Gallery*, 2 vols, London 1973

OWEN AND BROWN 1988
Felicity Owen and David Blayney Brown, *Collector of Genius: A Life of Sir George Beaumont*, New Haven and London 1988

OWEN AND BROWN EXH. CAT. 1988
Felicity Owen and David Brown, with catalogue by John Leighton, *'Noble and Patriotic': The Beaumont Gift 1828*, exh. cat., National Gallery, London 1988

PARRIS AND FLEMING-WILLIAMS 1991
Leslie Parris and Ian Fleming-Williams, *Constable*, exh. cat., Tate Gallery, London 1991

PASSAVANT, JOHANN DAVID
Kunstreise durch England und Belgien (Frankfurt, 1833), trs. by Elizabeth Rigby (later Lady Eastlake) as *Tour of a German Artist in England*, 2 vols, London 1836

PAULSON 1971
Ronald Paulson, *Hogarth: His Life, Art, and Times*, 2 vols, London 1989

PAULSON 1989
Ronald Paulson, *Hogarth's Graphic Works*, 3rd rev edn, London 1989

PENNY 1986
ed. Nicholas Penny, *Reynolds*, exh. cat., Royal Academy of Arts, London 1986

PIGLER 1956
Andor Pigler, *Barockthemen, eine Auswahl von Verzeichnissen zur Ikonographie des 17. und 18. Jahrhunderts*, 3 vols, Budapest 1956

POLITICAL AND PERSONAL SATIRES
British Museum, Department of Prints and Drawings: *Catalogue of*

Political and Personal Satires, Vols I–IV ed. F.G. Stephens, Vols V–XI ed. M. Dorothy George, London 1870–1954

POTTERTON 1986
Homan Potterton, *Reynolds and Gainsborough, Themes and Painters in the National Gallery*, Ser. 2 No. 3, London 1986

PROWN 1966
Jules David Prown, *John Singleton Copley in England*, 2 vols, Cambridge, Mass. 1966

RAWLINSON
W.G. Rawlinson, *The Engraved Work of J.M.W. Turner, R.A.*, 2 vols, London 1908–13

REDGRAVE, DICTIONARY
Samuel Redgrave, *A Dictionary of Artists of the English School*, 2nd edn 1878, reprinted in facsimile 1970

REYNOLDS 1960
Graham Reynolds, *Catalogue of the Constable Collection*, Victoria and Albert Museum, London 1960

REYNOLDS 1965
Graham Reynolds, *Constable: The Natural Painter*, London 1965

REYNOLDS 1984
Graham Reynolds, *The Later Paintings and Drawings of John Constable*, 2 vols, New Haven and London 1984

REYNOLDS 1996
Graham Reynolds, *The Early Paintings and Drawings of John Constable*, 2 vols, New Haven and London 1996

RIBEIRO 1983
Aileen Ribeiro, *A Visual History of Costume: the eighteenth century*, London 1983

RIBEIRO 1995
Aileen Ribeiro, *The Art of Dress: Fashion in England and France 1750–1820*, New Haven and London 1995

ROBERTSON 1978
David Robertson, *Sir Charles Eastlake and the Victorian Art World*, Princeton 1978

ROSENTHAL 1983
Michael Rosenthal, *Constable: The Painter and his Landscape*, New Haven and London 1983

RUSKIN 1857
John Ruskin, *Notes on the Turner Gallery at Marlborough House, 1856*, London 1857

RUSKIN, WORKS
ed. E.T. Cook and Alexander Wedderburn, *The Works of John Ruskin*, 39 vols, London 1903–12

SHANES 1990
Eric Shanes, *Turner's Human Landscape*, London 1990

SHAWE-TAYLOR 1990
Desmond Shawe-Taylor, *The Georgians: Eighteenth-Century Portraiture & Society*, London 1990

SHIRLEY
The Hon. Andrew Shirley, *The Published Mezzotints by David Lucas after John Constable, R.A.*, Oxford 1930

SITWELL 1936
Sacheverell Sitwell, *Conversation Pieces*, London 1936

SMART AND BROOKS 1976
Alastair Smart and Attfield Brooks, *Constable and his Country*, London 1976

SMITH 1860
Thomas Smith, *Recollections of the British Institution*, London 1860

TAYLOR 1971
Basil Taylor, *Stubbs*, London 1971

THICKNESSE 1788
Philip Thicknesse, *A Sketch of the Life and Paintings of Thomas Gainsborough, Esq.*, London 1788

WAAGEN 1838
Gustav Friedrich Waagen, *Kunstwerke und Künstler in England* (Berlin, 1837–8), trs. by H.E. Lloyd as *Works of Art and Artists in England*, 3 vols, London 1838

WAAGEN 1854
Gustav Friedrich Waagen, *Treasures of Art in Great Britain*, trs. Lady Eastlake, 3 vols, London 1854, with a supplementary vol., *Galleries and Cabinets of Art in Great Britain*, London 1857

WALKER 1985
Richard Walker, *Regency Portraits: National Portrait Gallery*, 2 vols, London 1985

WALPOLE, ANECDOTES
Horace Walpole, *Anecdotes of Painting in England with some account of the principal artists ... Strawberry Hill 1782*; ed. The Rev. James Dallaway, 5 vols, London 1826–8

WALPOLE CORRESPONDENCE
ed. W.S. Lewis et al., *The Yale Edition of Horace Walpole's Correspondence*, 48 vols, New Haven 1937–83

WARK 1971
Robert R. Wark, *Ten British Pictures 1740–1840*, San Marino 1971, reprinted 1985

WATERHOUSE 1941
Ellis Waterhouse, *Reynolds*, London 1941

WATERHOUSE 1953
Ellis Waterhouse, *Painting in Britain 1530–1790*, London 1953, 2nd edn 1962

WATERHOUSE 1958
Ellis Waterhouse, *Gainsborough*, London 1958

WATERHOUSE 1964
Ellis Waterhouse, *Three Decades of British Art* (Jayne Lectures 1964), Philadelphia 1965

WATERHOUSE, DICTIONARY
Ellis Waterhouse, *The Dictionary of British 18th Century Painters in Oils and Crayons*, Woodbridge 1981

WATTS, SEATS
William Watts, *The Seats of the Nobility and Gentry*, London 1779–86

WEBSTER 1978
Mary Webster, *Hogarth*, London 1978

WHITLEY 1915
William T. Whitley, *Thomas Gainsborough*, London 1915

WHITLEY 1928
William T. Whitley, *Artists and their Friends in England 1700–1799*, 2 vols, London 1928

WHITLEY 1928–30
William T. Whitley, *Art in England*, 2 vols (I: 1800–1820; II: 1821–1837, Cambridge 1928, 1930

WHITLEY PAPERS
Notes in MS and typescript on artists, collected by William T. Whitley and preserved in the Department of Prints and Drawings, British Museum

WILTON 1979
Andrew Wilton, *The Life and Work of J.M.W. Turner*, London 1979

WILTON 1987
Andrew Wilton, *Turner in his Time*, London 1987

WOODALL 1939
Mary Woodall, *Gainsborough's Landscape Drawings*, London 1939

WOODALL, LETTERS, 1963
ed. Mary Woodall, *The Letters of Thomas Gainsborough*, 1961, 2nd edn, London 1963

YOUNG GAINSBOROUGH, 1987
Susan Foister, Rica Jones and Olivier Meslay, *Young Gainsborough*, exh. cat. London, National Gallery, Norwich, Castle Museum, and Newcastle, Laing Art Gallery, 1997

EXHIBITIONS REFERRED TO IN ABBREVIATED FORM

When known, precise dates are given, as these may assist the pursuit of reviews and occasional controversy. Authorship of the catalogues of one-man or specialist exhibitions is given if stated.

1813	London, British Institution, *Pictures by the late Sir Joshua Reynolds* (with a Preface to the catalogue by Richard Payne Knight), Summer 1813
1814	London, British Institution, *Pictures by the late William Hogarth, Richard Wilson, Thomas Gainsborough, and J. Zoffani*, Summer 1814
1857	Manchester, Exhibition Hall, Old Trafford, *Art Treasures of the United Kingdom collected at Manchester in 1857*, 1857
1862	London, South Kensington Museum (later Victoria and Albert Museum), *International Exhibition*, 1862
1885	London, Grosvenor Gallery, *Thomas Gainsborough* (notes by F.G. Stephens), Winter 1885
1913	Leeds, City of Leeds Art Gallery, *Works by and after John Constable, R.A.*, 1913
1927	Ipswich Museum, *Bicentenary Memorial Exhibition of Thomas Gainsborough, R.A.* (notes by Percy Moore Turner), 7 October–5 November 1927
1930	London, 25 Park Lane, then Sir Philip Sassoon's house, *Loan Exhibition of 18th Century English Conversation Pieces*, March 1930
1934	London, Royal Academy of Arts, *Exhibition of British Art*, Winter 1934
1936	London, 45 Park Lane, Sir Philip Sassoon's house, *Gainsborough, Loan Exhibition in aid of the Royal Northern Hospital*, 18 February–31 March 1936
1938	Paris, Palais du Louvre, *La Peinture Anglaise XVIIIe & XIXe Siècles*, 1938
1946–7	New York, Chicago, Toronto: Metropolitan Museum of Art, New York, The Art Institute of Chicago, The Art Gallery of Toronto, *Masterpieces of English Painting: William Hogarth, John Constable, J.M.W. Turner*, 1946–7
1948	Paris, *Huit siècles de vie Britannique* (British Council), 1948
1949	Lisbon and Madrid: *A Hundred Years of British Painting* (British Council), 1949
1949–50	Hamburg, Oslo, Stockholm and Copenhagen: Kunsthalle, Hamburg, Kunstnernes Hus, Oslo, Nationalmuseum, Stockholm, and Statens Museum for Kunst, Copenhagen, *British Painting from Hogarth to Turner, Two Centuries of British Painting* (British Council), 1949–50
1950	Venice, The Biennale, *Works by John Constable, Matthew Smith, Barbara Hepworth* (British Council), 1950
1951–2	London, Royal Academy of Arts, *The First Hundred Years of the Royal Academy*, December 1951–March 1952
1953	Paris, Orangerie, *Le Paysage Anglais*, February–April 1953
1953	London, Tate Gallery *Thomas Gainsborough 1727–88* (Arts Council), cat. E.K. Waterhouse, May–August 1953
1954–5	London, Royal Academy of Arts, *European Masters of the Eighteenth Century*, 27 November 1954–27 February 1955
1955	Rotterdam, Museum Boymans, *English Landscape Painting from Gainsborough to Turner* (British Council), 5 March–28 April 1955
1956–7	New York, St Louis, San Francisco: Museum of Modern Art, New York, City Museum, St Louis, California Palace of the Legion of Honor, San Francisco, *Masters of British Painting 1800–1950*, 1956–7
1957–8	Montreal, Ottawa, Toronto, Toledo: Montreal Museum of Fine Arts, National Gallery of Canada, Ottawa, Art Gallery of Toronto, Toledo Museum of Art, *British Painting in the Eighteenth Century* (British Council), 1957–8 (later shown in part at the Tate Gallery)
1958	Munich, The Residenz, *The Age of Rococo: Art and Culture of the Eighteenth Century*, 15 June–15 September 1958
1959	London, Tate Gallery and Arts Council Gallery, *The Romantic Movement* (Arts Council for the Council of Europe), 10 July–27 September 1959
1960	Moscow and Leningrad: Pushkin Museum, Moscow, and Leningrad, The Hermitage State Museum, *British Painting 1700–1960* (British Council), Summer 1960
1961	Birmingham City Museum and Art Gallery, *Works by Sir Joshua Reynolds* (cat. John Woodward and Malcolm Cormack), 1961
1968–9	London, Royal Academy of Arts, *Royal Academy of Arts Bicentenary Exhibition 1768–1968*, 14 December 1968–2 March 1969
1971–2	London, Tate Gallery, *Hogarth* (cat. Lawrence Gowing), 2 December 1971–6 February 1972
1972	Paris, Petit Palais du Louvre, *La peinture romantique anglaise et les préraphaélites*, January–April 1972
1973–4	London, Tate Gallery, *Landscape in Britain* (cat. Leslie Parris), 20 November 1973–3 February 1974
1974–5	London, Royal Academy of Arts, *Turner 1775–1851* (Tate Gallery and Royal Academy cat. Martin Butlin, Andrew Wilton and John Gage), 16 November 1974–2 March 1975
1976	London, Tate Gallery, *Constable* (cat. Leslie Parris, Ian Fleming-Williams and Conal Shields), 18 February–25 April 1976
1979–80	London, National Portrait Gallery (at 15 Carlton House Terrace), *Sir Thomas Lawrence 1769–1830* (cat. Michael Levey), 9 November 1979–16 March 1980
1980–1	London and Paris: London, Tate Gallery, *Gainsborough* (cat. John Hayes), 8 October 1980–4 January 1981, and (with some changes), Paris, Grand Palais du Louvre, 6 February–27 April 1981
1983–4	Paris, Grand Palais du Louvre, *J.M.W. Turner* (British Council; cat. John Gage), 14 October 1983–16 January 1984
1984–5	London and New Haven: London, Tate Gallery (18 October 1984–6 January 1985) and New Haven, Yale Center for British Art (13 February–7 April 1985), *George Stubbs 1724–1806* (cat. Judy Egerton), 1984–5
1985/86	Paris, Grand Palais du Louvre, *Reynolds* (cat. ed. Nicholas Penny), 9 October–16 December 1985 (first showing of the exhibition later seen at the Royal Academy, London, in 1986)
1987–8	London, Tate Gallery, *Manners & Morals: Hogarth and British Painting 1700–1760* (cat. Elizabeth Einberg), 15 October 1987–3 January 1988
1988	Sudbury, Suffolk, Gainsborough's House, *Gainsborough's Family* (cat. Hugh Belsey), 11 June–18 September 1988
1988	Leningrad and Moscow: The Hermitage State Museum, Leningrad, and The Pushkin Museum, Moscow, *Masterpieces from the National Gallery*, London (no cat.), 1988
1990	London, Paris and New York: Tate Gallery, London (7 February–22 April), Grand Palais du Louvre, Paris (17 May–23 July), and Metropolitan Museum of Art,

	New York (6 September–2 December), *Wright of Derby* (cat. Judy Egerton), 1990
1991	London, Tate Gallery, *Constable* (cat. Leslie Parris and Ian Fleming-Williams), 13 June–15 September 1991
1991–2	London, National Portrait Gallery, *The Portrait in British Art: Paintings bought with the help of the National Art Collections Fund* (cat. John Hayes), 8 November 1991–9 February 1992
1992–3	London, Tate Gallery, *The Swagger Portrait: Grand Manner Portraiture in Britain from Van Dyck to Augustus John 1630–1930* (cat. Andrew Wilton), 14 October 1992–10 January 1993
1997	London, Norwich and Newcastle: National Gallery, London (29 January–31 March), Castle Museum, Norwich (19 April–15 June), and Laing Art Gallery, Newcastle (21 June–17 August), *Young Gainsborough* (cat. Susan Foister, Rica Jones and Olivier Meslay), 1997

OTHER ABBREVIATIONS

ADD. MSS	Additional Manuscripts, British Library
ARA	Associate [member] of the Royal Academy
BFAC	Burlington Fine Arts Club
BI	British Institution, London
BL	British Library
BM, P&D	British Museum, Department of Prints and Drawings
bt	bought (usually in the saleroom)
BT	Baronet
d.s.p.	died *sine prole* (without issue)
JWCI	Journal of the Warburg and Courtauld Institutes
LACMA	Los Angeles County Museum of Art
NACF	National Art Collections Fund
NAM	National Army Museum, London
NG	National Gallery, London
NGA	Washington National Gallery of Art, Washington, DC
NGS	National Gallery of Scotland, Edinburgh
NMM	National Maritime Museum, London
NPG	National Portrait Gallery, London
NT	National Trust
PRA	President of the Royal Academy of Arts
PRO	Public Record Office, London (Chancery Lane and Kew)
RA	Royal Academy of Arts; Royal Academician
RA, WINTER	Exhibitions presented at the Royal Academy during the winter months (and from 1871 to 1910 usually entitled Works by the Old Masters and by Deceased Artists of the British School), as distinct from the Summer exhibitions of works by living artists and their contemporaries
SA	Society of Artists, London
SBA	Society of British Artists, Suffolk Street, London
SNPG	Scottish National Portrait Gallery, Edinburgh
TS	*Turner Studies*, 11 vols, 1981–91, published by the Tate Gallery
V&A	Victoria and Albert Museum, London

List of Works

The National Gallery inventory number precedes the title of the work.

THE CATALOGUE

Part I

John Constable

1776–1837

Born in East Bergholt, Suffolk, son of Golding Constable, corn miller and merchant (his business centred on Flatford Mill), and his wife Ann Watts; educated chiefly at Dedham Grammar School. Worked for a few years for his father, meanwhile drawing. Early mentors include Sir George Beaumont and Joseph Farington RA. Entered RA Schools March 1799. Early – and enduring – enthusiasms include Gainsborough ('I fancy I see Gainsborough in every hedge and hollow tree'), Claude, Ruisdael and Rubens. Resolved to become a painter (with the reluctant consent of his father, who 'thinks He is pursuing a Shadow'). In May 1802 made his now-famous assertion: 'There is room enough for a natural painture' (in a private letter to his friend Dunthorne); in Suffolk the following year, began to make 'studies ... painted from nature' (and painted portraits, for income). Accumulated, in sketchbooks and oils, a store of Suffolk landscape studies on which he drew after settling in London in 1819 (living in Hampstead, and renting a studio in Charlotte Street).

Exhibited over a hundred works at the RA from 1802 to 1837, his first significant Suffolk landscape being *Dedham Vale: Morning*, exh. 1811. Determined to make monumental paintings of scenes known since boyhood which 'made me a painter' – 'all that lies on the banks of the Stour' – he exhibited a series of so-called 'six-footers' between 1817 and 1826, using themes and details from his stock of studies, transforming them in his Charlotte Street studio into paintings now considered to epitomise 'the Constable country'.

In 1829, began work on *English Landscape Scenery*, select images engraved in mezzotint by David Lucas, commercially a failure; subjects (not all published) include, besides Suffolk landscapes, Hampstead, Salisbury Cathedral, Stonehenge and Hadleigh Castle. From 1830, lectured in Hampstead, at the Royal Institution, and in Worcester on the history of landscape painting, probably the first artist in England to address himself to a subject generally considered low in the academic hierarchy.

Neither Constable's subject matter nor his palette appealed to academicians or connoisseurs of the day in England, though from the 1820s he had admirers in France. His self-confidence often faltered, needing frequent support from his friend Archdeacon Fisher, and he was often short of money, but he did not waver from his resolve to achieve a 'natural painture'. Public recognition was humiliatingly slow. Elected ARA 1814; not elected RA until 1829. Such slights determined his friends, after Constable's death (on 31 March 1837), to purchase *The Cornfield* (NG 130) and present it to the National Gallery.

References

Ed. R.B. Beckett, *John Constable's Correspondence*, I–VI, and *John Constable's Discourses*, Suffolk Records Society 1962–6, 1970; Andrew Wilton, *Constable's 'English Landscape Scenery'*, London 1979; Graham Reynolds, *The Later Paintings and Drawings of John Constable*, New Haven and London 1984; Graham Reynolds, *The Early Paintings and Drawings of John Constable*, New Haven and London 1996.

NG 2652

Weymouth Bay: Bowleaze Cove and Jordon Hill

1816–17
Oil on canvas, 53 × 75 cm (21 × 29½ in.)

Provenance

Unsold in Constable's lifetime; in his estate administrators' sale, Foster's 16 May 1838 (probably lot 41, 'Weymouth Bay, a sketch'[1]), £4.4.0, bt Swabey; ...; William Fuller Maitland, Stanstead Hall, Essex, sold Christie's 10 May 1879 (72), bt Daniel £157.10.0; ...; purchased 1890, £450, by George Salting (d.12 December 1909);[2] as part of the Salting Bequest, entered the National Gallery 1910.

Exhibited

London, Agnew's, *The Collection of Pictures and Drawings of the late Mr George Salting*, January 1910 (59, as 'Coast scene');[3] NG, Room XV, *Pictures from the Salting Bequest*, 1910 (no catalogue);[4] Tate Gallery 1937 (18); Chicago, New York, and Toronto 1946–7 (17); Madrid and Lisbon 1949 (4); Venice, Biennale, *John Constable, Matthew Smith and Barbara Hepworth*, 1950 (9); Rotterdam 1955 (10); New York, Saint Louis, and San Francisco 1956–7 (19); Tate Gallery 1991 (85).

At the Tate Gallery 1960–1.

Literature

Davies 1946, pp. 33–4; R.B. Beckett, 'Constable's Honeymoon', *Connoisseur*, CXXIX, no. 525, 1952, pp. 3–8; Davies 1959, pp. 21–2; Reynolds 1960, pp. 109–12; Parris, Fleming-Williams and Shields 1976, pp. 99–100; Rosenthal 1983, pp. 111 (fig. 141), 113; Reynolds 1984, pp. 32–3, cat. no. 19.10, plate 74; Parris and Fleming-Williams 1991, pp. 168–76 (no. 85, repr.), pp. 428–30.

Technical Notes

Cleaned in 1956. In very good condition, though the impasto has been a little flattened by the lining. The pinkish-buff ground shows through the thinly painted foreground and, in places, through the paint of the sky.

Fig. 1 *Weymouth Bay*, *c.*1816. Oil on millboard, 20.3 × 24.7 cm. London, Victoria and Albert Museum.

Constable became familiar with this landscape, under varying light, during the six weeks of his honeymoon (mid-October to early December 1816), which he and Maria spent at Osmington in Dorset, staying with the Reverend John Fisher[5] and his own recently married wife. Fisher, twelve years younger than Constable and since 1811 his firm friend, then held (among many other ecclesiastical sweets) the Dorset living of Osmington;[6] he had married the Constables in London on 2 October 1816, after previously inviting them to stay in his vicarage at Osmington, a small village in the downs some four miles north-east of Weymouth. 'The country here is wonderfully wild & sublime & well worth a painters visit', Fisher had written to Constable on 27 August 1816: 'My house commands a singularly beautiful view: & you may study from my very windows. You shall [have] a plate of meat set by the side of your easel without your sitting down to dinner: we never see company: & I have brushes paints & canvass in abundance.'[7]

Constable turned his stay at Osmington to good advantage, making many oil sketches and twenty or so drawings and watercolours of the bay and other views nearby.[8] As Parris and Fleming-Williams note, the coast of his native Suffolk had not so far attracted him as a subject;[9] but from Osmington short paths led down to the beach and to the fishing village of Osmington Mills, and up to panoramic views of the sea from the downs. Constable followed them, concentrating his attention on the smaller coves within the wide span of Weymouth Bay. Weymouth itself, a booming resort whose front was lined with lodging-houses and bathing-machines, did not offer him a congenial subject.[10] The only figures in his views of the bay are fishermen, a few saunterers on the sands and an occasional shepherd on the downs.

This view, established by Beckett 1952,[11] is of Bowleaze Cove, within the wide sweep of Weymouth Bay, looking west from Osmington, which is behind the painter's back (with Weymouth itself out of sight); 'the little Jordon stream' can be seen trickling over the beach, with Furzy Cliff and Jordon Hill beyond.

NG 2652 is one of three oil versions of the subject. The sequence in which they were painted is not documented. Reynolds argues (convincingly, for this compiler) that the first version is the small oil sketch on millboard with a stormy sky (fig. 1), almost certainly an open-air sketch from nature and, as he notes, similar in size to other oil sketches evidently made on the spot at Osmington: the 'little pictures' which, as Fisher observed, fitted into the lid of Constable's outdoor painting-box.[12]

NG 2652, also sketchy, was described by Davies as an 'unfinished' picture,[13] presumably because Constable has left some of the brownish-red ground unpainted, to 'tell' (on the beach) as Dorset-coloured sand and (in the sky) to give weight to the clouds. Its apparent spontaneity has inclined many to suggest that it was painted on the spot. If 'on the spot' means *en plein air*, with Constable painting his canvas on the Osmington shore, this is a possibility – Rosenthal notes that 'the canvas is near the 20¼ × 30¼ outdoor size'[14] – but cannot be established without further documentation. Parris and Fleming-Williams argued in 1985[15] that NG 2652 should be 'regarded as an open-air study', but appear to offer (in 1991) a compromise solution in suggesting that both the small V&A

sketch and the larger NG 2652 could have been painted at Osmington at much the same time: 'the small storm sketch gives the impression of having been executed very rapidly, perhaps during an interval of bad weather while Constable was working on the larger picture',[16] which perhaps implies that NG 2652 was painted in Osmington vicarage, half a mile away from 'the spot'. Beckett notes that Constable was 'still thinking of the clouds at Osmington' when making sky studies at Hampstead some six years later: on the back of one such study dated September 5th 1822 he wrote: 'Very appropriate to the coast at Osmington.'[17]

There is (so far) general agreement that a third, larger and more highly finished painting now in the Louvre (fig. 2)[18] is the final version, developed from both the others. In the Louvre picture, as in the V&A oil sketch, the sky is stormy and there are a few more figures than in NG 2652. There was formerly much uncertainty over whether the work which Constable exhibited at the British Institution in 1819 (44, as 'Osmington Shore, near Weymouth') was the Louvre or the National Gallery picture (or, conceivably, another, at present untraced work); Reynolds convincingly demonstrates that it was the Louvre picture.[19] It was primarily from the Louvre version that David Lucas engraved the mezzotint *Weymouth Bay, Dorsetshire* (for which Constable offered the alternative titles 'Tempestuous Afternoon' or 'Tempestuous Evening') for Constable's *English Landscape Scenery*, 1830.[20]

Fig. 2 *Weymouth Bay*, ?exhibited 1819. Oil on canvas, 88 × 112 cm. Paris, Musée du Louvre.

NOTES

1. Since two other sketches called 'Weymouth Bay' were offered in the same day's sale (one in a group of four sketches, lot 45, the other in a group of five, lot 47), some uncertainty remains over the lot number of the National Gallery sketch.

2. Salting recorded the purchase in his MS 'Pictures' notebook, NG Archives, A.1.6 31, [p. 24]: '90. Cost: £450 Chesil Beach. Weymouth Bay. study for picture in Louvre.'

3. Salting bequeathed 'my pictures or such as they, the Trustees may select' to the NG. His executors arranged for the NG Trustees to make their selection at Agnew's.

4. Probate was granted 22 January 1910 and the Trustees of the NG selected 164 paintings (from a total of 224) on 26 January 1910. The exhibition of 91 paintings from the Salting Bequest opened to the public at Agnew's on 12 February 1910 and was reviewed in *The Times*, 14 February 1910. In catalogues annotated by NG staff, the title 'Coast Scene' (59) is amended to 'Weymouth Bay'. The notebook in which Salting recorded his purchases is in the NG Archives; receipts from dealers are in the Guildhall Library, Archives of P.W. Flower and Sons (executors), MSS 19,473. For a full account of George Salting, his collections and bequests to various museums, see Stephen Coppel, 'George Salting (1835–1909)', in ed. Antony Griffiths, *Landmarks in Print Collecting*, London 1996, pp. 189–203.

5. Fisher is abundantly noticed in the Constable literature. For his correspondence with Constable, see *JCC*, vol. VI, *passim*; for his 'somewhat bewildering variety of ecclesiastical offices', see pp. 41–2. For Constable's portraits of Fisher and his wife, painted during the Osmington visit, now coll. Fitzwilliam Museum, Cambridge, see Reynolds 1984, cat. no. 17.3 (*Rev. John Fisher*, reproduced in this catalogue, p. 38) and Reynolds 1996, cat. no. 16.83, plate 1342 (Mary Fisher).

6. Fisher is sometimes described at this stage (1816) as 'Vicar of Osmington and Gillingham'; but Beckett in *JCC*, vol. VI, pp. 41–2, records that the Gillingham living was then held by Canon Douglas; after his death in March 1819 it was given to Fisher.

7. Fisher to Constable, 27 August 1816, *JCC*, vol. VI, p. 29.

8. For the oils painted during or shortly after his stay in Osmington (including a finished painting of Osmington village for Fisher), see Reynolds 1996 (under 1816). For the drawings, see Reynolds 1996 (under 1816); Fleming-Williams 1990, pp. 141–4; Parris and Fleming-Williams 1991, pp. 428–30.

9. 1991, p. 168.

10. For the growth of Weymouth see J. Britton and E.W. Brayley, *The Beauties of England and Wales*, vol. IV, London 1809, pp. 357–9, and Beckett 1952, *JCC*, vol. VI, p. 31. Since George III first visited it nearly thirty years earlier, Weymouth had boomed, with 'every spot of land which fronts the sands ... snatched up with the greatest avidity, and appropriated to the purpose of building lodging-houses', the building of Assembly Rooms and the erection of rows of bathing machines (not yet in the picturesque canon). The sketchbook Constable used during this stay (described by Reynolds 1960, p. 111) included a drawing inscribed 'View of Osmington and the Downs with the figure of George III on horseback at Sutton Poyntz.'

11. Beckett 1952, p. 6.

12. Reynolds 1960, p. 111, no. 155; V&A 330–1888. Reynolds notes that in NG 2652, Constable has developed the distant plume of water or smoke in the V&A oil sketch into the figure of a shepherd with a flock of sheep. For Constable's painting-box, used out of doors on his knee, its lid serving as an easel, see Beckett 1952, p. 7.

13. 1959, p. 21.

14. Rosenthal 1983, p. 111.

15. Reviewing Reynolds 1984 (*Burlington Magazine*, CXXVII, 1985, p.167 (under 17.30), they suggest that NG 2652 should be regarded as 'an open-air study' and should be 'brought forward to join the Boston *Osmington and Weymouth Bays* of 1816' (Reynolds 1984, cat. no. 24.7, plate 480, a different subject, but comparable in size).

16. 1991, p. 173, no. 85.

17. Beckett 1952, p. 8; he suggests that NG 2652, with two other paintings approximately the same size, *Osmington and Weymouth Bays* (Museum of Fine Arts, Boston; Reynolds 1984, cat. no. 16.81, plate 1341) and *Osmington Bay* (coll. John G. Johnson, Philadelphia, Reynolds 1984, cat. no. 24.7, plate 480), could have been painted in Hampstead around 1824.

18. Reynolds 1984, cat. no. 19.9; presented to the Louvre in 1873.

19. Reynolds 1984, p. 31, cat. no. 19.8; pp. 31–2, cat. no. 19.9.

20. Shirley no. 13.

NG 6510

Stratford Mill

exhibited 1820
Oil on canvas, 127 × 182.9 cm (50 × 72 in.)
Inscribed (by a later hand)

Provenance

Purchased from the artist in 1821 by Archdeacon John Fisher as a gift to his solicitor John Pern Tinney, of Salisbury; purchased from the latter's widow in 1848 by Charles Frederick Huth; after his death, in his sale, Christie's 6 July 1895 (77), bt Agnew, from whom purchased 1896 by Sir Samuel Montagu, Bt (cr. 1st Baron Swaythling, 1907); by descent to 3rd Baron Swaythling, by whom sold Christie's 12 July 1946 (19), bt Ellis & Smith for Walter Hutchinson (d.1950); Messrs Hutchinson & Co. (Publishers) Ltd, sold Christie's 20 July 1951 (85), bt Major Sir Reginald Macdonald-Buchanan for the joint collection of himself and his wife, The Hon. Lady Macdonald Buchanan; following his death (1981) and hers (1987), accepted in lieu of Inheritance Tax by HM Government, by whom allocated to the National Gallery 1987.

Exhibited

RA 1820 (17, as 'Landscape'); BI, *Pictures by Living Artists of the English School*, 1825 (114, as 'Landscape; a Water-mill, with Children angling'); *International Exhibition*, 1874 (59); RA Winter 1886 (158); RA Winter 1896 (126); Agnew's, *Twenty Masterpieces of the English School*, 1897 (2); Berlin, Königliche Akademie der Künste, *Aelterer Englischer Kunst*, 1908 (73); Copenhagen, Ny Carlsberg Glyptotek, *Aeldre Engelsk Kunst*, 1908 (2); Leeds City Art Gallery, *John Constable, R.A.*, 1913 (14); London, Wembley, *British Empire Exhibition*, 1924 (V 15); RA, *British Art*, 1934 (382 Y); London, Hutchinson House (Stratford Place), *National Gallery of British Sports and Pastimes*, 1951 (338); RA 1951–2 (213); Leicester Art Gallery, *A Hundred Years of British Landscape Painting*, 1956 (34); Christie's, *Christie's Bi-Centenary Exhibition 1766–1966*, 1967 (5); RA 1968–9 (88); Tate Gallery 1976 (177); Tate Gallery 1991 (100).

Literature

Smart and Brooks 1976, pp. 76–9, figs. 41–2; Graham Reynolds, 'Stratford Mill by John Constable RA', *Art at Auction: The Year at Sotheby's 1982–3*, 1983, pp. 48–53; Rosenthal 1983, pp. 120–4; Reynolds 1984, cat. no. 20.1, pp. 43–4, plate 129; Malcolm Cormack, 'Constable's Stratford Mill', in ed. John Wilmerding, *Essays in Honor of Paul Mellon*, Washington 1986, pp. 71–83; Ivy 1991, pp. 84–6; Parris and Fleming-Williams 1991, pp. 197–200, cat. no. 100, pp. 201–2.

Engraved

by David Lucas, mezzotint, published 1840, after Constable's death and with the title (unsanctioned by him) *The Young Waltonians*. Also etched by Brunet Debaines 1883.

Technical Notes

In very good condition, though the impasto has been crushed by an old lining. The X-radiograph shows two significant changes: a standing angler, directly above the girl, has been painted out, and the trees, centre left, have been made taller.

This was the second of the so-called 'six-footers' which Constable showed at the Royal Academy over the years 1819–25.[1] While continuing to paint a variety of subjects, from 1819 he was determined (in Graham Reynolds's words) 'to bid for attention at the Academy through monumental renderings of the Stour scenes which had first suggested pictures to him as a child'.[2]

The Stratford mill of the title, partly seen on the left, was a water-powered paper mill on an islet in the River Stour just outside the Suffolk village of Stratford St Mary; the site is about two miles to the west of East Bergholt, Constable's birthplace.[3] In boyhood, Constable would have had ample opportunity to watch (and, if he wished, occasionally to join) anglers along the Stour. He was to exhibit a different subject entitled *Boys Fishing* (near a lock on the Stour) in 1813.[4]

The composition of NG 6510 developed from an oil sketch now known as *Anglers at Stratford Mill*, made on the spot in the summer of 1811;[5] upright in shape, this concentrates on the close proximity of the mill islet to the river-bank, from which three boys are fishing, while other children fish or look on from the convenient perch of a low timber construction (serving the purpose of protecting the bank from the bumps of barges). The figure of a rider watering his horse on the left, already observed in this sketch, was to be retained throughout.

The 1811 sketch remained with Constable, among the material which accompanied him to London when he settled there in 1817. It was thus available for reference when, probably some eight years after making his sketch, he began to contemplate painting a large picture of the scene. Details from a pencil sketchbook used in Suffolk and Essex in 1813[6] were used around 1819 in the composition of *Stratford Mill*: a study of river weeds and water-lilies (chiefly of their leaves) was used for a detail in the foreground on the extreme right, and a study of four irregular bits of timber, conjoined, was used for a makeshift mooring-post on the river-bank, in the foreground right of centre. In this subject, with the mill-wheel on the extreme left, the willow dying (not growing) aslant the river, the wooden fence surrounding the islet and the odd chunks of timber serving as a fender to keep barges from bumping into the river-bank, there was ample scope for Constable to indulge his delight in 'the sound of water escaping from Mill dams ... Willows, Old rotten Banks, slimy posts, & brickwork'.[7]

In a small and swiftly painted oil sketch (fig. 1)[8] probably made in 1820 (possibly earlier), and roughly a quarter of the size of the eventual finished work, Constable roughed in his developing ideas for the composition of a large painting,

though many changes were to be made. This rapid sketch is horizontal in format to include a wider group of trees on the left bank and a broad stretch of the River Stour flowing from the right and meandering through the centre of the picture.

It was followed by a full-scale preparatory oil sketch (fig. 2),[9] now in the collection of the Yale Center for British Art, probably made shortly before the finished painting, following his procedure the previous year with *A View on the Stour near Dedham* (*'The White Horse'*). The Yale sketch clearly reveals how much Constable has added (not just in size) to the first idea of 1811. The landscape has broadened and greatly lightened. The small clump of trees in the upright sketch has widened, and has been divided into two by a river inlet, with shafts of sunlight playing between the trees and upon a narrow wooden gate[10] which serves as a focal point along the left bank; further along it, a dying willow leans over the river, and further still another rivulet allows a glimpse of a farmhouse. The River Stour, hardly conspicuous in the 1811 sketch, now plays a peaceable central role in the composition. On its further bank, an unladen barge is being moored to the bank, two men in it, another beside it, all seemingly with time to spare rather than at work;[11] beyond them, the river takes a leisurely bend towards distant green meadows and slopes where farm animals graze. The finished painting was to remain broadly faithful to the trees and river of the large oil sketch, though Constable handled many details differently; the dying willow is more starkly seen, and the feeling of distance is increased by a softer focus on the gate and farmhouse (fig. 3), by subduing detail on the distant slopes, and by piling up and darkening the clouds above them to suggest showers further off. But the most immediately noticeable changes are in the foreground figures.

Comparison of fig. 2 and NG 6510 makes most of these changes immediately apparent. In the Yale sketch, there are four foreground figures (and many pentimenti); the awkwardly leaning figure on the left, present in both small oil sketches, has been eliminated, his place taken in the Yale sketch and in the finished picture by part of an uprooted tree trunk, left lying to moulder on the bank. The dominant figure in the Yale sketch – the boy standing, wearing a red waistcoat and holding a long fishing rod fairly high over the water – was not included in the final picture. With his disappearance, the two younger children (a girl and a boy, both kneeling, in minor roles in the Yale sketch) are given different and more active parts in the scene. The boy, no longer a mere spectator, becomes an angler, his rod held high, casting over the water. The girl, now upright and leaning over the river-bank fender to watch, occupies a nearly central place in the foreground. Constable allots to her skirt the prominent patch of bright red which he had 'lost' when discarding the boy in the red

Fig. 1 Sketch for *Stratford Mill*, ?1820. Oil on canvas, 30.5 × 42 cm. Private collection.

waistcoat in the foreground in the Yale sketch; but he deploys the red waistcoat further off, on the back of the angler on the islet bank. Greater tension has been introduced into the figure of the angler seen in profile on the left of this group. In the finished picture his rod (instead of dipping) is held nearly level over the water, its line seemingly taut (that boy is 'undergoing the agony of a bite', Sir George Beaumont reputedly remarked[12]). The general effect of these changes is to free the figures from a somewhat huddled grouping and to concentrate their (and our) attention upon the business of fishing.

Unusually, Constable's correspondence does not record his progress with the picture. Probably his own confidence in it may be inferred from Farington's note on 1 April 1820 that 'Constable called & spoke of a picture he has prepared for the Exhibition but has not & does not intend to consult opinions upon it'.[13] When the Royal Academy exhibition was hung three weeks later, Constable must have been gratified to find that *Stratford Mill* was hung in the Great Room.[14] C.R. Leslie RA vividly remembered Constable's 'noble picture' hanging there; he particularly admired the barge in the middle distance, lying 'with extreme elegance of perspective on the smooth river' and the light clouds which 'throw their shadows over a rising distance of great beauty'. He added: 'It is a view, and when it was painted, was an exact one of Stratford Mill on the Stour, not far from Bergholt.'[15] The picture received generally favourable attention from reviewers; but it did not sell.

Some months later, Constable's friend Archdeacon John Fisher, who had bought *A View on the Stour* ('*The White Horse*') from the previous Royal Academy exhibition for himself, asked if he could purchase *Stratford Mill* to present to John Pern Tinney, the Salisbury solicitor who had recently won a lawsuit for him.[16] Constable agreed to sell it for 100 guineas, a price Fisher considered too low (later referring to the picture as 'our joint present'). But getting the picture away from Constable proved difficult. On its return from the Royal Academy, Constable had worked further upon it, and evidently continued to do so. 'When will Tinney receive his picture?', Fisher enquired on 14 February 1821,[17] nearly two years after it had been 'finished' and exhibited: to which Constable answered that it was 'getting on', and that as soon as its [?new] frame was ready he would 'dispatch it'.[18] Over the next few years Tinney was to discover that getting (and keeping) his picture out of Constable's hands was 'not unlike the gauze handkerchief in the bramble bush'.[19]

Stratford Mill appears to have reached Tinney by mid-July 1821,[20] but not to have been what Tinney most wanted in the house he had newly refurbished for his bride: Fisher reported that there it looked like 'an emerald in a dish of

Fig. 2 Full-scale sketch for *Stratford Mill*, 1820. Oil on canvas, 131 × 184 cm. New Haven, Yale Center for British Art, Paul Mellon Collection.

Fig. 3 *Stratford Mill*, detail

rubbish', in a room 'exactly like the best parlour of an opulent stockbroker', with an enormous brass chandelier and 'a clock stuck round with gilt cupids like the chimney peice ornaments in the breakfast scene of Marriage a la mode', hanging low, under a Venetian scene and surrounded by 'pannels of brown varnish yclept "old masters" '.[21]

The Tinneys might have been happier with their white elephant if Constable had been content to leave it alone; but as Reynolds notes, Constable 'found it difficult to relinquish control over his paintings even when they had been sold, and since he regarded *Stratford Mill* as one of his most important works he expected to have the use of it when he suited him'.[22] He borrowed it back three times, each time having to arrange (with Fisher's help) for a substitute in the Tinneys' drawing-room. Constable first requested its return to his studio in October 1823, so that he could work on 'toning' it. Tinney was reluctant; though he admired Constable's work sufficiently to have discussed two further commissions,[23] he was a solicitor and (not unreasonably) regarded a picture sold as a picture 'finished'. Moreover, as Fisher reported:

> he dreads your touching the picture. This of course is not his own thought, for he would not discover any alteration you might make. But it is the suggestion of [F.C.] Lewis the engraver. 'There is a look of nature about the picture', says Lewis, 'which seems as if it were introduced by magic. This, when Constable gets it on his easil, he may in an unlucky moment destroy: and he will never paint another picture like it, for he has unfortunately taken to copy himself.' You must take the sweet & the bitter together. Lewis seemed to speak, Tinney said, as if he reported the opinion of other artists as well as himself.[24]

After Archdeacon Fisher's assurances ('I have told Tinney that you only want to tone the picture down: & that you will not alter a line or leaf without consulting him'[25]), the picture returned to Constable's studio in Charlotte Street.

It stayed there for eight or nine months, during which time Constable 'got to work' at 'toning & improving Tinney's picture', with help from Sir George Beaumont, who happened to call on 3 June 1823 ('He thinks it one of my best & admirable in color & light & shade'[26]); he also 'did up' the frame. When the return of *Stratford Mill* was already long overdue, Constable announced that he would like to retain it for inclusion in the British Institution's first loan exhibition of works by living British artists, to be held in the summer of 1825. Tinney, recognising the importance of this exhibition, agreed to lend to it, but insisted that his *Stratford Mill* should meanwhile be returned to him ('He particularly wishes for it at the Music meeting, the 16th August. You will do well to send it directly....'[27]). When Constable later requested that *Stratford Mill* should proceed from the British Institution to the opening exhibition of the Royal Scottish Academy in Edinburgh, Tinney refused point blank. *Stratford Mill* was back in Salisbury by 26 November 1825, leaving Constable convinced that Tinney had acted like 'a dog in the manger', and hinting that he might ask for it again ('I want to copy the picture').[28]

In 1834, two years after Tinney's death, Constable borrowed *Stratford Mill* from a reluctant Mrs Tinney for David Lucas to engrave, though by now even he took her point that 'it completely unfurnishes the drawing room'.[29] It was away for another six months or so, returning only after Constable quarrelled with Lucas over the latter's proposal to publish his *Stratford Mill* engraving as a companion to one after another (unspecified) artist; then Constable demanded the picture's return, claiming: 'I want to have it again safely lodged in her house – not to be disturbed again, at least by me.' Lucas's mezzotint of the picture was eventually published in 1840, after Constable's death, with the engraved title *The Young Waltonians*; according to Constable's first biographer C.R. Leslie RA, this was 'a title he certainly would not have given it',[30] but one which was in some future loan exhibitions transferred to the painting itself. Perhaps thankfully, Mrs Tinney sold the picture in 1848 to George Salting's friend and fellow-collector Charles Huth.

NOTES

1. In order of their exhibition at the RA (and with their original exhibition titles followed by the titles by which they are now generally known), they are:
(i) 1819: 'A Scene on the River Stour' (*The White Horse*), 51¾ × 74 in.; Frick Collection, New York (R. 19.1).
(ii) 1820: 'Landscape' (*Stratford Mill*; after Constable's death sometimes called 'The Young Waltonians'), 50 × 72 in.; NG 6510 above.
(iii) 1821: 'Landscape; Noon' (*The Hay Wain*), 51¼ × 73 in., NG 1207, pp. 42–9.
(iv) 1822: *View on the Stour near Dedham*, 51 × 74 in.; Huntington Art Gallery, San Marino, California (R.22.1).
(v) 1824: 'The Lock' (*A Boat passing a Lock*), 56 × 47 in.; Thyssen-Bornemisza Collection, Switzerland (R.24.1).
(vi) 1825: 'Landscape' (*The Leaping Horse*), 56 × 73¾ in.; Royal Academy of Arts, London (R.25.1).

2. Reynolds 1984, p. xiii.

3. For a concise description of the course of the River Stour as depicted by Constable, see Smart and Brooks 1976, pp. 20–1 and map on p. 30; for Stratford Mill (replaced about 1850) and a photograph of its site (and much reduced substance), see ibid., pp. 76–7, fig. 42.

4. Exh. RA 1813 (266); present whereabouts uncertain. Reynolds 1996, cat. no. 13.3, pp. 179–80, Lucas's mezzotint repr. plate 990.

5. Exh. Tate Gallery 1991 (97, repr. in colour).

6. Reynolds 1963, pp. 77–86, cat. no. 121; sketchbook study of water-lilies p. 55 (plate 87), and of four pieces of timber p. 77 (plate 91); see also Reynolds 1984, p. 43.

7. Constable to Fisher, 23 October 1821, *JCC*, vol. VI, p. 77.

8. Private collection; Reynolds 1984, cat. no. 20.3, plate 131; exh. Tate Gallery 1991 (98, repr. in colour).

9. Reynolds 1984, cat. no. 20.2, p. 44, including a note on its false signature; exh. Tate Gallery 1991 (99, repr. in colour). This sketch, sold from Wynn Ellis's collection in 1876, re-emerged in 1982, was not accepted by many Constable experts at the time but was revealed after cleaning to be demonstrably authentic. See Cormack 1986, pp. 71–83, repr., with details.

10. See Ian Fleming-Williams in ed. Charles Leggatt, *Constable, A Master Draughtsman*, exh. cat., Dulwich Picture Gallery and Art Gallery of Ontario 1994, p. 188 and fig. 88, for the suggestion that the hut [or gate?] flanked by poplars is based on a sepia ink and grey wash sketch of 1798 (Reynolds 1996, cat. no. 98.22, plate 74).

11. A recent description of the figures in *Stratford Mill* as being 'absorbed in their tasks' (Bermingham 1987, p. 138) seems not to allow for the fact that labourers had some time off.

12. Leslie 1845, p. 84.

13. Farington, *Diary*, vol. XVI, p. 5487.

14. Of the 'six-footers' exhibited between 1819–25 (see note 1), *View on the Stour near Dedham* (1822) and *The Lock* (1824) were to be hung in the Great Room; the 'six-footers' of 1819, 1821 (*The Hay Wain*, NG 1207) and 1825 (like *The Cornfield*, NG 130) were hung in the Academy's School of Painting.

15. Leslie 1951, p. 77.

16. See *JCC*, vol. VI, pp. 60–1; as Beckett notes, correspondence does not cover negotiations over the sale of the picture, which was presumably discussed between Fisher and Constable in conversation.

17. Fisher to Constable, *JCC*, vol. VI, p. 62.

18. Constable to Fisher, '1821', *JCC*, vol. VI, p. 63.

19. Fisher to Constable, 21 November 1825, *JCC*, vol. VI, p. 209.

20. Fisher to Constable, *JCC*, vol. VI, p. 69.

21. Fisher to Constable, 16 February 1822, *JCC*, vol. VI, p. 84, enclosing a sketch showing the position of *Stratford Mill* and other pictures in Tinney's drawing-room. 'An emerald in a dish of rubbish', was evidently a quotation from Constable himself; Beckett (p. 84, n. 1) notes that he was to reuse the phrase in a lecture of 1836.

22. Reynolds 1984, p. 44.

23. For these, and the disputes they led to, see Reynolds 1984, p. 44.

24. Fisher to Constable, 2 October 1823, *JCC*, vol. VI, pp. 134–5.

25. Fisher to Constable, 23 October 1823, *JCC*, vol. VI, p. 141.

26. Constable's journal entries made for his wife, 3 June 1824, *JCC*, vol. II, p. 324.

27. Fisher to Constable, 6 August 1824, *JCC*, vol. VI, p. 179.

28. Constable to Fisher, *JCC*, vol. VI, p. 210. Constable adds 'I think it was unkind if not unjust in Tinney not allowing me the picture. I am now cut off from any prospects in that quarter [Scotland]...'; 14 January 1814, p. 213: 'it is on his [Tinney's] part a dog in the manger business – and he must re-win my good opinion, by some act of friendship – I want to copy the picture.'

29. Constable to Lucas, n.d. [1834], *JCC*, vol. IV, p. 409; and ibid., vol. VI, p. 263.

30. See *JCC*, vol. IV, pp. 409, 411–12; Leslie 1845, p. 84, n. [1].

NG 2651

Salisbury Cathedral and Leadenhall from the River Avon

1820
Oil on canvas, 52.7 × 77 cm (20¾ × 30¼ in.), including extensions of *c.* 3 cm at top and at each side (see Technical Notes below)

Provenance
Unsold during the artist's lifetime; by descent to Isabel Constable (d. 1888); presumably purchased from her executors by the dealers Boussod & Valladon, by whom sold to Agnew's 4 June 1891; purchased from Agnew's by George Salting 13 June 1891;[1] part of the Salting Bequest to the National Gallery 1910.

Exhibited
Probably London, Grosvenor Gallery, 1889 (294, 'Sketch for a "Salisbury", 20½ × 30 in., lent by Isabel Constable'[2]); NG, Room XV, *Pictures from the Salting Bequest*, 1910 (no catalogue); Tate Gallery 1991 (137).

At the Tate Gallery 1960–1.

Literature
Davies 1946, p. 33; R.B. Beckett, 'Constable at Leydenhall', *Burlington Magazine*, XCIV, 1952, pp. 115–16; Davies 1959, pp. 20–1; Reynolds 1977, pp. 12–14; Reynolds 1981, pp. 136–7, 141; Reynolds 1984, no. 20.51, plate 173; Parris and Fleming-Williams 1991, pp. 253–4, no. 137 (repr., with colour detail, p. 254).

Copy
by John Dunthorne, oil on canvas, 52.1 × 76.2 cm, made for Archdeacon John Fisher in 1827 (see p. 39).

Technical Notes
In good condition. There are additions approximately 3 cm wide at the top and at both sides. The X-radiograph shows that the main piece of canvas was cut at these three sides after it had been painted. The tacking margin at the bottom edge, where the canvas is markedly cusped, has also been removed. The additions, which are butt-joined to the main piece of canvas, are held in place by a lining canvas. The X-radiograph shows that the canvas of the additions has a slightly closer weave and a denser ground than the main piece of canvas. The paint on the additions is similar to and overlaps the paint on the main piece of canvas.

The warm buff-coloured ground shows through the paint of the sky, and has been left exposed in many places in the foliage and foreground.

Constable painted Salisbury Cathedral many times,[3] from different viewpoints and in a manner which varies from *plein air* oil sketches such as NG 2651 to large pictures painted for exhibition. He first visited Salisbury in 1811, returning briefly (twice) in 1816. NG 2651 was painted during his longest visit, for six weeks, with his wife and two children, in the summer of 1820. He was to return in 1821, for three weeks, and in 1823 for four days. His last visit, for about a month in July 1829, inspired *Salisbury Cathedral from the Meadows* (fig. 2), which Constable himself referred to as 'the Great Salisbury';[4] exhibited in 1831, it has been on loan to the National Gallery since 1983.[5]

Outside Suffolk, no other place was so often in Constable's thoughts as Salisbury; he felt himself 'almost abiding' there, 'so much does this city, by a singular chance associate to my life'.[6] That 'singular chance' was his encounter, in Suffolk and probably in 1798, with Reverend John Fisher DD, who in 1807 was to become Bishop of Salisbury; earlier, his benefices had included the living of Langham, near East Bergholt, where the Constable family lived. On one of the rare visits he actually made to his Suffolk parish, he was kind to the young Constable. As 'J. Sarum', as he signed himself from 1807 (the year in which he was also appointed Chaplain of the Royal Academy), the Bishop invited Constable to make his first visit to Salisbury. Constable spent about three weeks in the autumn of 1811 staying in the Bishop's Palace, with a commission to paint the Bishop's portrait.[7]

For Constable, Salisbury came to embody above all the most rewarding friendship of his life, with the Bishop's nephew and namesake, Archdeacon John Fisher:[8] it was there, he wrote, that 'our friendship ... first took so deep a root.'[9] Over the next twenty years, they met when Fisher came to London or when Constable could get away to Salisbury; as noted under *Weymouth Bay* (NG 2652, pp. 26–9), it was Fisher who performed Constable's marriage ceremony in London in 1816 and had the Constables to stay in Osmington Vicarage during their honeymoon. Constable's portrait of Fisher, presumably begun at Osmington, with a companion portrait of Fisher's wife Mary, is reproduced here (fig. 1).[10]

Fisher, twelve years younger than Constable, enjoyed all the preferments which nepotism could decently bestow; only those of immediate relevance are noted here.[11] A minor canon of Salisbury Cathedral from 1812, he was given the living of Osmington in Dorset the following year. At the age of 29, in 1817, Fisher was installed as Archdeacon of Berkshire, then in the diocese of Salisbury; two years later, he became a canon residentiary of Salisbury Cathedral, and was granted the use for his life of Leadenhall, the oldest canonical house in the Cathedral Close, where Constable was to stay on future visits to Salisbury.[12]

For over twenty years, Constable and Fisher corresponded, intermittently and unguardedly. Their letters (edited and fully annotated by R.B. Beckett[13]) offer the most revealing insight into Constable's personality apart from his own works. It was in correspondence with Fisher that Constable confided his ambitions to be a 'natural painter'; it was Fisher's account of feeling 'as happy as "a careless boy"' during a day's fishing

Fig. 2 Sketch for *The Hay Wain*, *c.*1820. Oil on paper on panel, 12.5 × 18 cm. New Haven, Yale Center for British Art, Paul Mellon Collection.

The dominant motif in *The Hay Wain* is of course the passage of the 'wain' or wagon through the water. As Reynolds notes, scenes showing a cart going through a ford recur in Flemish and Dutch landscape paintings.[24] Constable's sale in 1838 included two 'Landscapes' by Van Goyen, one with travellers in a cart, the other with wagons descending a hill; he also owned an 'Upright landscape with water and figures' by Siberechts,[25] and may have been familiar with the engraving of Siberechts's *Wagon crossing a Ford*,[26] to which *The Hay Wain* comes closest in subject matter. Knowledge that Flemish painters had made such unheroic incidents the focus of their paintings is likely to have fortified Constable from the start of his own career.

Some influence from Rubens's *An Autumn Landscape with a View of Het Steen in the Early Morning* (now NG 66)[27] is apparent in *The Hay Wain*, both in the breadth of its composition and in the oddly 'Flemish' appearance of the 'wain'. Rubens enthusiasts tend to see a greater influence here than do Constable scholars. In the catalogue of the 1996 *Rubens's Landscapes* exhibition, *The Hay Wain* was described as 'a profound meditation upon – as well as a reinterpretation of – the *Landscape with Het Steen*'.[28] Certainly Constable had studied the *Landscape with Het Steen* over the years, and greatly admired it. He first saw it in February 1804, when he was aged 27 and the 'great Rubens', newly acquired by his kindly mentor Sir George Beaumont, was *in restauro* in the studio of Benjamin West PRA.[29] Later that day Constable told Farington that it was the finest work by Rubens that he had seen;[30] but revealingly, he went on to comment on James Ward's almost equally large landscape *St Donat's Castle, Glamorganshire, Bulls Fighting*,[31] painted in direct emulation of the *Landscape with Het Steen*, and hanging with it in West's studio. Constable remarked that Ward's picture 'shewed How inferior a production made up upon a picture is to one that is founded on original observation of nature'. Constable's resolve to pursue 'a natural painture' predated his knowledge of the Rubens,[32] and was not shaken by it.

Constable had other opportunities to see landscapes by Rubens. He is unlikely to have missed the British Institution's *Rubens, Rembrandt and Vandyke* exhibition of 1815, in which some of the greatest of all Rubens's landscapes hung together in one room, presenting the unique chance to see together the

Fig. 3
Full-scale sketch for *The Hay Wain*, ?1820.
Oil on canvas, 137 × 188 cm.
London, Victoria and Albert Museum.

Fig. 4 *A cart and horses, with a carter and dog* (study for *The Stour Valley and Dedham Village*), 1814. Oil on paper, 16.5 × 23.8 cm (detail). London, Victoria and Albert Museum.

Landscape with Het Steen (10) and its companion, *The Rainbow Landscape* (8: now Wallace Collection), as well as the Duke of Buccleuch's *The Watering Place* (17: now NG 4815), Marquess Camden's *Landscape with a Wagon at Sunset* (18: now in the Museum Boymans-van Beuningen, Rotterdam) and the Earl of Mulgrave's *Landscape with Moon and Stars* (19: now Courtauld Gallery). In 1836, in the third of his lectures on the history of landscape painting, Constable described the *Landscape with Het Steen* and its 'companion' *The Rainbow Landscape* as among the finest works of 'the magnificent Rubens'.[33] Rubens, he declared, imparted a 'joyous and animated character' to landscape, 'impressing on the level monotonous scenery of Flanders all the richness which belongs to its noblest features'. He observed that Rubens 'delighted in phenomena – rainbows upon a stormy sky, – bursts of sunshine, – moonlight, – meteors, – and impetuous torrents ...'. If any of Constable's works were to be singled out as revealing a strong Rubens influence, it should perhaps be *Hampstead Heath with a Rainbow*,[34] painted in 1836, while Constable was giving this series of lectures. What Constable chiefly responded to was Rubens's skill in capturing 'effects' of nature: 'dewy light and freshness, the departing shower, with the exhilaration of the returning sun, effects which Rubens, more than any other painter, has perfected on canvas'; if Constable emulated Rubens, it was in striving to render similar effects of nature.[35] There is, surely, more 'original observation of nature' in *The Hay Wain* than there is a 're-interpretation' of Rubens. Contemporaries saw the influence of Ruysdael, not Rubens. Constable's admiration for the *Landscape with Het Steen* seems chiefly to have acted as a liberating force, stimulating him to introduce breadth and distance (though hardly a Rubensian 'world view') into his own picture of 'a small corner of Suffolk'.[36]

Constable himself did not call his picture *The Hay Wain*. That title was a nickname bestowed on it by Archdeacon Fisher when, asking about the picture's progress in a letter to Constable of 14 February 1821, he enquired 'And how thrives the "hay wain"?';[37] after that both friends several times refer to the picture as 'the wain'. The wagon Constable depicts does not conform to the usual design of hay wagons or carts of the period; as many correspondents (particularly from Suffolk) have pointed out, its sides are too low for carting hay, and it seems better suited to carting timber.[38] An artist's needs must on occasion modify accuracy. At that central point of his picture, Constable could not introduce a wagon which would bulk large, or nullify his carefully judged effect of surrounding water. By 1821 Constable had made many studies of other horses and carts;[39] but he had no material on hand for the sort of low wagon he had in mind. Tied to his London studio, he realised that he needed more local information. His brother Abram arranged for John Dunthorne, the East Bergholt-born artist who sometimes assisted Constable,[40] to make 'outlines of a scrave or harvest waggon'; in mid-February, Dunthorne obliged, though he 'had a very cold job'. The result appears to be much less robust than the high-loaded wagon we see in the hayfield itself. The slatted sides of Constable's 'hay wain' would enable it to carry an occasional load of hay, perhaps for a farmer lacking a cart appropriate to every purpose. From his request to Dunthorne for a sketch, Constable evidently recalled seeing something like this in Suffolk. He may also have wanted a cart similar to those in Rubens's landscapes; if his 'hay wain' is unlike any contemporary English hay wagon, it is curiously close to Rubens's chalk study of a hay-cart for *Return from the Harvest*.[41] The wheels of Constable's hay wain are typical of all wagon- and cart-wheels of this period. They are of wood, shod with hoops or tyres of iron; in hot weather, the wooden parts of the wheels contracted and the iron tyres came loose. The wagon's route through the shallows to the ford is not only the nearest way to the hayfield, but will also enable the wooden rims of the wheels to soak up water and expand to grip the tyres firmly.[42] There appear to be three horses: a pair, with a third horse harnessed in front.

Constable's fondness for touches of red finds expression here in the thick red fringes decorating the leather collars or housen worn above the horses' neck-harness (the hames, to which the harness was hooked, and whose two open ends can be seen behind each horse's neck).[43] Housen had evolved as a form of protection against rain (wet harness could blister horses' necks), and were chiefly used in winter. Coloured woollen fringes were sometimes added for decoration, but appear to have been reserved for special events, such as ploughing matches or other journeys away from the farm. On black or dark bay horses, red-fringed housen contributed a note of brightness which evidently pleased Constable so much that he adorned the housen of horses on quite humdrum tasks with red fringes; they appear for instance on the dark bay cart-horses beside a dunghill in *The Stour Valley and Dedham Village* exhibited in 1815 (see fig. 4),[44] and on those drawing a sand- or gravel-cart in the small *Hampstead Heath* of 1821,[45] painted at about the same time as *The Hay Wain*. To equally bright effect, red fringes decorate the eponymous *White Horse*, and finally appear on the cart-horses in *Salisbury Cathedral from the Meadows* (a work of 1831 which increasingly seems to hint at some conflation between two places particularly dear to Constable, Salisbury and Suffolk). David Lucas noted that one of Constable's father's barge men 'found fault with his puting housings on a towing horse when he had to explain to his satisfaction that the object in doing so was that he might have the oppertunity of introducing the bright red colour of the fringe as an contrasting one in opposition to the greens'.[46]

In answer to Fisher's enquiry of 14 February 1821 ('how thrives the "hay wain"?'), Constable replied that it was 'getting on'; but he confided: 'Believe – my very dear Fisher – I should almost faint by the way when I am standing before my large canvasses was I not cheered and encouraged by your friendship and approbation ...'[47] Abram Constable, who saw the picture in his brother's studio towards the end of February, had 'faint hopes' that it would be ready for the exhibition: 'there appear'd everything to do'.[48] Calling on Constable on 9 April, Farington 'saw his new picture in a frame'; the following day it was despatched to the Royal Academy,[49] with its given title 'Landscape: Noon'. Reviewers of the exhibition generally praised the picture, *The Examiner* declaring that it 'approaches nearer to the actual look of rural nature than any modern landscape whatever';[50] but it did not sell. When it returned to his studio, Constable did some further work on it, perhaps, as Reynolds suggests, improving the balance between sky and the other elements of landscape with the knowledge gained through a series of sky studies made at Hampstead in the summers of 1821–2.[51]

Constable was probably unaware at the time that two French visitors to England had seen his picture in the Royal Academy exhibition: the artist Géricault (then aged 30) and the writer Charles Nodier. According to Delacroix, Géricault returned to France 'quite stunned' by Constable's picture,[52] while the romantic writer Charles Nodier rhapsodised over it in his *Promenade De Dieppe aux Montagnes d'Ecosse*, published within a few months of the exhibition:[53] singling out Constable's picture, he suggested that French artists should similarly look to nature instead of solely to the 'voyage de Rome' for inspiration:

> La palme de l'exposition est due à un grand paysage de Constable, auquel les maîtres anciens et modernes ont peu de chefs-d'œuvre à opposer. De près, ce sont de larges empâtements de couleurs mal étendues qui offensent le tact à l'égal de la vue, par leur grossière inégalité. De quelques pas, c'est une campagne pittoresque, une maison rustique, une rivière basse dans les petits flots blanchissent sur les cailloux, un char de paysan qui traverse le gué. C'est de l'eau, de l'air et du ciel; c'est Ruysdael, Wouvermans, ou Constable.

Scenting a coup, the Anglo-French dealer John Arrowsmith came over from Paris when Constable re-exhibited the picture at the British Institution the following spring (priced at 150 guineas[54]), and offered him £70 for it. The figure was disappointing; but although Constable reported 'some nibbles' at the picture, they had come to nothing. Arrowsmith's talk of it forming 'part of an exhibition in Paris – to show them the nature of the English art' – was attractive, and might bring commissions; and he was very hard up ('painting these large pictures have much impoverished me', for they prevented him from undertaking 'jobs' for money). 'I hardly know what to do', Constable wrote to Fisher on 13 April 1822, in a letter which discusses his dilemma (and also begs for a loan of £20 or £30).[55] For the moment he did nothing. In July 1823 Fisher told Constable that much as he himself would have liked 'to possess your "wain"', he could at present afford to do no more than ask for first offer of it; he thought it would be 'of most value to your children, by continuing to hang where it is, till you join the society of Ruysdael Wilson & Claude'.[56] But when 'the Frenchman' returned to London in January 1824 to renew negotiations, this time proposing to exhibit the picture in the forthcoming Paris Salon and hinting that there it would be bought for the Louvre, Fisher's advice was crisp: 'Let your Hay Cart go to Paris by all means. ... The stupid English public, which has no judgment of its own, will begin to think that there is something in you if the French make your works national property.'[57] Constable followed this advice, driving something of a bargain with 'the Frenchman': he agreed to sell *The Hay Wain*, *View on the Stour near Dedham* (his latest six-footer) and a small *Yarmouth Jetty* to Arrowsmith for £250.[58]

Arrowsmith sent these three pictures to the Salon in 1824. A full account of the sensation they caused is given by Beckett 1956. Delacroix went at least twice to see them, returning to his studio to give new life to his *Massacres de Scio* by adding touches of pure colour in Constable's manner,[59] and Stendhal wrote enthusiastically about them ('Truth for me has an immediate and irresistible charm');[60] a more conservative critic considered that 'the swamps of M. Constable' were enjoying merely a fashionable success, and could detect in his work 'hardly more than a palette brilliantly set out'.[61] Constable commented almost bemusedly: 'Think of the lovely valleys mid the peacefull farm houses of Suffolk, forming a scene of exhibition to amuse the gay & frivolous Parisians.'[62]

The Louvre did not buy *The Hay Wain* (perhaps because Arrowsmith insisted in 1824 that the three pictures should be sold together for £500); but its Director (M. le Conte de Fourbin) publicly expressed his high admiration of it, while Frédéric Villot, its Keeper of Paintings, was to write that French landscape painting had hitherto awaited its messiah: 'Il se manifesta enfin, aux yeux des artistes étonnés, par des œuvres exposées au Salon de 1824, et ce messie se nommait Constable.'[63] The Salon exhibition prompted some commissions; but Arrowsmith's precarious finances (and the bankruptcy of his fellow-dealer Claude Schroth, also involved in negotiations with Constable) appear to have doomed *The Hay Wain* to be shuffled ingloriously around the Parisian art market for the next few years, and probably prevented S.W. Reynolds from carrying out his proposal to engrave it.[64] Recognition from abroad was a comparatively empty honour, when what Constable really wanted (but did not attain until 1829, and then only by one vote) was election as a full Royal Academician. Charles X, King of France, had 99 gold medals to award among the 2,180 exhibits at the Salon of 1824; one of them went to Constable, chiefly for *The Hay Wain* (fig. 5). He could not be persuaded to go over to collect it.[65]

Fig. 5 Gold medal awarded by King Charles X of France to 'Mr Constable, Peintre de Paysage'. Obverse, actual size. National Gallery Archives.

NOTES

References here are chiefly to Reynolds's catalogues raisonnés, 1984, 1996. It should be noted that Parris and Fleming-Williams's grouping of illustrations and commentaries on various material relating to The Hay Wain *(1991, pp. 133–43, plates 58–66; pp. 201–5, plates 100–1) also greatly assists its study.*

The compiler is indebted to John S. Creasey, The Rural History Centre, The University, Reading, for discussing and providing information on the 'wain' and its wheels.

1. An annotated copy of the sale catalogue (BL) includes (after the properties of Mme Preponnier, Demonville and Fossard) an additional MS entry (anon. owner): 'M. Constable, peintre anglais. Paysage, sur le premier plan une charette plein de foin traverse un gué auprès d'une ferme. Grande composition de ce peintre. 2300 fr., Boursault.'

2. See [Michaud], *Biographie Universelle, Ancienne et Moderne*, vol. V, Paris 1854, pp. 336–7. Born *c.*1760, Boursault began his career as an actor (with the stage name Malherbe), was involved in French Revolutionary politics and later made a fortune as theatrical manager. He formed a collection of pictures but sold it *c.*1838, several years before his death at the age of 80 in 1842.

3. Henry Artaria, *A Descriptive Catalogue of the Gallery of Edmund Higginson Esq. of Saltmarsh Castle*, London 1841, p. 285, as 'From the collection of M. Boursault, who bought it at the *Exhibition of English Masters* in Paris'.

4. A surgeon, George Young had been a friend of Constable; he assisted at Constable's post-mortem in 1837 (Beckett 1964, p. 369; Fleming-Williams and Parris 1984, p. 3 n.*) and subscribed ten guineas towards the purchase of *The Cornfield* for presentation to the NG (see NG 130).

5. The 'Waterloo Bridge' picture, laid aside, then begun afresh, has a complex history; it finally took shape as the picture exhibited in 1832, and now in the Tate Gallery. See Reynolds 1984, cat. no. 32.1, plate 819; Parris and Fleming-Williams 1991, pp. 369–72.

6. Farington, *Diary*, vol. XVI, p. 5582.

7. Reynolds 1996, cat. no. 12.1, plate 931.

8. Reynolds 1984, cat. no. 17.1, plate 5.

9. From the description of Flatford Mill, lot 2 in Abram Constable's sale, Ipswich, 31 March 1846, quoted by Beckett, *JCC*, I, p. 312. The property, which included a house and two millers' cottages, etc., was sold for £2000.

10. Davies 1959, p. 13.

11. See Smart and Brooks 1976, p. 135, for a clear and detailed account of the relationship of the various channels of water seen in NG 1207.

12. Smart and Brooks, ibid., note that a few years after Constable's death, Abram Constable agreed with the Stour River Navigation Company to the closing of the ford and the channel. For details of this area, see their reproduction (p. 19) of the East Bergholt Enclosure Award of 1817. The ford is no longer visible.

13. Reynolds 1996, cat. no. 02.13, plate 166; this view is from the south bank of the Stour.

14. For example, Sir Kenneth Clark, in *The Hay Wain*, National Gallery Books no. 5 [n.d.], p. 9.

15. Leslie 1843, p. 18 (1951 edn, p. 45).

16. Lott was a farmer of some substance. Reporting village affairs to their brother, Constable's sisters refer to him as 'Mr Lott' (e.g. 23 February 1817, p. 161; 1 March 1825, p. 219). In July 1824 Lott's Farm was put up for sale by auction at Ipswich (later withdrawn); reporting this to his brother, Abram Constable noted that the farm carried a high Land Tax of £6 18. 0., but he was considering offering £1800 for it: 'its greatest value to these premises as you justly observe is to keep disagreeable people away...' (*JCC* vol. I, p. 216). See J.F. E[lam], 'The Lott Family and "The Cottage"', *East Bergholt Society Newsletter*, no. 14, 1984, pp. 3–4.

17. Abram Constable to John Constable, from Flatford Mill, 2 August 1824, *JCC* vol. I, p. 216.

18. Reynolds 1996, cat. nos. 11.36 (27.3 × 24.2 cm (10¾ × 9½ in.), verso of 11.36), plate 921, and 11.37/38 (each 24.1 × 18.1 cm (9½ × 7⅛ in.), on one sheet of paper, R 11.37 recto, R 11.38 verso), plates 919, 920.

19. Reynolds 1996, cat. no. 16.23, plate 1291.

20. Ibid., cat. no. 14.46, plate 1192; see his cat. no. 14.47, plate 1193 for the small open-air oil sketch which precedes this. The painting was engraved by David Lucas in mezzotint for Constable's *Various Subjects of Landscape, Characteristic of English Scenery* (now generally known as *English Landscape Scenery*), 1831, with the title 'Mill Stream' (Shirley no. 25). See Michael Kitson, 'John Constable 1810–1816: A Chronological Study', *JWCI*, XX, 1957, pp. 339, 343, 351, 354–7.

21. Reynolds 1984, cat. no. 21.3, plate 215; see also Cormack 1986, pp. 128–9, but note that his plate 126 considerably enlarges the actual size of this sketch.

22. Ibid., no. 21.2, plate 214; as Reynolds notes, the sketch is marginally larger than the final picture. Both the full-scale sketch and *The Hay Wain* were formerly owned by Henry Vaughan, whose MS notes on both (NG Library) are discussed by Reynolds.

23. Reynolds 1996, cat. no. 09.77, plate 807.

24. Reynolds 1984, p. 68.

25. Sale Foster's, 15 May 1838, lots 2 and 13 by 'Van Goyen', lot 19 by 'Siberechts', 'Upright landscape with water and figures'; so far unidentified.

26. Museum Boymans-van Beuningen, Rotterdam; repr. E. Plietzsch, *Hollandische und Flamische Maler des XVII. Jahrh.*, Leipzig 1983, fig. 396.

27. In the third of his 1836 lectures on the history of landscape painting (Beckett, *Discourses*, 1970, p. 61), Constable discussed the work of 'the magnificent Rubens', with particular reference to 'the pair of landscapes, which came to England from Genoa, one of which is now in the National Gallery', i.e. *Landscape with a View of Het Steen* (NG 66), presented by Sir George Beaumont in 1826, and its 'companion', *The Rainbow Landscape*, which in 1836 belonged to Lord Orford, and is now in the Wallace Collection.

28. Brown 1996, p. 108.

29. Owen and Brown exh. cat. 1988, p. 24.

30. Farington, *Diary*, 10 February 1804; vol. VI, p. 2239: 'Constable called. – Had been to Mr West's, and seen the Landscape by Rubens belonging to Sr G. Beaumont, – which He thought the finest of the Master that He had seen...'

31. Oil on panel, 132 × 228 cm; V&A, repr. in colour, *100 Great Paintings in the Victoria and Albert Museum*, London 1985, p. 101. Very usefully, reproductions of the Rubens and the Ward are juxtaposed in Owen and Brown 1988, pp. 146–7, plates 61, 62.

32. Constable to John Dunthorne, 29 May 1802: 'For the past two years I have been running after pictures and seeking the truth at second hand ... I shall shortly return to Bergholt where I shall make some laborious studies from nature – and I shall endeavour to get a pure and unaffected representation of the scenes that may employ me. ... There is little or nothing in the exhibition worth looking up to – there is room enough for a natural painture.'

33. Lecture of 9 June 1836, given at the Royal Institution; Beckett 1970, p. 61.

34. Reynolds 1984, cat. no. 36.7, plate 1057; and see Parris and Fleming-Williams 1991, p. 382, no. 219.

35. The much-repeated statement that Constable painted a copy of *Landscape with a View of Het Steen* (e.g. Martin 1970, p. 140, under 'Copies'; p. 141 n. 31 referring to C.R. Leslie, *Memoirs of the Life of John Constable, Esq. RA*, ed. Shirley, London 1937, p. 156) appears to be mistaken. The only copy of a Rubens Constable is known to have made is the picture in his studio sale, 15 May 1838 (53), called 'Landscape and Cattle', perhaps copied from the 'lovely little Rubens' which Beaumont lent him in 1824, three years after *The Hay Wain* was finished. Leslie recounts that when Constable stayed with the Beaumonts at Coleorton in 1823, he 'made a sketch from a landscape by Rubens'. This was thereafter assumed to mean that Constable copied *Landscape with Het Steen*; but Constable's own letters from Coleorton (fully describing the copies from Claude which he made on that occasion) do not mention Rubens. Constable does however record that in the following year, 1824, Beaumont lent him 'his lovely little Rubens' ('Journal', 7 July 1824, *JCC*, vol. II, p. 356: this picture, possibly the 'little landscape' mentioned by Owen and Brown 1988, p. 23, is unidentified, but the phrase 'lovely little Rubens' cannot possibly refer to the *Landscape with Het Steen*.

36. Smart and Brooks's phrase, 1976, p. 133.

37. *JCC*, vol. VI, p. 62.

38. For extensive correspondence on this point see the *East Anglian Daily Times* (Ipswich), May–June 1977.

39. See Reynolds 1960, notably no. 132 (sketch-book used in Essex and Suffolk 1814) and nos. 134–5 (plate 99).

40. For an account of John Dunthorne, junior (1798–1832), see Fleming-Williams and Parris 1984, pp. 195–204. Constable's letter to Fisher of 17 November 1824 gives some idea of Dunthorne's assistance: 'I have my friend Dunthorne with me [in London] – he cheers & helps me so much that I could wish him always to be with me. He forwards me a great deal in subordinate parts such as tracing, squaring &c &c.' (*JCC*, vol. VI, p.181).

41. See the larger of two studies on the sheet in the collection of the Berliner Staatliche Museen, repr. Brown 1996, p. 49, fig. 43.

42. The compiler is indebted on this point (and many others) to John S. Creasey, The Rural History Centre, The University, Reading (in correspondence).

43. See Terry Keegan, *The Heavy Horse: Its Harness and Harness Decoration*, [Pelham Books] 1973, pp. 66–8. The compiler is indebted for information about red-fringed housen to R.J. and C.J. Clark of Weylands Farm, Stoke by Nayland.

44. Reynolds 1996, cat. no. 15.1 (noting preliminary studies of a cart and horses), plate 1221.

45. Reynolds 1984, cat. no. 21.8, plate 218.

46. Annotation to p. 51 of Lucas's copy of the first edition of C.R. Leslie's *Memoirs of the Life of John Constable Esq. R.A.*, 1843, one of many annotations collected and published by Parris et al. 1975, p. 58.

47. Not dated; *JCC*, vol. VI, p. 63.

48. Abram Constable to John Constable, 25 February 1821; ibid., p. 193.

49. Farington, *Diary*, vol. XVI, p. 5645; ibid., p. 65.

50. See Ivy 1991, pp. 91–3, for this and other reviews.

51. Reynolds 1984, cat. no. 21.1, pp. 68–9; the sky studies are discussed under cat. no. 21.66, p. 85. Constable's well-known letter to Fisher on the importance of the sky in landscape ('The sky is the "source of light" in nature – and governs every thing') was written on 23 October 1821, from Hampstead (*JCC*, vol. VI, pp. 76–8).

52. In a letter of 1858 to Th. Silvestre, Delacroix wrote: 'Constable, homme admirable, est une des gloires anglaises. Je vous en ai déjà parlé et de l'impression qu'il m'avait produite au moment où je peignais le *Massacre de Scio*. Lui et Turner sont de véritables réformateurs. Ils sont sortis de l'ornière des paysagistes anciens. Notre école, qui abonde maintenant en hommes de talent dans ce genre, a grandement profité de leur exemple. Géricault était revenu tout étourdi de l'un des grands paysages qu'il nous a envoyés' (ed. P. Flat and R. Piot, *Journal d'Eugène Delacroix*, I, Paris 1893, p. 9 n. 3).

53. Paris 1821, pp. 84–5, 86; an English trans. was published Edinburgh 1822 (quoted by Ivy 1991, pp. 93–4).

54. *JCC*, vol. VI, p. 86.

55. Ibid., pp. 86–8.

56. 5 July 1823, ibid., p. 123.

57. 18 January 1824, ibid., p. 151.

58. *View on the Stour near Dedham* (which Constable referred to as 'The Bridge'), was exh. RA 1822 and is now coll. Huntington Art Gallery, San Marino, California; Reynolds 1984, cat. no. 22.1. For the version of *Yarmouth Jetty* see Reynolds 1984, cat. no. 22.39.

59. See note 52. Delacroix, 23 September 1846, *Journal*, 2 (ed. P. Flat et R. Piot, 1893, cited in note 52), *Supplément*, pp. 451–2: 'Constable dit que la supériorité du vert de ses prairies tient à ce qu'il est composé d'une multitude de verts différents. Ce qui donne le défait d'intensité et de vie à la verdure du commun des paysagistes, c'est qu'ils font ordinairement d'une teinte uniforme. Ce qu'il dit du vert des prairies, peut s'appliquer à tous les autres tons.' See M. Florisoone, 'Constable and the "Massacres de Scio" by Delacroix', *JWCI*, XX, 1957, pp. 180–5.

60. *Journal de Paris*, 16 and 24 October 1824; see article XIV in the same series.

61. Etienne Delécluze, *Journal des Débats*, 4 April 1828, *Journal de Paris*, 30 November 1824, quoted by Beckett 1956, pp. 252, 250.

62. Constable to Fisher, 8 May 1824, *JCC*, vol. VI, p. 157.

63. 'John Constable', in *Revue Universelle des Arts*, IV, 1857, p. 290.

64. See *JCC*, vol. VI, p. 185, Constable to Fisher, 17 December 1824; vol. IV, pp. 266–7, S.W. Reynolds to Constable, n.d.

65. The medal, awarded for the three landscapes Constable had exhibited at the Salon in 1824, was presented to Constable in 1825 by the French Ambassador to England, the Prince de Polignac; it eventually found its way to an equivalent of Portobello Road and was purchased by Sir Charles Wakefield, who presented it to the NG in 1927. The medal is now in the NG Archives. Electrotype copies of the obverse and reverse of the medal are inset into the frame of *View on the Stour near Dedham* (see note 58), whose exhibition at the Salon of 1824 (359) had helped to earn Constable the medal.

NG 130

The Cornfield

1826
Oil on canvas, 143 × 122 cm (56¼ × 48 in.)
Inscribed *John Constable. f. London. 1826.* in brown, bottom right

Provenance
Unsold in Constable's lifetime; shortly after his death (31 March 1837), purchased from the administrators of his estate for 300 guineas by 113 subscribers, and presented by them to the National Gallery, December 1837.

Exhibited
RA 1826 (225, 'Landscape'); BI 1827 (101, 'Landscape: Noon'); Paris, Salon 1827–8 (219, 'Paysage avec figures et animaux'); Birmingham Society of Arts 1829 (122, 'Noon'); Worcester Institution 1835 (50, 'Harvest – Noon; a Lane Scene'); Tate Gallery 1976 (242, repr.); New York 1983 (23, repr. in colour); Tate Gallery 1991 (165, repr. in colour p.303, with detail p.302); NG, *At Home with Constable's Cornfield*, 1996 (exhibits unnumbered).

At the Tate Gallery 1960–1.

Literature
Davies 1946, pp. 22–3; Davies 1959, pp. 9–11; Reynolds 1965, pp. 105–8; Smart and Brooks 1976, pp. 107–19; Rosenthal 1983, pp. 172–9; Reynolds 1984, pp. 167–8; Parris and Fleming-Williams 1991, pp. 301–5.

Engraved
(1) in mezzotint by David Lucas (Shirley no. 36) as a pair to *The Lock* (Shirley no. 35), first published by F.G. Moon and others 2 June 1834, without a title (repr. Shirley facing p. 199); republished by F.G. Moon and others 1 July 1834, entitled *LANDSCAPE.*; (2) in line by C. Cousen for publication in the *Art Journal*, 1869, facing p. 10.

Copies
A faithful copy approximately the same size was made (? *c.*1840–50) by the artist Frederick Waters Watts (1800–70), Constable's emulator[1] (indistinctly inscribed and dated, sold Sotheby's 13 April 1994, lot 13, repr.). At least 85 copies were made (or attempted) by students and amateurs on 'Copying Days' at the NG between 1857 and 1889, the years in which the Gallery's annual reports published lists of 'Pictures most frequently copied'.

Technical Notes
Cleaned in 1941. There are no records of treatment between the picture's acquisition in 1837 and its cleaning in 1941, but evidence was found then of an earlier cleaning and restoration. By 1967 the canvas had become so fragile that lining was necessary; before that date there had been a double canvas, the first of which may have been an original loose lining. The picture retains its original turnover. The paint is in very good condition except for some slight abrasion in the sky. The signature is in very thin and transparent paint, not characteristic of Constable's handling.

This vision of a Suffolk lane in high summer was painted in Constable's studio in London during January–March 1826. The lane which winds as if into the cornfield is a recollection of part of Fen Lane, along which Constable had often walked as a schoolboy; the route he would have taken leads from his native village of East Bergholt towards Fen Bridge over the Stour, and thence to Dedham where he attended school (but the bridge and Dedham itself are out of sight in this picture, to the right). The lane still exists, recognisably; but the scene as a whole makes no claim to be an accurate depiction of the countryside beyond it. The church tower and cluster of red-roofed houses which provide a distant focal point beyond the bend of the river 'never existed', as the artist's eldest son, Charles Constable, was later to point out.[2] As any other landscape painter might have done, Constable invented the village for the sake of a vista. His resolve to be a 'natural painter' should not be interpreted as a determination to depict every detail faithfully.

Constable himself did not use the title *The Cornfield.* He first exhibited the picture as 'Landscape', and later with varying titles (given above under Exhibited) in which the word 'Noon' several times figured. He was content for Lucas's mezzotint of the subject to be published in 1834 with his original title, 'Landscape'. The picture seems first to have been dubbed *The Cornfield* by the committee which organised its presentation to the National Gallery in 1837; it has been known as *The Cornfield* ever since. The popular title is used here to avoid confusion; it has after all some sanction in Constable's own summary of the scene as 'inland – cornfields – a close lane, kind of thing...' (in a letter of 8 April 1826 to Archdeacon John Fisher,[3] more fully quoted from below).

Constable appears to have begun work on the picture by mid-January 1826, completing it by 8 April, when he 'dispatched' it to the Royal Academy for the forthcoming exhibition (opening to the public on 1 May). Shortage of time had forced him to work quickly. He had intended that his chief picture in the exhibition should be the large *Waterloo Bridge*, on which he had laboured during 1825; but progress with it was fitful. 'My Waterloo like a blister begins to stick closer & closer – & to disturb my nights', he confided to Fisher on 19 November 1825; by mid-January he reported 'My large picture is at a stand.'[4] For this he blamed 'the ruinous state of my finances', which compelled him to lay *Waterloo Bridge* aside in order to complete various commissions; but it seems that inspiration for it had failed. Working at Brighton during the last days of December and early January 1826, Constable had little trouble in painting the small *Mill at Gillingham, in Dorsetshire*, a commission which provided one good subject to send to the forthcoming Royal Academy exhibition;[5] but his need of a large picture to accompany it now became urgent.

Fig. 2 Sketch for *The Cornfield*. Oil on canvas, 59.7 × 49.2 cm. Private collection, on long loan to Birmingham, City Museums and Art Gallery.

Fig. 1 Study for *The Cornfield*. Oil on canvas, 33 × 20.8 cm. Indianapolis Museum of Art, The Clowes Fund Collection.

Though not one of his 'six-footers', *The Cornfield* was conceived on a sufficiently large scale to embody (in Graham Reynolds's phrase) Constable's 'determination to bid for attention at the Academy through monumental renderings of the Stour scenes which had first suggested pictures to him as a child'.[6] It was conjured up largely from material already in Constable's studio.

The motif of a wooded lane leading to a more sunlit prospect had often recurred in Constable's work since his *Woodland Scene* of 1801,[7] with its echoes from both Ruisdael and Gainsborough. *Dedham Vale from the Coombs*,[8] the following year, was to open up the prospect beyond the lane in a way which anticipates *The Cornfield*. What is probably Constable's first conception of *The Cornfield* is expressed in a very free oil sketch now in Indianapolis (fig. 2).[9] In this, most of the elements of the finished picture are present, but spontaneously dashed in rather than defined. The basic similarity of composition in the sketch and in the finished picture has previously prompted suspicion that the Indianapolis sketch might be a later artist's impression of Constable's finished picture.[10] Its authenticity was established in 1988 by Charles Rhyne, who suggested that that this may be the work described in Constable's sale, 16 May 1838 (part of lot 14), as 'The Corn Field; a study from nature, for the picture in the National Gallery'.[11] Both Rhyne and Reynolds date this sketch to 1816 (a year in which Constable made several visits to Suffolk), noting its stylistic resemblance to the oil sketch for *Flatford Mill*, exhibited in 1817.[12]

The oil study at present in Birmingham (fig. 1)[13] was almost certainly made in the studio shortly before Constable began work on the finished picture. Omitting all staffage, this study was evidently made to work out how the lie of the land (very broadly indicated in the Indianapolis sketch) is to be credibly represented. The need for 'mapping' was greater than may at first sight appear in the finished picture, since the lane, itself rutted and uneven, bends (and branches off to the right), the bank on the left (where the corn stands tall) is much higher than on the right, the cornfield slopes down towards the river and the more recent idea of a distant village (not present in the Indianapolis sketch) has to be worked in. The finished picture closely follows the landscape contours of the Birmingham study, and echoes most of the falls of light worked out in it. The most notable difference in the finished picture is that a dying tree is substituted for a vigorous one on the left. Minor differences include some reduction in the mass of the trees on the left, and bringing the glimpse of a red-roofed village on the horizon into more clarity on a site near the river-bend. In their catalogue of the 1991 *Constable* exhibition, Parris and Fleming-Williams prefer a different dating; they suggest that the Birmingham study is one of a group of studies from nature which Constable is known to have made in Suffolk in 1817, and is unlikely to have been made with *The Cornfield* specifically in mind;[14] and they see the Indianapolis sketch as the preliminary sketch made in the studio, shortly before Constable began work on the big picture.[15] To this compiler, Reynolds's reasoning is more convincing.

Some of the details were taken from other early studies, probably mostly made on the spot. The boy drinking is adapted from an oil sketch made some fifteen years earlier (fig. 3), probably also made in Fen Lane, though further along it.[16] Constable sometimes referred to his finished picture as 'the drinking boy'.[17] Reynolds suggests that the motif was 'an important symbol for Constable ... possibly recalling similar occasions when he slaked his own thirst when he was walking to school'.[18] The pool from which the boy drinks is presumably fed by an underground spring, of the sort which abound along the Stour; the gently rotting wooden barrier

Fig. 3 *A Lane near Flatford* ('The Drinking Boy'). *c.*1811. Oil on paper laid on canvas, 20.3 × 30.3 cm. London, Tate Gallery.

which protects the pool from encroaching water plants stands here for all the 'slimy posts' and 'old timber props ... &c &c' in which Constable delighted.[19]

On 8 April 1826 Constable was able to report to Fisher:

> I have dispatched a large landscape to the Academy – upright, the size of my Lock – but a subject of a very different nature – inland – cornfields – a close lane, kind of thing – but it is not neglected in any part. The trees are more than usually studied and the extremities well defined – as well as their species – they are shaken by a pleasant and healthfull breeze – 'at noon' – 'while now a fresher gale, *sweeping with shadowy gust the feilds of corn*' &c, &c. I am not without my anxieties – but they are not such as I have too often really deserved – I have not neglected my work or been sparing of my pains... My picture occupied me wholly – I could think of and speak to no one. I was like a friend of mine in the battle of Waterloo – he said he dared not turn his head to the right or left – but always kept it straight forward – thinking of himself alone.

He added: 'I do hope to sell this present picture – as it has certainly got a little more eye-salve than I usually condescend to give to them.'[20]

'More eye-salve' than usual presumably means more charm, or more picturesque details. He did not stint on these. Some of the details are adapted from his earlier works. The donkey cropping the hedgerow on the left in *The Cornfield* is an echo from *Dedham Vale: Morning*, exhibited in 1811;[21] but for *The Cornfield* he made a fresh oil study of the donkey, in the same attitude but with a foal beside her.[22] The decision to include donkeys may have been prompted by the fact that Constable had also turned back to a very early oil painting, perhaps the picture exhibited in 1802 as *Edge of a Wood* (fig. 4),[23] but unsold, which included (as well as a donkey) a tree which he needed for the extreme left of *The Cornfield*. He retained its shape and most of its branches, but converted a living, pollarded tree into one which is half-dying, its upper branches denuded; symbolism has been read into this, but perhaps Constable at that point in his picture chiefly needed to gain emptier space by losing the density of summer foliage. The plough conspicuously placed near the gateposts to the cornfield is taken almost exactly from a finely observed oil sketch inscribed *2d Novr. 1814*; left in the open outside the still unharvested cornfield, its presence there is premature. John Creasey suggests that Constable may have included it as a reminder (to the public) that ploughing follows harvest; but perhaps it was simply a detail which Constable considered too good to waste.[24] The black and white sheepdog (? of Border Collie breeding)[25] is similar to the dog in *The Hay Wain* of 1821 (NG 1207, pp. 42–9); Reynolds notes that its type recurs in *The Lock* of 1826 and *Hadleigh Castle* of 1829.[26] Reynolds[27] suggests that Constable may have derived the idea of sheep being driven along the lane from Gaspard Dughet's *Landscape in the Roman Campagna* (now NG 68), which David Cox RWS certainly knew, and which Constable could have seen when it was exhibited at the British Institution in 1822 (Reynolds adds, with characteristic sanity, 'though so obvious a motif need not be a reminiscence').[28]

Altogether, Constable loaded *The Cornfield* with picturesque detail: the 'drinking boy', two donkeys, fifteen sheep, a sheepdog whose concentration appears to have been distracted by the sight (or sound) of a wood-pigeon fluttering from the trees on the left, a church in a red-roofed village, a river meandering through level green meadows and more touches of poppy-red than in any other of his pictures. If there is, as Reynolds noted in 1965, 'a great reserve of emotion' about this image of the lane along which Constable had daily walked to school,[29] there is also, on the surface, the hope which Constable had frankly expressed to Fisher: 'I do hope to sell this present picture...'[30]

Much has been made of a letter written to Constable on 1 March 1824 by his botanist friend Henry Phillips who, having seen the picture at a fairly early stage (presumably in February), wrote:

> I think it is July in your green lane. At this season all the tall grasses are in flower, bogrush, bullrush, teasel. The white bindweed now hangs its flowers over the branches of the hedge; the wild carrot and hemlock flower in banks of hedges, cow parsley, water plantain &c; the heath hills are purple at this season; the rose-coloured persicaria in wet ditches is now very pretty; the catch-fly graces the hedgerow, as also the ragged robin; bramble is now in flower, poppy, mallow, thistle, hop, &c.[31]

This letter is quoted in full both by Reynolds[32] and by Parris and Fleming-Williams.[33] The latter authors state that Constable 'had plainly sought' help from Phillips over 'the correct plants to put in the foreground for the time of year he was depicting'. If so, he made little or no use of Phillips's list, which is evidently from an all-England reference book translated into Gilbert White prose. However appropriate Constable's 'wet ditch' may have been as the natural habitat of the 'rose-coloured persicaria',[34] he had no time to mug it up. Only Constable's standard summer plants, butterbur (in the wet patches in the foreground), cow parsley, bramble, and poppy (ubiquitously, in little touches of red in the corn on the left, under the group of elms and more improbably in the shade of the trees on the right) can certainly be identified in *The Cornfield*.[35] Constable made two studies of butterbur about this time,[36] probably using them for *A Mill at Gillingham*[37] as well as for *The Cornfield*. With his trees he was more confident, reporting to Fisher that in this picture they were 'well-defined as to species'. On the left is a dying (not dead) oak, then three elms, with more oaks and perhaps a silver birch in the wood on the right; the 'brushwood sheaf/ Round the elm tree bole'[38] (at which the donkeys nibble) is particularly well observed.

When exhibiting the picture for the second time, at the British Institution in 1827, Constable gave it the title 'Landscape; Noon', accompanied by a few lines from 'Summer', from Thomson's *The Seasons*[39] (they had been in his mind

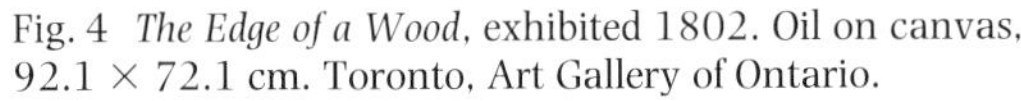

Fig. 4 *The Edge of a Wood*, exhibited 1802. Oil on canvas, 92.1 × 72.1 cm. Toronto, Art Gallery of Ontario.

Fig. 5 *The Cornfield*, detail

while he was working on the picture: he had quoted from them, not accurately, when writing to Fisher in April 1826, see p. 54). In his quotation for the 1827 exhibition catalogue, the italics are his own: 'A fresher gale/ Begins to wave the woods and stir the stream/ *Sweeping with shadowy gust the fields of corn.*'

It has been pointed out that Thomson's lines describe the approach of 'sober Evening',[40] while Constable himself specifies 'noon'; and the light breeze seemingly playing through the trees in his lane hardly echoes Thomson's fresher gale, gustily sweeping the fields of corn. But quotation has never yet been subject to precise rules. What Constable chiefly responded to in Thomson's lines was the idea of *fresher* air over fields of corn.

Probably Constable's scene represent high summer, perhaps mid- to late August, not long before harvesting. The cornfield itself is painted with masterly economy: a few vertical strokes of the brush at the field's edge are enough to inform us that the crop is corn (probably wheat), and that it has grown tall; then the brush broadens into a pale golden, slightly undulating sweep, and thereby creates an entirely convincing field (though not one swept by a shadowy gust). Corn growing at the very edge of a field on the left (fig. 5) informs us more exactly of the near-ripeness of the season. There is no point in the plough's presence outside the cornfield (except as a picturesque eye-stopper) unless harvesting is imminent and it is soon to be put to use ploughing through the stubble.

There has been much discussion over the degree to which Constable depicts a 'real' or 'illusory' countryside in *The Cornfield*.[41] Arguments over whether the sheep will wander into the cornfield while the boy slakes his thirst and the dog's attention is momentarily distracted,[42] over why the dead tree has not been cut down, or why the gate is off its hinges, are by no means uninteresting, but lose sight of Constable's larger source of inspiration. A 'fresher gale' must take us back to Constable's long love of Claude, whose general influence permeates this scene.

A compositional debt to Claude's *Landscape with Hagar and the Angel*, of which Constable painted a copy in the spring of 1800 (the *Hagar* was then in Sir George Beaumont's collection, and is now NG 61) has long been recognised, both in *The Cornfield* of 1826 and in the much earlier *Dedham Vale* of 1802, which in many ways anticipates it.[43] In the autumn of 1823 Constable spent six weeks at Coleorton as the Beaumonts' guest. Beaumont had already announced that he was to present most of his collection to the newly founded National Gallery; aware that 'Sir G. will not possess these things for longer than a room is ready in the Museum to receive them',[44] Constable concentrated his attention at Coleorton on Beaumont's Claudes.[45] He painted studious copies of *Landscape with the Death of Procris* (now NG 55)[46] and of *Landscape with Goatherd and Goats* (now NG 58), taking time over them – 'a sketch (of a picture) will not serve more than one state of mind & will not serve to drink at again and again.'[47] Constable not only copied Claude; he also 'slept with one of the Claudes every night', Beaumont indulging his guest to the point of letting him unhook a Claude from the breakfast room to hang in his bedroom. 'The Claudes are all I can think about while here', he wrote to his long-suffering Maria.[48]

The *Landscape with Goatherd and Goats* affected him powerfully. He wrote that 'It contains almost all that I wish to do in landscape', and set himself to make 'a nice copy from it to be usefull to me as long as I live'.[49] He described it as 'a noon day scene – which *"warms and cheers but which does not inflame or irritate"* – *Mr. Price.* [It] diffuses a life & breezy freshness into the recess of trees which make it enchanting.'[50] Constable's 'nice copy' is likely to have helped to inspire him to infuse a mood of 'noon day' and 'breezy freshness' into *The Cornfield.* While Constable's 'drinking boy' is outwardly a less idyllic figure than Claude's piping shepherd, each is proper to the landscape he inhabits, and each (in a sense) momentarily possesses it. Constable often referred to Claude in his lectures on the history of landscape painting, in one of them remarking that 'In Claude's landscape all is lovely – all amiable – all is amenity and repose; the calm sunshine of the heart.'[51] This, perhaps, was the mood which he tried to capture in *The Cornfield.*

Reviewers of the exhibition mostly admired *The Cornfield. The Times* reviewer, having devoted most of his column to portraits and history paintings, added: 'The best landscapes (beyond all comparison) in the exhibition are from the pencil of Mr Constable. One of them, No. 225 (*The Cornfield*) is singularly beautiful, and not inferior to one of Hobbima's most admired works.'[52] The most ardent praise was given by *The Examiner*'s reviewer, *R.H.* (Robert Hunt, brother of Leigh Hunt), who stressed that Constable

> has been faithful to his first love, Nature, from the commencement of his career... [No.] 225, *Landscape,* grows into higher admiration the more it is looked at, not only for the pure pastoral it contains, – the flock of sheep, the shepherd boy stretched on the ground to drink, the ploughed corn-field, the village church &c. but for its sapphire sky and silver clouds, its emerald trees and golden grain, its glittering reflexes of sun-light among the vegetation; in fine, its clear, healthful and true complexion, neither pale, nor flushed, nor artificial.[53]

When *The Cornfield* was exhibited at Worcester in 1835, *Berrow's Worcester Journal* also gave it high praise, but considered that 'the sky is rather too cold and stormy to suit the idea of heat, which the artist has excited by the colouring and action of the scene'.[54]

The picture failed to sell, either at the Royal Academy or in any of the four other exhibitions to which Constable later sent it: the British Institution exhibition in January 1827, the Paris Salon later that year, the exhibition arranged by the Birmingham Society of Arts in 1829 or that of the Worcester Institution in 1835.

Soon after Constable's death (on 31 March 1837), his Hampstead friend William Purton discussed with C.R. Leslie RA the idea of purchasing a painting from Constable's studio to present to the National Gallery, inviting subscriptions from a wide circle of Constable's friends and admirers. Such ideas do not always get off the ground; this one triumphantly (and quickly) did. A committee chaired by the 84-year-old Sir William Beechey RA met on 6 June 1837 in Constable's studio;[55] together they selected *The Cornfield,* as likelier to appeal 'to the general taste' than the more exuberantly mannered *Salisbury Cathedral from the Meadows* (see p. 39, fig. 2). The administrators of Constable's estate agreed to sell the picture for 300 guineas (£315), a figure probably established by Robert Vernon's purchase of *The Valley Farm* off Constable's easel two years earlier. An account was opened at Drummonds Bank; circulars flowed out; subscriptions (ranging from one to ten guineas) flowed in, from 113 men and women, their names later listed in a printed roll-call.[56] Many had known Constable at different periods of his life; others (not readily identifiable) perhaps knew Constable chiefly through the paintings he exhibited, the *English Landscape Scenery* mezzotints he published (at a loss) or the lectures he had given on landscape in Hampstead, Worcester and at the Royal Institution.[57]

Eight months after Constable's death, the picture he had repeatedly failed to sell fulfilled his admirers' determination that 'one of his Pictures should be permanently accessible to the Public'. On 1 December 1837, Sir William Beechey on behalf of the 113 subscribers formally offered *The Cornfield* to the Trustees of the National Gallery, who accepted it 'gratefully ... on the part of the public'. It was the first picture by Constable to enter the national collection.

NOTES

1. For Frederick Waters Watts and the occasional confusion of his work with Constable's, see Fleming-Williams and Parris 1984, pp. 205–11.

2. *Art Journal,* April 1869, p. 118. Refuting a suggestion in the *Journal* 's January issue (p. 10, accompanying C. Cousen's engraving of the picture) that the village 'looks like Dedham', Charles Constable wrote: 'I would rather it had been called "A Suffolk Lane". It was taken in the lane leading from East Bergholt (my father's native village) to the pathway to Dedham across the meadows, a quarter of a mile from East Bergholt Church, and one mile from Dedham Church, as the crow flies. The little church in the distance never existed: it is one of the rare instances where my father availed himself of the painters' licence to improve the composition...' It has been suggested that Constable 'moved' the village of Higham from some two miles away to this point; see Smart and Brooks 1976, p. 112, with a modern photograph of Higham repr. p. 111, fig. 66; but Parris and Fleming-Williams 1991, p. 305, note that Higham church tower has no stair-turret.

3. Constable to Fisher, 8 April 1826, *JCC,* vol. VI, p. 216.

4. Constable to Fisher, (i) 19 November 1825, *JCC,* vol. VI, p. 207; (ii) 14 January 1826, *JCC,* vol. VI, p. 212. The 'large Waterloo Bridge' was eventually completed and exhibited in 1832 as *The Opening of Waterloo Bridge seen from Whitehall Stairs, June 18th 1817* (Tate Gallery; Reynolds 1984, cat. no. 32.1, plate 819).

5. *A Mill at Gillingham, Dorsetshire* (50 × 60.5 cm), exh. RA 1826 (122), now coll. Yale Center for British Art; Reynolds 1984, cat. no. 26.4, plate 620.

6. Reynolds 1984, p. xiii. Constable's memory is ably discussed by Bermingham 1987, pp. 127–36.

7. Reynolds 1996, cat. no. 01.40, plate 149.

8. Ibid., cat. no. 02.7, plate 157.

9. Ibid., cat. no. 16.100, plate 1360.

10. In Robert Hoozee's *L'opera completa di Constable,* Milan 1979, it appears as H.692, among rejected or doubtful works.

11. In *John Constable RA.,* exh. cat., Salander-O'Reilly Galleries, New York 1988, pp. 18–19.

12. Reynolds 1996, cat. no. 16.1022, plate 1361.

13. Reynolds 1984, cat. no. 26.2, plate 612.

14. 1991, cat. no. 163, p. 299; they argue (i) that the Birmingham study, being 'devoid of incident', cannot have provided an immediate stimulus to the composition of *The Cornfield* ('Constable always needed some remembered or recorded incident...'); and (ii) that it is stylistically close to other Suffolk studies made in 1817, of which they give examples.

15. Parris and Fleming-Williams 1991, cat. no. 164, p. 300.

16. See Parris 1981, no. 10.

17. For example, Constable to David Lucas, 26 November 1833, asking for a proof of the engraving of the picture: 'I want to hang up a "Drinking Boy", if you could let me have one.' (*JCC*, vol. IV, p. 404)

18. Reynolds 1984, p. 168.

19. The phrases are taken from two of Constable's letters to Fisher: (i) letter of 23 October 1821, *JCC*, vol. VI, p. 77 (more fully quoted under NG 6510, p. 30); and (ii) letter of 23 January 1825, *JCC*, vol. VI, p. 191, where Constable expresses his delight in 'old timber-props, water plants, willow stumps, sedges, old nets, &c &c &c'.

20. Constable to Fisher, 8 April 1826, *JCC*, vol. VI, pp. 216–17.

21. Reynolds 1996, cat. no. 11.2, pp. 155–6, plate 890.

22. V&A (790-1888); Reynolds 1973, no. 287, plate 218; Reynolds 1984, cat. no. 26.3, p. 169, plate 613. Donkeys were one of Constable's favourite picturesque ingredients: the best-known example is probably the single donkey in *Cottage near a Cornfield* of 1833 (Reynolds 1984, cat. no. 33.3, pp. 246–7, plate 868).

23. Reynolds 1996, cat. no. 02.1, plate 150.

24. The oil sketch is Reynolds 1996, cat. no. 14.44 ('Two studies of a plough'), plate 1187. The compiler is grateful to John S. Creasey, The Rural History Centre, The University, Reading, for noting (in correspondence) that this is a common type of wheel plough, usually called 'the Norfolk wheel plough'. He notes that at its front, Constable has indicated the start of the linkage to attach the plough to a horse (or horses). He comments: 'I would not imagine that a plough with its whipple trees (or other linkage) would be left outside of the field unless it was to be used soon. Either Constable is expecting a rapid reaping of the harvest field, followed by an immediate ploughing of the stubble, or else he is using some artistic licence to balance his picture and perhaps to suggest the next task that must follow the harvest.'

25. For the dog and its likely behaviour, see Rosenthal 1983, p. 178.

26. Reynolds 1984, p. 168.

27. Reynolds 1965, pp. 106–7, and see Reynolds 1984, p. 168.

28. See Fleming-Williams and Parris 1991. Mention might be made here of two watercolours by David Cox (1783–1859). In *Kenilworth Castle*, a large watercolour of about 1806–7, Cox was inspired by 'a painting by Gaspard Poussin seen in the dealer Simpson's shop in Soho' (conceivably NG 68, which appears to have been on the market in London around this time, and may have been known then to Constable as well as to Cox) to introduce a boy driving a flock of sheep into the foreground. In *A Herefordshire Lane*, probably dating from the late 1800s, Cox depicts a boy driving sheep down a rutted lane (with a stream on the left, and trees either side) similar to that in *The Cornfield*. Both works are repr. in Stephen Wildman, *David Cox*, exh. cat., Birmingham Museums and Art Gallery, 1983, cat. nos 3 and 4, plates 1 and 3. The similarity of subject matter is worth noting, but is probably coincidental, to be accounted for by the similarity of country lanes in Herefordshire and Suffolk. No acquaintance between Cox and Constable is known (nor need a borrowing from Cox by Constable be supposed).

29. Reynolds 1965, p. 106.

30. Constable to Fisher, 8 April 1826, *JCC*, vol. VI, p. 217.

31. Phillips's letter is known only from this extract as published in Leslie 1951 (reprinted *JCC*, vol. V, p. 80).

32. 1984, pp. 167–8; Reynolds notes that Constable had not been in Suffolk in July since 1817.

33. 1991, p. 305.

34. *Polygonum persicaria L.*, sometimes known as peechwort.

35. The compiler is indebted to Frances Mount, whose Suffolk nursery garden is near Fen Lane, for her close study of NG 130 in the Chief Restorer's studio; this enabled identification only of the plants noted above. The answer to Parris and Fleming-Williams's question 'What else, one wonders, could the trained eye name?' (1991, p. 305) would appear to be 'nothing'.

36. Reynolds 1984, cat. no. 26.7, plate 615.

37. Reynolds 1984, cat. no. 26.4, plate 620.

38. The phrase is Browning's, in *Home Thoughts from Abroad*.

39. Summer, II, lines 1654–6.

40. Parris and Fleming-Williams 1991, p. 302.

41. For example, see Rosenthal 1983, p. 178, followed by Cormack 1986, p. 187; Parris and Fleming-Williams 1991, pp. 304–5.

42. Shepherds consulted by the NG think not: a cornfield has nothing to entice sheep, and the elders of the flock know that bloat will result from eating cornseed. The leading sheep seems to be turning, following a (probably familiar) direction along the lane's continuation to the right; the rest will follow.

43. Reynolds (1965, p. 107) goes so far as to say that the whole effect of *The Cornfield* is as a mirror image of Claude's *Hagar and the Angel*. See ibid. p. 21, for Constable's first sight of the picture. Beaumont so loved the *Hagar* that he took it with him when travelling, and thus was able to show it to the young Constable first on a visit to Dedham, and later whenever Constable called on him in London.

44. Constable to Fisher, from Coleorton, 19 October 1823, *JCC*, vol. VI, pp. 139–40.

45. The intensity of Constable's response to Beaumont's Claudes is expressed in his letters from Coleorton to his wife and to his friend John Fisher; see *JCC*, vols II, pp. 294–7, and VI, pp. 142–8. Besides the two Claudes of which he painted copies, Constable also greatly admired *Landscape with Narcissus and Echo* (now NG 19), writing to his wife on 2 November 1823: 'I am now going to breakfast – before the "Narcissus" of Claude. How enchanting and lovely it is, far very far surpassing any other landscape, I ever yet beheld' (*JCC*, vol. II, p. 294). Rosenthal 1983, p. 177, suggests that although Constable's 'drinking boy' had appeared in an earlier sketch, his inclusion in *The Cornfield* might also refer obliquely to Claude's *Narcissus*.

46. Writing to Fisher, Constable called it 'a most pathetic and soothing picture' (*JCC*, vol. VI, p. 142). Then thought to be by Claude, it is now recognised as a seventeenth-century copy.

47. Constable to Fisher, from Coleorton, 2 November 1823, *JCC*, vol. VI, p. 142. Constable's copies after Beaumont's Claudes remained in his studio and were in his sale, Foster's 15 May 1838 (46, 48, 49).

48. From Coleorton, 9 November 1823, *JCC*, vol. II, p. 297; the letter includes the remark 'If any thing could come between our love, it is him.'

49. Constable to Fisher, from Coleorton, 5 November 1823, *JCC*, vol. II, p. 295; see also p. 293. For Constable's 'nice copy' (now coll. Art Gallery of New South Wales, Sydney), see Reynolds 1984, cat no. 23.36, plate 424.

50. Constable to Fisher, 2 November 1823, *JCC*, vol. VI, p. 142.

51. *JCD*, p. 53. Delivered on 2 June 1836, the second in a course of four weekly 'Lectures on the History of Landscape Painting' given by Constable at the Royal Institution, London, 26 May–16 June 1836, developed from a series of three lectures given to the Worcester Institution for promoting Literature, Science and the Fine Arts at the Athenaeum, October 1835. For Constable's lecture notes, edited and published by R.B. Beckett, see *John Constable's Discourses*, 1970, pp. 28–74.

52. *The Times*, Saturday 29 April 1826 (after a preview the previous day), p. 3 [b].

53. Ivy 1991, p. 119, and partly quoted by Parris and Fleming-Williams 1991, p. 302.

54. Quoted in Lord Windsor, *John Constable R.A.*, London and New York 1903, pp. 126–8.

55. The committee included, beside Purton and Leslie, the RAs A.E. Chalon, William Etty and Clarkson Stanfield, the ARAs J.J. Chalon and F.R. Lee, the bookseller William Carpenter (later Keeper of Prints and Drawings in the British Museum), the publisher John Murray and the collector John Sheepshanks.

56. Copy in NG Archives.

57. For the subscriptions to and presentation of the picture, see Judy Egerton, *NG News*, February 1996 [p. 2].

NG 1272

Cenotaph to the Memory of Sir Joshua Reynolds, erected in the grounds of Coleorton Hall, Leicestershire, by the late Sir George Beaumont, Bt.

exhibited 1836
Oil on canvas, extended by strips of wood to 132 × 108.5 cm (52 × 42¾ in.)
Inscribed *REYNOLDS* on the face of the cenotaph, in paint, as if carved in stone, followed by similarly feigned (but illegible) lines of Wordsworth's verse.

Exhibited with these lines:

> Ye lime trees ranged before this hallowed urn
> Shoot forth with lively power at spring's return,
> And be not slow a stately growth to rear,
> Of pillars branching off from year to year,
> Till they have formed a darksome aisle,
> Like a recess within that sacred pile,
> Where REYNOLDS mid our country's noblest dead,
> In the last sanctity of fame is laid;
> And worthily within those sacred bounds
> The excelling painter sleeps – yet here may I,
> Unblamed amid my patrimonial grounds,
> Raise this frail tribute to his memory –
> An humble follower of the soothing art
> That he professed – attached to him in heart,
> Admiring, loving – and, with grief and pride,
> Feeling what England lost when Reynolds died.
>
> *Inscribed by Wordsworth, at the request, and in the name of Sir George Beaumont.*

Provenance

Unsold in the last year of the artist's life; his administrators' sale, Foster's 16 May 1838 (71), bt William Carpenter (£42) on behalf of Constable's children; bequeathed by the artist's daughter Isabel Constable, as the gift of Maria Louisa, Isabel and Lionel Bicknell Constable, to the National Gallery 1888.

Exhibited

RA 1836 (9, with title followed by Wordsworth's lines as given above); International Exhibition, 1862 (British Division, Class XXXVIII, 286); RA Winter 1871 (44); Leeds City Art Gallery, *John Constable R.A.*, 1913 (85); RA 1968–9 (79); Tate Gallery 1976 (330).

Literature

Davies 1946, pp. 27–8; Taylor 1975, p. 209; Parris, Fleming-Williams and Shields 1976, pp. 186–8; Paulson 1982, pp. 133–9; Reynolds 1984, cat. no. 36.1, pp. 285–6, plate 1052; Owen and Brown 1988, pp. 136, 208 (plate 92), 218–22, 230; p. 233, Appendix 1: 'Plan of Coleorton Hall and Grounds'; Ivy 1991, pp. 213–19, quoting contemporary reviewers.

Technical Notes

In very good condition; unlined. The construction of the support is unusual in three respects. Firstly, strips of wood were added to all four sides of the stretcher to increase its dimensions before the canvas was attached. Secondly, a loose lining canvas was attached to the stretcher before the canvas on which the picture is painted. Thirdly, further strips of wood were added at the right and bottom edge, and the painting continued over them.

Based on a pencil drawing (see below) dated 28 November 1823, made on the last day of Constable's six-week stay at Coleorton with the Beaumonts (see p. 55, and under Beaumont's portrait by Hoppner, NG 6333, pp. 370–5).

Sir George Beaumont, thirty years younger than Reynolds, had been his friend and remained his profound admirer. Meeting Beaumont in Rome in 1822, Joseph Severn noted that all Beaumont's artistic recollections 'were made to centre round the pivot of Sir Joshua Reynolds who was top of his admiration both as a man and as an artist'.[1]

In 1812, twenty years after Reynolds's death, Beaumont erected a stone 'urn' dedicated to Reynolds's memory in the grounds of Coleorton Hall. Having recently rebuilt the house, he intended to redesign the gardens.[2] Following the example of William Shenstone at The Leasowes, Beaumont proposed to include memorials dedicated to his friends and those he revered in the grounds of Coleorton. On this he consulted William Wordsworth, who spent about a month at Coleorton during July–August 1810, and undertook to compose memorial inscriptions.[3]

The memorials were to include a boulder stone placed in commemoration of Richard Wilson in January 1818 (drawn by Constable in 1823) and a memorial grove honouring Beaumont's ancestor, the poet Francis Beaumont. By far the most important was to be the 'urn' dedicated to Reynolds. Both Beaumont and Wordsworth used the word 'urn' as the much-revered William Shenstone had used it in his *Unconnected Thoughts on Gardening* (first published in 1764), to denote a sepulchral monument to someone buried elsewhere; it was evidently Constable who promoted the 'urn' to a 'cenotaph', in his 1836 title. In planning the Reynolds memorial, Beaumont no doubt heeded Shenstone's dictum that 'URNS are more solemn, if large and plain; more beautiful, if less ... ornamented. Solemnity is perhaps their point, and the situation of them should still cooperate with it' (see fig. 3).[4]

The Reynolds urn was to be placed at the end of an avenue of lime trees, near the Hall (for its site, see Owen and Brown 1988, Appendix 1). The avenue of limes appears to have been planted or at least marked out during Wordsworth's visit, for he had it in mind when composing the lines for the memorial inscription, which begin 'Ye lime trees ranged before this hallowed urn...'. Wordsworth's lines foresee the 'stately growth' of the lime trees at Coleorton forming a 'darksome aisle' recalling the 'sacred pile' where Reynolds was in fact buried (the crypt of St Paul's Cathedral).

Fig. 1 The Coade stone terms of Raphael (left) and Michelangelo as they now stand at the end of the lime avenue in the grounds of Coleorton. Photograph by John Crocker.

Wordsworth sent the first draft of his lines to Beaumont in November 1811.[5] Discussing and revising them took nearly a year (during which Lady Beaumont lost the first draft 'through redundancy of care'[6]). Minor variations were still being mooted on 23 October 1812, when Joseph Farington and William Owen RA were guests at Coleorton. The construction of the urn finally began on 30 October 1812. Farington that day recorded:[7]

> At noon today Sir George & Lady Beaumont Owen and myself walked to [the] Arbour in which Sir George had given directions to have a monument to the memory of Sir Joshua Reynolds erected, and there the workmen being assembled the first stone was laid with due form by Sir George, Lady Beaumont, Owen, & myself; and afterwards each of us in turn struck the stone with a mallet Lady Beaumont saying 'May nothing but – Time – destroy this Monument'.

Near the start of the lime avenue, as Constable shows in his painting, were placed busts of Michelangelo and Raphael, each mounted as a term on tall tapering blocks of stone. These have often been supposed to have been 'invented' by Constable ('intended, no doubt, to add a further dimension to his tribute to past art, perhaps even to suggest a pedigree for British art'[8]); but the presence of Michelangelo and Raphael, revered by Reynolds as well as by himself, was part of Beaumont's carefully pondered memorial. Far from being the figments of Constable's imagination, Michelangelo and Raphael were the products of Mrs Coade's Artificial Stone Manufactory.[9] Despite some minor mishaps, they still preside, on either side of the end of the lime avenue (fig. 1).[10] Although Beaumont's order to Mrs Coade in 1817 for 'a pair of busts Milton and Shakespeare to be finished as terms 7 guineas each' (installed looking towards the memorial to Sir Francis Beaumont)[11] is recorded, his order for Michelangelo and Raphael is not; but it is likely to have been placed at about the same date.

In 1823 Constable had spent some six weeks at Coleorton as the Beaumonts' guest; during this visit (20 October to 28 November) he was chiefly preoccupied with making copies of Beaumont's Claudes (as noted under NG 130, p. 55). He spent some of his time time sketching and looking for subjects out of doors and, in a letter to Fisher of 2 November 1823, mentioned that 'In the dark recesses of these gardens, and at the end of one of the walks, I saw an urn – & bust of Sir Joshua Reynolds – & under it some beautifull verses, by Wordsworth.'[12] But it was not until 28 November 1823, the day of his departure from Coleorton, that Constable found time to make a pencil and grey wash drawing of the Reynolds memorial (fig. 2) in a sketchbook, inscribing on the back of the page the lines 'written by Mr W. Wordsworth and engraven on the Urn, in the Garden'.[13] On the same day, he made two sketches of the massive 'Stone in the Grove, Coleorton Hall dedicated to the Memory of Richard Wilson'.[14]

Constable's drawing of the Reynolds memorial was made from a fairly close viewpoint, concentrating on the cenotaph itself, but showing something of the surrounding trees, their trunks still slender but their boughs already forming a dense screen behind the stonework. Although Michelangelo and Raphael were almost certainly *in situ* by then, they would have been behind his line of vision; he does not include them in his drawing, and perhaps at that time he did not realise their significance. When he mentioned in his letter of 28 November to Fisher that he saw ('in the dark recesses of the garden') 'an urn – & bust of Sir Joshua Reynolds', he may have mistaken either Michelangelo or Raphael for Reynolds (he was, after all, drawing in the late November light, and in the hurry of departure from Coleorton that day).

Ten years later, Constable began to turn the pencil drawing made on the spot into the oil painting which he was to entitle *Cenotaph to the Memory of Sir Joshua Reynolds*; meanwhile he referred to the subject variously as 'my Sercophagi',[15] 'the Wood'[16] or 'the Avenue'.[17] In an undated letter to C.R. Leslie, probably written early in February 1833, Constable announced: 'I contemplate a half length of my Sercophagi', adding that Vaughan advised '"not less" than a small half length'.[18] He began the subject on a canvas of what he habitually defined as half-length (i.e. 50 × 40 in.), later adding strips of wood which enlarged the height of the painted surface by 2 inches and its width by 2¾ inches (details of the placing of these wooden strips are given above under Technical Notes). He appears to have worked on his painting during February and early March 1833; then, probably in late March, wrote to C.R. Leslie: 'I have laid by the Cenotaph for the present. I am determined not to harrass my mind and HEALTH by scrambling over my canvas – as I hitherto so often have done!'[19] Inspiration was evidently flagging; the drawing which now provided the basis for his painting had after all been made ten years earlier.

Three years later, Constable took up the subject again, this time with a positive incentive to finish it. The approaching Royal Academy exhibition of 1836 would be the last to be held in Somerset House, where exhibitions had been presented since 1780 (the Royal Academy was to move to new premises in Trafalgar Square, shared with the National Gallery). Constable had time to finish only one oil painting for the 1836 exhibition.[20] He had to choose between the *Cenotaph* and *Arundel Mill and Castle*, commissioned by George Constable (no relation, but a friend from 1832). Old loyalties prevailed; he wrote to George Constable on 12 May 1836, 'I found I could not do both – and so I preferred to see Sir Joshua Reynolds's name and Sir George Beaumont's once more in the catalogue, for the last time in the old house.'[21] On the same day he wrote (with less than complete confidence) to Charles Boner, 'I ... am finishing the scene in Coleorton grounds with the cenotaph–or rather I am about such things.'[22] He appears to have had both large and small worries over his picture, one of the latter being how best to represent Wordsworth's engraved lines in paint; he confided his worries to C.R. Leslie, who replied, 'I trust you are quite wrong about your beautiful picture', and sent him a rough sketch suggesting how the lines of verse might be feigned, with the word 'REYNOLDS' alone legible, advice which Constable faithfully followed.[23]

Constable's introduction of a stag into the picture gives an appropriate sense of the sequestered grove in which the memorial stands, but a false idea of its actual size. The total height of the 'cenotaph', from the ground to the top of the

Fig. 2 Study of 'the Urn in the garden', inscribed 'Coleorton Hall. Novr. 28. 1823'. Pencil and grey wash on paper, 26 × 18.1 cm. London, Victoria and Albert Museum.

capstone, is just under seven feet (the central block on which Wordsworth's lines are carved is only two feet square).[24] The stag in front of it is a fully mature animal, which appears to have started off as a red deer but acquired the palmated antlers of a fallow buck during the picture's progress.[25] To the tip of its antlers, the stag must be taller than the cenotaph by at least a foot, yet it is depicted as only half its size. Thus is the monument exalted. The idea of a stag as staffage is not far-fetched; deer are natural denizens of the woods in this part of Leicestershire, and it has also been suggested[26] that its presence near the memorial erected by Beaumont may be an association of ideas with the theme of Jacques and the Wounded Stag, which both Beaumont and Constable had addressed.[27] Constable takes even greater licence with the avenue of lime trees, Wordsworth's 'darksome aisle' which leads one to the memorial itself. This avenue in fact is 31 yards long, but Constable drastically foreshortens it to allow Michelangelo and Raphael to act as ushers in the foreground: each term in reality is 79 inches high. Constable has thinned out the lime trees more drastically than nature could have done. The robin, perched on the right-hand tip of the memorial's capstone (and red-breasted, predictably), may have been added as some counterpoint to the picture's general sombreness.

In the end, Constable referred to his 'Cenotaph' as 'a tolerably good picture'.[28] Reviewers saw it primarily as a homage to Reynolds or as an illustration to Wordsworth. The *Gentleman's Magazine* pronounced Constable's picture to be of interest 'chiefly for the illustrious name with which it is associated, namely that of Sir Joshua Reynolds, having otherwise less to captivate the spectator than is usually to be found in the compositions of the same artist'. The reviewer for *Blackwood's Magazine* observed that Wordsworth's inscription was 'solemn, sepulchral', and only '"dim religious"' light was appropriate to it. 'If ever subject required chaste and sober colouring it is this; yet is it flickering throughout with impertinent lights, and dots of all colours, utterly ruinous to the sentiment', 'scratchy and uncomfortable in execution, painted, it would seem, on a principle of contrast and interception, ill-suited to the subject'. *The Morning Chronicle*'s reviewer alone was able to detach himself from the subject matter, instead reminding spectators that Constable's paintings ought not to be too hastily judged: 'The peculiar manner in which Mr Constable's pictures are painted makes them appear singular at first, but by choosing a proper distance for observing them, by degrees the effect seems to grow upon us until we are astonished that we did not like them better before. If exceeding truth to nature, finish without littleness, and pure, rich colouring are admirable in a picture, then surely Mr Constable's must be generally liked.'

This was the last oil painting which Constable exhibited at the Royal Academy. It did not find a purchaser.

Fig. 3 A Memorial Urn. Illustration to William Shenstone, 'Elegy I', as published in his *Verse and Prose*, II, 1764.

NOTES

Coleorton was until recently a property of the British Coal Corporation. The compiler is particularly indebted to John Crocker and Jeremy Winter, past and present curators of its grounds, for detailed information about the Reynolds memorial.

1. Quoted by Owen and Brown 1988, p. 3.

2. For Coleorton and its rebuilding, see Owen and Brown 1988, ch. VIII, pp. 107–28.

3. For Beaumont's long friendship with Wordsworth, see Owen and Brown 1988, *passim*.

4. For Shenstone, see J. Dixon Hunt and P. Willis, *The Genius of the Place*, London 1975, including a reprint of *Unconnected Thoughts on Gardening*, pp. 289ff. (the quotation used here is from p. 293), and quoting Richard Pococke's description of the urns at The Leasowes (1756), p. 266.

5. Enclosed in a letter (November 1811) suggesting that 'Had there been room at the end of the small avenue of Limetrees for planting a spatious Circle of the same trees, the Urn might have been placed in the centre', and offering four alternative lines describing a circle of trees whose branches would in time meet overhead (ed. E. de Selincourt, *The Letters of William and Dorothy Wordsworth, II, Part 1, 1808–1811*, 2nd edn, rev. M. Morrison, Oxford 1969, p. 513); but Beaumont was evidently content with a simple avenue.

6. Owen and Brown 1988, p. 136.

7. In a travel notebook whose entries, 15 September–16 October 1812, precede his diary entries of the same dates in Farington, *Diary*, vol. XII, p. 4231.

8. See Taylor 1975, p. 209, and Parris et al. 1976, p. 187, followed by Paulson 1982, p. 135.

9. Alison Kelly, *Mrs Coade's Stone*, Upton-on-Severn 1990, p. 137; see pp. 137–8 nn. 80, 81.

10. The compiler is indebted to John Crocker for the following information (in correspondence, 1992). The Reynolds Memorial is approached from the east. The aisle of lime trees (31 yards long) is aligned due west, and is paved with cobblestones, which finish in a circle around the memorial. Michelangelo and Raphael stand on either side of the end of the avenue. Their present position, facing each other, as in Constable's painting, is not certainly their original position. When Mr Crocker first knew the site, in the early 1950s, both busts looked down the aisle, towards the memorial. Over the years, the growth of tree roots toppled both terms, and Raphael's nose was broken off. They lay on the ground under lichen and moss for some twenty years. In the 1970s, Mr Crocker had them raised to their present position, their exact siting being determined by problems of root disturbance. At the same time, Raphael's nose was repaired by the Ceramics Department of Loughborough College of Art and Design, but as Mr Crocker notes, 'unfortunately they gave Raphael a Roman nose rather than his own graceful profile as depicted by Constable'.

11. Kelly 1990 (cited in note 9), pp. 139, 145 n. 81. *Milton* and *Shakespeare* cost 7 guineas each. For a photograph showing them *in situ*, see Frederick A. Whiting, 'A Garden Planned by Wordsworth', *Country Life*, 24 September 1964, p. 773, fig. 3.

12. Constable to Fisher, *JCC*, vol. VI, p. 143.

13. Reynolds 1996, p. 126, no. 23.31, plate 419. Reynolds 1960, pp. 161–2, no. 259, gives a transcript of Constable's rendering of the lines, plate 196.

14. Coll. V&A; Reynolds 1960, cat. nos. 260–1, plate 197.

15. Constable to C.R. Leslie, ? February 1833, *JCC*, vol. V, p. 93.

16. Constable to his son Charles, 6 March 1833, *JCC*, vol. V, p. 144.

17. Constable to C.R. Leslie, 26 March 1836, *JCC*, vol. III, p. 136.

18. *JCC*, vol. III, p. 93. Henry Vaughan, later a collector of works by Constable, Turner, etc., presented *The Hay Wain* to the NG in 1886.

19. *JCC*, vol. III, p. 96.

20. The only other work he exhibited at the RA in 1836 was a watercolour, *Stonehenge* (Reynolds 1984, cat no. 36.3, plate 1055).

21. *JCC*, vol. V, p. 32.

22. Constable to Charles Boner, his children's tutor, *JCC*, vol. V, p. 197.

23. Undated letter, of which only part survives; Parris et al. 1975, p. 244.

24. The compiler is indebted to Jeremy Winter, present curator of Coleorton grounds, for making a measured drawing of the component parts of the memorial. Its measurements (height before width) are as follows:

Main block with carved inscription:
24 × 24 in.
capstone: 8 × 30 in.
first step below block: 15 × 15 in.
second step below block: 12 × 55 in.
third step below block: 12 × 81 in.
fourth step below block: 12 × 104 in.
Total height: approximately 7 ft.

Mr Winter also measured the overall height of the busts and terms of Michelangelo and Raphael: 79 in. (each 22 in. shoulder to top of head, and 12 in. wide × 10 in. deep). He reports that the lime tree aisle is 31 yards long, and that its floor is made up of flint cobbles laid with brick in symmetrical patterns (traditionally thought to have been laid by Lady Beaumont).

25. Daphne Hills, Mammals Section, Department of Zoology, British Museum (Natural History), to whose comments (in correspondence, 1996) on Constable's depiction of the deer and also on its likely height the compiler is indebted. The stag's head and antlers closely follow those in a small pencil study made (perhaps from a stuffed animal) while Constable was working on the painting. Reynolds 1984, cat. no. 36.2, plate 1051 (NG Archives, transferred to the Department of Prints and Drawings, British Museum).

26. See Paulson 1982, pp. 135–6.

27. Beaumont's painting *Jacques and the Wounded Stag* (repr. Owen and Brown 1988, p. 199, fig. 87) was exh. RA in 1818. For drawings and watercolours of the subject made by Constable in 1832 and 1835, see Reynolds 1984, cat. nos. 34.9–12, 35.32–38.

28. Constable to George Constable, 12 May 1936, *JCC*, vol. V, p. 32.

"My dear Sir,

"You have thanked me handſomely, for what has not been handſomely done *;—but I intend you ſhall have ſomething better ſoon.

"Mr. Boydell brought the large Landscip you ſpeak of, for ſeventy-five guineas, laſt week, at Greenwood's:—It is in ſome reſpects a little in the *ſchoolboy* ſtile—but I do not reflect on this without a ſecret gratification; for—as an early inſtance how ſtrong my inclination ſtood for Landskip, this picture was actually painted at Sudbury, in the year 1748: it was begun *before I left ſchool*;—and was the means of my Father's ſending me to London.

"It may be worth remark, that though there is very little idea of compoſition in the picture, the touch and cloſeneſs to nature in the ſtudy of the parts and *minutiæ*, are equal to any of my latter productions.—In this explanation, I wiſh not to ſeem vain or ridiculous, but do not look on the Landſkip as one of my riper performances.

"It is full forty years ſince it was firſt delivered by me to go in ſearch of thoſe who had *taſte* enough to admire it!—Within that time, it has been in the hands of twenty picture dealers, and I once bought it myſelf during that interval for *Nineteen Guineas*:—Is not that curious?

"Your's, my dear Sir,

"Moſt ſincerely,

"THOMAS GAINSBOROUGH."

Pall-Mall, *March* 11, 1788.

To ******, Eſq.

* Some drawings which Mr. Gainſborough ſent as a preſent.

Fig. 1 Letter from Gainsborough to Henry Bate Dudley concerning his painting *Cornard Wood*, published in *The Morning Herald*, 11 March 1788.

these various things. Its right half, empty of figures, is shaded, and still. Branches of trees are clearly reflected in two adjoining ponds; such ponds, fed by springs, are still to be found in this part of Suffolk.

Such scenery, and such activities, must have been familiar to Gainsborough since childhood. He told Philip Thicknesse, his friend, early patron and anecdotalist, that even before he learnt to draw, 'there was not a Picturesque clump of Trees, no, nor hedge row, stone, or post, at the corner of the Lanes, that he had not so perfectly in his mind's eye, that had he known he could use a pencil, he could have perfectly delineated'.[11] He began teaching himself to draw and paint by studying and copying the landscapes of Dutch artists, particularly Jacob van Ruisdael; his close copy in black chalk of Ruisdael's *Woodland Ford with Figures and Cattle* ('*La Forêt*') is frequently reproduced.[12]

The taste for Dutch landscape was one Gainsborough shared with many others before him and in his own time. In *English Taste in Landscape in the Seventeenth Century*[13] (a rich yet strangely neglected source), H. and M. Ogden trace a long line of Dutch artists working in England between 1660 and 1700. Andrew Moore's valuable study of Dutch and Flemish paintings in East Anglian collections[14] shows the increasing popularity of Dutch landscapes with English collectors during the eighteenth century. Dealers stocked Dutch pictures since they had a wide appeal to those who preferred the recognisable reality rather than the unrealisable, Claudian ideal. Growing up in Sudbury, Gainsborough could have seen Dutch paintings in East Anglian collections, and probably knew others in the form of engravings. In the work of Ruisdael and Cuyp, Pynacker and Saftleven,[15] he could have recognised 'a common, native landscape' (Andrew Moore's phrase)[16] to which he could respond, which he could readily adapt, and which was also marketable. Gainsborough appears to have had contacts with dealers from the 1740s, particularly with Panton Betew, a Suffolk-born dealer in London, who handled several of his early Suffolk landscapes and commissioned engravings of them.[17] In 1748, when *Cornard Wood* was (in Gainsborough's own phrase) 'first delivered by me to go in search of those who had taste enough to admire it', it is likely that he took it to Panton Betew, who bought it, outright or on commission, and placed it for sale in his shop in Old Compton Street, Soho.

Hayes cites two pictures listed in a sale catalogue of 1766 as evidence that Gainsborough did some hack work for dealers, 'repairing a Dutch landscape, and putting figures into a landscape by Wijnants'; but it should be noted that the latter name in fact appears in the sale catalogue as 'Wynants', and that Adrienne Corri has traced a Francis Wynants working in Suffolk with whom Gainsborough might have collaborated, rather than undertaking the more difficult exercise of superimposing figures on a much earlier artist's work.[18] Whether on this occasion he 'put figures' into a landscape painted by the Wijnants who died in 1684 or collaborated with a Wynants of his own day remains unclear; but in either case, too much should not be made of this.[19] Many artists, especially when young and needy, were willing to oblige dealers with a bit of restoration: after all, they had brushes and paints to hand, and 'obliging' might help if their own works were to be accepted for sale.

Forty years after painting the picture we now know as *Cornard Wood*, Gainsborough wrote that it was 'actually painted at Sudbury, in the year 1748'. He states this in a letter dated 11 March 1788, written from his home in Pall Mall to his friend Henry Bate Dudley, who published it in the *Morning Herald*. Gainsborough's letter is reproduced here in full (fig. 1), for quite apart from being a characteristic example of his letter-writing style, it is an important document for *Cornard Wood*. Though this letter recalls a picture painted forty years earlier and, like all Gainsborough's letters, is written impulsively, there is no good reason to disbelieve anything in the artist's own statements in it.

The letter was prompted by the fact that three days earlier, *Cornard Wood* had unexpectedly resurfaced in Greenwood's saleroom, where it was purchased by the well-known collector and print-publisher Alderman John Boydell. As a good newspaper man, Bate Dudley judged that the reappearance of an early 'large Landscip' by an artist known in the 1780s chiefly as a fashionable portraitist would make an interesting news item; he therefore asked Gainsborough for information about it. Gainsborough's response was the letter reproduced here; but evidently thinking that Gainsborough's letter-writing style was too whimsical for his readers, Bate Dudley published his own genteel (and misleading) paraphrase of it the next day,[20] publishing the letter itself only after Gainsborough's death.

Gainsborough thinks of the picture as 'in some respects a little in the schoolboy stile', and as 'an early instance of how strong my inclination stood for LANDSKIP'. He then states perfectly clearly that 'this picture was actually painted at SUDBURY, in the year 1748', adding that 'it was begun before I left school; – and was the means of my Father's sending me to London'. Gainsborough's recall of events of 1748 is likely to have remained particularly clear: that was the year of his father's death, and his own return from London to live and work in Sudbury.[21] By the spring of 1788, when he was asked to recollect *Cornard Wood*, he owned to being in 'bodily pain' (he died of cancer in August);[22] but other letters show a mind still keen and work still progressing. Hayes however believes that 'the date of 1748 is open to question on stylistic grounds, and it is conceivable that after forty years, Gainsborough's memory played him false.'[23] Hayes prefers to date *Cornard Wood* to '*c.*1746–7', and later writers have fallen into line behind him.

Of nearly 200 landscapes painted over the years by Gainsborough, only one is actually dated – the so-called *Rest by the Way* now in Philadelphia, dated 1747.[24] Hayes's dating of '*c.*1746–7' orders *Cornard Wood* into a position four works earlier than the Philadelphia picture, largely, it seems, because he considers that *Cornard Wood* 'suffers from the inclusion of too many unrelated motifs'[25] and demonstrates that 'subject-matter of any clearly defined or meaningful description ... was not [yet] within Gainsborough's grasp'. But there is a subject in *Cornard Wood*, perhaps more obvious to economic historians than to art historians: this is the common just outside Sudbury, used by the villagers for small gainful activities – much as similar figures abound in Jan van der Heyden's *Cross Roads in a Wood*, a painting of about 1675 whose likely influence upon Gainsborough, noted by Bachrach in 1971,[26] is ignored by Hayes and his followers.

Admittedly, the common seems over-crowded; but it is crowded not by 'unrelated motifs' but by people with distinct purposes. A year or two later, Gainsborough amply demonstrated his ability to handle clearly defined subject matter, with a landscape recently identified by the Suffolk historian Norman Scarfe as *Holywells Park, Ipswich* (fig. 3), in which the ponds are man-made, constructed to supply Cobbold's Brewery with pure water from Holywells' natural springs.[27] Cornard Wood is more 'picturesque' (or less realistic) than Holywells Park; but at its core it retains a sense of a real place, however unreally crowded with picturesque staffage.

Using the evidence of exhibition and saleroom catalogues, newspaper reviews, engravings and a few surviving receipts, Hayes has constructed a valuable list of 'Datable Landscapes';[28] but such supporting evidence is sparse for the early landscapes. Here his chronological order must be surmised 'on stylistic grounds', which inevitably produces chain-dating,[29] and does not admit the possibility that a work might hang

Fig. 2 *Cornard Wood*, detail

Fig. 3 *Holywells Park, Ipswich*, *c.*1748–50. Oil on canvas, 50.8 × 66 cm. Ipswich, Christchurch Mansion.

about in an artist's room, picked up now and then, reviewed and either discarded or finally pulled together. Hayes acknowledges that 'very few of the landscapes are precisely datable, especially in the early and middle years of Gainsborough's career'.[30] Gainsborough himself has stated that *Cornard Wood* was 'actually painted ... in the year 1748', which would place it a year later than the Philadelphia picture; to this compiler, that seems perfectly credible. In the absence of any reason to disbelieve him – other than the inevitably subjective perception of 'stylistic grounds' – this compiler prefers to respect Gainsborough's own date of 1748.

Gainsborough's recollection that *Cornard Wood* 'was begun before I left school' is less specific (or more ambiguous), than the statement later in his letter that 'this picture was actually painted ... in the year 1748'. It has sometimes been taken to mean that Gainsborough began the painting (or possibly even completed it) at the age of twelve or thirteen, in 1740, the year in which he probably left home for London, to study drawing in the St Martin's Lane Academy.[31] Even a small knowledge of Gainsborough's habitually airy, allusive and wholly undocumentary letter-writing style[32] suggests that his phrase 'begun before I left school' does not literally mean 'before I left Sudbury Grammar School',[33] but rather while he was still learning his art, drawing studies from nature on scraps of paper which (as Thicknesse recalled) he called 'his Riding school', and painting (in his own phrase) 'a little in the schoolboy stile'. Hayes's interpretation of Gainsborough's wording seems reasonable enough: 'the most obvious explanation is that he had made drawings and sketches of the scene while he was still a schoolboy and only took them up again several years later';[34] but it should be noted that he makes rather too large a claim for his evidence in saying that 'X-ray photographs show that he did not deviate one iota from his composition once he had started work upon the canvas; the inescapable conclusion is that every detail had been carefully thought out beforehand – one only regrets the many lost drawings.'[35] The X-ray photographs in question, taken by the National Gallery at Dr Hayes's request, are of the middle section of the picture only, and are not easy to interpret, since they chiefly show the picture's ground rather than the paint.[36]

Gainsborough himself remarks in his letter of 1788 that 'though there is very little idea of composition in the picture, the touch and closeness to nature in the study of the parts and *minutiae*, are equal to any of my latter productions'. This claim is abundantly justified, as a detail shows (fig. 2). Some pride in and affection for this early work are evident in his letter; but he hopes not to sound 'vain or ridiculous' in expressing them, and adds 'do not look on the Landskip as one of my riper performances'. Writing about *Cornard Wood* perhaps prompted him (two months later, in a letter to his

Fig. 4 *Wooded Landscape with Herdsman seated near a Pool*, *c.*1747–8. Sudbury, Gainsborough's House.

Norfolk friend Thomas Harvey) to recall 'my first imitations of little Dutch landscapes'.[37]

Attention has been drawn to the 'grey skies' in *Cornard Wood*;[38] but they were not always so grey. As observed in the Technical Notes, the sky is painted with a weak tint of Prussian blue which has faded, except where the canvas was turned over at the top edge. While the sky itself now appears to be grey, with greyer clouds, it must once have been as blue as the skies in the small and probably slightly earlier canvas called *Landscape with a Peasant on a Path*,[39] and in the *Wooded Landscape with Herdsman*[40] (fig. 4) which Hayes dates '*c.* 1746–8', but which appears to this compiler to be close in date (and place) to *Cornard Wood*, and thus likely also to have been painted in 1748.

Cornard Wood belonged for some years to John Constable's uncle, David Pike Watts; it hung in his house in Portland Place, where Constable could often have seen it. When his uncle lent the picture to the British Institution in 1814, it was catalogued as 'A woody scene, in his early manner'; it may have been Constable who recognised the scene as near Cornard, and helped to evolve the title under which it descended to his cousins. Constable was born within ten miles of Gainsborough's birthplace.[41] When, as a young man of 23, he first called on Joseph Farington RA (on 25 February 1799), the conversation turned to Gainsborough's work. Farington records that 'Mr J. Constable of Ipswich calld ... thinks first pictures of Gainsborough his best, latter so wide of nature.'[42] Painting near Woodbridge in Suffolk the following summer, Constable wrote to J.T. Smith: 'tis a most delightfull country for a landscape painter, I fancy I see Gainsborough in every hedge and hollow tree.'[43] At this stage in Constable's development, what he looked for and found in Gainsborough's early landscapes was truth to nature. By the time he gave his lectures on landscape painting in 1836, he could respond to something less particular and more elusive in Gainsborough's pictures: 'On looking at them, we find tears in our eyes, and know not what brings them.'[44] Constable discussed Ruisdael in these lectures, bringing into the lecture hall a copy he had himself recently made of a Ruisdael winter scene in order to demonstrate 'that Ruysdael understood what he was painting'.[45]

The influence of Dutch artists passed on to the next generation of East Anglian landscape painters. It is evident, for instance, in the *Landscape: A View through Trees* painted by James Stark in the 1820s, and now in the Castle Museum, Norwich.[46] In a letter to Stark of 1816, his master John Crome gave the general advice that 'Trifles in Nature must be overlooked that we may have our feelings raised by seeing the whole picture at a glance, not knowing how or why we are so charmed.'[47] Gainsborough was to be praised by

Théophile Thoré (later better known as Thoré-Bürger) for just such wisdom, which Thoré discerned in a group of his later landscapes exhibited in the Manchester *Art Treasures* exhibition of 1857. Of these Thoré wrote: 'Il ébauchait tout d'un trait son tableau et le poussait harmonieusement de haut en bas, sans isoler son attention sur de petits fragments, sans s'obstiner aux détails; car il cherchait l'effet général, et il le trouvait presque toujours ... d'un seul coup d'œil.'[48] He went so far as to say that the Louvre should acquire a landscape by Gainsborough even if it meant paying for it ('honnêtement et par le simple vertu des livres sterling').[49] When Gainsborough painted *Cornard Wood*, at the age of twenty, he put too many 'petits fragments' in it, and charming as these individually are, they distract us from 'seeing the whole picture at a glance' (in Crome's phrase), 'd'un seul coup d'œil' (in Thoré's). Gainsborough's own awareness of this no doubt explains why, forty years later, he pronounced his picture to be 'a little in the schoolboy stile'. Undoubtedly it is unsophisticated in composition; as certainly, there is a note of reverie about it which sets it wholly apart from the realism of the 'little Dutch landscapes' he had studied in his youth.

Perhaps unexpectedly, the last word might go to Roger Fry. In 1934, discussing the weaknesses – but still more the strengths – of *Cornard Wood*, aware of the artist's models yet still more aware of his individuality, he writes:

> *Cornard Wood* ... is in effect a transposition of a Dutch landscape into an English mood, and with a freshness and delicacy of feeling which is entirely personal to Gainsborough; and with that, a franker acceptance of the colour of nature than Hobbema or Ruysdael allowed. Beside them, no doubt it would look a little fragile and over subtle; it lacks their forcible construction and vigorous relief. But though it is not overemphasised, the relief and the spatial construction are none the less felt, and perhaps that very delicacy and understatement of contrast conduces to the dreamy tranquillity of its mood.[50]

NOTES

1. Farington, *Diary*, 26 March 1808, vol. IX, p. 3247. Josiah Boydell asked Farington's help in selling two pictures inherited from his uncle Alderman Boydell, Reynolds's portrait of Lord Heathfield and 'the Landscape by Gainsborough', saying that 'He wd. take 300 guineas' for *Lord Heathfield* 'and 150 gs. for the Landscape by Gainsborough'.

2. David Pike Watts (1754–1816), collector and a governor of the BI, was John Constable's uncle; see *JCC*, vol. I, 1962, p. 319.

3. See Ilam Gallery Catalogue 1827, 1828, p. 14, and anon., *History and Topography of Ashbourn*, Ashbourn 1839, p. 181.

4. The picture was completed in 1748, thirteen years before Gainsborough exhibited any work; and he seems never to have given it a specific title. In 1790, two years after his death, Mary Prestel's aquatint of it was published with the engraved title *Gainsborough's Forest*, probably invented by Alderman John Boydell, then the owner of the painting and publisher of the engraving. It was exhibited at the BI in 1814 as 'A woody scene, in his early manner', at the BI in 1843 as 'A woody landscape' and at the Manchester *Art Treasures* exhibition of 1857 simply as 'Landscape'. The specifically descriptive (and nearly accurate) title 'Wood scene: the Church and Village of Cornard, near Sudbury, Suffolk, in the distance' had meanwhile been evolved for it in the Ilam Gallery Catalogue, 1828.

In time this was contracted to the deservedly popular title 'Cornard Wood', used for many years in National Gallery catalogues. Davies (1946 and 1959) thought that since the 1790 engraved title antedated the 1828 Ilam Gallery title, the painting should be called 'Gainsborough's Forest ("Cornard Wood")'; but there is no great validity in a title invented after the artist's death, and Cornard Wood itself cannot by any stretch of the imagination be called a forest. *Cornard Wood* is therefore preferred here as the key phrase in the picture's title.

In Hayes 1982, II, p. 342, NG 925 appears as *Wooded Landscape with Woodcutter, Figures, Animals, Pool and Distant Village (Gainsborough's Forest)*; but this title is geared to Hayes's need (in a catalogue of 187 landscapes) to distinguish between their salient features. It will not do for general use.

5. The second 'J. Boydell' is Josiah, nephew of Alderman John Boydell, founder of the firm and by 1790 the owner of Gainsborough's picture.

6. The compiler is very grateful to Hugh Belsey for explaining the viewpoint on the spot, and for subsequent discussion of the picture.

7. Originally 'Abbess', from its ownership by the Abbey of Malling, Kent; see Eric Sandon, *Suffolk Houses*, Woodbridge 1977, pp. 306–7. It still stands.

8. It may be noted here that the sale of Lord Dover's pictures at Robinson & Fisher, 21 May 1895 (by order of the late Viscount Clifden's executors), included, as lot 778, a small canvas by Gainsborough: 'Landscape and Figures with Views of Henney Church, near Sudbury in Suffolk, where Gainsborough was born' (bt Wallis). The identification of Henny Church in the background is hardly likely to have been invented; but this landscape appears to be unidentifiable in Hayes 1982; nor does he identify any other views of Henny.

9. N. Pevsner rev. E. Radcliffe, *Suffolk*, 1974, p. 186, describes the tower of St Mary's, Great Henny, as 'the lower parts ... Norman, the diagonal buttresses and the broach-spire C 15 or later'.

10. Soil consisting of clay and chalk, much used in Suffolk and elsewhere as a fertiliser; sometimes spelled 'marle'.

11. Philip Thicknesse, *A Sketch of the Life and Paintings of Thomas Gainsborough, Esq.*, privately printed, and sold in London, 1788, p. 6.

12. Gainsborough's copy of the Ruisdael (Hayes 1970, cat. no. 80, plate 248; coll. Whitworth Art Gallery, Manchester) was first discussed and illustrated by Mary Woodall (1935, pp. 40 and 45, repr. p. [41]; also repr. Foister et al. 1997, fig. 1. Ruisdael's *Woodland Ford with Cattle and Figures ('La Forêt')* is in the collection of the Louvre (on long loan to Douai, Musée de la Chartreuse), and is repr. in colour in Walford 1991, p. 136, fig. 145. Waterhouse 1958 (cat. no. 826, plate 46) notes that Gainsborough's so-called 'Drinkstone Park' landscape now in the São Paulo Museum of Art is a freer variation on the same Ruisdael. Hayes (1982, as '*c.*1747', cat. no. 20, repr.) considers the São Paulo landscape to be later than *Cornard Wood*, which to this compiler seems unlikely.

13. Henry V.S. Ogden and Margaret S. Ogden, *English Taste in Landscape in the Seventeenth Century*, Ann Arbor 1955; see particularly chapter XII, pp. 114–26.

14. Andrew W. Moore, *Dutch and Flemish Painting in Norfolk*, exh. cat., Norwich Castle Museum, London 1988, *passim*. A fuller idea of the scope of this study is given by its subtitle, 'A history of taste and influence, fashion and collecting'.

15. Jacob van Ruisdael (*c.*1628/9–82); Jan Wijnants (active 1643, d.1684); Aelbert Cuyp (1620–91); Adam Pynacker (1621–73); Herman Saftleven (1609–85).

16. Moore 1988 (cited in note 14), p. xvi. While Dutch landscapes were no doubt among Gainsborough's early and abiding loves, by the end of his life his collection of over fifty works by old masters included (as well as three works by Ruisdael, three by Molijn, two by Wijnants and others by

Pynacker, Berchem and Poelenburgh) two large canvases by Snijders, seascapes by Van de Velde, and works by Poussin, Francisque Millet, Sébastien Bourdon, Ghisolfi and others. See Hayes 1982, II, p. 130.

17. See Hayes 1982, I, p. 64.

18. Hayes 1982, I, p. 60, and n. 2. The sale of 'Italian, Flemish and English Pictures of Mr Oldfield', was held by Mr Prestage, Savile Row, 7–8 February 1766; the two lots mentioned were 'Mr Gainsborough. A Dutch Landscape, repaired by', first day's sale, 7 February 1766 (17) and 'Wynants. A Landscape, the Figures by Mr Gainsborough', second day's sale, 8 February (56). The second day's sale also included four paintings by Gainsborough (14, 33, 34, 53).

The anglicised (or phonetic) spelling 'Wynants' or 'Wynantz' is frequently used in English eighteenth-century collections and salerooms for the Dutch 'Wijnants'. In a review of the National Gallery's *Young Gainsborough* exhibition of 1997 (*Evening Standard*, 6 February 1997, p. 28), Brian Sewell rightly drew attention to the fact that Adrienne Corri had traced (through entries in bank books) a Francis Wynantz 'working in Suffolk in 1735', who received various payments from *c.*1733 to 1740 from the Suffolk-based Fonnereau family at much the same time as they made payments to Gainsborough and to Francis Hayman; see Adrienne Corri, (i) 'Gainsborough's Early Career; new documents and two portraits', *Burlington Magazine*, CXXV, 1983, p. 210 including n. 56; (ii) *The Search for Gainsborough*, London 1984, pp. 199–201. Corri suggests that the picture in the 1766 Oldfield sale – 'Wynants. A Landscape, the Figures by Mr Gainsborough' – may have been a collaboration between this Francis Wynantz and the young Gainsborough. If Francis Wynantz is certainly an artist, this may well be so. 'Putting figures' into a picture by the earlier Dutch artist Wijnants would have meant over-painting: has a painting by Ruisdael with considerably later over-painted figures been found?

19. See Foister et al. 1997, p. 7, where two entries in the Oldfield sale catalogue of 1766 – a 'Dutch landscape repaired by Mr Gainsborough' (first day, lot 17) and a 'Wynants' including 'Figures by Mr Gainsborough' – are taken as evidence that 'Gainsborough was paid for repairing Dutch landscapes'; further, that these two pictures (neither of which has been traced) provide 'the clearest indication that Gainsborough not only made copies of Dutch landscapes but actually worked on the paintings themselves'; and still further: 'it would seem a simple transition from such repair work to the production of Gainsborough's own landscapes.' Simple!

20. Under the heading 'Mr Gainsborough', *Morning Herald*, 12 March 1788 [p. 3, col. a]. Bate Dudley misunderstands Gainsborough's letter; by combining several of Gainsborough's phrases into the statement 'He painted it at Sudbury in the year 1748, at which time he was a schoolboy', Bate Dudley has caused much confusion. His version is reprinted from the *Morning Herald* in Whitley 1915, pp. 297–8 (punctuation, etc. revised, and a last paragraph added).

21. John Gainsborough died 29 October 1748. For Gainsborough's portraits of his father, see *Gainsborough's Family*, exh. cat., Gainsborough's House, Sudbury 1988, cat. nos. 4, 5. Gainsborough returned to live in Sudbury either late in 1748 or early in 1749. David Tyler notes that in the Rate Book for Hatton Garden March 1748/9 Gainsborough's name has been entered but crossed through ('Thomas Gainsborough's days in Hatton Garden', *Gainsborough's House Review 1992–3*, Sudbury 1993, p. 32 n. 24).

22. Letter to Thomas Harvey of Catton Hall near Norwich, from Pall Mall, 22 May 1788; Woodall 1961, no. 43, p. 91.

23. Hayes 1982, II, p. 345; paraphrased on p. 312.

24. Coll. Philadelphia Museum of Art. Hayes 1982, II, cat. no. 22 (as 'Wooded Landscape, with Peasant resting...'). See Richard Dorment, *British Painting in the Philadelphia Museum of Art from the Seventeenth through the Nineteenth Century*, London 1986, cat. no. 26, p. 111, repr.

25. Hayes 1982, I, p. 51. Foister 1997 carries this rather further, alleging (p. 3) that the picture 'is made up of a number of motifs which are near-quotations from seventeenth-century Dutch painters', though no such 'near-quotations' are actually adduced.

26. Coll. Thyssen-Bornemisza, repr. *Shock of Recognition*, Mauritshuis, The Hague, and London, Tate Gallery, exh. cat., 1971 (65), with the entirely pertinent note 'cf. Gainsborough no. 30 [*Cornard Wood*]'.

27. *Holywells Park, Ipswich* (Hayes 1982, II, cat. no. 26, as *Extensive Landscape with Reservoirs, Sluice Gate House and Seated Figure*) was acquired for Ipswich, Christchurch Mansion, in 1992; for the identification of the view, see *NACF Review 1992*, 1992, pp. 122–3.

28. Hayes 1982, II, pp. 312–18, followed by exhibited and datable but unidentifiable landscapes (pp. 319–21), with a 'Summary of the Chronology Proposed' (pp. 324–5).

29. See Martin Butlin's review of Hayes 1982, *Burlington Magazine*, April 1983, p. 233, for the weakness inherent in chain-dating.

30. Hayes 1982, II, p. 309.

31. No records of dates of student admissions to St Martin's Lane Academy appear to have survived. Gainsborough was baptised 14 May 1727, so would have turned thirteen on 14 May 1740, the year in which he is usually said to have begun to study in London; e.g. Waterhouse 1958, 'Chronology', p. 8: '1740. He is sent to London by his father to study; he remains there until 1748.' Bate Dudley, writing in the *Morning Herald*, 4 August 1788, two days after Gainsborough's death, noted that 'after painting several landscapes from the age of ten to twelve, he quitted Sudbury in his 13th year, and came to London'. This notice is fully quoted in Horace Walpole, *Anecdotes of Painting*, vol. V (ed. F.W. Hiles and P.B. Daghlian), New Haven and London 1937, pp. 36–9.

32. Roger Fry observed that 'However plain and direct a statement Gainsborough makes, he can never make it in prose. Always there is just that heightening of the emotional pitch which makes it poetry' (*Reflections on British Painting*, London 1934, p. 71). Fry was discussing Gainsborough's paintings, but his comment is also applicable to Gainsborough's letters.

33. There are no surviving records for pupils at Sudbury Grammar School: W.W. Hodson gives an account of the school's history in 'Sudbury Grammar School', *Proceedings of the Suffolk Institute of Archaeology and Natural History*, VII, 1891 [or 1890 ?], pp. 312ff. and states (p. 318), 'It was here that Thomas Gainsborough, the painter, received his education' – quoting Fulcher 1856.

34. Hayes 1982, II, p. 312, and see p. 345.

35. Hayes 1982, I, p. 76.

36. National Gallery Conservation Department records.

37. Letter of 22 May 1788 to Thomas Harvey of Catton, near Norwich; Woodall 1961, no. 43, p. 91. For Thomas Harvey (1748–1819) and his collection, see Andrew Moore 1988 (cited in note 14), particularly pp. 26–30.

38. See Foister et al. 1997, p. 4.

39. Coll. Tate Gallery (N 01485), 22.2 × 17.9 cm; Hayes 1982, II, cat. no. 16 (as '*c.*1746–7'), repr. p. 342.

40. Hayes 1982, II, cat. no. 11, as *Wooded Landscape with Herdsman seated on a Bank near a Pool, Cows and Distant Village*, repr. p. 337 (then private collection).

41. See Felicity Owen, 'Early Influences on John Constable', in ed. Hugh Belsey, *From Gainsborough to Constable*, exh. cat., Gainsborough's House, Sudbury 1991, pp. 17ff. For Gainsborough's influence on Constable, see also Hayes 1982, I, pp. 291–3.

42. Farington, *Diary*, 25 February 1799, vol. IV, p. 1164.

43. Constable to John Thomas Smith (1766–1833; from 1816, Keeper of Prints and Drawings in the British Museum), 18 August 1799; *JCC*, vol. II, p. 16.

44. Ed. R.B. Beckett, *John Constable's Discourses*, Ipswich 1970, p. 76, in Lecture IV of four lectures on the history of landscape painting given at the Royal Institution, May–June 1836; p. 67.

45. Ibid., p. 64.

46. Discussed and reproduced in Moore 1988 (cited in note 14), cat. no. 92, p. 134, repr. p. 92. Stark's dates are 1794–1859.

47. Quoted by Moore 1988, p. 58.

48. W. Bürger, *Trésors d'art exposés à Manchester*, Paris 1857, p. 394.

49. Ibid., p. 393.

50. *Reflections on British Painting*, London 1934, p. 72.

Perhaps more interesting than Plampin himself is his pose. Most writers have followed Waterhouse in believing that it is derived from Watteau's portrait of Antoine de la Rocque, painted in about 1719, which depicts a veteran of the wars, wounded at Malplaquet, sitting under a tree with his gammy leg extended; and perhaps it partly is. Artists in England could have become familiar with de la Rocque's pose through Lépicié's engraving of about 1734;[13] both Hogarth and Hayman are thought to have adapted it, Hogarth for the drunken rake with his leg up on a table in the brothel scene of *A Rake's Progress*,[14] and Hayman, more repetitively, in *Stealing a Kiss* and *The Wapping Landlady* (two paintings of about 1741 for Vauxhall Gardens supper-boxes),[15] in his double portrait of David Garrick and William Windham of about 1745 (fig. 1) and in the portrait uncertainly identified as of Philip Thicknesse.[16] The latter is probably of much the same date as *John Plampin*, and is so similar in style that it was long thought to be by Gainsborough rather than by Hayman. Gainsborough, at this time a great friend of Hayman, would have been very familiar with his use of the pose; there is an approximation to it in his pencil drawing (? of the early 1750s) of a young man reclining on a bank beneath a tree[17] and he uses it for a figure in the foreground of *Landguard Fort*,[18] a landscape painted for Philip Thicknesse which has not survived, and is now known only in the form of Thomas Major's engraving (fig. 2), published in August 1754.

But good artists rarely adapt an idea unless it appeals to their imagination on more than one level. An earlier source which may have been in Gainsborough's (and indeed in Watteau's) mind is the figure of the shepherd piping in Arcadia, in Rubens's *Pastoral Landscape with Rainbow* (fig. 3), painted about 1635 and engraved by Schelte à Bolswert.[19] Rubens's figure is a pictorial image of the shepherd whom Virgil envied, free to enjoy the beauty of nature, and to play his pipes 'stretched out beneath a spreading beech';[20] and his image goes back a long way.

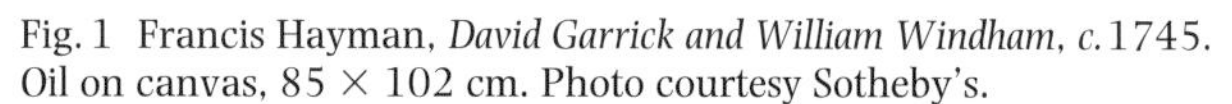

Fig. 1 Francis Hayman, *David Garrick and William Windham*, *c.*1745. Oil on canvas, 85 × 102 cm. Photo courtesy Sotheby's.

Gainsborough's modishly dressed John Plampin is no artless shepherd; yet despite his dress, he seems at home here, and the lie of the land he occupies has some echoes of the Rubens, as does the inclination of his dog's head. Gainsborough, like Reynolds, could allude to more than one source at a time. There is also, surely, in this as in Hayman's various versions of the pose, an element of cocking a snook (or in this case a leg) at the rules set by masters of deportment. François Nivelon's *Rudiments of Genteel Behaviour*, published in 1737 with illustrations by Bartholomew Dandridge, has taught Plampin what to do with his hands: '... the bend of the Elbow at its due Distance, will permit the Right Hand to place itself in the Waistcoat easy and genteel', while the left hand should be employed in 'holding the Glove in an easy, careless manner'.[21] But there is defiance in the legs, which are far from genteelly disposed. As John Hayes memorably observed, 'all the forms radiate outwards from the waist of the sitter as though they were spokes in a wheel, but elegant, serpentine spokes which closely reflect the theories advanced in Hogarth's *Analysis of Beauty*, published in 1753, at just about the date of this picture. Even the dog is absorbed into these predominating rhythms.'[22]

Aileen Ribeiro (1983) observes that Plampin wears a deep blue frock-coat trimmed with gold braid, a white satin waistcoat with gold tasselled frogging, black breeches and a tricorn hat with 'a sharp front pinch, called the Kevenhuller cock, worn by those with military and sporting inclinations'; she also notes that his square-buckled flat-heeled black leather shoes are suitable for a country walk. Plampin is accompanied by a small gun dog, probably a pointer cross; his collar-plate bears no inscription. Gainsborough evidently liked the dog's pose (seen from the left, one foreleg just in front of the other, the body slightly sloping, as if walking delicately down a small incline), for it recurs (with variations) in dogs in other Suffolk portraits of the 1750s.[23] X-rays show that Plampin's dog was added after Plampin himself was virtually complete; the dog's muzzle is painted over his master's breeches.

Fig. 2 (left) Detail from *Landguard Fort*, engraved by Thomas Major after Gainsborough's lost painting and published 5 August 1754.

Fig. 3 Peter Paul Rubens, *Pastoral Landscape with Rainbow*, detail, *c.*1635 (oil on canvas, 81 × 129 cm). St Petersburg, The State Hermitage Museum.

NOTES

1. Register of Baptisms, St Mary's, Bury St Edmunds, Suffolk: John, son of John and Ann Plampin, baptised 18 May 1727. There is much information about various generations of the Plampin family in the Davy MSS, BL, Add. MSS. 19078, 19145; from this source, briefly skimmed by the compiler, a few notes are given below. Portraits of earlier Plampins are recorded at Nowton Court by Revd Edmund Farrer, *Portraits in Suffolk Houses*, London 1908, pp. 275–6.

2. Waterhouse 1958 did not suggest a specific year for this portrait, describing it as 'from the earlier 1750s'. The date of 'about 1752' for Plampin's portrait is proposed by Hugh Belsey, who is engaged on a catalogue of Gainsborough's portraits; that dating seems more likely than 'about 1753–4' proposed by Hayes 1975, p. 205.

3. See ed. Jane Fiske, *The Oakes Diaries*, 2 vols, Suffolk Records Society vols XXXIII–IV, Woodbridge 1990, 1991.

4. For the history of the manors of Shimpling and Chadacre, see W.A. Copinger, *The Manors of Suffolk*, vol. I, London 1905, pp. 195, 198. Chadacre is a few miles north-west of Lavenham and six miles south of the county town of Bury St Edmunds. Chadacre Hall, rebuilt in the nineteenth century, is now an Agricultural Institute.

5. The compiler owes this identification to Hugh Belsey, who took her to see the church and gave her many pointers to information about the Plampin family. For All Saints, Lawshall, see Pevsner 1974, p. 328.

6. *Al. Cantab.*, Part 1, vol. III, 1924, p. 368; adm. Jesus College, Cambridge, 17 February 1745/6; matriculated 1746.

7. From this connection, Plampin derived several benefits, of which the Davy Papers (cited in note 1) quote one, reported in the *Ipswich Journal*, 23 August 1788: 'John Plampin Esq. of Chadacre Hall, in this county, was lately appointed Secretary to the Grand Duke of Tuscany, by the Earl of Bristol, a sinecure of £200 a year.'

8. The eldest son John (*c.*1754–1823), heir to the manor of Shimpling, was Rector of Whatfield and Stanstead, Suffolk; George (d.1795) was Rector of Depden and Stanstead. Robert Plampin (1762–1834, noticed in *DNB*) became a Vice-Admiral. Of the three daughters, Harriet married James Harrington, surgeon, of Hartest, near Shimpling; Sophia married John Macklin, of Devonshire, and ended up in Dublin; and Elizabeth Frances married Orbell Oakes, son of James Oakes, whose *Diaries* are cited in note 3.

9. Pevsner 1974, p. 416.

10. i.e. one who rotates his crops, leaving some fields to lie fallow (thereby regaining natural nourishment) before resowing. See John G. Gazeley, *The Life of Arthur Young 1741–1820*, Philadelphia 1973, p. 159. Arthur Young lived and farmed at Bradfield Combust, some five miles from Chadacre.

11. Ed. M. Betham-Edwards, *The Autobiography of Arthur Young, with selections from his correspondence*, 1898, p. 154. See also Norman Scarfe, *A Frenchman's Year in Suffolk*, Suffolk Records Society vol. XXX, Woodbridge 1988, p. 107. Foreign visitors at the Plampin's ball, fully identified by Scarfe, included the Duke of Liancourt, his two sons and Maximilien de Lazowski.

12. Fiske 1990, 1991 (cited in note 3), vol. I, pp. 179, 216, 309, 310, 311.

13. Lépicié's engraving of Antoine de la Rocque is not reproduced here because recent reproductions of it are available in Potterton 1976, Allen 1987 and Foister et al. 1997.

14. See Paulson 1984, cat. no. 134, pp. 93–4, plates 134–134a.

15. Both are repr., with the engraving after Watteau, by Potterton 1976, p. 15.

16. Coll. St Louis Art Museum, Missouri. 'Philip Thicknesse' was catalogued by Waterhouse as by Gainsborough (1958, cat. no. 660, plate 12). For the attribution to Hayman, see Allen 1987, pp. 41–2, fig. 22, reproduced above Lépicié's engraving of Watteau's *Antoine de la Rocque*. Waterhouse reproduces 'Philip Thicknesse' above John Plampin, making the two easy to compare.

17. Private collection; Hayes 1970, cat. no. 9, not repr.; Woodall 1939, repr. plate 28.

18. Hayes 1982, II, cat. no. 37; his plate 37 reproduces Major's complete engraving.

19. Coll. The State Hermitage Museum, St Petersburg; Jaffé 1989, cat. no. 1218. See Christopher Brown, *Rubens's Landscapes*, exh. cat., NG London 1996–7, cat no. 48, p. 81, plate 74 (in colour), with Rubens's pen and ink study for this and other figures, plate 75. The engraving by Schelte à Bolswert (*c.*1586–1659) is in reverse; repr. Rooses 1886–92, IV, plate 338. His engravings after Rubens were widely known and studied in England.

20. From a passage in Virgil's *Eclogues* quoted by Brown (cited in note 19), p. 79. As Brown notes (p. 80), Virgil's pastoral poems had inspired artists before Rubens, including Giorgione, Titian and Giulio and Domenico Campagnola.

21. Quoted by David Mannings, 'A Well-Mannered Portrait by Highmore', *Connoisseur*, 189, 1975, pp. 16–19.

22. Hayes 1975, p. 204.

23. For instance in *Major Dade in Shooting Dress* (see p. 83, fig. 3); Waterhouse 1958, cat. no. 759, 'middle 1750s' and in the portrait of an unidentified man, W.758, as '1750s', with Agnew's, 1969. Plampin's dog also recalls Robert Andrews's longer-haired gun dog in NG 6301.

NG 1811

The Painter's Daughters chasing a Butterfly

? *c.*1756

Oil on canvas, 113.5 × 105 cm (44¾ × 41¼ in.)

Provenance

Revd Robert Hingeston (1699–1766), Master of Ipswich School: unless given to him by Gainsborough, probably purchased at Gainsborough's own sale before leaving Ipswich, 22–23 October 1759 (no cat.); then by descent[1] through his son, Revd James Hingeston, Vicar of Reydon, near Southwold, Suffolk (d.1777), to his grandson James Hingeston; Owen Roe, Ipswich, by 1856; Henry Vaughan, by 1871, by whom bequeathed to the National Gallery 1900.

Exhibited

BFAC, *Old Masters*, 1871 (72); RA Winter 1886 (48); Munich 1958 (63); NG, *The Painter's Daughters chasing a Butterfly: Painting in Focus No. 4*, 1975; Tate Gallery 1980–1 (36, repr.); Paris, Grand Palais, 1981 (9); Tate Gallery 1987–8 (217); London (NG), Norwich and Newcastle 1997 (8).

Literature

Davies 1946, pp. 60–1; Fulcher 1856, pp. 48–9, 231; Waterhouse 1958, cat. no. 285, plate 52; Davies 1959, pp. 38–9; Michael Levey, *The Painter's Daughters chasing a Butterfly*, exh. cat., NG, London 1975 (*passim*; n.p.); Hayes 1975, fig. 12 in colour, p. 207 n. 31; Belsey 1988, pp. 25–30, fig. 8; David Tyler, 'Thomas Gainsborough's Daughters', *Gainsborough's House Society Annual Report 1991–2*, Sudbury 1992, pp. 50–66.

Technical Notes

The ground is pinkish brown, clearly showing through Margaret's dress, her apron and her outstretched foot, and also exposed in the space between Mary's right arm and body and in her foot. This priming is a mixture of lead white, chalk (calcium carbonate) and orange ochre: the same constitution as in the *lower* priming layer in *The Painter's Daughters with a Cat* (NG 3812).

Two samples of bright, slightly greenish yellow from the impasto of Mary's dress were analysed: the pigment is pure Naples yellow (lead antimonate) in the strongest-coloured areas, with lead white intermixed where the tint is paler.

The colour of the yellow in Mary's dress is unusually good for an eighteenth-century specimen. Naples yellow in eighteenth-century pictures was often of a poor hue, traces of impurities (particularly iron) in its manufacture commonly giving it a distinctive orange (or sometimes pink) tinge; by the early nineteenth century improved methods of manufacture gave rise to much purer lead antimonate yellow pigments.

The mid- and light green of Margaret's underskirt is made up of white lightly tinted with Prussian blue and a little black pigment (a pyrolised vegetable pigment, but not charcoal). The dull grey-blue of the sky, upper left, is the same combination of pigments with more black, although a little vermilion is also incorporated rendering the paint both duller and denser.

The sombre greenish-brown background above Mary's head contains the usual complex combination of pigments Gainsborough employed for his duller-coloured foliage paints: here it is Prussian blue, yellow, orange and red ochres, a little vermilion, red lake and possibly also a yellow lake. The paint surrounding the girl's head appears to have been overthinned with diluent and has dried with the shrinkage cracks characteristic of this.

The girls are Mary and Margaret, the artist's daughters by his wife Margaret Burr, and their only children to survive infancy.[2] Both daughters were born while Gainsborough was living and working in Sudbury, his own birthplace. Mary was baptised at All Saints, Sudbury, on 3 February 1750. Margaret was baptised at St Gregory's, Sudbury, on 22 August 1751. In neither register of baptisms is the date of birth recorded, but if the Gainsboroughs followed the general custom of baptising their children within a month or so of birth, then Mary is likely to have been born in January 1750 and Margaret in July 1752. There was probably only eighteen months' difference in age between them.

Mary's and Margaret's dates of baptism were established by David Tyler in 1992.[3] Previously it had been inferred (from erroneous inscriptions on their shared tombstone in St Mary's, Hanwell[4]) that Mary was born in 1748 and Margaret in 1752, with four years' difference in age between them. Waterhouse in 1953 gave Mary's dates as 1748 to 1826 and Margaret's as 1752 to 1820; later writers accepted those birth dates and based their dating of Gainsborough's various portraits of his daughters upon them. It is much to the credit of Martin Davies, a confirmed bachelor, that he alone observed (when cataloguing the two National Gallery double portraits in 1959) that it is 'hard to believe that there is about four years difference in age between the girls'.[5]

Between about 1756 and 1770, Gainsborough is known to have painted six double portraits of his daughters (listed below), as well as separate portraits of each of them.[6] None of the double portraits is dated. Suggesting at least approximate dates for them must largely be based on estimating the girls' probable ages in each picture from the dates of their baptisms. Other open-air portraits painted at about the same time as the earlier double portraits of his daughters might be expected to help with dating but do not: not only are few of them dated or easily datable, but the decorous style of his commissioned portraits is different both in scale and manner to the freedom with which he portrays his daughters.

The Painter's Daughters chasing a Butterfly is likely to have been painted in Ipswich in or about 1756. Mary, in yellow, appears to be about six years old, and Margaret about four or five. In Ipswich, where he lived for seven years (1752–9), Gainsborough rented a house opposite the Shire Hall; its garden adjoined that of the much larger house in Lower Brook

NOTES

1. The Hingeston line of descent is elaborated here because it was confused by Fulcher 1856 (pp. 48–9), followed by Davies 1959 (p. 39) and by Einberg, exh. cat., Tate Gallery, London 1987 (217). It was the Revd Robert Hingeston (not James) who was Gainsborough's friend and sitter (see note 10). The compiler is indebted to John Bensusan-Butt for a copy of his genealogical table of the Hingeston family.

2. There is a strong probability that the 'Mary Gainsborough Hatton Garden' who was buried on 1 March 1747 at St Andrew's, Holborn, was the infant daughter of Thomas and Margaret Gainsborough. This record was first traced by Adrienne Corri, as noted by Hayes 1982, vol. I, p. 89 n. 5. The dates of birth and baptism of this Mary Gainsborough remain untraced. See David Tyler, 'Thomas Gainsborough's Days in Hatton Garden', *Gainsborough's House Review 1992–3*, Sudbury 1993, pp. 27–32 (and n. 21).

3. Tyler 1992, p. 50, and *passim*.

4. The tomb still stands. Its lettering reads: 'Sacred/to the Memory of/ MISS MARGARET GAINSBOROUGH/ who departed this life December/ 1820 in the 68th year of her Age/ Also MRS MARY FISCHER/ Sister to the above who died 2nd Day of July 1826/ Aged 78 Years [***] "and in their deaths they/ were not divided." '

5. Davies 1959, p. 38.

6. For Gainsborough's single portraits of Mary and Margaret, see Waterhouse 1958, pp. 68–9, and Belsey 1988, *passim*.

7. An advertisement in the *Ipswich Journal* after the Gainsboroughs' departure describes the property as consisting of 'a Hall, and two Parlours, a Kitchen, a Wash-House, with a Garden and Stable, good Cellars, and well supply'd with Cock-Water, five Chambers and Garrets, with other Conveniences' (quoted by Whitley 1915, p. 25). The house no longer stands; its site is occupied by 34 Foundation Street. The Master's House was in Lower Brook Street. See W.M.M., 'From out the More Distant Past', in *Old Ipswichian Magazine*, October 1961, pp. 68–70.

8. W.370, 371. Revd Robert Hingeston's portrait is repr. in colour in John Blatchly, *The Town Library of Ipswich*, Woodbridge 1989, facing p. 57. Blatchly notes that Hingeston was an Usher of Ipswich School 1721–43, and Master (i.e. Headmaster) 1743–66. He was thus an usher at the school when Gainsborough was a pupil there.

9. Quoted by Whitley 1915, p. 22.

10. Fulcher 1856, pp. 28–9, publishes a letter from Hingeston's son (Revd James Hingeston) recalling his father's friendship with Gainsborough and his ownership of several of Gainsborough's works, including 'a picture of Gainsborough's two daughters ... chasing a butterfly', two portraits and several drawings.

11. Private collection; W.290, plate 8; Belsey 1988, fig. 23.

12. Coll. Yale Center for British Art, New Haven; see Cormack 1991, p. 52, repr. p. 53.

13. Coll. Fitzwilliam Museum, Cambridge; see Goodison 1977, pp. 80–1, plate 17; Hayes 1980, cat. no. 58, colour detail p. 91. Dated by Goodison to *c.*1750, by Hayes to 'early to mid 1750s'.

14. Levey 1975 [p. 2].

15. These observations were made by Canon Peter Hawker, FSA and entomologist, in an undated letter to the Tate Gallery while the picture was on loan to the *Gainsborough* exhibition, 1980–1.

16. See Brian Boyd, *Vladimir Nabokov: The American Years*, London 1992, p. 121.

17. Levey 1975 [p. 1].

18. Ibid.

19. In letters to James Unwin, 24 July 1763; *c.*1764; and 21 January 1765; see Woodall 1961, pp. 147, 157, 163.

20. Whitley 1915, p. 352: 'In early catalogues of picture sales landscapes by Miss Gainsborough are occasionally mentioned'; but none is recorded in the Getty Provenance Index 1801–10.

21. Millar 1969, cat. no. 800, plate 79.

22. For the later years of the Gainsborough sisters, see Tyler 1992, pp. 50–60; and David Tyler, 'The Gainsborough family: births, marriages and deaths re-examined, in *Gainsborough's House Review 1992–3*, Sudbury 1993, pp. 45–8.

23. Quoted by Tyler 1992, p. 55.

24. Purchased as a double portrait by Charles William Macready and John Forster, jointly, some time after 1831, then cut vertically into two; the two halves were later rather imperfectly reunited by Forster, who bequeathed the painting to the V&A in 1876.

25. W.284, plate 50; Levey 1975, fig. 6; Belsey 1988, fig. 9.

26. See 'M.W.T.' in anon., *100 Great Paintings in the Victoria and Albert Museum*, London 1985, p. 70, repr. in colour p. 71; Belsey 1988, p. 27, repr. fig. 9.

27. W.283; Belsey 1988, p. 87, quoting Pyne's review in the *Somerset House Gazette*, 7 August 1824, repr. in colour p. 19.

28. W.287, plate 90; Belsey 1988, pp. 88–91, repr. in colour p. 89. See St. John Gore, in [ed. anon.] *European Paintings in the Collection of the Worcester Art Museum*, Worcester, Mass. 1974, pp. 30–3. A chalk study for this painting (Hayes 1970, cat. no. 25, plate 90; Belsey 1988, cat. no. 21, repr.) was acquired by Gainsborough's House in 1996.

29. Quoted by Allen 1987, p. 100.

30. Woodall 1963, p. 151.

31. W.288; Belsey 1988, repr. p. 30, fig.11.

NG 3812

The Painter's Daughters with a Cat

? *c.*1760–1
Oil on canvas, 75.6 × 62.9 cm (29¾ × 24¾ in.)

Provenance

Passed after the deaths of Gainsborough and his wife to their younger daughter, Margaret (d.1820), who bequeathed a life-interest in her property to her elder sister Mary (d.1826), the property to be divided thereafter between the three daughters of Gainsborough's sister, Mrs Susannah Gardiner, or their heirs;[1] inherited in 1827 by Susannah Gardiner's grandson, Revd Gainsborough Gardiner (d.1869), then by his son Revd Edward R. Gardiner; passed to the widow of Edward Netherton Harward, Gainsborough's great-great-nephew, by whom sold Christie's 11 May 1923 (101), bt Knoedler (3045 guineas), from whom purchased by the National Gallery 1923.

Exhibited

Amsterdam, Stedelijk Museum, *Twee Eeuwen Englische Kunst*, 1936 (40); Paris, Louvre, 1938 (48); Paris, Musée des Arts Décoratifs, *Le Siècle d'Elégance: La Demeure Anglaise au XVIIIe Siècle*, 1959 (209); Ottawa, National Gallery of Canada, *Masterpieces of European Painting*, 1960 (10); Leningrad and Moscow 1988 (no cat.); London (NG), Norwich and Newcastle 1997 (9).

Literature

Davies 1946, p. 63; Waterhouse 1953, p. 44; Waterhouse 1958, cat. no. 286, plate 51; Davies 1959 pp. 40–41; Michael Levey, *The Painter's Daughters chasing a Butterfly*, exh. cat., NG, London 1975 (*passim*; n.p.); Hayes 1985, p. 209 n. 43, detail repr. plate 41; Belsey 1988, pp. 27–8, fig. 20.

Engraved

(1) in line by Peter Tomkins, n.d.; (2) lithograph by Richard J. Lane, with title *The Orphans*, published 1 January 1827 by J. Dickinson, 'from a sketch in the Possession of E.R. Gardiner Esqr.'

Technical Notes

The painting is in good condition, apart from some fine flaking, for example on Mary's forearm. The picture had been lined at some point before 1923. An annotated copy of the National Gallery's *British School Catalogue*, 1923, reads: 'The lower part a mere sketch. The painting had never been varnished, and was very dirty when bought [by Knoedler, in 1923] at Christie's. The dirt was removed by M. de Wild, at Messrs Knoedler's, with peroxide of hydrogen, the resulting condition being good. The cleaning was more drastic than that which we usually favour: C.J.H.' The initials are those of Sir Charles Holmes, then Director of the National Gallery.

In this unfinished sketch, the ground colour is clearly visible, particularly in the lower right. Two layers of priming are present: the lower a light pinkish brown, and the upper a darker brown variation of the lower ground. By analysis each layer is a mixture of lead white, chalk (calcium carbonate) and an orange-coloured natural ochre; the upper layer contains in addition some red ochre, giving it a stronger warm colour than that beneath. The lower ground here is identical in composition to the single pinkish-brown priming on *The Painter's Daughters chasing a Butterfly* (NG 1811); others of Gainsborough's canvases have virtually pure white primings.

A sample was taken from one of the white sketch-like broken lines seen in the lower right; these are directly on the ground and presumably are part of an initial design for the composition. Elsewhere this is worked in diluted brownish-black paint. The white sample was separated from the ground and analysed in an attempt to establish whether it might be paint or 'chalk' (pastel). The result is not wholly conclusive: the layer contains high levels of silicon and aluminium with a little lead, calcium and iron. The last three elements could arise from the ground layer, leaving aluminium and silicon as the main components of the white material of the line. This is consistent with china-clay (kaolinite, as well as a number of other white aluminosilicate minerals). It is possible that china-clay pressed into sticks was used as a drawing material. Kaolin is mentioned as an incorruptible white in a French source, *Traité de la Peinture au Pastel* (Paris 1788). This interpretation remains, therefore, speculative, but the lines seem not to be in paint. Their similarity to painted lines as we now see the picture is partly explained by the fact that they have imbibed varnish, binding the white particles together.

The two differing yellows in the picture were analysed. The dull mustard-coloured patch partially concealing the cat's unfinished head is pure yellow (natural) ochre; the paler, more primrose highlights on Mary's sleeve are Naples yellow (lead antimonate yellow: see comments under NG 1811) combined with white.

A thin layer of dull blue-green of the sky at the upper left edge of the composition comprises a mixture of white, Prussian blue, black and some orange and yellow-coloured earth pigment. A dull green colour was clearly intended. The constitution of the paint here is similar to many of Gainsborough's foliage paints.

The Painter's Daughters with a Cat is likely to have been painted in Bath a year or so after the Gainsboroughs had moved there (in late 1759). Mary appears to be aged about ten or eleven, and Margaret about eight or nine. This is essentially a sketch, left unfinished. The Technical Notes above are of particular interest here, for they suggest that after priming his canvas, Gainsborough sketched the subject in white chalk or pastel, working directly on the ground, and probably swiftly. In particular, the cat held above Margaret's clasped hands is merely suggested, though the shape is a good deal more credible as that of a cat than the object in Mrs Andrews's lap (see NG 6301, p. 84, fig. 4) is as that of a pheasant (as has sometimes been suggested).

portrait, begun before 1774, was completed in 1779, after Gainsborough left Bath. Gainsborough's letter of 31 July 1779 to Mrs Ditcher about her husband's newly finished portrait establishes that that portrait was painted in lieu of fees;[10] he may have been similarly generous in declining payment for portraits of his other doctors. Palmer's letter of 1771 to Garrick (cited above) notes that Gainsborough has 'sent home the pictures of Moysey and his family, which he had painted *gratis* for him, and the old doctor paid for the frames'.[11] Gainsborough also painted portraits of Dr Rice Charleton and of his two children (see p. 100, fig. 2), reputedly in lieu of medical fees; while no documentary evidence for this appears to exist, it seems particularly likely in the case of a physician who was also a friend and a collector of Gainsborough's landscapes. Gainsborough's own current portrait charges almost certainly far exceeded his doctors' fees. He had no trouble in finding sitters in Bath at 60 guineas for a full-length portrait (for most of the 1760s), rising to 100 guineas in 1769, while Dr Charleton's fee of one guinea per consultation was probably the going rate for other 'top physicians' in the town.[12] But Gainsborough may have found more rewarding material for portraiture in the attentive expressions of his doctors than in the faces of most of his fashionable Bath sitters.

Dr Ralph Schomberg is datable to around 1770. It has strong affinities with other robust, outdoor male full-lengths which Gainsborough painted in Bath between 1768 and 1774, particularly with *Viscount Kilmorey* of about 1768 and *Sir Benjamin Truman*, early 1770s (both in the Tate Gallery),[13] and with *Ralph Bell* of 1772 (North Carolina Museum of Art).[14] *George Pitt, 1st Lord Rivers*,[15] can hardly be much earlier than Schomberg's portrait; *Sir William Johnstone Pulteney*[16] of about 1772 (in a pose closely similar to Schomberg's) cannot be much later. A less well-known full-length, that of *Arthur, 1st Marquess of Donegall* (fig. 1), is likely to be even closer in date to *Dr Schomberg*.[17] Graves tentatively identifies *Dr Schomberg* with the 'Portrait of a gentleman; whole-length' exhibited at the RA in 1770 (84);[18] while the date is suitable, no contemporary corroboration of the identification has been traced, and conceivably the work exhibited in 1770 was Lord Donegall's portrait rather than Schomberg's.

The nuances of class distinction in this group of portraits are subtly observed. Lord Donegall is portrayed in the 'foolish cross-legged pose' of the fashionable idler who has come to Bath for pleasure. The 10th Viscount Kilmorey, a product of Eton and the Grenadier Guards, faces us squarely and masterfully. Schomberg's stance by contrast is slightly oblique, his attitude subtly deferential; he, after all, attends professionally upon the aristocrats who come to Bath to take the waters, and he seems less at ease than they in the countryside in which he finds himself. Each of the sitters in this group carries – with varying assurance – a walking-stick or cane, secured in the prevailing fashion by means of a black ribbon threaded through the top, then wound round the wrist. Dr Schomberg's more demure manner of holding his cane conforms to the deportment proper to physicians, who were described (in 1808) as assuming 'an air of gravity and meditation' by carrying their canes 'perpendicularly in front of the body, with the head [usually containing pungent herbs] pressed close under the nose'.[19]

The romantically wild yet artificial landscape background, with a wooded hillside on the right tumbling diagonally down, under a darkening sky, to more level ground on the left, is echoed in other full-length portraits of this period, including the (more dramatically lit) background in *Jonathan Buttall ('The Blue Boy')*, exhibited in 1770.[20] As Bomford, Roy and Saunders observe, the background in *Dr Schomberg* is painted 'with enormous speed and sureness', with brushstrokes so fluid that 'at the bottom left, dark paint has run down the canvas and Gainsborough either did not notice or did not care to correct it'.[21] Before Schomberg's crimson frock-coat faded, the depth of colour in the landscape's greens and browns must have been a brilliant foil to its skirts.

Dr Schomberg was aged 56 in 1770. His origins were German and Jewish; born in Schweinsberg on 14 August 1714, he was the eldest son of Meyer Löw Schomberg, an Ashkenazi Jew and MD of Giessen who, having emigrated with his family to England in 1720, began his London career as physician to the poor at the Great Synagogue in the City of London.[22] He and almost all his family (including his son Ralph) abandoned Judaism once in England.[23] Dr Meyer Schomberg was sufficiently assimilated by 1734 to be Steward of the Corner Stone Lodge of Freemasons, of which Hogarth was a member; he prospered, and by 1740 was reckoned to be one of the most successful physicians in London, with an annual income of 4000 guineas.

Ralph Schomberg, the seemingly benevolent sitter in NG 684, was in fact the black sheep of the family. He was educated at Merchant Taylors' School, 1726–31; he then travelled abroad, matriculating at Giessen University in 1733, but living beyond his means and constantly incurring debts. Fitful glimpses of him embarking on a career as a Notary Public, then travelling to Barbados as tutor to two young Lascelles,[24] then wandering on the Continent, are all shadowed by debts, which his father eventually refused to pay. In 1747 he sued his father for a fictitious debt;[25] not surprisingly, his father's will was to cut him off with a shilling. Marriage in 1742 to Elizabeth Crowcher, daughter and heiress of Joseph Crowcher, Master of the Vintners Company in the City of London, temporarily redeemed his worldly position. She was a Christian, and all their ten children were to receive infant baptism. Abandoning the profession of notary, Ralph decided to follow his father and his own twin brother Isaac into medicine; he graduated MD at Rotterdam in 1745, obtained a further MD from Aberdeen and then (his father and brother presumably having advised him to stay away from London medical circles) practised at Yarmouth until his move to Bath in 1761.

The career of Ralph Schomberg's twin brother, Dr Isaac Schomberg MD, FRCP (1714–80), was both distinguished and unmarred by scandal;[26] the contrast between them might have furnished Hogarth with a 'modern moral subject', not wholly unlike the contrast between the two apprentices in the earlier scenes of his *Industry and Idleness* engravings of

Fig. 1 *Arthur, 1st Marquess of Donegall*, *c*.1770. Oil on canvas, 232.4 × 152.4 cm. Belfast, Ulster Museum.

1747.[27] Both brothers were, to different degrees, friends of David Garrick.[28] Garrick, who suffered from gout and went frequently to Bath to take the waters, was the patient of both the Schomberg twins, Ralph ('my good Dr Ralpho') attending him in Bath[29] and Isaac in London. Ralph (or possibly Isaac) Schomberg commissioned a replica of Gainsborough's portrait of Garrick (full-face, with a book), painted about the same time as NG 684; it remained in the Schomberg family until sold by a descendant in 1904.[30] Ralph Schomberg was a tireless but untalented 'scribbler'.[31] His various publications (eighteen are listed in the *DNB*) included not only medical treatises but also poems, plays and polemics. His addiction to writing verse melodramas[32] which he pressed upon Garrick, evidently in the hope that as actor-manager he would wish to stage and even perform in them, repeatedly tried Garrick's patience. Garrick exploded by post on receiving Schomberg's rewriting of *Richard III* in 1773, then wrote to John Taylor (in a letter of 21 June 1773) to tone down his exasperation: 'I am afraid my letter to Schomberg, which I have inclos'd to You, will be a little too rough – tho I would cure him of Scribbling, I would not shock him – will you be so good to alter ye phrase of his Murdering Shakespear to something more mild ... if you think ye Dr wants a rough purge to be cleans'd from his play-writing let it go as it is.'[33] Isaac Schomberg, a more reliable friend, attended Garrick in his last illness in 1779.

Fig. 2 Thomas Hudson, *Dr Isaac Schomberg*, *c.*1755–60. Oil on canvas, 76 × 63.5 cm. San Marino, California, Huntington Art Gallery.

Fig. 3 William Hogarth, *Sir Alexander Schomberg, RN*, dated 1763. Oil on canvas, 61 × 48.5 cm. London, National Maritime Museum.

Ralph Schomberg's final fall from grace occurred on 14 December 1777, when donations were invited in aid of the Bath Hospital. He was among those appointed to collect money from boxes in various churches, the Pump Room and the Hospital – with the result recounted in a letter from William Jones to Lady Spencer, from Bath, 30 December 1777:

> Lawyers have been noted for cheating; but what shall we say of a physician at Bath, Dr Schomberg, who was appointed last Sunday to hold a plate for charity at the Church door, where a large collection was expected for the Hospital, and was detected by several persons in stealing the money? Above seven pounds in guineas and half crowns were found in his coatpocket, when he was charged with the fact. Yet this man, who was base enough to attempt this uncharitable fraud, married a woman with eight hundred a year. I am heartily sorry for her and for their family: He has left Bath, and must hide his face for ever.[34]

Presumably knowing that the scandal would have reached London, Schomberg settled in Reading, and died there 29 June 1792.[35]

Portraiture by different artists of members of the same family is not a subject which seems to have received much attention, yet it can throw light both on the range of portraiture available at the time and on artists' ability to catch a likeness. The Schomberg twins and their younger brother Alexander all sat to different portraitists. Dr Isaac Schomberg (fig. 2) was painted around 1755–60 by Thomas Hudson, who had also painted Dr Meyer Schomberg.[36] Captain Sir Alexander Schomberg RN (1720–1804) was painted by Hogarth, on a canvas dated 1763 (fig. 3). The three brothers' portraits were painted within at most fifteen years of each other. There appears to be little record of why sitters chose different portraitists. In the case of Ralph Schomberg, it appears that the initiative was taken by Gainsborough. The result is a portrait of a man whose aspect was described in 1838, as 'bland, gentlemanly, benevolent, and intelligent, with a *tout ensemble* bearing no inconsiderable resemblance to our abstract ideas of the good Samaritans of the old school of medicine, the solemnity and elevated pretensions of whose first-rate wigs were firmly sustained below by a sedate reserve of gold-headed canes... We believe ... that the tenor of his way was noiseless. He looks contented, and probably "Ne'er had chang'd, nor wish'd to change his place"'.[37]

During the short period in 1835–6 when *Dr Ralph Schomberg* first hung in the National Gallery as a gift from the Schomberg family (see Provenance), it attracted praise from two reviewers. The critic of *Blackwood's Magazine*, whose scornful comments on Gainsborough's *The Watering Place* ('a dingy ditch...') are quoted under NG 109, was happy to add that 'the portrait of Ralph Schomberg ... redeems poor Gainsborough's fame. Gainsborough's forte was portrait, in that he stands almost unrivalled among those of his day, and in that walk he is original. He is more natural than Sir Joshua.'[38] *The Spectator's* reviewer wrote of *Dr Ralph Schomberg*: 'A more living transcript of individual character was never put upon canvas: it is identity, as you look, it almost seems to breathe...' He also noted with approval that the portrait was hung under a skylight, and was the only picture in the National Gallery which could be seen in a natural light.

NOTES

The compiler is greatly indebted to Susan Legouix Sloman, Keeper of Art, Victoria Art Gallery, Bath, who has generously supplied all the information from Bath newspapers and Rate Books.

1. Susan Sloman notes that Jones's misrepresentations of pictures were notorious: see Graham Reynolds, 'Auctioneers, Dealers, Constables and Crooks', *Apollo*, CXXXV, 1992, pp. 368–71.

2. Issue of 22 January 1761.

3. Letter of 11 April 1766, published in ed. Brigitte Mitchell and Hubert Penrose, *The Revd John Penrose, Letters from Bath 1766–67*, Gloucester 1983, p. 27.

4. Susan Sloman has kindly supplied the following information, chiefly from City Rate Books, Bath Record Office. The earliest of these records rate-payers assessed on 24 June 1766, and lists Dr Schomberg in Orange Grove; he last appears there in 1769. By June 1769 he is listed at Prince's Buildings, one of the two terraces on the north side of

George Street, newly developed by Prince Hoare, the sculptor brother of the portraitist William Hoare; he is last listed there in January 1778. William Hoare, Dr Rice Charleton and Captain William Wade lived in the adjoining terrace, Edgar Buildings.

5. Wade sat to Gainsborough in 1770–1. See Susan Legouix Sloman, '"The immaculate Capt. Wade": "Arbiter Elegantiae"' *Gainsborough's House Review 1993–4*, Sudbury 1994, pp. 46–61, repr. p. 47. Purchased by the Victoria Art Gallery, Bath City Council, 1988.

6. For Charleton, see Ann Sumner, *Gainsborough in Bath*, exh. cat., Holburne Museum, Bath 1988, pp. 11–12, 30.

7. See Susan Legouix Sloman, 'Gainsborough and "the lodging-house way"', *Gainsborough's House Society Annual Report, 1991–2*, Sudbury 1992, pp. 23–43.

8. Ed. David M. Little and George M. Kahrl, *The Letters of David Garrick*, 3 vols, London 1963, II, no. 776, p. 878.

9. *Dr Rice Charleton*: 90 × 60 in., Holburne Museum, Bath, W.136, plate 87; *Robert and Susannah Charleton*: 57 × 46 in., Virginia Museum of Fine Arts, Richmond, Virginia, W.137, plate 149; see Sumner 1988 (cited in note 6), pp. 11–12, cat. no. 13, repr. front cover.

10. Ditcher's portrait is W.196, 'probably mainly painted before 1774, but only finished in 1779'. Gainsborough's letter to Mrs Ditcher, dated 'Bath, July 31st 1779', is published in Woodall 1963, p. 53; 'Madam – I am very glad the picture arrived safe and meets with your approbation. With regard to the price of the picture and frame I must acknowledge myself overpaid abundantly by my worthy friend's attention to my family while we lived at Bath.' He adds: 'If you can, pardon my neglect in not paying the carriage, which I fully intended doing, but for the hurry I was in the day it went away. You must rest assured, Madam, that what remains unpaid is from us to you.'

11. *Dr Abel Moysey*: private collection, W.505, plate 91; *Abel Moysey the Younger*: private collection, on long loan to Gainsborough's House, Sudbury, W.506, plate 137; see Hugh Belsey, *The Moysey Family*, exh. cat., Gainsborough's House, Sudbury 1984 (1, repr. front cover, 6 and 7, repr. [pp. 2–4]).

12. For Gainsborough's fees at this period, see Hayes 1975, p. 42. On physicians' fees, Belsey 1984 (cited in note 11), [p. 2], quotes Parson Woodforde, whose father consulted Dr Moysey in Bath, January 1771: 'My Father gave him a guinea for prescribing as usual...', from ed. John Beresford, *The Diary of a Country Parson. The Revd. James Woodforde*, I, London 1924, p. 104.

13. *John, 10th Viscount Kilmorey*, 92 × 61 in., W.411, plate 116; *Sir Benjamin Truman*, 93 × 58½ in., W.674, plate 117.

14. W.61. See Hugh Belsey, 'A Case of Mistaken Identity: Thomas Gainsborough's *Ralph Bell*', *North Carolina Museum of Art Bulletin*, XV, 1991, pp. 44–50, fig. 1.

15. W.577, plate 110; exh. RA 1769 (36); now Cleveland Museum of Art. Repr. in colour in E.K. Waterhouse, 'Bath and Gainsborough', *Apollo*, XCVIII, 1973, plate 11. Private collection.

16. W.565, plate 144; possibly RA 1772. Coll. New Haven, Yale Center for British Art; repr. in colour Cormack 1991, plate 40.

17. For the portrait of *Arthur, 1st Marquess of Donegall* (1739–1799) and its sometime identification as of Lord Archibald Hamilton, see *NACF 64th Annual Report*, 1967, p. 34.

18. It cannot be the 'Portrait of a Gentleman' exh. 1772 (96), for which see *London Chronicle*: 'a noble portrait in which ease and gracefulness are remarkably conspicuous' (*17): hardly apt to Schomberg's solidity.

19. The compiler is indebted to Susan Sloman for these quotations, from anon., *Hints to the Bearers of Walking-Sticks and Umbrellas*, London 1809. She notes that the *New Bath Guide*, the collection of satirical verses by Christopher Anstey first published in 1766, includes a line describing departing doctors as 'Brushing off, each his cane at his nose'.

20. Exh. RA 1770 (85), Huntington Art Gallery, San Marino, California, W.106, plate 127. For an illuminating essay on this, see Wark 1971, chapter III, 'Gainsborough's *The Blue Boy*', pp. 29–41.

21. *NG Technical Bulletin*, 12, 1988, p. 45.

22. For the careers of Dr Meyer Schomberg and the twin brothers Dr Ralph and Dr Isaac Schomberg (and the prolonged dispute over the latter's eligibility for admission to the Royal College of Physicians), see Alex Sakula, 'The Doctors Schomberg and the Royal College of Physicians: an eighteenth-century shemozzle', *Journal of Medical Biography*, 1994, 2, pp. 113–19.

23. Arthur Barnett, *The Western Synagogue through Two Centuries 1761–1961*, London 1961, p. 109, notes that at a time when the professions were still largely barred to Jews, 'the whole of the Schomberg family forsook their faith and found their path to fame made easier by way of the portals of the Church; all except one' [Alexander Schomberg of Bath, ? nephew of Ralph Schomberg]. Evidence is scrappy. The only one of Ralph Schomberg's ten children whose baptism has been traced (by Susan Sloman) is Robert Sandford, baptised in Bath Abbey on 5 January 1764.

24. Probably the children of Henry Lascelles, a Yorkshireman who made a fortune in the West Indies: see Eileen Harris, *The Townsend Album*, exh. cat., NPG, London 1974 (14).

25. Sakula 1994 (cited in note 20), p. 117 n. 30, cites the case: Schomberg v. Schomberg, Chancery, PRO C12/2230/13.

26. For an outline of Dr Isaac Schomberg's career, see Sakula 1994 (cited in note 22), pp. 116–17.

27. Paulson 1989, cat. nos. 168–79, repr. pp. 350–62.

28. For Isaac Schomberg's relationship as 'physician-friend' to Hogarth, see Paulson 1971, II, pp. 324, 420, 470, 508. Isaac Schomberg built up a collection of Hogarth's engravings. Hogarth's will included the following 'Item': 'that a Ring value Ten Guineas be presented to Dr Isaac Schomberg in remembrance of me.' For his friendship with and professional services to Garrick, see Little and Kahrl 1963 (cited in note 8), *passim*.

29. See Little and Kahrl 1963 for Garrick's frequent references to gout and other ailments: his letter from Bath to George Colman, 12 April 1766 (II, no. 397, pp. 504–5), reports on his ills and Dr Schomberg's treatment: 'I have a very serious fit of ye Gout, & how long it will last, & when I shall see you, ev'n my good Dr Ralpho can't tell me – I am in general cent p cent better for my present purgatory – Qualms – pukings, purgings, & Yellowness have left me, & I have no complaint but my gouty leg...' Garrick's letter of 2 April 1766 to Richard Berenger (II, no. 399, p. 507), also from Bath, reports that 'the waters have made me better, but left a kind of hoarseness, & weakness in my Bowels, which our Friend Dr Schomberg combats most wisely with Rhubarb, Magnesia &c. I am now much better, but I fret myself a little to think I cannot possibly venture upon Macbeth; which is a treble mortification to me, as I fear his Majesty has a desire to see it...'

30. W.307, perhaps a copy rather than a replica; sold by E.C. Schomberg, Christie's, 7 May 1904; later acquired by Paul Mellon, by whom sold Christie's 18 November 1981 (184, as by 'T. Gainsborough'). The original version, W.305, exhibited at the RA in 1770 (86 or 87) is now coll. NPG (5054).

31. He was described as 'long a scribbler, without genius or veracity' (Reed, *Biographica Dramatica*, I, 635–6, quoted in *DNB*).

32. One quotation from Schomberg's 'play-writing' must suffice, from *The Death of Bucephalus*, a burlesque tragedy performed in Edinburgh in 1765: Act I ends with a would-be assassin declaiming:

> 'Well, let me see – oh! ay! I've hit the means,
> I'll mingle deadly nightshade with his beans.'

33. Little and Kahrl 1963 (cited in note 8), II, no. 776, p. 878.

34. *The Bath Chronicle* of 25 December 1777 records the collection for the benefit of the Hospital, without mentioning Schomberg. Jones's letter is published in G. Cannon, *The Letters of Sir William Jones*, Oxford 1970, I, pp. 256–7, and in Trevor Fawcett, *Voices of Eighteenth-Century Bath*, Bath 1995, p. 156, no. 362. The compiler is indebted (as always) to Susan Sloman for both pieces of information.

35. He was buried in what appears to have been a family vault in St George's in the East, London. Two of his sons became Church of England parsons.

36. Repr. Sakula 1994 (cited in note 20), p. 115, fig. 2.

37. Anon., *The National Gallery*, London [1838], n.p.

38. *Blackwood's Edinburgh Magazine*, XL, no. CCL, August 1836, p. 211.

William Hallett (third in his family line of that name) was born on 24 June 1764 in Soho Square,[10] the son of William Hallett II (1730–67) and his wife Hannah Hopkins, daughter and heiress of the successful financier and South Sea Stock speculator, John 'Vulture' Hopkins. Three years old when his father died, he was largely brought up by his grandfather, William Hallett I (?1707–81), who, having made a fortune as a highly fashionable cabinet-maker,[11] in 1748 bought the newly cleared site of the 1st Duke of Chandos's once princely mansion at Canons in Middlesex, with much of the estate, and in due course built himself a villa there.[12] In Francis Hayman's group portrait of *The Hallett Family*, 1756,[13] William Hallett I is portrayed holding a plan for the house. On his grandfather's death in 1782, William Hallett III (Gainsborough's sitter)[14] inherited his house and the estate of Canons,[15] with a considerable fortune; his sister's portion was £70,000, but his own much larger one is unrecorded. He was then still a minor. After spending two years abroad on the Grand Tour,[16] he recorded: 'I returned home, and was married on 30th day of July 1785 to Miss Elizabeth Stephen with a fortune of nearly 20,000 [pounds].'[17]

Elizabeth Stephen's background is so far comparatively sketchy. The marriage certificate of 1785 describes her as 'spinster, of the Parish of St James's, Westminster'. She is believed to be the child born to James and Elizabeth Stephen on 8 February 1764, and baptised in St James's, Westminster, on 5 March 1764;[18] if so, both bride and bridegroom were aged 21 when they married, though Elizabeth Stephen was the elder by four months. Reporting the marriage, the *Gentleman's Magazine* described her as 'only daughter of the late Mr S., surgeon, with a handsome fortune'; but neither his professional qualifications, his will nor any further information about either of her parents has been traced. At the time of her marriage, she was described as 'of Breakspears, Co. Middlesex'. Breakspears, an ancient house not far from Canons, was then owned by the Partridge family; John Partridge was a witness of the marriage,[19] and the Partridges may have been friends or relatives with whom she was staying.

Elizabeth Stephen and William Hallett were married in the richly decorated church of St Lawrence, Little Stanmore, which the 1st Duke of Chandos had rebuilt in 1715 in the style of a private chapel and which he commissioned Louis Laguerre and Bellucci to decorate; it was for this church that Handel composed the Chandos Anthems. Mr and Mrs Hallett may have sat to Gainsborough in their wedding garments. Mrs Hallett's dress is of fine ivory silk, caught at the waist with a black silk band; a frilled muslin kerchief covers her breast, with a knot of pale grape-green ribbon under it, and this delicate colour is repeated in the extravagant bow beneath the ostrich feathers on her hat. Ribeiro, whose observations are largely drawn on here, notes that the filmy gauze silk stole over Elizabeth Hallett's arms echoes the 'contrived carelessness' of her hair and dress, and makes it seemingly easy for Gainsborough to merge gauze into foliage. William Hallett wears a black silk velvet frock-suit;[20] his hair is powdered, and he carries a black round hat.

Without the dog, the mood might have seemed a little solemn. The dog appears to be a Pomeranian sheepdog. A similar dog belonged to Gainsborough's friend Carl Friedrich Abel, the composer and viola da gamba player, and is depicted lying at his master's feet in Gainsborough's full-length portrait of him, exhibited in 1777; for Abel, Gainsborough also painted the *Pomeranian Bitch and Puppy* now in the Tate Gallery.[21] Gainsborough's pleasure in suggesting the thick, soft creamy coat of this breed through what are in fact sparse, light brushstrokes is also evident in his portrait of Mrs Robinson in the Wallace Collection.[22]

Waterhouse 1967 singles out 'a small group of late Gainsborough portraits which show the sitter walking forward towards the spectator' – first exemplified by the small-scale figures taking the air in *The Mall in St James's Park* of 1783–4,[23] studied 'from a home-made doll' – as 'among the most original and poetic inventions of English eighteenth century portraiture',[24] though owing something to both Watteau and Van Dyck. Gainsborough's enchanting studies for a projected picture known as 'The Richmond Water-Walk' (see fig. 1) are close in spirit to the figures in *The Mall*, and in turn infuse the mood in which he portrays (on a large scale) *Mr and Mrs Hallett* and *Lady Sheffield* (also of 1785). Their portraits, Waterhouse suggests, are closer to Gainsborough's 'fancy pictures' of the 1780s than to portraiture: 'their portrait content is no more positive than a lingering fragrance.'[25] Richard Graves's poem *On Gainsborough's Landskips with Portraits; full length Figures less than life, drawn in pairs walking thro' woods, etc.*[26] includes the pleasing fancy that Gainsborough subverts *Paradise Lost*: without specifying the image he has in mind, he writes:

> [in] that blest pair, by Gainsborough's pencil drawn...
> We find the pleasing cheat so well sustained
> Each landskip seems 'a Paradise regain'd'.

Waterhouse called *Mr and Mrs Hallett* 'an incomparable picture of young love';[27] later writers try variations on the same theme, one deeming it to be 'as much as portrait of the romance of young love as it is a likeness of the two individuals',[28] another that it is 'a universal statement about wedded bliss'.[29]

William Hallett may in fact be preoccupied less with thoughts of wedded bliss than with speculation about which horse was likely to win the next race. Racing was his great passion; betting and gambling were to be his downfall. The chief source of information about William Hallett is contained in his own will, which he drew up himself in an extraordinarily informal autobiographical style shortly before his death.[30] From this it is clear that even before his marriage, racing was his chief interest. Living in the country bored him, and Canons, the property he had inherited from his grandfather, held no charms for him: 'I was fond of sporting, and it was situated too near London.' He and his wife never lived at Canons, and Gainsborough's portrait never hung there; Hallett had let the estate to the racehorse owner and breeder Colonel Dennis O'Kelly in 1783,[31] two years before his marriage, and sold it in 1786.[32] William Hallett is listed among subscribers to the *Racing Calendar* from at least 1794 to 1825. His racing colours are given as 'orange, with black sleeves'.[33]

It is not clear where the Halletts (or the Gainsborough) were housed immediately after the marriage. In 1788 Hallett purchased the estate of Little Wittenham, near Wallingford, Berkshire, where he built 'a small house'; but soon afterwards they moved to Faringdon House, where they lived for twenty years. In 1807 he made two disastrous property deals, at Denford Park and 'the Townhill property', losing heavily on both, and in the process quarrelling irrevocably with his eldest son, William Hallett (IV). Finally the Halletts settled in a newly built house known as Candys, in South Stoneham, near Southampton.[34]

By 1830 nothing was left of William Hallett's fortune. His will records that he lived with his wife Elizabeth 'most happily for nearly 48 years, as it was impossible to do otherwise with such a woman'. Nothing is known of the life she led after she was painted by Gainsborough, sauntering in filmy stuffs through a glade; but it may be surmised that it was not an easy one. The couple had two sons and four daughters.[35] Elizabeth Hallett died on 16 April 1833,[36] aged 69, and was buried in the Hallett family vault in St Lawrence, Whitchurch.

Having remarried in 1834,[37] William Hallett consigned Gainsborough's portrait of himself and his first wife to Foster's saleroom in August of that year (see note 2); but it did not sell. In December 1834 he made his will.[38] It is a curious document, drawn up by himself and more like an informal, almost Shandean narrative of his life than any conventional will and testament (but, having been signed and sealed in the presence of witnesses, it was legally accepted as such). He lamented that he had no riches to bestow on his children, but added that 'they will enjoy all my late wife's fortune' (presumably it had been tied up in trust funds). He was in debt, and had little to leave. He left 'my picture of my late wife to my dearest daughter Lettice Elizth Hilliard which was painted before I married July 30th 1785':[39] and although 'my picture of my late wife' does not immediately suggest a double portrait of himself and his wife, presumably this self-effacing reference does indeed refer to Gainsborough's double portrait. He left a miniature (unidentified) of his late wife to his daughter Charlotte, his religious books to his clerical son-in-law, Revd Fulwar Fowle, his law books to his son-in-law Nash Crosier Hilliard, five guineas for a ring to his friend William Crowdy and the 'rest and residue' to his second wife Mary Jane, 'hoping sincerely that it may turn out better than expected'. As for his funeral, it should be simple. 'I should like to be taken in a concealed manner (for the sake of cheapness) to the Crane Inn at Edgeware and from thence by ten poor labourers such as the clergymen of the Parish of Little Stanmore may name ... to be buried in my family vault near my late wife' (adding 'where my present wife may like to join the party if not better engaged').[40] William Hallett died on 21 November 1842, aged 78. He was duly buried beside his first wife in the Hallett vault in St Lawrence, Whitchurch, where they had been married 57 years earlier.

When the double portrait was shown in the British Institution's Gainsborough exhibition of 1859, *The Times* reviewer commented that 'Mr Hallett is only known to fame as a patron of the Turf. As he is here presented it would be difficult to conceive a more perfect realisation of youthful elegance and high breeding. He is worthy of the sweet young woman who wears the budding honours of wifehood with such pretty pride, her hand resting with a fond and confiding pressure on the new husband's arm. Happy young couple to be handed down to posterity, before the world had withered the young wife's roses, – before the turf and the bottle has soured the husband's brow, and reddened his nose, or the gout stiffened and swelled those shapely legs of his.'[41]

The popular title 'The Morning Walk' appears to have been invented for the picture almost a century after it was painted, probably around 1884, when it changed hands (via Agnew's) from family ownership to that of the Rothschilds who, having no connection with the sitters, may have preferred an impersonal title. 'The Morning Walk' had already been conjured up by Christie's in 1859 as a title for Gainsborough's portrait of Miss Elizabeth Haverfield.[42] The phrase 'the morning walk' is recollected from Thomson's *The Seasons* (Part III: 'Summer'), which had long been a useful mine of quotations for artists.[43] John Linnell quoted the lines '...when every Muse/ And every blooming pleasure wait without,/ To bless the wildly-devious

Fig. 1 Study of a lady, probably for 'The Richmond Water-Walk', *c.*1785. Black chalk and stump and white chalk on buff prepared paper, 49.2 × 31.1 cm. New York, Pierpont Morgan Library.

morning-walk' to accompany a painting which he titled *The Morning Walk* and showed at the Royal Academy in 1847 (265);[44] it may have been Linnell who made the title popular. The exuberance of the lines is more suited to *Miss Haverfield* (a child in an outsize hat among foxgloves) than to the more reticent mood of *Mr and Mrs Hallett*. Fancy names are perhaps most commonly bestowed on portraits which seem to express an elusive mood, as well as attempting to catch a likeness. By a process of association, Romney's double portrait of Sir Christopher and Lady Sykes (and a dog), painted the year after *Mr and Mrs Hallett* and on much the same scale, was known earlier this century as 'The Evening Walk'.[45]

In the course of reviewing some of the British pictures in the International Exhibition of 1862, the poet and critic Théophile Gautier wrote:

> On éprouve, en face du portrait de sir William Hallet et de sa femme, une sensation rétrospective bizarre, tant l'esprit du siècle dernier y vit avec une illusion intense. On croit voir en réalité ces jeunes époux qui marchent en se donnant le bras dans l'allée d'un jardin. La femme, romanesquement jolie, est habillée d'une robe de mousseline à l'Angelica Kauffmann, et d'une écharpe de gaze dont sa main délicate chiffonne distraitement le bout. Un chapeau à la Pamela cerclé d'un ruban blanc pose sur ses beaux cheveux bleu-cendré qui se rendent à la mode du temps en un énorme chignon. Le mari porte l'habit à la française et la culotte courte de la façon la plus gracieuse du monde et jette un regard amoureuse à sa femme; un chien blanc, ennuyé de ce tête-à-tête, court en jappant après le couple comme pour réclamer sa part habituelle de caresses.[46]

Beatrix Potter's judgement was sterner. In February 1885 (then aged nineteen, and already a regular exhibition visitor), she saw the the exhibition of works by Gainsborough at the Grosvenor Gallery. 'The papers have praised them up in an extraordinary manner', she noted; but she was unimpressed. On this occasion she barely mentions the Hallett double portrait, remarking in general that compared with Reynolds's portraiture 'all Gainsborough's faces' are too composed, 'the more expressive ones melancholy, there is scarcely a laughing face here'. She proceeds to compare Gainsborough with Reynolds: whereas 'Reynolds presents to us a cheerful, pleasant race, the men refined, kindly and thoughtful, the women fresh, gay, natural and clothed in rich colour', Gainsborough's men look 'careworn instead of cheerful', and his ladies 'long faced and depressed'. She considered that 'Neither Reynolds nor Gainsborough were great draughtsmen, but the former's deficiencies were generally concealed by the force and movement of his figures'.[47] Curiously, Beatrix Potter's opinions in some sense anticipate the profounder judgements of Ellis Waterhouse, who observed that whereas Reynolds had excelled in the portraiture of 'the solid British male', Gainsborough in his latest years was 'supremely fitted to paint the portraits of creatures who were all heart and sensibility'.[48]

Fig. 2 *Mr and Mrs William Hallett*, detail

NOTES

1. See note 8.

2. See Whitley 1930, p. 287: 'A PICTURE BY GAINSBOROUGH. Messrs Foster and Son will have the honour to submit to Public Auction, at the Gallery, 54 Pall Mall, on Saturday, August 9th, unless a favourable offer should be previously made ... a capital picture, whole-length, by Gainsborough... It represents a lady and gentleman in the dress of forty-eight years ago, including a landscape and a Pomeranian dog, admirably executed... It may be viewed at Messrs Foster's Gallery, 54 Pall Mall, where tickets and particulars may be obtained.' Before the sale, it was also shown at Mr Peel's, 17 Golden Square, London. In the auctioneer's copy of the sale catalogue in E.K. Waterhouse's collection (now coll. Paul Mellon Centre), the picture is marked as 'passed'; in the V&A copy, as 'withdrawn'. Evidently there were no offers. Davies 1959, p. 44 n. 5, following up a passage in *The Critic*, XVIII, 25 June 1859, believed the picture may also have been offered for sale about the same time at John Allnutt's gallery, Pall Mall, but there may be some confusion with Foster's of Pall Mall here.

3. Agnew's stock-book records that on 15 April 1884 two paintings were purchased together from 'Hilliard' (no initial, no prefix), 'Whole length of Mr & Mrs Hallett' and 'Snyders Still-Life'. W.E. Hilliard was believed by some branches of the family to have sold a picture which in fact belonged to his wife, having had a copy made to hang in its place; alternatively, he was believed by others to have accepted the picture as a pledge for loans made to one or more Halletts.

In 1958 Mrs Eland presented to the NG a collection of papers from the estate of her father, Maurice Brockwell, who had compiled a history of the Halletts and Hilliards under the title 'The Morning Walk', unpublished. The Brockwell Papers include family trees and some correspondence, though the bulk is the typescript of the projected book. Family traditions appear to have been discrepant. Brockwell seems to have concluded that W.E. Hilliard was in fact acting for the Hilliard family in general.

4. See Lord Rothschild (Chairman of the Trustees of the NG 1985–91), *NG News*, May 1992 [pp. 1–3]; he recounts that negotiations between his father and the NG for the purchase of the picture began in April 1947 and took almost seven years to complete.

5. Comments on the 1936 exhibition by Martin Davies (on condition) and E.K. Waterhouse, typescript, NG Library.

6. Alan Clutton-Brock, a Trustee of the NG, describing the picture's first public appearance after cleaning in April 1954 ('The "Morning Walk" Purchased', *Christian Science Monitor*, Boston, Mass., 24 April 1954, expanded from a note in *The Times*, 3 April 1954, p. 8) noted a remarkable freshening of colour after the removal of discoloured varnish: 'Mrs Hallett's dress has now become the palest ivory white', against which her 'apple-green' ribbons tell effectively.

7. This point is established by William Hallett's will, dated 3 December 1834, and signed ('by his running his pen over his name') and sealed in the presence of witnesses 9 September 1836, in the Public Record Office (PROB 11 /1998 ff. 315–7). A typescript copy among the Brockwell Papers has been checked by the compiler against the official copy in the PRO and, apart from changes of spelling and punctuation, found to be reasonably accurate.

8. Hayes 1963, p. 370. Hayes traced a payment of £126 to Gainsborough entered in the ledgers of William Hallett's account with Drummond's Bank under the date of 4 March 1786. He adds: 'Clearly, the picture was executed shortly after the couple's marriage, which took place on 30th July 1785'; but William Hallett's will states that the picture was painted before their marriage.

9. Hayes 1963.

10. According to his own statement in his will; but there may be some confusion with the date of his baptism, recorded as 24 July 1764 in the Register of Baptisms, St Anne's, Soho, London.

11. William Hallett's will describes his grandfather as 'an Upholster at the corner of Long Acre and St Martin's Lane ... in business about 20 years and as he assured me, was never in bed more than four hours in any night during that time'. The fullest account of William Hallett I is in Percy McQuoid and Ralph Edwards, *Dictionary of English Furniture*, vol. II, rev. edn, London 1954, pp. 252–3. McQuoid and Edwards call Hallett 'probably the most fashionable furniture maker of George II's reign'. He worked in Great Newport Street 1732–53, and from 1753 at the corner of St Martins's Lane and Long Acre (where he may have been in partnership with William Vile). Hallett's clients included Thomas Coke, 1st Earl of Leicester, Lord Folkestone, and Lord Cardigan; but only one pattern chair is now identifiable as his. See also Sir Ambrose Heal, *The London Furniture-Makers*, London 1953, pp. 64–5. Horace Walpole several times refers to Hallett, notably in a letter to Richard Bentley, 5 July 1755, about a visit to Latimers: 'Half of the ornaments are of [Batty] Langley's bastard Gothic, and half of Hallett's mongrel Chinese. I want to write over the doors of most modern edifices "Repaired and beautified, Batty and Hallett, churchwardens"' (*Walpole Correspondence*, vol. XXXV, p. 233).

12. For the Halletts' connection with Canons, see C.H. Baker and Muriel I. Baker, *The Life and Circumstances of James Brydges, First Duke of Chandos*, Oxford 1949, pp. 437ff., and R.B. Pugh, *Victoria County History: Middlesex*, V, Oxford 1976, pp. 116ff. The 1st Duke of Chandos's mansion had been stripped of its contents and pulled down by 1753, when William Hallett I began to build his house. The North London Collegiate School now occupies the site, with William Hallett's house still standing at its core.

13. Private collection; repr. Allen 1987, p. 104, with informative notes, pp. 103, 105. Gainsborough's sitter is not included in Hayman's family group of 1756 as he was not born until 1764; but his father William Hallett II is portrayed, in the foreground.

14. A 'Mr Hallet' sat to Reynolds in 1764, but according to Graves and Cronin, this was probably Christopher Hallett, who died *c.*1770.

15. See *Gentleman's Magazine*, LII, 1782, pp. 45–6: obituary of William Hallett I. A view of the house he built at Canons as it appeared in 1782, engraved after J.A. Gresse, was published in *Watts's Seats of the Nobility and Gentry*, London 1782, repr. Baker and Baker 1949.

16. William Hallett may be the 'Mr Hallett' whom Mary Berry encountered at an evening party in Rome on 21 November 1783 (ed. Lady Theresa Lewis, *Extracts from the Journals and Correspondence of Miss Berry, 1783–1822*, I, London 1866, p. 56).

17. William Hallett's will.

18. Register of Baptisms, St James's, Westminster.

19. *Gentleman's Magazine*, 1785, p. 664; the other witness was John Dolben English, William Hallett's brother-in-law.

20. Ribeiro 1995, p. 50.

21. *Carl Friedrich Abel*: 88 × 58 in., exh. RA 1777 (135), coll. Huntington Art Gallery, San Marino, California; W.1, plate 171. *Pomeranian Bitch and Puppy*; *c.*1777, 83.2 × 111.8 cm, Tate Gallery, London (N 05844); W.821, plate 290c.

22. Wallace Collection, 229 × 153 cm; W.579, plate 238: John Ingamells, *The Wallace Collection Catalogue of Pictures*, I: *British, German, Italian, Spanish*, London 1985, pp. 93–7, repr. p. 94.

23. Frick Collection, New York; W.987, plate 243.

24. Ellis Waterhouse, *The James A. de Rothschild Collection at Waddesdon Manor: Paintings*, Paris 1967, p. 4, where *Sophia Charlotte, Lady Sheffield* is cat. no. 10, repr.; also repr. Hayes 1975, plate 100.

25. Waterhouse 1958, pp. 28–9.

26. Richard Graves (1715–1804) was Rector of Claverton, Bath. Marcia Pointon draws attention to Graves's poem in 'Gainsborough and the Landscape of Retirement', *Art History*, 2, no. 4, 1979, p. 450. First published in 1762, it was included in William Shenstone's MS 'Miscellany', first ed. Iain A. Gordon, as *Shenstone's Miscellany 1759–1763*, Oxford 1952, pp. 125–6.

27. Waterhouse 1953, p. 178.

28. Hayes 1975, cited above, p. 227.

29. Andrew Wilton, *The Swagger Portrait*, exh. cat., Tate Gallery 1992, p. 148.

30. See note 7.

31. For O'Kelly, an eminent breeder of racehorses and a patron of Stubbs, see *DNB*.

32. William Hallett's will; Baker and Baker 1949, pp. 439–9, and Pugh 1976, p. 116 (both cited in note 12).

33. William Hallett is listed in *Racing Calendars* between (at least) 1794 to 1825. His colours are given in the *Racing Calendar* for 1800 (p. liii).

34. Information about William Hallett's property transactions is taken from his will.

35. (i) William Hallett IV, b. 8 August 1786; d. 29 September 1859; (ii) Lettice Elizabeth (who inherited the Gainsborough), b. 2 September 1787; m. Nash Crosier Hilliard; d. 29 September 1859; (iii) Caroline, b. 19 August 1791, d. aged three weeks; (iv) Charlotte, ?–1788; (v) Emily, b. ? (vi) Richard Stephen (named after Mrs Hallett's father, the untraced surgeon ?), b. 9 July 1794; Lieut., 52nd Foot, d. 6 August 1812.

36. *Gentleman's Magazine*, CIII, 1833, (i), p. 379: 'In Southampton Street, after a married life of forty-eight years, Elizabeth, wife of Wm. Hallett, esq., of Candy's near Southampton.' If she made a will, it has eluded search.

37. His will names his second wife as Mary Jane Croudace, but does not record the date of this marriage.

38. William Hallett's rambling will suggests that by then he may not have been entirely in his right mind.

39. Maurice Brockwell (see Brockwell Papers) firmly believed that the following bequest in William Hallett's will, 'I give my picture of my late wife to my dearest daughter Lettice Elizth Hilliard wch. was painted before I married', referred to Gainsborough's double portrait; he wrote on this point to *The Times*, 13 July 1953, p. 7. It may be noted that Lettice Hilliard did inherit the double portrait and, so far as is known, no other portrait of her mother. That William Hallett's phrase 'picture of my late wife' may mean 'picture which belonged to my late wife' is supported by his phrasing 'three pictures of my said wife, namely one of her mother, another of her aunt... and a third of her sister...' in an inventory attached to his will. The compiler is grateful to her colleague Humphrey Wine LLB for advice on this point.

40. All the facts in this paragraph are derived from William Hallett's will. Two codicils: (i) 29 November 1834, appointing his two sons-in-law, Nash Crosier Hilliard and Revd Fulwar William Fowle, 'to act in conjunction with' his [second] wife and his friend William Crowdy; (ii) 29 November 1836, altering 'the Executorship', with his wife's consent. His will directs his executors to 'pay into the hands of my said wife twenty-five pounds before they commit my body to the earth, and the further sum of fourteen pounds to defray expenses of housekeeping for one fortnight, commencing from the day of my decease'.

41. *The Times*, 6 June 1859. This sardonic note was picked up and carried still further (and inaccurately) in *The Critic*, XVIII, 25 June 1859, p. 616: '...that loveable woman now standing before us died soon after her marriage, and he (now rendered immortal by Gainsborough), known to fame only as a patron of the turf, became a low, debauched, gambling roué, gouty, bloated and poverty-stricken, married again "some low person" and with this strange, eventful history exit Mr Hallett...'

42. 126.2 × 101 cm, sold Christie's 26 March 1850 (72, as 'The Morning Walk, Portrait of Miss Haverfield'), Wallace Collection (P44); W.355; see Ingamells 1985, p. 99, repr. p. 98.

43. James Thomson, *The Seasons* (first published in parts 1726–30), 1792 edn, p. 60, lines 78–80. Shawe-Taylor 1990 suggests that lines 936–44 from 'Spring' in Thomson's *The Seasons* might also be apt to the picture: '...Perhaps thy loved Lucinda shares thy walk,/ With soul to thine attuned. Then Nature all/ Wears to the lover's eye a look of love.../ You, frequent pausing turn, and from her eyes,/ Where meekened sense and amiable grace/ And lively sweetness dwell, enraptured drink/ That nameless spirit of ethereal joy./ Inimitable happiness! which love/ Alone bestows, and on a favoured few'

44. Untraced by this compiler.

45. Waterhouse 1958, p. 213, plate 184; see also Shawe-Taylor 1990, p. 131, fig. 6, repr. in colour. Romney could have seen *Mr and Mrs William Hallett* in Gainsborough's studio.

46. Théophile Gautier, 'Exposition de Londres', *Le Moniteur Universel*, 5 June 1862. An extract translated into English but giving no source was published by Whitley 1915, p. 258, and repeated by Hayes 1975, p. 227, and Hayes 1991, p. 118, without source or date. For tracing the source, the compiler is much indebted to Dr Robert Snell, and for providing a photocopy of *Le Moniteur Universel* to Danielle Le Nan, Directeur, Département des Périodiques, Bibliothèque Nationale.

The following translation is offered here: 'One experiences, in front of the portrait of William Hallett and his wife, a strange retrospective sensation, since the spirit of the last [eighteenth] century pervades it so intensely. One seems truly to see this young couple walking with linked arms along the garden lane. The lady, romantically beautiful, is dressed in a muslin gown in the style of Angelica Kauffmann, her delicate hand carelessly toying with her filmy stole. A hat which Pamela might have worn, circled with a band of white ribbon, surmounts her beautiful ash-blue hair, dressed in the fashion of the day in an enormous chignon. The husband, dressed in the French style, with knee-breeches of the greatest elegance, throws a look of love towards his wife; a white dog, vexed at the couple's absorption in each other, runs after them, barking to reclaim his usual share of their caresses.'

47. *The Journal of Beatrix Potter from 1881 to 1897*, transcribed and ed. Leslie Linder, London 1996, pp. 126–7. When Beatrix Potter saw *Mr and Mrs William Hallett* again in the Royal Academy's Winter exhibition the following month, she noted: 'It is not the best by a good deal'; she found the figures stiff, the technique 'scratchy', Mr Hallett's legs 'quite out of drawing' and the dog 'spirited but very sketchy'; she liked 'the lady' best, even though she conformed to 'the Gainsborough type' (pp. 134–5).

48. Waterhouse 1953, pp. 177–8.

NG 80

The Market Cart

1786
Oil on canvas, 184 × 153 cm (72½ × 60¼ in.)

Provenance

Purchased from the artist in or by May 1787, for 350 guineas, by Sir Peter Burrell Bt, MP (cr. 1st Baron Gwydir 1796); his sale, Christie's 8–9 May 1829, 2nd day (87), as *A Grand Upright Landscape, with Figures, representing peasants with a market cart making their way over the uneven surface of a glade...*, 1050 guineas, bt [William] Seguier for the Governors of the British Institution,[1] by whom presented to the National Gallery 1830.

Exhibited

by Gainsborough, with other pictures for sale, in his apartment in Schomberg House, Pall Mall, London, from the end of December 1786 until sold in May 1787; BI, *Italian, Spanish, Flemish, Dutch and English Masters*, June 1829 (88, as 'Landscape with Market-people'); Tate Gallery, 1953 (167); Tate Gallery, 1959 (167); Tate Gallery, 1973–4 (60); Paris, Grand Palais, 1981 (76); Birmingham, City Museum and Art Gallery, and Toronto, Art Gallery of Ontario, *Thomas Gainsborough: The Harvest Wagon*, 1995 (24).

At the Tate Gallery 1951–86.

Literature

Morning Herald, 30 December 1786, 1 January and 7 May 1787; *The World*, 12 January 1787 (transcripts in Whitley Papers, BM); MS 'Inventory of the Household Furniture at Grimsthorpe Castle in the County of Lincoln the Property of the Right Honourable Lord Gwydir ... 1st January 1812', Lincolnshire Archives Office, BRA 305 (typescript extract in NG Archives); Whitley 1915, pp. 263–4, 270–5, 304, 323, 332, 355–6; Woodall 1939, pp. 67–70, cat. no. 450, plate 90; Davies 1946, pp. 55–6; Waterhouse 1958, pp. 34, 40, cat. no. 1002, plate 286; *Smith College Museum of Art Bulletin*, no. 40, Northampton, Mass., 1960, p. 32; Hayes 1964, p. 26, fig. i; Michael Clarke, 'Gainsborough and Loutherbourg at York', in *Preview, York City Art Gallery Quarterly*, XXXVI, 1973, pp. 931–5; Hayes 1975, pp. 44, 47, 227, plate 162; Hayes 1982, I, pp. 161, 176–8, 238, cat. no. 184, pp. 566–9, repr. pp. 176 (fig. 212), 567; Paul Spencer-Longhurst and Janet M. Brooke, *Thomas Gainsborough: The Harvest Wagon*, exh. cat., Birmingham and Toronto 1995, pp. 54–5.

Engraved

after Gainsborough's death, by (1) H. Robinson, published by J. Major 1 September 1832; (2) E. Goodall, published by John Pye 1 July 1836; (3) W. Taylor, for *The National Gallery of Pictures by the Great Masters*, published by Jones & Co., London [1838], n.p.

Copies

innumerable (see Waterhouse 1958, p. 40; some are listed by Davies 1946, p. 55). The closest to the original is probably (as noted by Davies 1946, p. 55 n. 4 and Hayes 1982, II, p. 568) the picture exhibited BI 1817 (72) as by Gainsborough, lent by Sir Thomas Neave, now coll. Detroit Institute of Arts. The faithful copy sold Christie's 28 October 1949 (?61) appears to have been made from one of the nineteenth-century engravings.

Technical Notes

In good condition, though the impasto was crushed by a lining in the late nineteenth century. Cleaned and relined in 1955. The paint is thin and transparent. There is a pentimento in the horse's head, which seems originally to have been painted slightly nearer the cart.

The title *The Market Cart* was given to the picture after it entered the National Gallery in 1830.[2] While Gainsborough's picture was on display in his own 'Picture Gallery'[3] in Pall Mall, it was untitled. Gainsborough himself evidently felt no more need to elaborate titles for his landscapes than Constable, his admirer, who first exhibited the pictures now known as *The Hay Wain* (NG 1207) and *The Cornfield* (NG 130) as 'Landscape: Noon' and 'Landscape'.[4]

This six-foot-high canvas, on the same scale as some of the grandest of Gainsborough's full-length portraits, was begun in the latter months of 1786; it was finished in the last few days of December,[5] hardly more than eighteen months before Gainsborough's death. The landscape elements – the disposition of the trees, and the angle of the gently sloping uneven track – are largely taken from a very beautiful unfinished oil sketch (fig. 1).[6] The spontaneous quality of this sketch suggests that it was begun as a picture in its own right rather than designed as a preliminary study for *The Market Cart*. More purely pastoral than *The Market Cart*, and less than half its size, the sketch was probably left unfinished because its own beauty quickly suggested the possibilities of a larger, more elaborate picture. That slightly diagonal sloping track which permits the spectator to glimpse rather than confront the scene, those towering trees and the fall of light upon them, provided the basis for the larger canvas and heightened spectacle of *The Market Cart*, in which the solitary herdsman in the sketch, following his cows towards a watering-place, is replaced by a heavily laden market cart about to trundle through the water.

'You know my cunning way of avoiding great subjects in painting', Gainsborough wrote to his fellow-RA Sir William Chambers in 1783.[7] The two-wheeled cart drawn by a single horse through this picture is far from being in itself a 'great subject'; it is an ordinary country cart, adaptable to various uses, from carting produce to transporting labourers to a harvest field. A canvas cover could be hooped over the top to provide shelter from sun, wind or rain; an extra horse (or

Fig. 8 Charles-Nicolas Cochin after Jean-Siméon Chardin (1699–1779), *La Petite Fille aux Cerises*. Engraving, published 1738.

Fig. 9 Charles-Nicolas Cochin after Jean-Siméon Chardin, *Le Jeune Soldat*. Engraving, published 1738.

brightness of the foreground still life. The elder girl's flower-trimmed cap and blue, lace-trimmed dress are closely echoed in Gainsborough's early 'Portrait of a Girl', now known (with a portrait of a boy) only as fragments of what must have been quite a large double canvas;[57] Gainsborough in the early 1740s would have encountered Hogarth at Slaughter's Coffee House, and may have had a chance to see *The Graham Children*.

Of the four children, it is of course Henrietta, the eldest, who makes us most aware that childhood is a brief, transitory state, for she is already passing out of it. She is allotted the role of minding the baby, and given a pose which perhaps began to seem too grown-up, or too staid; and so, at the painter's request, she has caught up the lower folds of her long muslin apron and tucked them over her left arm. This gives Hogarth the chance to paint one of the finest passages in the picture, as the soft folds of lace-edged muslin tumble and fall in a long S-curve embodying Hogarth's 'line of beauty'.

Henrietta's upraised arm also compels attention to two cherries dangling from her hand, and to their likely significance. It has been suggested that the cherries are symbolic of the 'fruit of Paradise, traditionally associated with childhood'[58] (perhaps like the two cherries the Virgin dangles before the Child in Joos van Cleve's *Holy Family* in New York[59]). Conversely, it has been noted that cherries are 'quite well-known erotic symbols in the eighteenth century':[60] but symbols of what, precisely? Recourse to dictionaries of slang suggests that what Hogarth has in mind (or at least partly in mind) is the cherry as the symbol of virginity, because of its supposed resemblance to the hymen. 'To lose one's cherry' is an old expression (still current) meaning to lose one's virginity.[61] Henrietta, who is only nine years old, still has hers, but will not remain forever in this world of childish innocence. The cherries will be taken from her, or perhaps willingly given. Or, as Brian Sewell suggests, a pair of pendant cherries can connote the male sex: this 'pair of testicular cherries' for which the baby (in his unisex infant clothes) seems to reach may indicate his gender.[62] Only because Hogarth draws such deliberate attention to the cherries held against Henrietta's stomacher do we look for an explanation more complex than that the girl has simply taken a pair of cherries from the basket of fruit on the floor to bob them up and down to amuse the baby, or that the artist selects cherries because their bright, clear red provides an ideal colour contrast to the blue and white of her dress. This small but deliberately focused detail invites larger questions about Hogarth's use of symbols and allusions throughout the picture, to which there can be no certain answers, since Hogarth combined many different levels of meaning, sometimes with deliberate ambiguity. Composing a picture is more complex than driving home a moralising text.

Among the many possible meanings of the cherries, it seems probable that there is also a specific but seemingly hitherto unnoticed allusion to the painting by Chardin now known as *La Petite Fille aux Cerises* (fig. 8). Chardin had exhibited this at the Salon in 1737, entitled *Une petite fille assise s'amusant avec son déjeuner*, with a companion picture entitled *Un petit enfant avec des attributs de l'enfance*, now known as *Le Jeune Soldat* (fig. 9).[63] Both pictures were engraved by C.-N. Cochin in 1738,[64] with couplets suggesting that the innocence with which the children now amuse themselves will not last; below the image of the child playing with cherries, holding a pair of them, with others in her lap and basket, is inscribed: *'Simple dans mes plaisirs, en ma colation, / Je sçais trouver aussy, ma recreation.'* The engravings are likely to have been in London printsellers' shops by the end of 1738, and a painting of *La Petite Fille aux Cerises* (possibly the picture exhibited at the Salon) was up for sale in London that year.[65] Hogarth would almost certainly have known the engravings. They are quite small (the paintings, destroyed during World War II, were not large); but in each, the single figure of the child largely fills the picture. Chardin's manner in these two subjects of focusing attention on the child, as well as his intimation that childish innocence will pass, is likely to have provided a very real stimulus to Hogarth in his portrayal of the Graham children a few years later. The extent to which Hogarth may have been indebted to Chardin deserves fuller investigation; meanwhile Henrietta's cherries may be noted as some evidence of that debt.

At the age of nineteen, in 1752, Henrietta married her second cousin Daniel Malthus, whose friendship with Rousseau was held by his contemporaries to account for many 'eccentricities' (such as not allowing his wife to wear her wedding ring).[66] She bore him seven children, to whom she is said to have been 'a most affectionate and indulgent mother'; she lived just long enough for her son the Revd Thomas Robert Malthus[67] to place in her lap his *Essay on the Principle of Population, as it affects the Future Improvement of Society* (1798), then died in 1800. Her younger sister Anna Maria married Thomas Ryves FSA.

Richard Robert Graham, having followed his father to Harrow School and served an apprenticeship to him, succeeded to a largely sleeping partnership in the Pall Mall business, which appears to have ended by 1800, by which date there were new tenants in the house. He also succeeded to the post of Apothecary to Chelsea Hospital, where he employed a deputy to do the work; having married in 1767, he lived in Chelsea, reputedly in affluence.[68] Farington records a visit on 7 May 1805 with Sir George Beaumont and Thomas Lawrence 'to Mr Grahams at Chelsea where we saw a picture of portraits of Children painted by Hogarth in 1742. – The Portraits were of Mr Graham and his Sisters. – Mr Graham said He was then between 8 & 9 years old.'[69] In 1805 Richard Graham was nearly seventy. The picture became more widely known when he lent it to the British Institution exhibition of 1814; it was presumably after Richard Graham's death at the age of 82 in 1817 that it was secured by William Seguier for the keenest and most affluent of Hogarth collectors, George Watson Taylor MP. With Seguier's help, Watson Taylor assembled a 'Hogarth Room' in his house, Erlestoke Mansion, near Devizes, and there (until his sudden bankruptcy in 1832[70]) *The Graham Children* hung with Hogarth's *Self Portrait, The Shrimp Girl, A Scene from the Beggar's Opera*, and other works, with Roubiliac's terracotta model of Hogarth's dog Trump for company.

NOTES

1. The picture was still in R.R. Graham's possession in 1814, when he lent it to the BI exhibition. MS annotations (given here in double quotation marks) by Nichols to the list of Hogarth's works in Nichols and Steevens 1817, III, p. 168, are as follows: 'The Family of R.R. Graham, Esq., "formerly with" [in the possession of] R.R. Graham Esq. "and since sold to Mr Seguier".'

2. Christie's stencil *890 FX* on the backboard relates to this transaction.

3. Lord Duveen made it a condition of his gift that the picture should remain unglazed: see NG Board Minutes, 9 October 1934, vol. 11, p. 138.

4. Wartime tour organised under the general title *World's Fair Touring Exhibition*; shown in different venues mostly under that heading, and under the title *Masterpieces of Art from Foreign Collections* (with some variations).

5. Among pictures at Somerley, Waagen notes: 'HOGARTH. – Portraits of two girls with their little sister and a boy; also a cat and a bullfinch. A very interesting picture by the master, great transparency being combined with the animation peculiar to him. The execution is also very careful.'
See also Max Roldit, 'The Collection of Pictures of the Earl of Normanton at Somerley, Hampshire', ii, *Burlington Magazine*, III, 1903, pp. 219–25.

6. A small tear near the bottom edge (in a dark square of the floor, left of centre) caused during transport within the Gallery in 1950 was repaired before relining.

7. Reynolds seems to have been quite fond of orpiment, and Gainsborough used 'a preparation of orpiment' for his bright yellows, while certain intense greens in Wright of Derby's *Mr and Mrs Coltman* (NG 6496) contain mixtures of orpiment and Prussian blue. The use of realgar and orpiment (both highly toxic pigments) might by this date be regarded as rather archaic.

8. Various earlier identifications most commonly supposed the children's father to be Robert Bontine Cunninghame Graham, of Gartmore (see for example Sitwell 1936, p. 92; R.B. Cunninghame Graham, *Doughty Deeds*, 1925, p. 167; letters from Mrs B.J. Walz, a descendant of Richard Robert Graham, NG Archives 1957). The fourth and youngest Graham child was commonly identified as Anna Maria (in fact the third child), which necessitated supposing that her place in the picture was filled by the children's elder step-sister Elizabeth.

9. Daniel Graham and Mary Crisp were married in the parish church of St George the Martyr, Southwark, 30 October 1732 (Register of Marriages, GLC Archives). Her maiden name is sometimes given as Cripps.

10. For the professional qualifications and royal service of Daniel Malthus, Thomas Graham and Daniel Graham, see Leslie G. Matthews, *The Royal Apothecaries*, London 1967, pp. 140–8. Daniel Graham was apprenticed to his uncle Daniel Malthus for eight years from 6 December 1709; admitted a freeman of the Society of Apothecaries

7 November 1721; appointed apothecary to George I August 1721; reappointed by George II 1728, and retained in his service until 1741, when his cousin Thomas Graham (d.1761) succeeded him. Appointed Apothecary to Chelsea Hospital in 1739, ? for life, obtaining (in 1747) a grant of his place in reversion to his son Richard Robert, then aged 13 (see C.T.G. Dean, *The Royal Hospital, Chelsea*, London 1950, p. 221). Matthews 1967, p. 147, notes that in 1776 (less than two years before his death), Daniel Graham was brought back into the royal service, on the death of John Gowland, Apothecary to George III: 'Although by that time Daniel Graham would have been about eighty-one years old, and on the face of it too old for such an appointment, there were many extraordinary things done during George III's bouts of illness, and it has not been possible to trace another Daniel Graham of that period.'

11. They prepared the anointing oils for the coronation of George II and Queen Caroline in 1728, at a charge of £206 (Matthews 1967, p. 146).

12. For a description of Daniel Graham's Pall Mall houses (demolished *c.*1818 for the formation of Waterloo Place) and some account of their occupants, see *Survey of London*, vol. XXIX, *Parish of St James's, Westminster*, Pt 1, 1960, p. 323, and Appendix p. 547. It is noted here that each of the houses was four storeys high and three windows wide. J. Coney's street elevation of this part of Pall Mall, 1814 (reproduced in this *Survey* and in Matthews 1967, plate 9), shows some later additions.

13. Dean 1950 (cited in note 10), p. 221.

14. Walpole to Seymour Conway, 3 July 1765, *Walpole Correspondence* 1974, vol. XXXIX, p. 3. In a letter to Mann, 27 August 1768 (vol. XXII, p. 333), Walpole recalls consulting Daniel Graham's father: 'Thomas Graham the Apothecary used on every occasion when you complained of any disorder, to reply with much solemnity, "Humph! it is very extraordinary, and yet it is very common"', a phrase Walpole thinks more appropriate to 'self-murder'. Walpole reports on Lady Townshend and Lady Caroline Fitzroy's visits to Daniel Graham to be blooded (vol. XXXVII, pp. 196–7). In his notes to Sir Charles Hanbury-Williams's *Poems*, Walpole refers to Daniel Graham as 'one of the most eminent apothecaries of the day'.

15. Walpole to Lady Suffolk, 17 July 1766; ibid., vol. XXXI, 1961, p. 124.

16. Register of Baptisms, III, Parish of St James's, Westminster (City of Westminster Archives Centre); this Register, in which the children's dates were first traced by Mary Webster 1989 [1], records dates of birth as well as of baptism. Henrietta Catherine Graham, Anna Maria Graham and Thomas Graham are all recorded as the childen of 'Daniel Esqr & Mary'. By what is presumably an error, Richard Robert Graham is recorded as the son of 'Thos & Mary' (perhaps a confusion with a Thomas Graham (and his wife Ann) whose daughter was baptised there in 1732/3. There can be no doubt that Richard Robert Graham was in fact the son of Daniel Graham and his wife Mary. Daniel Graham's will, dated 1776 (PRO, PROB 11/1040/ q.109), refers to 'my only son Richard Robert Graham'.

17. Size 94 × 58 cm (239 × 147½ in.), 1740, coll. Thomas Coram Foundation for Children, London; exh. cat. Tate Gallery 1987–8, p. 173, repr. in colour.

18. 'Children in Early Modern England', in ed. Gillian Avery and Julia Briggs, *Children and their Books*, Oxford 1989, 4 (pp. 45–77), pp. 58–9. The compiler is much indebted to this stimulating essay. The research of Keith Thomas (and of Linda Pollock, *Forgotten Children*, Cambridge 1983) corrects the view of J.H. Plumb, 'The New World of Children', *Past and Present*, 67, 1975 (much quoted by art historians), that parents were not indulgent to or demonstrably fond of children before the 'new world' of the eighteenth century.

19. The quotation is by Thomas in Avery and Briggs 1989 (cited in note 18), p. 59, from ed. Albert Hartshorne, *Memoirs of a Royal Chaplain, 1729–1763. The Correspondence of Edmund Pyle*, London 1905, p. 33.

20. Walpole, *Anecdotes*, 1780, vol. IV, p. 135.

21. 'The Dumb Rhetoric of the Scenery', *Apollo*, XCV, 1972, p. 14.

22. Ed. Burke 1955, pp. 86–7. The duck-machine Hogarth describes (*c.*1763) was 'brought from France some years ago'. He calls it a 'silly but much extoll'd machine'. His description of it occurs in a passage in which he contrasts the beauty and simplicity of 'nature's machines' with the artificiality of 'those made by mortal hands'.

23. Reproduced by Ambrose Heal, *London Furniture Makers*, London 1953, p. 55. The compiler is indebted to Christopher Gilbert (in correspondence) for discussing examples, and in particular for drawing her attention to Foulger's trade card, in which the go-cart appears top centre.

24. Sold Christie's 15 December 1993 (20, reproduced in colour); private collection. In *The FitzPatrick Children*, *c.*1752–3 (coll. Marquess of Tavistock and the Trustees of the Bedford Estate), George Knapton depicts a similar red-painted go-cart out of doors; it has a carved scalloped seat and a gilded lion and shield on the axle. Repr. in colour Tate Gallery 1987–8, cat. no. 195, p. 208; see also cat. no. 188 in the same exhibition, a Devis family group of 1749 repr. p. 200. Another outdoor go-cart is depicted in David Allan's *The Family of Sir James Hunter Blair*, 1785 (repr. Mario Praz, *Conversation Pieces*, London 1971, p. 142, fig. 103).

25. See Ronald Paulson, *Hogarth's Graphic Works*, 3rd edn, London 1989, p. 42 (giving details of Hogarth's apprenticeship in 1714 to the silversmith Ellis Gamble, terminated probably in 1720, before Gamble's apparent partnership 1723–8 with Paul de Lamerie); p. 73, cat. no. 114 (for the design on the Walpole salver); and p. 200, cat. no. 254 (engraving of the *Arms of Paul de Lamerie*, noted by Paulson as not certainly by Hogarth). The Walpole salver is illustrated and discussed in ed. Andrew Moore, *Houghton Hall*, exh. cat., Norwich Castle Museum and Kenwood House, Iveagh Bequest, London 1996 (60), p. 142.

26. See *Paul de Lamerie ... England's Master Silversmith (1685–1751)*, exh. cat., Goldsmiths' Hall, London 1960, cat. no. 83, p. 129, where one of the Woburn baskets is reproduced opposite a colour detail from NG 4756 showing Hogarth's basket for comparison; see also *Treasure Houses of Britain*, exh. cat., NGA, Washington 1985, no. 457.

27. Department of Metalwork; acc. no. 292-1976.

28. For the change from Old Style ('O.S.') to New Style ('N.S.') dating, see C.R. Cheney, *Handbook of Dates*, London 1970, pp. 10–11. Briefly, the Old Style of dating the New Year from 25 March was retained in England until an Act passed in March 1751 decreed that the New Year would thereafter begin on 1 January.

29. See Webster 1989 [1], p. 172, and, for her evidence from the burial register of St Mary's, Harrow-on-the-Hill, p. 217 n. 2. Daniel Graham had been educated at Harrow School, of which both he and his father were Governors. A memorial tablet placed in the south wall of St Mary's, Harrow-on-the-Hill, records his death in 1778 at the age of 83, after 43 years of happy marriage, leaving one son and two daughters ('Filius. & duæ filiæ').

30. Hogarth's group portrait *The Cholmondeley Family*, 1732 (repr. Tate Gallery 1987–8, no. 67, p. 88 in colour), includes the figure of Lady Malpas, who had in fact died the previous year, signifying this by an old convention of cherubs hovering over her head. Presumably neither the Grahams nor Hogarth wished to resort to this in 1742.

31. Webster 1989 [1], p. 173, fig. 2.

32. Black and red chalk on grey paper, 22.9 × 27.6 cm. BM 1895-12-14-1; repr. A.P. Oppé, *The Drawings of William Hogarth*, London 1948, cat. no. 92, plate 87; M. Ayrton and B. Denvir, *Hogarth's Drawings*, London 1948, plate 32. Oppé notes (under cat. no. 91) that Nichols and Steevens 1817, p. 66, mention 'a head of a sleeping child in colours, as large as life' in Dr Lort's collection of drawings by Hogarth, sold in 1791, but is unable to establish whether this is the drawing now in the BM.

33. Black chalk heightened with white, inscribed 'Dead Child' verso; private collection; repr. Daphne Foskett, *Samuel Cooper and his Contemporaries*, exh. cat., NPG, London 1974, no. 137, p. 69. Compare also the *Dead Child*, seventeenth-century northern school, Musée des Beaux-Arts, Besançon, repr. Philippe Ariès, *Images of Man and Death*, Cambridge, Mass., and London 1985, p. 207, fig. 296.

34. Repr. Alastair Smart, *Allan Ramsay*, New Haven and London 1992, p. 75, plate 59.

35. Ballpoint, pencil, watercolour, gouache, 1978, Henry Moore Foundation; repr. *Henry Moore*, exh. cat., RA 1988 (218).

36. Anthony À Wood, notice of Henry Marten, *Athenae Oxonienses*, ed. Philip Bliss, London 1817, vol. III, p. 1242.

37. Ickworth (NT); see Laing 1995, cat. no. 20, repr. p. 63.

38. Engraving, 1580s; Hollstein, vol. VIII, H.250; reproduced in Paul Taylor, *Dutch Flower Painting 1600–1750*, exh. cat., Dulwich Picture Gallery, 1996, p. 18, fig. 8. The compiler is much indebted to Taylor's stimulating introduction and (though he is not here concerned with Hogarth) to his liberating discussion of symbolism in flower painting.

39. See Thomas in Avery and Briggs 1989, p. 47, and Pollock 1983, 'Illness and Death', pp. 124–42, particularly pp. 138–9 (both cited in note 18).

40. *NG News*, March 1994: 'Trustee's Choice' [p. 1].

41. If read correctly (this area is dark), the time conceivably alludes to the fact that Thomas died before he was two years old.

42. See, for comparison, H. Cescinsky and M.R. Webster, *English Domestic Clocks*, London 1913, p. 284, where figs. 307 and 308 illustrate two eight-day striking clocks of *c.*1720, each in an oak case veneered with ebony, made respectively by George Graham (? no relation of Daniel Graham) and Thomas Tompion and Edward Banger.

43. The compiler is grateful to John Leopold, Department of Mediaeval and Later Antiquities, British Museum, for this observation.

44. Painted 1758–9; Albright-Knox Art Gallery, Buffalo, New York; Tate Gallery 1987–8, cat. no. 210, repr. in colour p. 225.

45. Ed. Michael Kitson, 'Hogarth's "Apology for Painters"', *Walpole Society 1966–68*, XLI, 1968, p. 86.

46. Ibid., p. 86, lines 197–201.

47. David Tallis, *Musical Boxes*, London 1971, p. 75, notes that the collection in the Paris Conservatoire includes a bird-organ in the shape of a book whose spine is lettered *L'Art d'élever les Serins*, or 'The Art of Teaching Canaries'.

48. *Lady with a Bird-Organ (La Serinette)*. Frick Collection, New York (26.1.22).

49. By the 1760s, serinette cases could be highly ornate and inlaid with elaborate marquetry designs. See Carole Patey, *Musical Boxes at the Victoria & Albert Museum*, London 1980, p. 10 and plate 6.

50. Hogarth had begun his career as a silver plate engraver, and the fact that he was a long-standing friend of Jonathan Tyers, proprietor of Vauxhall Gardens, has led to his name being associated with the design of Vauxhall Gardens season tickets; but the 'Orpheus' scene on the side of the bird-organ appears to be the first clear link between a design by Hogarth and its engraving on some of the season tickets. See Warwick Wroth, *Tickets of Vauxhall Gardens*, reprinted from *The Numismatic Chronicle*, Third Series, vol. XVIII, pp. 73–92, London 1908, *passim*: for Hogarth's likely role in their design, see particularly pp. 76–7. Wroth's cat. nos. 6a–c, closely approximate to the design painted in NG 4756: 'Orpheus, wearing laurel-wreath and cuirass, seated facing, playing lyre; near him are various animals (giraffe, bear, rabbit, dog, and an ape playing a violin); behind, tree on which is a squirrel...'

51. Hogarth depicts a male bullfinch, identifiable by its varied plumage – bright red breast, coal-black head and quills. The *Encyclopaedia Britannica* notes that the bullfinch's 'engaging disposition in confinement makes him a popular cage-bird – to say nothing of the fact ... of his readily learning to "pipe" a tune, or some bars of one.' Peter Quennell (*Hogarth's Progress*, London 1955, p. 192) notes that Hogarth himself had a favourite bullfinch 'and when it died, gave it decent burial beneath a stone (which has now vanished) bearing the inscription, carved and embellished by himself: 'Alas poor Dick!/ 1760/ Aged eleven.'

52. See G. Bernard Hughes, 'Old English Bird-Cages', *Country Life*, 24 September 1953, pp. 973–4, reproducing NG 4756, p. 973.

53. This description is based on that given by Desmond Morris in *Catwatching and Cat Lore*, London 1992, p. 71. The compiler is indebted to Malcolm Hadley and Deborah Trentham for this source.

54. See Lorenz Eitner, 'Cages, Prisons and Captives in Eighteenth-Century Art', in ed. K. Kroeber and W. Walling, *Images of Romanticism*, London and New Haven 1978, pp. 6, 18; William L. Pressly, 'Goya's *Don Manuel Osorio de Zuniga*: A Christological allegory', *Apollo*, January 1992, p. 12; Shawe-Taylor 1990, p. 211.

55. David Mannings, 'A Well-Mannered Portrait by Highmore', *Connoisseur*, 189, 1975, pp. 116–19, reproduces (fig. 3) a detail from NG 4756 showing Anna Maria dancing, and quotes from Nivelon's *Rudiments of Genteel Behaviour*, 1727: 'Each Forefinger and Thumb must hold the Petticoat, and the other Fingers be a little separated; the Body should have a little Swing in its Motion ... and let the Feet appear well turn'd and without any Affectation.'

56. The *Morning Herald* noted 12 April 1788 [p. 3]: '*Artificial flowers* are at present much worn in the caps of our fashionable fair; – they are made to imitate nature as nearly as possible, and a large bunch of *red* or *white* roses at the side of the cap, have assumed the place of *Ostrich Feathers!*'

57. The two fragments are in the collection of Gainsborough's House, Sudbury, whose curator Hugh Belsey dates them to about 1743–4.

58. See for instance Elizabeth Einberg, *Manners & Morals*, London 1987, p. 141; Shawe-Taylor 1990, p. 209.

59. Coll. Metropolitan Museum of Art, New York.

60. Conisbee 1986, p. 161.

61. See Eric Partridge, *A Dictionary of Slang and Unconventional English*, 8th edn, London 1984, p. 205; Tony Throne, *Dictionary of Contemporary Slang*, London 1990, p. 89. Partridge suggests that the expression dates from the late nineteenth century; Hogarth's use of the motif suggests that it was current by 1742. Alternatively, a pair of cherries may allude to testicles.

62. In a consistently stimulating review of *Hogarth the Painter* at the Tate Gallery, 1997, *Evening Standard*, 17 April 1997, pp. 28–9.

63. The paintings were on panel, 58 × 46 cm. Destroyed in London 1939/40, they are catalogued and reproduced in G. Wildenstein, *Chardin*, Oxford 1969, p. 173, cat. 150–1, figs. 67–8. The subjects are discussed and the engravings reproduced in Conisbee 1986, pp. 159, 161; he notes (p. 170) 'a painting of *A Girl with Cherries* was already up for sale in London in 1738, perhaps the picture seen at the Salon of 1737'.

64. Emmanuel Bocher, *Les Gravures Françaises du XVIIIe Siècle...., III, Jean-Baptiste Siméon Chardin*, Paris, 1876: *La Petite Fille aux Cerises* is cat. no. 43, pp. 43–4; *Le Jeune Soldat* is cat. no. 30, p. 31. *Jeune Fille à la Raquette* might also be considered in this group, but it was not engraved until 1742.

65. Conisbee 1986, p. 170.

66. See Patricia James, *Population Malthus*, London 1979, p. 13, quoting from the *Recollections* (1852) of Louisa Bray, a granddaughter of Daniel and Henrietta Malthus; since Louisa was born the year her grandmother died, her report that 'My Grandmother would not have been supposed a happy woman by those who knew her, yet towards the close of her life, she said she would willingly pass it over again' is at second hand.

67. For T.R. Malthus (1766–1834), political economist, see *DNB*, and James 1979 (cited in note 66), *passim*. In his 'Picture Choice', *NG News*, March 1994 [p. 1], Sir Keith Thomas sees irony in the fact that one of the daughters in *The Graham Children* (Henrietta) should become the mother of 'the gloomy economist, T.R. Malthus, who would blame the world's miseries on an excess of children!'

68. For R.R. Graham, see Matthews 1967, pp. 147–8; Dean 1950 (both cited in note 10), p. 221. Daniel Graham's will (see note 16) states that his son married Ann Bowles.

69. *Diary*, vol. VII, p. 2550.

70. Watson Taylor's entire collection was dispersed in a sale at Erlestoke conducted by George Robins, 9–31 July 1832. The works by Hogarth were sold on the fourteenth day, 24 July 1832. Of those mentioned here, the *Self Portrait* (43) is perhaps that now in the Yale Center for British Art, repr. Tate Gallery 1987, cat no. 73, p. 94. *The Shrimp Girl* (47) is NG 1162. *A Scene from the Beggar's Opera* (53) is the version now coll. Birmingham Museum and Art Gallery. Roubiliac's terracotta model of *Trump* (171, sold the following day) has been untraced since this sale; for the porcelain copy in the V&A, see J.V.G. Mallet, 'Hogarth's Pug in Porcelain', *Victoria & Albert Museum Bulletin*, vol. III, No. 2, 1967, pp. 45–54.

Fig. 3 Detail from Scene 1: *The Marriage Settlement*

father, whose gout may be a side-effect of rich living but is unconnected with the disease. The black spot will be the Viscount's most conspicuous attribute throughout, though it will appear on others as well.

The bride is in her wedding finery, but not in a bridal mood (fig. 3). This marriage has been forced upon her by her father. She may be no more than sixteen or seventeen. Hogarth makes no attempt throughout the story to depict

Fig. 4 Detail from Scene 1: *The Marriage Settlement*

her as intelligent; but he portrays her with his invariable response to youthfulness, bloom and health in women. Resisting any temptation to mock her attire, he lavishes his painterly skills on its delicate colours and soft textures in each scene she appears in. Here her dress has nuances of mother-of-pearl in its whiteness, and its gold trimmings lack the brazen quality of the Earl's. An exquisite little knot of flowers on her lace cap is as restrainedly charming as those the still carefree girls wear in *The Graham Children* (see p. 135). But the bride feels anything but carefree. Distractedly, she shuttles a gold ring along the veil she will have to don for the ceremony. The Alderman's black-gowned lawyer takes advantage of his position in the background to lean familiarly over her. This is unlikely to be their first meeting. Horace Walpole observed that in *Marriage A-la-Mode* 'an intrigue [is] carried on throughout the piece'.[80] If the girl and the lawyer are not already lovers, they soon will be. Since the lawyer has neither money nor breeding, the Alderman would never consent to his daughter marrying him. We learn later that the lawyer has the odd name of Silvertongue. Hogarth's contemporaries would have recognised the allusion to the proverb: 'A man that hath no money in his purse must have silver in his tongue.' Silvertongue must rely on charm and wiles to keep the intrigue going. In this he succeeds, up to the penultimate scene. And the girl remains loyal to him throughout. It is to her credit that in this scene she is not swayed by the prospect of rank and riches.

The pictures in the room make their own comment on events. They are almost all copies of 'dark old masters' which connoisseurs of the day thought safe and Hogarth disliked, if only because they were eagerly purchased by ignoramuses who disdained the work of British artists. The pictures nearest to the bride evoke the sense of outrage she herself cannot express. *Medusa* (after Caravaggio),[81] inset into a wall sconce hanging over the bride, sets the tone: screaming, with vipers writhing in her hair, she gives vent to rage: the bride may wish she could do the same. She may even feel that the martyrdoms depicted on *Medusa*'s right – *Saint Lawrence* (after Le Sueur)[82] roasted over burning coals and *Saint Agnes* (after Domenichino),[83] whose martyrdom had included being forced to enter a brothel before having her throat cut – are as nothing compared to her own imminent fate. In Silvertongue's corner, aggression largely takes over from martyrdom. To the left of his head, *Cain slaying Abel* (after Titian)[84] is a bad omen for the events of Scene 5, while above it *Tityus and the Vulture* (also after Titian)[85] hints at perpetual torment for seducers. On the window wall, *David slaying Goliath* (after Titian)[86] hangs above two smaller pictures. Hogarth may have invented the picture of Saint Sebastian knocked sideways by arrows to echo Silvertongue's pose as he leans over the girl, sharpening his quill; presumably he is also sharpening plans for the continuation of their affair after her marriage. Guido Reni's *Judith with the Head of Holofernes*[87] completes this group.

The largest painting of all, hanging by the window, is a portrait of Lord Squander himself in his younger days (fig. 4).[88] He is portrayed as half-General, half-Jupiter, in cuirass and fluttering sash, with a thunderbolt in his hand and wearing round his neck the Order of the Golden Fleece, an honour in fact awarded to no Englishman between Henry VIII and the Duke of Wellington;[89] well-founded doubts about his right to wear this Order can only add to doubts about the authenticity of his family tree. In this portrait, Hogarth mocks the flamboyant style of French portraitists such as Hyacinthe Rigaud (1659–1743) and Nicolas de Largillière (1656–1746).[90] Hogarth had a wide knowledge of French art; and it is characteristic of him that even while mocking, he could himself learn something from such portraiture. As Frederick Antal observed in 1947, Hogarth's portrait of the essentially English *Captain Coram* is largely derived from Drevet's engraving (1729) of Rigaud's portrait of the French financier *Samuel Bernard*.[91] By contrast, Lord Squander's portrait, as Gautier recognised, is 'emphatically ridiculous'.[92] Lord Squander himself does not appear after this scene. A painting on the ceiling depicts *The Drowning of Pharaoh in the Red Sea* (after Titian); as Cowley notes,[93] the imperious but doomed Pharaoh also wears a coronet.

A few years earlier, in a room seen from much the same angle, Hogarth had depicted *The Strode Family* decorously taking tea; but in that room, well-stocked bookshelves stand against one wall and agreeable landscapes hang on the other. Both rooms in their different ways illustrate Horace Walpole's observation that 'the very furniture of his [Hogarth's] rooms describe the characters of the persons to whom they belong'.[94] Books do not furnish any of the rooms in which the characters of *Marriage A-la-Mode* exist. Throughout its six scenes there is not a book in sight, apart from *Hoyle on Whist* (in Scene 2), the sanctimonious steward's tract on *Regeneration* in the same scene, the published treatise of *M. de la Pillule* in Scene 3 and the erotic novel *Le Sopha* in Scene 4. The characters in *Marriage A-la-Mode* exist in a moral void, without literature, philosophy or religion to sustain them.

NG 114: *The Tête à Tête*

NG 114

Scene 2: The Tête à Tête

Some months after the marriage. The phrase 'Tête à Tête' implies a private conversation, with no third party present; in Dr Johnson's *Dictionary* it is rendered as 'cheek by jowl'. The scene is the double drawing-room of (probably) the pseudo-Palladian house we saw out of the window, completed with the Alderman's money, as badly designed internally as externally,[95] and now occupied by the young couple. A Viscount's coronet surmounts the chandelier;[96] the old Earl is thus presumably still alive, but he does not reappear, and the Viscount will soon succeed as the next Earl of Squander.

This whole scene is designed to confound contemporary expectations of what a conversation piece should be. Where Arthur Devis, for instance, portrays a decorously mannered couple like *Mr and Mrs Dashwood* in a sparsely but tastefully furnished room (fig. 5),[97] Hogarth portrays a husband and wife whose marriage is (and has always been) such a sham that each has reverted to type, snatching at whatever form of diversion each likes best; and the room which they unhappily co-habit betrays all too clearly that they share no notions of presenting a common front to the outside world. The Squanderfields' drawing-room is a battleground for mute

Fig. 5 Arthur Devis (1712–1787), *Mr and Mrs Robert Dashwood at Home*, 1750. Oil on canvas, 112 × 96.5 cm. Private collection.

antipathy between themselves and flagrant disharmony among their possessions.

A wall-clock shows the time to be about 12.20pm, or shortly after noon. This was the fashionable hour to rise; but the Viscount has evidently just come home from an all-night debauch. Now, in a pose defying all treatises on elegant deportment,[98] he sprawls in a chair, his gaze unfocused, his complexion pallid, his hair dishevelled under the hat he has forgotten to take off. A poodle[99] sniffing at his coat-pocket detects one cause of the Viscount's lassitude: a girl's muslin cap. A similar cap hangs on the bed-curtains in Hogarth's scenes *Before* and *After*,[100] whose one-word titles suffice to indicate the nature of the activities which take place in them. A second muslin cap wound round the hilt of the Viscount's sword suggests that collecting such little feminine trophies is part of the night's sport. A *galant* subject by Jean-François de Troy of 1734 suggests that this was a French custom.[101] It depicts a girl whose pose and dress are not *comme il faut* (she is *en négligé*, and careless of the fact that she is exposing an ankle) tying a newly purchased ribbon round the sword-hilt of her lover. The Viscount's sword lies on the floor, broken, but not in combat, for it is still in its scabbard. The broken sword may symbolise the Viscount's impotence. He himself is too dazed to know or care how his weapon was broken. He is likely to pass out at any minute.

This image of the Viscount is probably the best-known single figure in all Hogarth's work. It drew the highest admiration from Gautier, who declared in 1868 (when Hogarth was chiefly known through engravings) that for this figure alone, Hogarth deserved fame as a painter. He particularly praised the modelling of the face (fig. 7), in which the painter had to retain the appearance of youth while showing the evidence of 'nature's revolt' against dissipation.[102] For the Viscount's pose, Hogarth partly drew on a red chalk drawing by Charles-Nicolas Cochin known as *A Party of Revellers* (fig. 6),[103] engraved in 1739, in which a man has fallen asleep, evidently after returning from a masquerade; a lady with a mask looks on, teasingly, while a painting behind them reveals

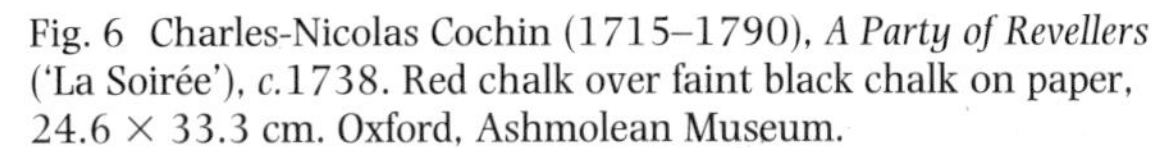

Fig. 6 Charles-Nicolas Cochin (1715–1790), *A Party of Revellers* ('La Soirée'), *c.*1738. Red chalk over faint black chalk on paper, 24.6 × 33.3 cm. Oxford, Ashmolean Museum.

Fig. 7 Detail from Scene 2: *The Tête à Tête*

Juno gazing adoringly as Endymion sleeps, making (rather more mildly) the sort of ironic pictorial juxtaposition which Hogarth makes throughout *Marriage A-la-Mode*.[104]

Seated on the other side of a portable table[105] laid with breakfast for one, the Viscountess stretches, seemingly only half-awake. Probably Hogarth knew Jonathan's Swift's poem *The Journal of a Modern Lady*, which includes the lines:

> The modern dame is waked by noon,
> Some authors say, not quite so soon;
> Because, though sore against her will,
> She sat up all night at quadrille.
> She stretches, gapes, unglues her eyes,
> And asks if it be time to rise...[106]

But as the Viscountess stretches, there is nothing simple about her expression. A copy of *Hoyle on Whist*[107] near her feet and a scatter of playing cards under the arch are usually taken to mean that while her husband was out, his wife passed a harmless evening entertaining visitors to a card party. But it is unlikely that she 'sat up all night at quadrille'; if visitors indeed came to play cards, one of them may have stayed on. In the left foreground, an overturned chair has not certainly been overturned in excitement over a game of whist. Two fiddles in cases – one case open, revealing the fiddle's base and tailpiece – lie on top of each other in a manner which suggests sexual innuendo. A music book lying open over the chair is inscribed with a tune which is perfectly playable, but which has so far eluded all attempts at identification. It may be the tune of a song, perhaps popular in Vauxhall Gardens in 1742–3, whose words (if they survive) might aid interpretation.[108]

With half-closed eyes, the wife takes in the evidence of her husband's debaucheries. They don't seem to disconcert her; by now she is probably used to them. But everything

Fig. 8 Detail from Scene 2: *The Tête à Tête*

Fig. 9 Pierre-Antoine Baudouin (1723–1769), *La Lecture*, *c*.1760. Gouache on paper, 29 × 22 cm. Paris, Musée des Arts Décoratifs.

about this unlikely Viscountess suggests that she has a secret of her own which enables her to regard her husband with an air of sly triumph. The manner in which she thrusts her body forward as she stretches is usually taken to indicate that she is pregnant. If so, the child is probably her husband's; but we cannot be sure that she is faithful to him. Several details strongly suggest that she is enjoying an affair of her own. It is likely to be with Silvertongue, who may have been with her late last night, and may still be concealed somewhere in the house. Painted (or carved) on the side of the chimneypiece, just about level with her left cheek, is the head of a man, suggesting a third party in this marital *tête à tête* (fig. 8). It has previously escaped notice, probably because it is less conspicuous in the engraving. There is no matching head on the husband's side of this otherwise symmetrical chimneypiece. Hogarth had already (and ironically) introduced a bust of William Kent into the right side of the chimneypiece in *The Assembly at Wanstead House*, 1730–1;[109] his capacity for allusion is virtually unlimited. Something is reflected in the small folding pocket-mirror[110] which the wife raises in her right hand; it is unlikely to be her tea-cup. Can she be signalling to someone whom we do not see? The picture hanging high up in the further room suggests that something clandestine is or has been going on. Originally Hogarth painted a *Madonna and Child* within this frame (see Technical Notes);[111] but all that can now be seen in it is a large bare foot at an angle which indicates somebody lying down, and presumably engaged in an activity so indecent that the picture has to be largely concealed. The Viscountess's pose – or perhaps both her pose and her husband's – is likely to have inspired the still more indiscreet pose of the lady in *La Lecture* (fig. 9), by Pierre-Antoine Baudoin (1723–69), Boucher's son-in-law, who exhibited small subjects of this sort at the Salon from about 1765.[112]

The unmistakable message of this scene as a whole is that the Squanderfields have bad taste. The badly proportioned chimneypiece itself is often said to be a satire on the designs of William Kent, the most fashionable interior designer of his day, whom Hogarth disliked; but it does not resemble any of Kent's published designs, nor is there is anything particularly Kentian about the room.[113] A cherub in the painting inset in the overmantel is playing (on the bagpipes) a popular song about once-happy days when 'all was love';[114] the phrase *Oh happy groves*, lettered on his music, serves to emphasise how far removed the home life of the Squanderfields is from 'happy groves'. In his *Analysis of Beauty*, Hogarth noted that 'Custom and fashion will, in length of time, reconcile almost every absurdity whatever to the eye',[115] instancing cherubs. 'A painter's representation of heaven would be nothing without swarms of these little inconsistent objects, flying about, or perching on the clouds'; in general they are so agreeable that the eye 'overlooks the absurdity', but a cherub playing a popular song on the bagpipes is near absurdity, and sets the tone for the whole ludicrous assemblage of *objets d'art* nearby.

On the mantelshelf, an antique female bust, broken at the neck and nose, recalls the busts of Cicero, Julia and Germanicus newly purchased by the Rake (and still bearing their sale lot numbers) in *The Marriage Contract*,[116] the precursor of Scene 2 of *A Rake's Progress* (and, to some extent, of Scenes 1 and 2 of *Marriage A-la-Mode*). The Squanderfields' bust was no doubt acquired to parade some respect for classical antiquity; but they have placed it inappropriately in the centre of a collection of bogus chinoiseries: 'squatting, round-bellied, open-mouthed orientals made in imitation, or rather in travesty, of Chinese images of Pu-Tai, the god of happiness'.[117] These were known as 'pagods', or pagoda figures, and were made in quantity in European porcelain factories to satisfy the 'China-mania' of the 1740s. The writer John Shebbeare (1709–88) observed that in one room of every fashionable house 'all the pagods and distorted animals of the east are piled up, and called the beautiful decorations of a chimney-piece'.[118] Hogarth, who considered the 'pagods of China' to be absolutely void of elegance,[119] has piled them up on the Squanderfields' mantelshelf, with a couple of baleful jade toads for good measure. Some bulbous glass completes the ensemble.

Next to the chimneypiece is a wall-clock of extravagant fantasy, set in metallic foliage on which a cat perches, a fish swims and a Buddha squats, extruding a pair of twisted candle-holders from his loins. Perhaps this represents a whim of one or other of the Squanderfields, but it was evidently designed by Hogarth in parody of highly elaborate French clocks of the period which incorporate porcelain (usually Meissen) flowers and figures.[120] In the further room, a slovenly footman who should be putting things to rights merely shambles about, yawning, still in his hair-curlers. The three tall paintings are of Saints Matthew, Andrew and John the Evangelist, who would have been in happier company if the painted-out 'Madonna and Child' had been left alone. No pictures have been painted in the lower four frames.

Exiting left, the steward of the household rolls his eyes towards heaven. With his *Ledger* under his arm and a stack of unpaid bills in his hand, he had come to 'help' his master; but his master is in no fit state to settle accounts. So the steward leaves, self-righteously, with a tract lettered *Regeneration* (the title of one of the Revd George Whitefield's most popular Methodist sermons[121]) sticking out of his coat-pocket. Despite his minor role, the steward is unforgettable. His face and his demeanour exemplify the distinction which Hogarth drew between 'characters' and 'caricaturas', and which Hazlitt was to expand as 'His [Hogarth's] faces go to the very verge of caricature, and yet never ... go beyond it... They exhibit the most uncommon features with the most uncommon expressions, but which are yet as familiar and intelligible as possible, because with all the boldness they have all the truth of nature.'[122] Dangling from the steward's little finger is a spike with a single piece of paper on it; this paper is inscribed *Rec^{d} 1743*, thus neatly recording the date of the painting itself.[123]

NG 115: *The Inspection*

NG 115

Scene 3: The Inspection

The scene is a doctor's consulting room. The Viscount has evidently been here before. This time he is accompanied by a young girl. The manner in which the Viscount sits (sideways) on a chair at once suggests at least four things: that he is the principal patient; that the pill-box placed near his groin contains pills previously prescribed for venereal disease; that the very young girl standing in the space between his outstretched legs is (at least temporarily) 'his' young girl; and that since he sits while she stands, she is decidedly his social inferior.

Brandishing his cane, the Viscount appears to be protesting that the doctor's pills don't work. They haven't cured him; and now the young girl appears to be infected with the same disease. She too holds a pill-box in one hand; with the other she dabs at what may be a syphilitic rash near her mouth. The Viscount lacks the imperiousness of the old Earl; he appears to be simultaneously blustering and entreating. His upraised cane may be an echo of the philosopher's wand in Vandergucht's illustration of *The Pin and the Needle* in one of Gay's *Fables* of 1727; but the Viscount is in no sense a philosopher. Although he needs help, he is slow to realise that neither rank nor money can procure a speedy cure for his disease.

While it has long been recognised that this scene turns on the subject of venereal disease, the parts played by the individual characters in it have baffled previous commentators. At a time when every detail in Hogarth's scenes was being scrutinised for meaning, Nichols and Steevens 1808 wrote of 'no two persons having hitherto agreed in their explanation' of this scene. Hazlitt called it 'very obscure and enigmatical'; Davies 1959 thought that 'Hogarth himself may have become lost among the details of the main theme and the subsidiary matter it pleased him to insert', and subsequent writers have offered no very coherent explanations.[124] Davies's question 'Why, for instance, are there three pill-boxes?' surely overlooks the fact that here Hogarth is using a simple pictorial device of links in a chain of cause and effect: the box by the Viscount's groin indicates the source of his disorder, the box he himself holds indicates his need for further treatment for his infection and the box the young girl holds suggests that through him, she too has become infected.

The pills themselves deserve attention. They are quite clearly black. The principal treatment for venereal disease at this time was a concoction of mercury, made up into pills.[125] Hogarth's perfectly rounded black spots are the symbols of the perfectly rounded black (because their principal constituent was mercury) pills which some of his characters take because they are infected with the disease (a point already made on p. 156). Venereal disease was rife in this period, and easily caught. Most 'cures' had unpleasant side-effects ('Two minutes with Venus: two years with mercury'[126] was a lesson many learnt painfully), and not all were effective. Doctors all over London openly advertised their pills for this 'disorder', usually on the back pages of newspapers,

The doctor polishes his spectacles on a handkerchief which by no means inspires confidence in his attention to hygiene. He has generally been assumed to be a figure of fun, made laughably ugly to undermine his pretensions and to show that he is a 'quack doctor'. This scene was for long known as 'The Visit to the Quack Doctor'; but Hogarth himself did not call it that. The most noticeable thing about the doctor is that he himself is riddled with venereal disease (fig. 10). This has escaped the notice of art historians, but not that of medical men. The doctor's 'dish face', and particularly the sunken bridge of his nose, his bulging forehead, thick lips and probable toothlessness, are characteristics of the 'bulldog facies' of an advanced degree of congenital syphilis (such as Gérard de Lairesse reveals in his *Self Portrait* of *c*.1675,[127] fig. 11); his deformed legs, bowed or 'sabred', also indicate congenital syphilis.[128] While Hogarth has undoubtedly based this figure on direct observation, William Schupbach makes the interesting suggestion[129] that Hogarth may also have had in mind the two diseased men in Raphael's cartoon *The Healing of the Lame Man*;[130] the doctor's face resembles that of the lame man (and through his father-in-law James Thornhill's copies of them, Hogarth knew the Raphael Cartoons well).[131] On a table beside the doctor is a human skull, not in itself a surprising object for a medical man to keep, perhaps for demonstration purposes. But this skull is riddled with small black holes which indicate syphilitic erosions.[132] The long and not always helpful anonymous poem 'in Hudibrastic verse' written in 1746 about the six scenes is at least to the point on the subject of the skull:

> And tho' it was extremely thick
> The p-x ten holes did in it pick.

Fig. 10 Detail from Scene 3: *The Inspection*

There is also a virago in the room, and a positively threatening one. Her dress is too gaudy to be ladylike; but she was once a fine figure of a woman, and is still quite handsome, despite two tell-tale black spots on her face (every human being in this room, as well as the once-human skull, is infected to some degree with venereal disease). Even more tell-tale is the tattoo *FC* above her left breast, said to have been inflicted on convicted prostitutes (the letters are now difficult to see in the painting, but are fairly clear in the engraving).[133] As the Viscount brandishes his cane, she is ready with a weapon of her own: a vicious-looking knife of the type which might be used in a doctor's surgery for blood-letting.

The woman's seeming fury and her relationship (if any) to the other three people in this room have puzzled previous commentators. She has been variously supposed to be the doctor's mistress, indignant at criticism of the efficacy of his pills, and/or the manageress of the establishment's sideline, who has procured the young girl for the Viscount and now appears to be furious that one of her girls should have been brought back infected with his disease.

She may well be both these things: but if one looks at the painting rather than the engraving of this scene, colour is a positive aid to interpretation. Hogarth has provided an unmistakable clue to the fact that the relationship between the furious woman and the seemingly helpless young girl is one of mother and daughter. The girl's skirt is of an unusual brocade, patterned with red flowers on a gold background. The woman's sleeves are of exactly the same material,[134] suggesting that she has used remnants of an old gown to make a skirt for her daughter and a bodice for herself. Hogarth's attention to detail was meticulous; he would never have repeated the same fabric on two figures in the same scene if he had not wanted to inform us of a close domestic relationship between the two people. There is a further implication of 'Like mother, like daughter', an adage as old as the Book of Ezekiel,[135] the girl is already following her mother's career. That a mother should put her young daughter out to prostitution was all too common in this period. In his capacity as a magistrate, Fielding observed that many prostitutes were 'under the age of eighteen, many not more than twelve, and these, though young, half eaten up with the foul Distemper'.[136] The Viscount is unlikely to be the girl's first client. Who gave her the pox – if indeed she has the pox and is not just acting, like her mother – cannot be certain; but it looks as if this may not be a pathetic scene of innocence wronged but a carefully rehearsed scene in which the Viscount will end up paying handsome damages for uncertain responsibility.

This scene is full of extraordinary objects; it takes time to realise that they represent fairly random fields of enquiry rather than true learning. Some unpleasant-looking iron machinery on the right immediately arouses the sort of apprehension commonly felt on entering a doctor's surgery; the pulleys above do nothing to allay it. The title-page of an open volume – *EXPLICATION / DE DEUX MACHINES SUPERBES: L'UN POUR REMETTRE/ LES EPAULES / L'AUTRE POUR SERVIR DE TIRE-BOUCHON* – tells us that one of these machines is for setting shoulders; the other is for drawing corks. The title-page also informs us that the machines are the invention of *MONS^{R} DE LA PILLULE*, and that both have been approved by the Royal Academy of Sciences in Paris. Facing the title-page is an engraved portrait of M. de la Pillule,[137] the author and inventor: presumably a portrait of this doctor, in better days. William Schupbach's research[138] suggests that here Hogarth may be only mildly satirical at the expense of the doctor's inventions; he may have known the magnificent volumes which summarise and illustrate the vast variety of machines and inventions approved by the Académie Royale des Sciences in Paris.

The evidence in the room suggests that the doctor practises simultaneously as physician, surgeon, barber-surgeon, apothecary and chemist. An open door on the right offers a glimpse of his distilling room.[139] Shelves against the left wall are lined with jars containing drugs, identified by labels; beneath them are drawers of herbs used to make up the drugs. So far, these are standard equipment. Beyond the shelves are two pictures of *lusus naturae*, commonly known as freaks: one is a man with his head growing below his shoulders, the other appears to be a double-headed hermaphrodite. Below them are the squat shapes of two painted mummy cases, of dubious medicinal value,[140] but sought after by collectors in the 1740s.

If the objects on the left wall are odd, those on the end wall are bizarre. A handsome cabinet, of the type used by more erudite collectors as a cabinet of curiosities, occupies most of the wall. Slung from it, on the left, is the horn of a narwhal (*Monodon monoceros*), about five feet long.[141] On top of the cabinet and on the wall beyond it are ranged – more or less in this order – a pile of bricks (perhaps to be heated to allay pain);[142] a barber's shaving bowl; a conspicuously large urine flask; a head of the sort which might hang outside an apothecary's shop, with a pill in its movable jaw; a giant's femur, hanging behind it; a small (but significant) tripod; an ivory comb, perhaps Eskimo (or Lapp); a tall hat, possibly North American, and a pair of moccasins; an outsize spur, with a stuffed reptile below it; an ancient long-handled sword and buckler; and a dark picture of a malformed child. Presiding over all this is a stuffed crocodile which has produced an ostrich egg. A crocodile *volant* is a time-honoured ingredient in pictures of alchemists.[143]

Fig. 11 Gérard de Lairesse (1640–1711), *Self Portrait*, *c.*1675. Oil on canvas, 89 × 73 cm. Florence, Uffizi.

Many of these strange objects could be matched in the 'cabinets of curiosities' formed by men far more eminent than this doctor.[144] Dr Richard Mead, physician to George II and one of the most learned men of his day, had several 'walnut tree cabinets' full of curious items; it took a five-day sale to disperse them.[145] He owned 'an Egyptian mummy, well preserved, with its original coffin', numerous 'serpents [pickled] in glasses', 'a monstrous embryo of a hog with 8 legs', a crocodile or two and a narwhal horn six-and-a-half feet long, as well as an even greater curiosity, the double horn of a rhinoceros. But as a connoisseur, Dr Mead owned things of beauty which this doctor could never aspire to: antique sculpture, carved gems and two paintings by Watteau, his patient in 1719.[146] Hogarth respected Dr Mead, knew his collection and would have had no wish to make fun of it; but he may have picked out some of the more commonplace objects in it to furnish this room. Acquired by those with true intellectual curiosity, 'curiosities' served as reminders that knowledge was not finite, and held out to enquiring minds possibilities for comparative studies based on informed research. But for such study, a well-stocked library was essential. That is what this doctor most conspicuously lacks. A truly learned physician would have had shelves full of books; here, apart from the doctor's own treatise, there are none.

One of the cabinet doors has swung open, to reveal a skeleton, an écorché (the sculpted figure of a man whose muscles and tendons are exposed as if the covering skin had been removed) and a periwig on a wig-maker's block and

Fig. 12 Detail from Scene 3: *The Inspection*

pole (fig. 12). A skeleton and an écorché figure can each be of value for teaching purposes, and were often found in anatomy theatres ('a skeleton in one niche and an écorché in an answering niche'[147]). But something more surreal is going on here. The skeleton is making advances to the écorché, one bony hand between its legs; the écorché, open-eyed and with far more expression in its face than such a figure would normally have, seems uncertain how to respond.[148] The tripod (mentioned above) seems to be placed directly over the écorché's head. It serves as an omen of the three-sided gallows-tree whose shadow is to loom over the last scene, and perhaps as a clue to the écorché's own fate; the only corpses which anatomists could lawfully obtain were those of executed criminals. The shadowy face on the wig-block[149] seems to watch not only what is going on in the cabinet but the goings-on in the room itself. This face is traditionally thought to represent the late Dr John Misaubin, who died in 1734. In his house in St Martin's Lane (not far from Slaughter's Coffee-House), Dr Misaubin had specialised in pills for the treatment of venereal disease; Watteau had drawn a caricature-sketch of him, complete with his long wig (engraved by Arthur Pond in 1739 with the caption *Prenez des Pilules*[150]), and Henry Fielding dedicated his play *The Mock Doctor* (first performed in 1732) to Dr Misaubin, for 'that Little Pill' which had rendered him 'so great a blessing to mankind'.[151] The long wig on the wig-block seems to be in his style, and although the shadowy face does not resemble that in Hogarth's pen and ink sketch of *Dr Misaubin and Dr Ward* nor in Louis Goupy's gouache of *Dr Misaubin and his Wife*,[152] Dr Misaubin's ghostly presence in this room might be considered appropriate to the sort of consultations which evidently frequently take place in it.

NG 116: *The Toilette*

NG 116

Scene 4: The Toilette

This scene takes place in the young Countess of Squander's bedroom; an Earl's coronet over her bed informs us that the old Earl must recently have died, and the young couple have lost no time in displaying evidence of their new rank. Like the front drawing-room in their house, the Countess's bedroom is painted olive-green, a colour much in vogue from about 1730,[153] but one which makes her pink bed hangings look distinctly vulgar. Another coronet surmounts the silver-framed looking-glass which stands on the Countess's dressing-table.

The Countess is following the fashion set by the French court and aped by the London *beau monde* of receiving visitors during the concluding stages of the *toilette* which follows her *levée*: that is, she has got up, and is now half-dressed (*en déshabille*), and is sufficiently presentable to receive visitors. The word *toilette* originally meant the little *toile* or piece of linen draped over the shoulders (as over the Countess's) while the hair was being dressed. By the 1740s, its meaning was extended to include the ritual of receiving visitors while completing one's dressing.[154] A *toilette* could also mean the 'toilet set' of silver brushes, tweezers, wig-powder shakers and boxes of paints, powders, patches and pomatums. The Countess's silver toilet set, in which the coroneted looking-glass is the chief piece, is comparatively simple, though probably costly; it could have been made by one of the leading goldsmiths of the day, such as Paul de Lamerie.[155] Some ladies needed a formidable battery of cosmetics, perfumes and unguents and several hours with which to make themselves up. Jonathan Swift's scabrous lines on *The Lady's Dressing Room* begin:

> Five hours, (and who can do it less in?)
> By haughty Celia spent in dressing...

and describes:

> Gallipots and vials placed,
> Some filled with washes, some with paste;
> Some with pomatum, paints and slops,
> And ointments good for scabby chops...[156]

But the Countess still has youth on her side, and what Gautier calls 'a certain plebeian freshness';[157] she can present herself in less than five hours. However foolishly she behaves, Hogarth continues to portray her in delicate colours. Here she wears a soft yellow wrapper over a pale lavender underskirt, with a blue bow on her bodice such as Chardin might have added; and as Hazlitt observed, Hogarth arranges the

Fig. 13 Detail from Scene 4: *The Toilette*

curl-papers around her head 'almost like a wreath of half-blown flowers'.[158] As her French hairdresser tests the heat of his curling-tongs on paper, a little puff of smoke arises. While the Countess awaits his attentions, she leans an arm over the back of her chair; and we see a baby's teething-coral hanging from a red ribbon over it,[159] indicating that she is now a mother, and sees her child occasionally, though it does not appear until the last scene. It does not of course occur to the Countess to meditate upon her reflection in the glass, as more thoughtful ladies do in *vanitas* paintings.[160] She has eyes only for Silvertongue, who is now evidently openly admitted to the house, and demonstrates his privileges and his lack of manners by putting his feet up on the sofa.

While Silvertongue continues his intrigue with the Countess, she has arranged a diversion for her visitors: a recital by an Italian singer whose beringed fingers, jewelled pendant, extravagantly curled wig and earrings indicate that he is a castrato (fig. 13). He has been variously identified as Farinelli, Carestini (in fact not a castrato but a counter-tenor) or Senesino, each of whom had sung for several seasons in London opera houses during the previous decade.[161] All three had been idolised by audiences, but had returned to Italy by mid-1740; but others arrived to sing their roles, Handel's operas alone demanding castrati. The porcine features of Hogarth's castrato are closest to those of Senesino in engravings after Thomas Hudson and Joseph Goupy;[162] but it is unlikely that Hogarth would have included a specific portrait of one individual in this series of invented characters; still more unlikely that either Farinelli, Carestini or Senesino would have deigned to sing at the Squanders' when they could command colossal fees in Covent Garden or the King's Theatre. Farinelli would not allow any of his singers to take outside engagements that would tire their voices. This castrato is probably a generalised portrait of the sort of 'foreigner' who (to Hogarth's disgust, as expressed in his engraving *Masquerades and Operas* of 1724) took London by storm. The singer has evidently brought his own accompanist with him, a vaguely Watteauesque flautist who adds yet another fashionably 'foreign' note to the scene.

A black manservant offers cups of chocolate while the castrato warbles on. Only two people in the room appear to be listening to him. One, a woman in white, falls into a pantomime of rapture. The other, a man with a fan attached to his wrist, has the face of a toady, not improved by a black spot on his lower lip. Behind him, another man is frankly dozing. A spindle-shanked, effeminate man sips chocolate with an abstracted air; his hair is still in curl papers (grotesquely horn-shaped), which suggests he is an habitué of the house, perhaps as a dancing-master, and is thus permitted to 'go about with it all morning in papers, and dress it out in the afternoon'.[163] The line-up against this wall is thus a castrated man (the singer), an elderly man (the flautist), an effeminate man, a likely homosexual (if wearing a fan is properly interpreted to indicate homosexuality) and a man who is frankly asleep. Silvertongue's portrait hanging above them (and above *The Rape of Ganymede*, also hinting at homosexuality) shows a man whose appearance is by contrast notably commonplace; but his uncomplicated masculinity is perhaps just what attracts the Countess. The only other active man in the room is the black man serving chocolate, who laughs at 'the nature of the white society he serves'.[164]

The Countess's present visitors do not appear to have quite the same social *cachet* as those new acquaintances whose cards lie in a careless scatter in the foreground on the left: Count Basset (who takes his name from a card game, but who is evidently either illiterate or a foreigner) *beg to no how Lade Squander Sleapt last nite*; Lady Heathan invites her to a Drum major 'next Sunday' (as only a 'Heathan' would), Miss Hairbrain to a Rout, Lady Townly to a Drum on Monday.[165] There are echoes here from Henry Fielding's play *The Modern Husband*, first performed in 1731: Mrs. Modern's engagement book reads 'Monday ... at Mrs. Squabble's; Tuesday, at Mrs. Witless's; Wednesday, at Lady Matadore's; Thursday, at Mrs. Fiddlefaddle's; Friday, at Mrs. Ruin's; Saturday, at Lady Trifle's; Sunday, at Lady Barbara Pawnjewel's'.[166]

As further evidence of the Countess's own bad taste, her latest purchases have been spread out before her. Still bearing their lot numbers, they have come from a sale whose catalogue lies on the floor (lettered *A CATALOGUE / of the / Entire*

Collection / of the Late Sr Tim^y Babyhouse / to be sold / by Auction). Attending auction sales and being seen to bid recklessly demonstrated not only wealth but also the fashionable qualities of whim and caprice. The Countess's latest purchases are lined up as a parade of folly on the floor: more 'pagods', toads and *grotesqueries* and, in a basket, a silver platter embossed with a design of Leda and the Swan (yet another image of sexual encounter in disguise), inscribed *Iulio Romano*. The Countess may have taken a perverse pleasure in securing Lot 1000, a figure of Actaeon, whose horns can appropriately enough represent a cuckold, such as she has proved her husband to be. This image of the absent master of the house is causing the small black page some merriment.

As usual, paintings on the walls add point and counterpoint to the story. Immediately behind the castrato is a version of Michelangelo's *Rape of Ganymede*; in Hogarth's version, the beak of the eagle (Jupiter in disguise, pouncing on a handsome boy) is dangerously lowered, as if one quick snap will result in castration if Ganymede resists. Above Jupiter hangs a recent portrait of Silvertongue, proof of his continuing advance in the Countess's favours. On the wall behind the Countess's dressing table hang two utterly different images of sexual encounter: Io in ecstasy in the embrace of Jupiter thinly disguised by a cloud in the shape of a bear, after Correggio, side by side with Lot's daughters making their father drunk so that he will sleep with them and thus perpetuate the human race, after (?) Caravaggio.[167] Perhaps the contrast is between sex as delight and sex as duty; but it is doubtful whether the Countess herself draws any conclusion from this contrast.

Turning her back on the singer and on her visitors, the Countess listens only to Silvertongue. As if his attitude were not enough to inform us that his mind is not on the castrato, Hogarth tucks behind Silvertongue's feet a copy of *Le Sopha*, a collection by Crébillon *fils* of erotic tales reflecting the moral depravity of the day, and consequently a best-seller:[168] it was translated into English and published in London in 1742. Silvertongue takes advantage of the music to put a proposition to the Countess. With one hand he offers her a ticket for a masquerade; it is inscribed *1 Door 2^d Door 3^d Do..*, and we understand that if she can make her way to the masquerade, he will meet her inside. He gestures with his other hand towards a painted screen, on which Hogarth has depicted a masquerade in progress. In a large room lit by chandeliers, men and women wearing masks and disguises mingle more freely than they could do with propriety at a formal ball. Silvertongue indicates one of the foreground figures: it is a man dressed as a friar, conversing with a woman dressed as a nun. Unlike Jupiter, who in this room alone is seen ingeniously disguised as an eagle, a bear and a swan, Silvertongue is not imaginative. The commonest disguises worn at masquerades were the loose-fitting costumes (or dominoes) of 'friars' and 'nuns', which could be readily hired and worn over one's own clothes, and that is how he proposes that he and the Countess should go to the masquerade. Henry Morland's painting, first exhibited in 1769 as *A Lady in a Masquerade Habit* and quickly popular as an engraving entitled

Fig. 14 Giuseppe Grisoni (1699–1769), *A Masquerade in the Long Room of the King's Theatre in the Haymarket*, *c.*1724. Oil on canvas, 104.2 × 111.8 cm. Private collection.

The Fair Nun Unmask'd,[169] depicts a 'nun' who has discarded her habit (except for a veil) but still toys with a mask similar to those lying on the floor in Hogarth's next scene.

Masquerades had become increasingly popular from the early eighteenth century, though frequently denounced as encouraging immoral behaviour.[170] Probably the most fashionable masquerades in Hogarth's day were those held in the Long Room which formed part of the King's Theatre in the Haymarket. To boost the theatre's revenues, the Swiss impresario Count John James Heidegger, its manager from 1708, staged masquerades there.[171] As many as 700 people might attend a masquerade in the Haymarket, giving an illusion of a congress of 'Turks, Italians, Indians, Polanders, Venetians, &c.', but all masked. *A Masquerade at the King's Theatre in the Haymarket*, one of several such subjects by Giuseppe Grisoni,[172] probably painted about 1724, shows a masquerade in full swing (fig. 14). Champagne and other wines were continually available from buffets at either side of the room. Supper was served at 11pm, 'the whole diversion continuing from nine o'clock till seven the next morning'.[173]

In the small space available to him on a painted screen in Scene 4, Hogarth suggests the attractions of a masquerade. In earlier engravings, he had been more savage. In *Masquerades and Operas* (or *The Bad Taste of the Town*), published in 1724,[174] he had charged Heidegger with debasing 'the English Stage'. His *Masquerade Ticket*, published in 1727,[175] includes an altar to Priapus on the left, and on the right an altar to Venus. A pair of long-case 'lecherometers' measure sexual appetites. Heidegger's bewigged head appears on the clock's face; its pendulum, inscribed *Nonsense*, moves incessantly, registering *Impertinence* every minute and *Wit* only once an hour. Since Heidegger was the subject of his particular dislike, Hogarth is likely to have had the King's Theatre in the Haymarket in mind when sending Silvertongue and the Countess off to a masquerade.

NG 117: *The Bagnio*

NG 117

Scene 5: The Bagnio

The anglicised word bagnio is derived from the Italian *bagno*, a bath or bathing-house. Probably the earliest bagnio in London was in Newgate Street, where John Aubrey notes that Turkish merchants established Turkish baths in 1679; others were soon opened, mostly operating – often under the sign of The Turk's Head – as Turkish baths with a coffee-house attached.[176] While some bagnios were perfectly respectable establishments, others became known as houses of ill repute. 'Carry her to a Bagnio, and there you may lodge with her', says Frankly to an eager lover in Benjamin Hoadly's play *The Suspicious Husband*, 1747.[177] In *Night*, one of *The Four Times of the Day* painted in about 1736 and engraved in 1738,[178] Hogarth depicts the outside of two such dubious houses near Charing Cross; on one side of the street a sign is hung out reading *Bagnio*, on the other *The New Bagnio*.

Scene 5 is set at night and by firelight. A crumpled bill lying on the floor (payment here is probably strictly in advance) is headed *The Bagnio*, with a picture of a Turk's head on it. The chief piece of furniture is a bed. Two gate-leg tables by the wall suggest that the room can also be hired for gambling; but tonight they are folded. Off-stage to the left, a fire must be burning low; we see only the long, slanting shadows cast by firelight.

Silvertongue and the Countess have come on from the masquerade to spend the night here. They have peeled off their dominoes and thrown aside their masks. The Countess's hooped underskirt lies like a half-collapsed Chinese paper lantern on the floor, beside her 'bearded lady' mask (with its frill to disguise the mouth) and her fashionable shoes with their upturned toes. She has tossed off her whaleboned stays (objects which had some fascination for Hogarth[179]) with such abandon as to overturn a chair; they fall across a bundle of faggots, plausibly there as firewood, but in addition recalling that a 'faggot' was a low term for a harlot. The firelight is brightest in this corner, casting coppery light and low shadows over this bizarre still life, which ends, in the far left, with a pair of crossed sticks, the upper one red-hot at one end; hidden meanings are likely here, as well as the most obvious one that the situation is potentially disastrous ('Kindle not a fire that you cannot extinguish' is a proverb already old in Hogarth's day[180]). The bed is rumpled, and the candle has burnt low; but how long Silvertongue and the Countess have spent in the room is uncertain.

Their plans for a night of bliss in the bagnio have miscarried. The Earl himself has burst into the room. It was probably he who broke the door lock off its hinges (it now lies on the floor). How he reached this room is uncertain. It is usually suggested that he followed Silvertongue and the Countess from the masquerade, bent on revenge, and challenged Silvertongue to a duel. But such positive, premeditated action would be out of character. It is just as likely – perhaps more likely, given the evidence of the Earl's nocturnal habits in Scene 2 – that this bagnio was one of his regular ports of call, and that some 'friend' tipped him the wink that his wife was in the next room. Such a scenario would be more in keeping with farces of the day. But this scene is not a farce. Things have gone seriously wrong, and will get worse. Perhaps he burst in with his sword already drawn, hoping to frighten Silvertongue or 'give him a lesson' (we saw him in Scene 3 brandishing his cane towards the doctor as if to exert his authority). But Silvertongue, again showing that capacity for effective action which the Earl lacks, reached for his own sword and used it first, and to fatal effect. This surprise encounter is usually described as a duel, but wrongly: duels were arranged by protocol, requiring formal challenge, acceptance and the presence of seconds. Silvertongue's sword now lies near the Countess's hoops, stained with the Earl's blood. The Earl, who may well have drunk pretty deeply before having the courage to rush in to a confrontation, may have had no time to wield his sword before being fatally stabbed. Now it has dropped to the floor and become fixed there, point downwards, as impotent in action as the Earl himself has always been.[181]

The Countess falls on one knee beside the Earl, her hands clasped, two distinct tears glistening on her cheek.[182] Just what emotions possess her at this moment is impossible to say: perhaps a mixture of shock, horror, remorse and fear for her own future. Of all the six scenes, this one was the least carefully worked out in advance. The Technical Notes above (pp. 149–50) should be closely studied here. They show that during the painting process major alterations were made and are visible in X-rays and in an infra-red reflectogram.[183] Hogarth appears to have changed his mind completely over the part the Countess plays in the scene. Originally he depicted the figure of a loosely clad woman hurrying off to the left edge of the scene, seemingly aghast, and clutching a sword diagonally across her body, its hilt by her face;[184] this figure was presumably Hogarth's first idea for the Countess, fleeing with the evidence of Silvertongue's guilt. He then painted out that figure, and placed the Countess kneeling at her husband's feet.

Hogarth's own indecision about how to stage this scene communicates itself to us: we are uncertain about how to react to it. Although the narrative line concerns death, desertion and despair, there are too many burlesque elements for us to feel true concern for any of the characters. That may of course be precisely what Hogarth intended. On one level, the Countess kneeling before the dying Earl suggests remorse. On another level, it is pure theatrical parody: in innumerable plays and operas, the wife/daughter kneels before her husband/father, clasping her hands to beg forgiveness, protest her innocence or just gain time while a lover hides in a laundry basket.[185] In Hogarth's own paintings of *The Beggar's Opera* (first staged in the Lincoln's Inn Theatre in 1728), Polly Peachum kneels before her father and Lucy Lockit before hers, both hoping to save Macheath from hanging.[186]

Fig. 15 Detail from Scene 5: *The Bagnio*

But if the Countess's attitude is a theatrical cliché, the Earl's situation is more serious. Whether or not the Countess fully realises it, he has received a mortal wound. Hogarth depicts him in a slow dying fall, his long ungainly legs just beginning to cave in. Hazlitt observed that the Earl's pose is 'one in which it would be impossible for him to stand or even to fall'.[187] There is probably an element of theatrical parody of actors or opera singers who took a long time in 'dying' here, as well as in the Countess's pose. It has been suggested that the Earl's pose 'can only be an echo, and a conscious one, of a *Descent from the Cross*',[188] with the Countess in the pose of a Mary Magdalen, and the night watchman's lantern throwing the shadow of a cross on the door. If Hogarth borrowed ideas for the collapsing body of the Earl from some (unspecified) representation of the deposition of Christ's body from the cross, the Earl's own habitual physical awkwardness and the sheer theatricality of the pose are also elements in the result Hogarth achieved. As the Earl falls, his head is seen within the frame of what is probably a looking-glass, perhaps to remind us that on his first appearance in Scene 1, the young man was idly contemplating his own image.[189] As death overtakes the Earl, the black spot on his neck is as conspicuous as ever.

An enigmatic shadow is thrown by firelight on the floor in the foreground (fig. 16). It is ostensibly the shadow of an ordinary pair of firetongs, which must be hanging up out of sight to our left (Hogarth even includes the shadow of the hook on which they hang). This shadow is very deliberately introduced; equally deliberately, Silvertongue's blood-stained sword is painted lying over the shadow, as if thrusting through it. The shadow is perhaps the schematic image of the long-legged man who is collapsing to the floor as we watch. The sword which mortally wounded him in the breast now lies, deeply stained with his blood, as if piercing the shadow through the groin. The sword alone has been able to 'cure' Lord Squander's venereal disease, at the cost of death. But there is probably a double meaning. In contemporary slang (then and now), a man's penis is his 'weapon'. Silvertongue's 'weapon' has reduced what is almost certainly the last of the Squanders to a shadow.

Predictably, the pictures on the walls are a bizarre assortment. A tapestry of *The Judgement of Solomon* hangs on the back wall, and a painting of Saint Luke with his ox and ass above the door. Near the window hangs a wicked parody of the sort of 'Portrait of a Lady as a Shepherdess' painted by the fashionable portraitist Thomas Hudson, Hogarth's near-contemporary:[190] but this is the 'Portrait of a Harlot', who may have dressed for the masquerade as a shepherdess in a tilted hat, but who holds a squirrel (contemporary slang for a harlot) perched on one hand and, with the other, dangles the handle of (?) a parasol below her waist; since her portrait is hung over another picture in which we see only a man's legs, the implications are lewd. The oddly angled gaze of the painted 'Lady' appears to be fixed upon the 'penitent' Countess, as if to suggest that they are each as bad as the other. The legs of the man in the lower picture are in buskins; otherwise, what we see of them (which is only from the knees down, the position of the right leg corrected by Hogarth) echoes the pose (in tartan socks) of *Samuel McPherson Corporal in his Highland Regimentals*; shot for desertion in July 1743, he was the subject of a popular engraving published the following month.[191] If the legs are indeed intended to echo those of the deserter, they are appropriately placed near the naked legs of Silvertongue, who is deserting the Countess.

A candle flame below the double picture veers wildly between the draughts from the open window and the open door. The proprietor of the *Turk's Head*, having heard a commotion, has come to investigate its cause. For his figure, simultaneously advancing and recoiling at what he sees, Hogarth draws on the pose of the doctor in one of Watteau's *Commedia dell'Arte* scenes, engraved by C.-N. Cochin in 1729 with lines which begin *'Belle n'écoutez rien, Arlequin est un traitre...'* ('Beautiful girl, do not listen to Harlequin, for he is a deceiver...'), advice which in this case is sound, but too late.[192] The proprietor has summoned a constable, who carries his staff of office, and the night watchman, who holds his lantern high, its bars casting the shadow of a cross on the door, its pattern of holes at the top throwing pools of reflected light up to the ceiling. These three advance through the open door. Silvertongue has not a moment to lose; with one quick backward glance he makes what he hopes is his escape through the open window (fig. 15). In his nightshirt, and once the alarm is raised, he will not long escape arrest. Hogarth's handling of this episode is restrained in comparison with that of John Collett (1725–80), his occasional plagiarist. In an engraving published in 1781 with the title *Fielding's Myrmidons spoiling Bob Booty's Morning Draught* (Stephens 1977, cat. no. 5947), Collett used the elements of Hogarth's scene, adding a man with two girls in bed and the legs of another (presumably drunken) man beneath it; he retained the stays and mask on the floor, the watch entering through the door and the overturned chair. One crude painting on the wall is presumably included in imitation of Hogarth.

Fig. 16 Detail from Scene 5: *The Bagnio*

NG 118: *The Lady's Death*

NG 118

Scene 6: The Lady's Death

In contrast to the first scene, which was set in the sumptuous house of a spendthrift, the last scene is set in the frugal house of a penny-pincher. The wretched Countess, dogged by the scandal following Silvertongue's arrest, trial and sentence to death for the murder of her husband, has returned to the house of her father the Alderman. A newly printed broadsheet lettered *Counseller Silvertou.../ last dying Speech...* lies at her feet. On it is the image of Tyburn's 'triple tree', the three-sided gallows foreshadowed by the tripod in Scene 3. Like the idle apprentice finally meeting retribution in the penultimate scene in *Industry and Idleness*, Hogarth's longest 'modern moral history' (engraved from drawings and published as a series of twelve plates in 1747),[193] Silvertongue will have been taken in a cart to Tyburn, but before being hanged from the triple tree which looms ahead, he will have been exhorted by a preacher to make a last speech from the scaffold professing repentance. The last speeches of condemned men, usually with macabre woodcut illustrations, were widely popular as reading-matter. The broadsheet is probably by now on sale all over town.

With Silvertongue dead, the Countess thought only of suicide. She has drunk laudanum, probably the entire contents of the bottle now lying empty on the floor. Death appears to have come swiftly. She may not even have thought of her child, but an old nurse lifts a child of about two years old to kiss his or her mother. Whether the child is a girl or boy is left ambiguous (boys were dressed in long skirts until they were 'breeched' at about eight years old). What is all too clear is that the child has congenital syphilis to an advanced degree. The black spot on its cheek and the sunken bridge of its nose are enough to indicate that; but as the child is lifted, we see also its pitiful legs, deformed by the disease (like the doctor's, in Scene 3), and encased in surgical boots and braces. The black spot on the cheek may suggest that this is the Earl's child; but the Earl will have passed on the infection to his wife, and the child's parentage remains in question. This group of mother, nurse and child parodies the final scene in many a novel of virtue rewarded. Above all, it is a parody of Samuel Richardson's novel *Pamela* (then much-acclaimed, but to many – including Fielding – tedious[194]) which Hogarth had been invited to illustrate, though not finally employed to do so. Gravelot's illustration of the virtuous Pamela who, after strenuously defending her honour through many trials, is rewarded at the end by marriage and a bouncing baby ('Billy is brought into my Presence, all smiling...'), is reproduced here (fig. 17). The Countess has not been so careful, nor so lucky. The child, an innocent in this story, has not been lucky at all. It is unlikely to survive long.

Suicides' chattels were forfeit; prudently, the Alderman removes a ring from his daughter's hand. In grabbing her arm to do so, he denies her her last chance to return her child's embrace. The Alderman is dressed exactly as he was in Scene 1; he was never a man of fashion. Nor is he a man of taste. The pictures in his house are all of the Dutch low-life school: pictures with broad bourgeois jokes, such as a man urinating against a wall (near the clock), a ham skewered by a rapier in the pile-up of food next to it, or a drunkard lighting his pipe at another's nose (on the left).

Fig. 17 Hubert-François Gravelot (1699–1773), illustration to Samuel Richardson, *Pamela, or Virtue Rewarded* (3rd edn, 1742): 'Billy is brought into my Presence, all smiling.' Pen, ink and sepia wash, 12.8 × 7.6 cm (detail). Formerly collection Captain E.G. Spencer-Churchill; present location unknown.

Fig. 18 Detail from Scene 6: *The Lady's Death*

The room is sparsely furnished; it contains little of comfort, and the boards are bare. A plain old-fashioned clock hangs on the wall. The Alderman does not spend money on whims. His wealth is not displayed; but we can be sure that it is measured and accounted for, down to the last groat. He has unlocked the door of a corner cupboard, presumably to stow away his daughter's ring; in it we see his ledgers, his most important possessions. Even within the cupboard, the ledgers are turned back to front.

The Alderman's civic gown and hat hang by the clock, and a silver punch bowl lends a solitary note of splendour to the table – but that was probably presented to him after a period of office rather than purchased by him. An open window reveals a view of London Bridge, at that date still with houses on it. We are somewhere in the City of London, probably near Blackfriars Bridge. Having been unwillingly married from her father's house, the Countess may never have revisited it until now. Perhaps the cruellest thing about her appearance as death approaches is the way her toes turn up within shoes designed for frivolity: she wore similar shoes in Scene 2, and appears to have worn them (and quickly discarded them) to the masquerade which was to have ended so blissfully. Now what was once high fashion simply expresses the onset of rigor mortis.

A doctor has been called: but there is nothing he can do, and he wanders off behind the Alderman, appearing to admire his fire precautions (a row of buckets lettered *S*, presumably for *Sand*). All we see of him is the back of his full wig and the top of his gold-handled cane. More in evidence is the apothecary, to the right of the Countess, with a nosegay in his buttonhole to counteract the odours in which he has to move, and what looks like the top of a stomach pump and a bottle of julep in his pocket. He is making a great show of accusing a half-witted servant of procuring the Countess's fatal draught of laudanum; but it is possible that the apothecary was himself treating the Countess with laudanum for a sexual infection (or for countering the adverse effects of mercurial pills), and now fears blame because she has drunk the lot. The servant is not certainly guilty. Clad seemingly in some cast-off of the yellow-green livery worn by the old Earl's servants in the courtyard in Scene 1, his hair in curlers in a vain attempt to keep up something of the old style, he is perhaps the only one loyal enough to have remained in the Countess's employment.

The table by the window is laid for the Alderman's next meal. It is meagre. A boiled egg is set upright in a dish of rice ('It is hard to shave an egg': old proverb[195]). A starved dog is about to make off with a pig's head whose upturned snout and closed eyes bear a ghoulish resemblance to the face of the dying Countess across the room. The platters appear to be of pewter, and the large jug on the floor is probably stoneware. The still life on a round table covered with a white cloth may be a deliberate parody of Chardin – for instance of *The White Tablecloth* of 1731–2 (fig. 19) – whose work Hogarth might have seen in Paris in 1743.

Fig. 19 Jean-Siméon Chardin (1699–1779), *The White Tablecloth* ('La Nappe'), *c.*1731–2. Oil on canvas, 96.6 × 123.5 cm. The Art Institute of Chicago, Mr and Mrs Lewis Larned Coburn Memorial Collection.

NOTES

1. 'Mr. HOGARTH'S PROPOSALS For Selling, to the Highest Bidder, the Six Pictures call'd The HARLOT'S Progress: The Eight Pictures call'd The RAKE'S PROGRESS: The Four Pictures representing MORNING, NOON, EVENING, and NIGHT: And that of a Company of Strolling Actresses Dressing in a Barn...'

An explanation of the bidding system and a statement of conditions of sale is followed by: 'N.B. The Six pictures call'd *Marriage A-la-mode*, will be sold in the same manner, but thc Book for that Purpose cannot be closed till about a Week after the Plates now engraving from them are finish'd, of which public notice will be given.

Marriage-A-la-Mode
1. The Marriage Settlement
2. The Tête à Tête
3. The Inspection
4. The Toilette
5. The Bagnio
6. The Lady's Death'

BL, Add. MSS 33,402 (Dodd MSS, vol. lx, ff. 62–3).

2. The ticket, known as *The Battle of the Pictures* (from a paper lettered thus, lower left), is headed *The Bearer hereof is Entitled (if he thinks proper) to be a Bidder for Mr Hogarth's Pictures, which are to be sold on the last day of this Month.* See Paulson 1989, pp. 113–14, cat. no. 157, plate 157.

3. See *European Magazine*, 1791, ii, p. 159 (Deaths): 'John Lane, at Hillingdon in Middlesex, 8 July 1791, aet. 87.'

4. The compiler is indebted to her colleague Humphrey Wine for communicating the following from the Angerstein Papers (F/ANG/066-1, Box no. 6) in the archives of the Corporation of London, Islington:
(i) 4 April 1792: J.F. Cawthorne & Messrs. Boydell. Agreement as to engraving Hogarth's pictures *Marriage A-la-Mode* (this was the set engraved in mezzotint by Richard Earlom and published by Boydell 1795–1800, as noted under Exhibited); (ii) 15 June 1795: J.F. Cawthorne to Holmes. Mortgage of Hogarth's pictures above mentioned.
(iii) 10 February 1797: Catalogue of sale of Hogarth's pictures above mentioned. Explanation of said pictures. (iv) 24 February 1797: Holmes to J.J. Angerstein. Assignment of said pictures on Mr Angerstein's purchase thereof and receipt for purchase money.

5. Two additional works by Hogarth were entered in pen and ink in Christie's copy of the catalogue, and were sold first: 'The Portrait of Hogarth... 1', bt Angerstein £45 3s. 0d. (*The Painter and his Pug*, now Tate Gallery, N 00112); and 'The Portrait of Sr John Thornhill... 2', bt Walton £5 5s. 0d.

6. Paulson 1971, II, p. 122.

7. *Morning Chronicle*, 5 May 1792, 'The six pictures of Hogarth's *Marriage A-la-Mode*, now exhibiting in Pall Mall...'

8. For an assessment of Lichtenberg's commentaries, see Paulson 1989, I, pp. 25, 28, noting an earlier translation by Innes and Gustav Herdan, *The World of Hogarth, Lichtenberg's Commentaries on Hogarth's Engravings*, Boston 1966.

9. Over 1000 lines long, and fairly described by Moore 1948, p. 56, as typical of the 'execrable Hudibrastic creations [of its time] which combine lewd suggestion and cant moralizing. While giving a faithful narration of Hogarth's story, the poet misses most of the pertinent satiric and often dramatic details that cram each picture.'

10. The anon. writer describes this set as 'painted in an exceedingly free and sketchy manner', noting (in detail) numerous variations from NG 113–18, but considers that 'they are evidently the finished sketches from which he afterwards painted the pictures now in the National Gallery'.

11. Davies 1959, p. 54.

12. Ed. Burke 1955, p. 216. Hogarth's 'Autobiographical Notes' are coll. BL, Add. MS, 27,991.

13. Ed. Burke 1955, p. 216.

14. There are of course precedents for some aspects of Hogarth's 'new' form of art in an old European tradition (Italian and Dutch as well as English) of popular engraving of a satirical, emblematic and moralizing nature. See Kurtz 1957 and David Kunzle, *The Early Comic Strip*, Berkeley and Los Angeles 1973.

15. Ed. Burke 1955, p. 206.

16. Walpole, *Anecdotes*, 1780, edn 1827, p. 140.

17. Henry Fielding, Preface to *The History of the Adventures of Joseph Andrews, and of his friend Mr Abraham Adams*, London 1742.

18. Gautier's review was partly published in *Le Moniteur Universel*, 24 May 1862; expanded and republished in *L'Artiste* (of which he was then editor), 1868. He probably knew the paintings well from earlier visits to London.

19. Only the engravings survive. The paintings, bought by William Beckford at Hogarth's auction in 1745, were destroyed by fire at Fonthill in 1755 (Scenes 2 and 4 perhaps survive in the form of two very damaged paintings in the Rosebery collection). For the engravings and the subscription ticket for them, see Paulson 1989, cat. nos. 120–6, pp. 75–83, repr. pp. 287–93.

20. 'George Vertue, Notebooks', vol. III, *Walpole Society 1933–4*, XXII, Oxford 1934, p. 58.

21. The paintings are coll. Sir John Soane's Museum, London. For the engravings, see Paulson 1989, cat. nos. 132–9, pp. 89–98, repr. pp. 300–18.

22. From Hogarth's advertisement of 2 April 1743, partly quoted above.

23. For a fuller account of the complex allusions and meanings of *Masquerades and Operas* than is possible here, and for Hogarth's satire on the 3rd Earl of Burlington and the cult of Palladio, see Paulson 1989, cat. no. 44, repr.

24. Painted for Hogarth's wealthy patron Mary Edwards (d.1743), now private collection. Engraved without Hogarth's sanction in 1746; see Paulson 1971, pp. 466–7.

25. 'Vertue Notebooks', III, ed. 1934, p. 58.

26. Ed. Burke 1955, p. 211–12; in preceding drafts (p. 206) he writes of training himself 'by retaining in my mind *lineally* such objects as fitted my purpose best'.

27. Oppé 1948, pp. 11–12.

28. Within a year of Hogarth's first announcement that he would employ French engravers on *Marriage A-la-Mode*, Anthony Highmore (a friendly rival) advertised that he would employ 'the best French engravers' for his illustrations to Samuel Richardson's *Pamela*, see *London Evening Post*, 26 February 1744 (and again in the *General Advertiser*, 12 April 1745).

29. Coll. Schloss Charlottenburg, Berlin; repr. Michael Levey, *Painting and Sculpture in France 1700–1789*, New Haven and London 1993, plate 32, with detail on facing page.

30. See Paulson 1989, pp. 14–16, for biographical notes on Hogarth's engravers. Paulson gives Scotin's first names as Louis Gérard rather than Gérard Jean-Baptiste. Hogarth's engraver signs himself 'G. Scotin'.

31. 'Vertue Notebooks', III, ed. 1934, p. 85. Baron's status can to some extent be measured by his inclusion in Gawen Hamilton, *A Conversation of Virtuosis ... at the Kings Arms*, 1735 (coll. NPG 1384; repr. Kerslake 1977, cat. no. 340, plate 951). He is likely to be the subject of Watteau's red chalk drawing (BM, 1874-8-8-2270) known as *An Engraver working at his Table* repr. Egerton 1997, fig. 34. E. de Goncourt (*Catalogue Raisonné de l'œuvre paint, dessiné et gravé d'Antoine Watteau*, Paris 1875, pp. 347–8) noted an inscription in the hand of Hugh Howard, the drawing's (?) first owner and Baron's contemporary, reading 'M. Baron, the graver, by A. Watteau'; presumably on an old mount, this was later lost, and the drawing was given a generalised title. See Paul Hulton, *Watteau Drawings in the British Museum*, exh. cat, British Museum, London 1980, cat. no. 54, p. 30, repr. Baron engraved Plate 3, *Evening*, of Hogarth's *The Four Times of the Day* (Paulson 1989, cat. no. 148, repr. p. 329).

32. See Paulson 1989, pp. 14, 16.

33. Ravenet engraved two plates after Hayman for [E. Moore and H. Brooke] *Fables for the Female Sex*, London 1744.

34. An authoritative collection of engravings after Watteau: first part 1726–8, second part 1735–6. See E. Dacier, J. Hérold and A. Vuaflart, *Jean de Jullienne et les Graveurs de Watteau au XVIIIe Siècle*, 4 vols, Paris: I, *Notices et documents biographiques*, 1929; II, *Historique*, 1922; III, *Catalogue*, 1922; IV, *Planches*, 1921; *passim* (see index under engravers' names).

35. Ibid., vol. III, *Catalogue*, 1922, Recueil cat. nos. 204 and 23; the painting is E. Camesaca and P. Rosenberg, *Tout l'œuvre peint de Watteau*, Paris 1970, new edn 1983 (203, repr.).

36. The painting of this title engraved by Baron while in Dr Mead's possession is now lost. A different painting of the same title, in the collection of Frederick the Great, is now coll. Berlin, Staatliche Schlosse und Gärten, Château de Charlottenburg, see E. Camesaca and P. Rosenberg 1983 , no. 174, repr.

37. 'Vertue Notebooks', III, ed. 1934, p. 156.

38. The impression of *Characters and Caricaturas* issued as a receipt to John Huggins, a sitter to Hogarth about this time, is dated 12 April, only ten days after Hogarth advertised the subscription (repr. Egerton 1997, p. 4). Paulson (1989, p. 113) notes other receipts dated in April and May 1743; December 1743; March and April 1744.

39. Repr. Bindman 1994, p. 52, fig. 41.

40. A five-day excursion down the Thames made by Hogarth, Samuel Scott, Ebenezer Forrest, John Thornhill and William Tothall in May 1732; see Paulson 1971.

41. See Paulson 1989, pp. 114–15.

42. Ed. Burke 1955, p. 230: Hogarth relates that Rouquet's *Lettres* were written for the entertainment of Marshal Belleisle, a French dignitary who had been arrested abroad by Hanoverian agents and subsequently detained in England, with his brother, during February–August 1745, when they purchased sets of Hogarth's prints. Hogarth encouraged Rouquet to 'fit [his explanations] for the press. as I h[ad] begun to find by my Prints going much abroad ... that such a thing might be acc[epta]ble since when I have always sent one of his exp[?lic]ations with such books of my Print as have gon abroad'.

43. Francis Haskell, *History and its Images*, New Haven and London 1993, p. 149.

44. For a detailed list and critical assessment of 'Commentaries and Catalogues', see Paulson 1989, pp. 24–9.

45. Walpole, *Anecdotes*, 1780, edn 1827, p. 132.

46. See Paulson 1971, I, pp. 478–9, and Paulson 1989, pp. 6–7, for the suggestion that Hogarth painted 'backward' or in reverse in subjects which were to be engraved, and that thus 'The reading structure is embodied in the engraving, not in the painting.'

47. Paulson 1971, I, p. 479.

48. Ed. Burke 1955, pp. 125, 131.

49. The double-plot of Dryden's tragi-comedy *Marriage A-la-Mode* (first published 1673) is summarised in ed. Margaret Drabble, *The Oxford Companion to English Literature*, Oxford 1985, p. 621: 'The main plot concerns a usurper's discovery that his daughter and his (lawful) predecessor's son have ... fallen idealistically in love. The comic plot is a double intrigue involving two friends and their pursuit respectively of the wife of the one and the betrothed of the other...'

50. 1758 edn, n. p. Johnson adds 'It is used likewise by shopkeepers for a kind of thin silken manufacture.'

51. *Wit a-la-mode* was first advertised in the *Gentleman's Magazine*, April 1745, p. 224, as by 'Cooper', presumably John Gilbert Cooper (1723–69), ? a possible candidate for authorship of the anon. *Marriage a-la-Mode: an humorous tale, in six canto's, in hudibrastic verse; being an explanation of the six prints lately published by the ingenious Mr. Hogarth*, London, printed for Weaver Bickerton 1746. The compiler is grateful to Dr Mervyn Jannetta, British Library, for his help over ephemera with 'a-la-mode' titles.

52. J.H. Hexter, *Reapppraisals in History*, London 1961, p. 78 and p. 79, noting 'the general truth that before the Tudor period country families had discovered the tonic effect on their more or less blue blood of a transfusion of *aurum potabile* from the City'. See chapter 5, pp. 71–116, *passim*.

53. Anthony Trollope, *The Way We Live Now*, first published 1875; reprinted London 1995, p. 433.

54. Joseph Addison, Richard Steele and others, *The Spectator*, ed. G.G. Smith, London 1945; vol. II, no. 220 [Steele], 12 November 1711, pp. 152–5. This begins: 'Sir, Why will you apply to my Father for my Love? I cannot help it if he will give you my Person; but I assure you it is not in his Power, nor even in my own, to give you my Heart.'

55. *Love in Several Masques*, in ed. Leslie Stephen, *The Dramatic Works of Henry Fielding*, vol. VIII, London 1882, pp. 30, 33.

56. Four versions known; see ed. David Bindman and Scott Wilcox, *'Among the Whores and Thieves', William Hogarth and The Beggar's Opera*, exh. cat., Yale Center for British Art and Lewis Walpole Library, 1997, p. 45, for evidence that a supposed fifth version (Walpole Library, Yale University) is an early eighteenth-century copy, probably of the version in Birmingham.

57. *David Garrick as Richard III* is coll. Walker Art Gallery, Liverpool; repr. Bindman 1994, p. 139, fig. 108. *David Garrick with his Wife* is coll. Her Majesty The Queen; see Oliver Millar, *The Tudor, Stuart and Early Georgian Pictures in the Collection of Her Majesty the Queen*, London 1963, p. 185, cat. no. 560, plate 211.

58. See Allen 1987, pp. 11–23.

59. Ed. Burke 1955, pp. 209, 215, 210.

60. Bertelsen 1983, p. 139.

61. See Paulson 1989, pp. 113–14, cat. no. 157, repr. p. 340.

62. From one of Nichols's unnamed correspondents, quoted in John Nichols, *Biographical Anecdotes of William Hogarth*, London 1781, p. 185.

63. John Lane's account of the sale and his resolve, despite later high offers, to keep the paintings 'as long as he lived' is among the papers of John Nichols, coll. NPG Archives, f. 273 ff.; revised and published in Nichols 1781, pp. 107 ff. Little is otherwise known of him. He lived at Hillingdon, Middlesex, some thirteen miles from the centre of London. His will, signed 24 April 1789 (PRO: PROB.11/1206), refers to lands and 'warehouses' which he owned there; apart from a few specific bequests of money, it leaves his landed property and the 'residue and remainder of Real and personal estate in goods chattels and effects whatsoever and wheresoever' to John Fenton Cawthorne, who is to be sole executor. Neither *Marriage A-la-Mode* nor any other work of art is mentioned by name.

64. Lane MS, NPG Archives.

65. The paintings hanging on the wall behind her are not decipherable but are unlikely to be from *Marriage A-la-Mode.*

66. Lane MS, NPG Archives.

67. The son of James Fenton, Recorder of Lancaster, an old friend of William Lane, he added the name Cawthorne on succeeding to estates of his mother's family. He was also the heir of William Lane's brother Richard. He is noticed in eds. Namier and Brooke 1964, vol. II, p. 418. For the Commons debate on his expulsion, see *Hansard's Debates*, 1795–7, XXXII, 1818, col. 1007–20. Cawthorne was re-elected in 1806.

68. The painting is coll. Thomas Coram Foundation for Children, London (repr. Webster 1978, p. 153); for the engraving, see Paulson 1989, pp. 141–5, cat. no. 184, repr. p. 366.

69. This guide repeats much of the material used in Egerton 1997, published to accompany an exhibition at the NG. For more detailed explanations, see Davies 1959 and Cowley 1983; for the engravings, see Paulson 1989.

70. Cowley 1983, pp. 28–9, is surely right in correcting previous descriptions of the canopy as a 'canopy of state' to a 'bed canopy'.

71. For marriage settlements in the eighteenth century, see Robert Robson, *The Attorney in Eighteenth-Century England*, Cambridge 1959, pp. 92 ff.

72. Thomas Fuller, *Gnomologia*, London 1732, p. 14, no. 350. The compiler's colleague Jacqui McComish notes (in discussion) that Chardin's *The Young Draughtsman* (coll. Musée du Louvre, Paris) wears two pins in his sleeve, as does the young model in Chardin's *House of Cards*, 1737 (coll. National Gallery of Art, Washington); both repr. Philip Conisbee 1986, plates 23, 136. Conisbee notes that *The Young Draughtsman* was one of the first Chardins to come to England, where it was engraved in mezzotint by J. Faber, 1740 (p. 33, plate 25).

73. Rouquet 1746, p. 30.

74. See J. Horace Round, *Peerage and Pedigree*, 2 vols, London 1910, I, pp. xvii–xxiii, and 'Tales of the Conquest', pp. 284–323.

75. See Andrea Palladio, *I Quattro Libri dell'Architettura*, first published Venice 1570, p. 55, plate 57 (Dover facsimile reprint, New York 1965). The compiler is grateful to John Harris for this suggestion, in discussion.

76. Eric Partridge, *Dictionary of Historical Slang*, London 1972, p. 566, dating the expression to 'mid 18thc.'

77. 'Viscount Squanderfield' is evidently a courtesy title, borne by the young man during the lifetime of his father, who is styled the Earl of Squander. For a note on such courtesy titles borne by the real-life nobility, see Davies 1959, pp. 57–8, n. 3. By Scene 4, Viscount Squanderfield has succeeded his father as the next Earl of Squander; the cards received by his wife in that scene are addressed to 'Lady Squander'.

78. Ed. Pat Rogers, *Jonathan Swift: The Complete Poems*, New Haven and London 1983, pp. 343–4. Gay's *Fable XIV* concludes:

> Thus the dull lad, too tall for school,
> With travel finishes the fool,
> Studious of ev'ry coxcomb's airs,
> He drinks, games, dresses, whores and swears,
> O'erlooks with scorn all virtuous arts,
> For vice is fitted to his parts.

79. It has long been recognised that venereal disease plays a part in *Marriage A-la-Mode.* There are references in the Poem of 1746 ('in Hudibrastic verse') to 'a slight Thing call'd a Cl–p' or to 'the P–x'. Most art historians who discuss this series are well aware that venereal disease plays a part in it, but assume that the function of the 'black spot', which appears, for instance, on the Viscount's neck, is to 'cover the mark of syphilis' or 'hide a venereal sore', leaving their readers with the impression that venereal disease took the form, at least in the Viscount's case, of a sore on the neck which could be covered by a neat round patch. The manifestation of the disease is not so tidy. Venereal disease customarily takes the form of a rash in the area of the groin, the torso and around the mouth, which may break out into lesions there (and elsewhere). Basically, Hogarth was restricted to the head and neck to indicate pictorially that the Viscount (and others) had the disease. The compiler is indebted to Dr Adam Lawrence, Head Physician in Genitourinary Medicine, Chelsea and Westminster Hospital, London (in discussions), for observing that Hogarth's symmetrical, perfectly round 'black spots' could not 'cover the marks of the disease', and for perceiving that Hogarth in fact uses the 'black spots' as symbols for those who are taking the round black mercurial pills which were then the most common form of treatment for the disease. See Morton 1990, Lowe 1992 and 'Two Minutes with Venus: two years with mercury: mercury as an antisyphilitic chemotherapeutic agent', *Journal of the Royal Society of Medicine*, June 1990, 83 (6), pp. 392–5.

80. Walpole, *Anecdotes*, 1780, edn 1827, p. 126.

81. Caravaggio's *Head of Medusa* (almost circular, 60 × 55 cm) is coll. Uffizi, Florence; see Michael Kitson, *The Complete Paintings of Caravaggio*, Harmondsworth 1969, p. 90, cat. no. 28 (repr.). Davies 1959, n. 17, notes that a version (or copy) was in the sale of Sir James Thornhill, Hogarth's father-in-law, 24 February 1735 (85), and that a (different) Medusa's head on a shield is included (among various stage properties on the floor) in Hogarth's engraving *Strolling Actresses dressing in a Barn*, 1738 (Paulson 1989, cat. no. 150, repr. p. 332).

82. Eustache Le Sueur (1616–55), *The Martyrdom of Saint Lawrence*, coll. Duke of Buccleuch; see Alain Mérot, *Eustache Le Sueur*, Paris 1989, cat. no. 158, fig. 354; engraved by G. Audan. The lower half of the composition owes something to Titian's version of the subject (Gesuiti, Venice).

83. Domenichino, *The Martyrdom of Saint Agnes*, *c.*1619–22/5; coll. Pinacoteca Nazionale, Bologna; see Richard E. Spear, *Domenichino*, New Haven and London 1982, cat. no. 63, plate 229. Hogarth gives only the lower half of the composition.

84. Titian, *Cain slaying Abel* and *David slaying Goliath*: two of three ceiling paintings in the Sacristy of S. Maria della Salute, Venice, *c.*1543-4; see H.E. Wethey, *The Paintings of Titian*, London 1975, III, cat. nos. 82, 84 (plates 157, 159). Hogarth shows both paintings in reverse, evidently having copied them from engravings; and although both the original paintings are upright in format, he makes a rectangular picture out of *David slaying Goliath*.

85. Titian: *Tityus* is one of a set of pictures known as the *Four Condemned* and documented 1548–9. Only *Tityus* and *Sisyphus* (both coll. Museo del Prado, Madrid) are now known; *Tantalus* and *Ixion* are lost. Tityus (sometimes confused with Prometheus) violated Latona; his punishment was to be endlessly tortured by a vulture preying on his liver.

86. See note 84.

87. Guido Reni, *Judith with the Head of Holofernes*, 1625–6, Sedelmayer Collection, Geneva; see D. Stephen Pepper, *Guido Reni*, Oxford 1984, cat. no. 104, plate 134.

88. It has been variously noted that the signet ring worn by the 'real' Earl on the little finger of his left hand reappears in the portrait on the wall.

89. See Davies 1959, p. 59, note 14.

90. Examples of the sort of flamboyant military portraits Hogarth may have had in mind are Hyacinthe Rigaud, *Louis XIV*, 1701 (coll. Prado) and Nicolas de Largillière, *Portrait of François-Armand de Gontaut, Duc de Biron*, 1714 (coll. Boston Museum of Fine Arts): see M.N. Rosenfelf, *Largillière and the Eighteenth-Century Portrait*, exh. cat., Museum of Fine Arts, Montreal 1981 (51, repr.).

91. F. Antal. 'Hogarth and his Borrowings', *The Art Bulletin*, XXIX, no. 1, 1947, pp. 43–4, reproducing *Captain Coram*, fig. 15, and Drevet's engraving after Rigaud, *Samuel Bernard*, fig. 16. Antal notes other influences on Coram, particularly Van Dyck.

92. Gautier 1868, p. 164.

93. 1983, p. 48, reproducing a detail of the engraving.

94. See note 16.

95. Assuming that the chimneypiece is in the centre of the wall of the nearer room, neither room is large enough to justify the pretentious arch supported by pairs of *verde antico* marble pillars and pilasters, with gilt Ionic capitals and medallions (gilding was often found in Palladian interiors). The room with the chimneypiece is painted olive green, a fashionable colour from *c.*1730 (see Ian C. Bristow, *Interior House-Painting Colours and Technology 1615–1840*, New Haven and London 1996, pp. 162–3); the walls of the further room are papered with a damask pattern, probably at a high cost. The over-mantel of the chimneypiece appears to be of veined white marble; the chimneypiece itself of a different colour. Such a combination was not uncommon, but here the relative proportions of the two are ill-judged.The far left corner of the carpet appears to have been cut to fit round the base of the columns. One darker and more deliberately defined square in the carpet seems to claim attention, but if this has a meaning, it has eluded this compiler. Possibly all it indicates is that the carpet is made up of different squares.

96. For the plausibility (or otherwise) of a Viscount with a mere courtesy title thus displaying a coronet, see Davies 1959, pp. 60–1, n. 27.

97. Almost any of the conversation pieces painted by Arthur Devis (1712–87) illustrate his manner; as a contrast to Scene 2 of *Marriage A-la-Mode* one might equally adduce *Mr and Mrs Richard Brill*, 1747 (New York University, Institute of Fine Arts), or *William Atherton and his wife Lucy, of Preston, Lancashire* (Walker Art Gallery, Liverpool).

98. The correct deportment for a seated gentleman is shown in *A Man seated in an Interior*, a chalk drawing by Carle van Loo (1705–65), dated 1743, and thus exactly contemporary with Hogarth's painting (coll. Nelson-Atkins Museum of Art, Kansas City Missouri, repr. Roger Ward, *Dürer to Matisse, Master Drawings from the Nelson-Atkins Museum of Art*, exh. cat., Kansas City 1996, p.150). The pose is upright, the hat tucked under the arm, the sword concealed under the skirts of the frock-coat, visible at knee-level. It should be noted that this and other figures in interiors by Carle van Loo are 'seen against a wall hung with canvases', as observed by Pierre Rosenberg, *French Master Drawings of the 17th and 18th centuries in North American collections*, exh. cat. 1972, pp. 216–17. Two figures (a seated lady and a seated man) from the same suite of drawings by Carle van Loo, both dated 1743, are coll. Pierpont Morgan Library, New York; see Cara Dufour Denison, *Le dessin français: Chefs-d'œuvres de la Pierpont Morgan Library*, exh. cat., Musée du Louvre, Paris, and Pierpont Morgan Library, 1993–4 (57, 58, both repr.).

99. Probably a poodle, such as the Viscount's taste for things French would incline him to choose, but perhaps of mixed breeding, like its owners. In *The Analysis of Beauty* (ed. Burke 1955, p. 49), Hogarth wrote: 'There is something extremely odd and comical in the rough shock dog'. The *Concise OED*, 1976, defines 'shock-dog' (obsolete) as 'shaggy-haired poodle'. The dog in Scene 2 has been variously identified, e.g. by Gautier 1868, p. 166, as a griffon and by Cowley 1983, p. 59, as a terrier, while Paulson 1989, p. 117, calls it 'the wife's lap-dog, a Bedlington terrier'.

100. Hogarth painted two versions of *Before* and *After*, (1) in outdoor settings, 1730–1, coll. Fitzwilliam Museum, Cambridge; repr. *Treasures from the Fitzwilliam*, exh. cat., Fitzwilliam Museum and tour 1989–90, p. 119, cat. nos. 122a and b, repr. in colour; (2) indoor settings, *c.*1731, coll. Getty Museum, Malibu; repr. Paulson 1971, I, p. 232; engraved by Hogarth, published 1736; see Paulson 1989, pp. 99–100, cat. nos. 141–2, repr. pp. 320–1.

101. Dr Richard Mead (1673–1753) reputedly owned a collection of De Troy's 'small fêtes galantes of the 1720s' (Fitzwilliam Museum and tour 1989–90, p. 119).

102. Gautier 1868, p. 167: 'Ici Hogarth mérite tout à fait le nom de peintre qu'on lui refuse parfois et fort injustement. La figure du jeune comte anéanti dans son fauteuil a une valeur d'exécution très remarquable. La tête pâle, exténuée, morbide, trahissant les révoltes de la nature contre les exigences de la débauche, se détache du chambranle grisâtre de la cheminée avec une prodigieuse finesse de ton. Le modèle du masque où il s'agissait de conserver l'apparence de la jeunesse et de distinction à travers la sénilité et l'hébètement précoces du libertinage est d'une justesse vraiment merveilleuse.'

103. As noted by Paul Oppé, *Burlington Magazine*, XCIX, 1957, p. 209. Cochin's red chalk drawing is coll. Ashmolean Museum, Oxford (K.T. Parker, *Catalogue of the Collection of the Drawings in the Ashmolean Museum*, Oxford 1938, I, pp. 237–8, no. 482). The title *A Party of Revellers* is used by Jon Whiteley, *Drawings by Contemporaries of Voltaire ... from the Print Room of the Ashmolean*, Ashmolean Museum, exh. cat., Oxford 1994 (32, repr.). If Hogarth did not know Cochin's drawing, he could have known the engraving of it (in reverse) by Claude Gallimard, 1739, known as *La Soirée*.

104. Hogarth had already depicted pictures hanging in interiors – for instance, in *The Strode Family*, *c.*1738 (coll. Tate Gallery; see Einberg and Egerton 1988, repr. p. 92, in colour) – but in such interiors, the pictures are mostly conventional landscapes such as the sitters might themselves have owned. In *Marriage A-la-Mode* Hogarth develops what might be called the 'ironical picture' to an art form in itself. The 'Endymion' painting in the background of Cochin's *Party of Revellers* may well have helped to stimulate this idea, as may other works by French artists which Hogarth may have seen on his visit to Paris at the end of May–June 1743. Watteau's *L'Enseigne de Gersaint (Gersaint's Shop Sign)*, painted in 1721 for his friend the picture- and print-dealer Edme-François Gersaint, shows the interior of Gersaint's shop hung frame-to-frame with pictures ranging from biblical, classical and mythological scenes to portraits. The medley shows the range of Gersaint's stock rather than commenting ironically on it; but if Hogarth saw it, he can hardly have failed to draw from it.

105. A similar table has been carried outside and placed (with books on it) on a terrace for *The Edwards Family*, 1733–4; private collection, repr. Bindman 1994, p. 135, fig. 104.

106. *The Journal of a Modern Lady* was first published in 1729; reprinted in Rogers 1983 (cited in note 78), pp. 365–72 and p. 788 n. The quotation is from p. 366, lines 38–43. 'Quadrille' here refers to the fashionable eighteenth-century card game for four people with 40 cards, which could involve heavy gambling.

107. The book Hogarth depicts is the first edition of *A Short Treatise on the Game of Whist. Containing the Laws of the Game... By a Gentleman*. London 1742. The author was Edmond Hoyle (1672–1769); the book went into many editions. The first edition of 1742 was a small book, as Hogarth suggests; its pages measure 15.2 × 8.3 cm.

108. Those who have kindly tried to identify the tune (but without success) include Carl Dolmetsch (at Martin Davies's invitation, 1956–8) and, at this compiler's invitation,

Robert R. Wark, The Huntington Library, San Marino, California, and Michael Burden, Director of New Chamber Opera. Curiously, in the engraving (Plate II) the notation is jumbled, and the tune thus becomes unplayable, possibly at its composer's request. It is possible that Hogarth himself invented the tune.

109. *The Assembly at Wanstead House* is coll. Philadelphia Museum of Art; see Richard Dorment, *British Paintings in the Philadelphia Museum of Art*, Philadelphia 1986, p. 159, repr.

110. If that is what it is. Gautier thought it might be either a *bonbonnière* (a little box for sweets) or a miniature case.

111. Also see Bomford and Roy in the *NG Technical Bulletin*, 1982, pp. 51–2, and figs. 8–10.

112. Among the works Baudoin exhibited at the Salon in 1765 were 'Several little subjets & portraits in miniature, under the same number' (97) and 'Several portraits in gouache, under the same number' (101).

113. See letter from Sir John Summerson to Martin Davies, 10 October 1956, NG Archives.

114. Its first verses are given in Thomas D'Urfey, *Wit and Mirth: or Pills to Purge Melancholy*, London 1719, vol. IV, p. 310, with a tune (by John Barrett) used by John Gay for song no. LVIII in *The Beggar's Opera*.

115. Ed. Burke 1955, pp. 49–50.

116. Coll. Ashmolean Museum; see Christopher Woodward, 'Hogarth's Marriage Contract', in *A Rake's Progress, from Hogarth to Hockney*, exh. cat., Sir John Soane's Museum, London 1997, pp. 13–14, with a colour repr. (1) and colour detail of the three foreground busts (2). The compiler is grateful to Alex Kayder for the observation (in correspondence) that the bust appears to be of the kind restored (in quantity) in Bartolomeo Cavaceppi's studio in Rome, and purchased by Englishmen on the Grand Tour (see Carlos A. Picon, *Bartolomeo Cavaceppi, Eighteenth-Century Restorations of Ancient Marble Sculpture from English Private Collections*, exh. cat., Clarendon Gallery, London 1983, *passim*).

117. Hugh Honour, *Chinoiserie*, London 1961, p. 53.

118. Shebbeare, writing as 'Batista Angeloni', is quoted by Hugh Honour, ibid., p. 130.

119. Hogarth, Preface to *The Analysis of Beauty* (ed. Burke 1955), p. 17.

120. The compiler is indebted to John Leopold, Department of Mediaeval and Later Antiquities, British Museum, for advice over the clock. As illustrations of French examples which are in some degree comparable, he suggests Tardy [pseudonym of Henri Gustave Sengellé], *French Clocks the World Over*, Paris 1981, vol. I, pp. 194, 291.

121. Davies 1959, p. 61 n. 33, notes that the first of the sermons published by George Whitefield (1714–70) as *Twenty-Three Sermons on Various Subjects*, new edn, 1745, is *On Regeneration*, and that it is identical with the sermon published in 1737 under the title *The Nature and Necessity of our New Birth in Christ Jesus*.

122. Hazlitt 1824, edn 1843, pp. 150–5.

123. In the engraving, where the painting's date would be irrelevant, the paper is more precisely inscribed 'Rec^{d} June 4 1744'.

124. Nichols and Steevens 1808, vol. I, p. 121; Hazlitt 1824, edn 1843, p. 145; Davies 1959, p. 52. Among later writers, Webster 1978, p. 105, notes that 'The exact meaning of this scene has been notoriously difficult to explain ever since the eighteenth century'; Paulson 1989, p. 119, notes various different interpretations; and see Cowley 1983, p. 85.

125. The compiler is grateful to Dr Adam Lawrence (see note 79) for drawing her attention to ed. E. Allen, J.L. Turk and Sir R. Murley, *The Case Books of John Hunter FRS*, London 1993. Dr John Hunter (1728–93), physician, surgeon, anatomist and probably the most enlightened medical man of his day, undertook the care of patients from all classes with all sorts of ailments. In the published *Case Books* noted above, he prescribed mercurial treatment for venereal disease (cases no. 351–401) both internally (in the form of pills) and externally in the form of ointment. Numerous other medical practitioners, some probably far less qualified than John Hunter, openly advertised pills for venereal disease. A list of doctors, their pills and what those pills were used for was published in the *Gentleman's Magazine*, 1748, pp. 348–9. The back pages of most newspapers regularly carried advertisements for pills to cure venereal disease (or 'gleets').

126. See '"Two minutes with Venus, two years with mercury": Mercury as an anti-syphilitic chemotherapeutic agent', *Journal of the Royal Society of Medicine*, 1990, vol. 83 (6), pp. 392–5.

127. See Alain Roy, *Gérard de Lairesse (1640–1711)*, Paris 1992, where his sufferings from syphilis are discussed p. 53; the Uffizi portrait is repr. p. 50 (and also in Morton 1990, p. 216; Egerton 1997, p. 29, with other portraits pp. 53–4).

128. Dr Adam Lawrence observes (in discussion) that the doctor's profile may be compared with plate 95 in A. King, C. Nicol and P. Rodin, *Venereal Diseases*, London 1980, and that the deformity of the doctor's legs indicates advanced gummatous osteo-periostitis of the ulna; he draws attention to plate 58 of King, Nicol and Rodin 1980. See also Morton 1990, p. 216.

129. In correspondence with the compiler during 1996.

130. Coll. Her Majesty The Queen; on long loan to the V&A. See John White, *The Raphael Cartoons*, London 1972, plate 3, with details plates 28, 30.

131. See Bindman 1994, p. 99. In the early 1730s, Thornhill was working on his copies of the Raphael Cartoons while Hogarth was lodging with him. Hogarth may have intended to engrave a set of Thornhill's copies. Bindman reproduces (fig. 72) Hogarth's engraving *Four Heads from the Raphael Cartoons* (Paulson 1989, cat. no. 264).

132. William Cheselden FRS, *Osteographia*, London 1733 (which Hogarth may have known), includes an illustration (two views) of the *Skull of a Woman who died of Venereal Disease*, repr. Barbara Maria Stafford, *Artful Science*, Cambridge, Mass. 1994, p. 103; the skull is far more heavily eroded than that which Hogarth depicts. A skull with syphilitic caries, coll. Royal College of Surgeons Museum, was included in the exhibition *Fatal Attractions: AIDS and Syphilis*, Wellcome Institute for the History of Medicine, London 1995.

133. For various interpretations of the letters, see Paulson 1989, p. 119.

134. The compiler is indebted to Dr Ashok Roy, National Gallery Scientific Department, for confirming this observation.

135. 'As is the mother, so is her daughter'; Book of Ezekiel, ch. 16, v.44

136. See I. Pinchbeck and M. Hewitt, *Children in English Society*, London 1969, pp. 117–20. The quotation from Fielding is on p. 119.

137. This is a common nickname for a doctor, especially one treating patients with mercurial pills for venereal disease. Watteau's semi-caricature sketch of Dr Misaubin, engraved by Arthur Pond, was lettered *M... de la Pilule* (de Goncourt 1875, cited in note 31, p. 38).

138. The compiler is indebted to William Schupbach, Curator of the Iconological Collections, Wellcome Institute for the History of Medicine, for kindly communicating the following note: Below the open volume is another, lettered *Tom.2*, which suggests that Hogarth is alluding to the magnificent multi-volume works describing the machines and inventions submitted to the approval of the Académie Royale des Sciences. There were at least three such works (and probably more) in Hogarth's time: (1) P. Demours, *Table générale des matières contenues dans l'Histoire & dans les Mémoires de L'Académie Royale des Sciences*, 8 vols, Paris 1729–after 1748. Each volume lists the *Machines ou Inventions approuvées par l'Académie* year by year. They include orthopaedic apparatus like that mentioned on the title-page of the volume Hogarth depicts (e.g. vol. 5, covering 1731–40, includes 'Espèce de Hausse-Col, pour obliger les Enfans à porter la tête droite...'). The engravings representing the machines could easily be represented in paint, as Hogarth has represented the machinery in the painting. There does not appear to be a corkscrew, but there are similar devices. (2) M. Gallon, *Machines et inventions approuvées par l'Académie Royale des Sciences*, vols 1–6, Paris 1735; vol. VII, Paris 1777. (3) *Histoire de l'Académie Royale des Sciences avec les Mémoires de Mathématique et Physique*, Paris 1748. *Machines ou inventions approuvées par l'Académie* in 1744 include a mill, an improved fire engine, a coal fire, a machine for cleaning dockyards, a lamp post, etc.

139. Schupbach suggests that this appears to be inspired by the spectacular engraving of the chemical and pharmaceutical laboratory of Ambrose Godfrey Hanckwits, FRS (1660–1741). His laboratory was in Southampton Street, Covent Garden, London. An impression of the engraving is coll. Wellcome Institute Library.

140. Cowley 1983, p. 89, asserts (without references) that 'The rare and costly substance, mummy, was used to encourage longevity and restore life.'

141. Schupbach notes that a narwhal horn was a feature of many cabinets of curiosities. There is one in the Wellcome Institute Library.

142. Cowley 1983, p. 89, identifies them as tea bricks.

143. Stuffed crocodiles suspended in the air seem to have been a feature of many such scenes. Hogarth may have borrowed several ideas (the Viscount's pose with upraised cane, as well as the crocodile) from Vandergucht's illustration to Gay's *Fables*, 1727, no. XVI, an illustration which appears also to have influenced 'A second view of practical chemistry' published by 'Chemicus' in *The Universal Magazine*, 1748 (repr. Cowley 1983, p. 90, fig. 23a).

144. See (1) Arthur MacGregor, 'The Cabinet of Curiosities in Seventeenth Century Britain'; and (2) William Schupbach, 'Some Cabinets of Curiosities in European Academic Institutions', both in ed. O. Impey and A. MacGregor, *The Origins of Museums*, Oxford 1985, pp. 147–85; pp. 169–178.

145. For Dr Richard Mead (1673–1753), see *DNB*. His portrait by Allan Ramsay, dated 1747, is coll. Thomas Coram Foundation for Children, repr. in colour in Einberg 1987, p. 176. Dr Mead's sale was conducted by Mr Langford, Covent Garden, 11–15 March 1755.

146. The two paintings painted for him by Antoine Watteau are noted in Egerton 1997, p. 62, n. 41.

147. William Schupbach, Wellcome Institute, in correspondence.

148. Is Hogarth's scene the source of the phrase 'a skeleton in the cupboard'? The *OED* gives the earliest usage of the phrase (as meaning 'a source of shame') as by Thackeray, in 1845, but notes that 'it is known to have been current at an earlier date'.

149. It has often been suggested that this face is that of Dr Misaubin. It bears a resemblance to that of a doctor in a near-caricature sketch by Watteau, engraved by Arthur Pond in 1739. The engraving is lettered *Prenez des Pilules, prenez des Pilules* (E. de Goncourt 1875, cited in note 31, p. 36, no. 26), and is thought to portray Dr Misaubin, who was famous for 'pillules' to treat venereal disease.

150. *Pers. and Pol. Satires*, III, ed. Stephens 1877, cat. no. 1987.

151. Henry Fielding, *The Mock Doctor or, The Dumb Lady Cured. A Comedy done from Molière. As it was acted at the Theatre Royal in Drury Lane, 1732.* Reprinted in *Dramatic Works by Henry Fielding Esq.*, II, 1882. Dr John Misaubin, born in France, member of the Royal College of Physicians 1719, is noticed in *DNB*. Schupbach notes that according to Jean Savaré, 'Le docteur Misaubin, de Watteau', *Revue d'Histoire de la Pharmacie*, 1966–7, 18, pp. 596–607, similar pills invented by Misaubin's brother-in-law were advertised during April 1743 as available from his son, at Misaubin's widow's house, 96 St Martin's Lane. Perhaps the face on the wig-block represents Misaubin's continuing influence in that sense.

152. Hogarth's pen and ink sketch of Dr Misaubin and Dr Ward (their names inscribed below by a later hand) is coll. Her Majesty The Queen; see Oppé 1948, p. 31, cat. no. 19, plate 15. The gouache by Louis Goupy is coll. Wellcome Institute.

153. See note 95, which includes a reference on this point to Bristow 1996.

154. This is also how Jonathan Swift uses it (though he anglicises *toilette* to 'toilet') in *Cadenus and Vanessa*, in a long passage about female diversions: '...Every trifle that Employs/ The out or inside of their heads/ Between their toilets and their beds.' See Rogers 1983 (cited in note 78), pp. 131, 139.

155. Fourteen pieces from a toilet set of 28 pieces made in 1724 by Paul de Lamerie (1688–1751) or in his establishment, coll. Ashmolean Museum, are illustrated in *Paul de Lamerie*, exh. cat., Goldsmith's Hall, London 1990, p. 57, below a detail of the Countess's dressing-table from NG 116.

156. Rogers 1983 (cited in note 78), pp. 448, ll. 1–2; p. 449, ll. 33–7. See p. 827 n. This devastating poem was one of the most popular in Swift's lifetime; seemingly first printed in 1732, it went through a whole range of editions in England and Ireland.

157. Gautier 1868, p. 165: 'une certaine fraîcheur plébéienne'.

158. Hazlitt 1824, edn 1843, p. 147.

159. As Davies 1959, p. 13, n. 58, and others note, Hogarth had depicted a similar teething-coral (on a blue ribbon) in *Lord Grey and Lady Mary West as Children*, 1740; repr. Bindman 1994, p. 141, fig. 111, in colour.

160. One example from many such paintings is Nicolas Regnier (or Renieri), *Vanité*, coll. Musée des Beaux-Arts, Lyon; repr. *Les Vanités dans la peinture au XVIIe siècle*, exh. cat., Musée des Beaux-Arts, Caen 1990, F.39, repr. p. 171.

161. See Highfill et al. 1984: (1) for Farinelli (the stage name of Carlo Broschi), V, pp. 145–52; (2) for Giovanni Carestini, 1705–60, V, pp. 57–9; (3) for Senesino (stage name of Francesco Bernardi), XIII, pp. 249–55.

162. For the engraving of Francesco Bernardi, called Il Senesino, by Alexander van Aken after Thomas Hudson, see *Thomas Hudson 1701–1779*, exh. cat., Iveagh Bequest, Kenwood House, 1979, cat. no. 5, repr. following catalogue entries (n.p.); for the engraving by E. Kirkall after Joseph Goupy (BM impression), see O'Donoghue 1908, vol. I, p. 177.

163. Henry Fielding, *Joseph Andrews*, London 1903 edn, p. 15.

164. Dabydeen 1987 suggests (p. 76) that the black manservant 'is a symbol of the type of hottentot fertility that is lacking in the white Opera singer. His coarse, natural, paw-like fingers are deliberately depicted in contrast to the bejewelled, effeminate fingers of [?] Senesino. His type of sexuality plays an intricate part in the network of sexual innuendoes in the picture.'

165. A 'drum' was an evening party; a 'drum major' a large evening party; a 'rout' was a particularly large (and probably late) evening party.

166. *The Modern Husband, A Comedy, as it was acted at the Theatre Royal in Drury Lane, 1731*, reprinted in *Dramatic Works by Henry Fielding Esq.*, London 1882, II; the quotation is from scene ii, p. 78.

167. Correggio's *Jupiter and Io* (Vienna, Kunsthistorisches Museum) illustrates Ovid's lines 'the god hid the wide land in a thick, dark cloud, caught the fleeing maid and ravished her' (*Metamorphoses*, I, lines 599–600; trans. F.J. Miller, Harvard edn, 1966) by showing Jupiter shrouding himself in thick grey cloud, rendered by Hogarth as bear-like brown. Hogarth probably knew the Correggio through E. Desrochers's engraving of 1705, and the Caravaggesque *Lot and his Daughters* through an engraving by the London-based L. du Guernier (1617–1716).

168. Claude-Prosper Jolyot de Crébillon (1707–77). *The Sopha. A Moral Tale* was listed in *The Gentleman's Magazine*, May 1842, p. 280: *Register of Books for May 1742*, no. 40, price three shillings.

169. Coll. Leeds City Art Galleries, Temple Newsam; see Helena Davis, 'The Fair Nun Unmasked', *Leeds Art Calendar*, no. 85, Leeds 1979, pp. 5–10.

170. For the general subject of masquerades, see Edward Croft-Murray and Hugh Phillips, 'The Whole Humours of a Masquerade', *Country Life*, 2 September 1949, pp. 672–5. For masquerade dress, see Aileen Ribeiro, *The Dress worn at Masquerades in England, 1730 to 1790, and its Relation to Fancy Dress in Portraiture*, PhD dissertation, New York and London 1984. See also Terry Castle, *Masquerades and Civilization*, Stanford 1986.

171. As the century progressed, masquerades were also held in Vauxhall Gardens, Ranelagh Gardens, Carlisle House in Soho Square, and the Pantheon in Oxford Street (opened in 1772).

172. For Giuseppe Grisoni (1699–1769), see Edward Croft-Murray, *Decorative Painting in England 1537–1837*, London 1970, pp. 214–15. A different *Masquerade on the Stage of the King's Theatre in the Haymarket*, 'perhaps by Giuseppe Grisoni', is repr. Croft-Murray and Phillips 1949 (cited in note 170), p. 673, then coll. Sir Osbert Sitwell. A smaller *Masquerade on the Stage of the Haymarket Theatre*, 1724, attributed to Grisoni, is coll. V&A, P.22-1948.

173. Most of this information is from a report in Mist's *Weekly Journal* for 15 February

1718, quoted by Croft-Murray and Phillips 1949.

174. See note 23.

175. Fully described and discussed by Paulson 1989, pp. 70–1, cat. no. 108, repr. 277.

176. See Bryant Lillywhite, *London Coffee Houses*, London 1963, pp. 95–7.

177. Benjamin Hoadly, *The Suspicious Husband*, first performed at Covent Garden 12 February 1747, with David Garrick as Ranger. For the text see ed. Mrs Inchbald, *The British Theatre*, vol. XIX, London 1824; the quotation is from Act II, Scene iv, p. 35.

178. For the painting of *Night*, see Laing 1995, pp. 58–9 (19a), repr. in colour p. 60. For the engravings of *The Four Times of the Day*, see Paulson 1989, pp. 103–8.

179. Discarded stays figure prominently in Scene 3 ('The Tavern Scene', sometimes called 'The Orgy') of *A Rake's Progress*; the painting (1733) and the engraving (1735) are repr. in exh. cat. Sir John Soane's Museum 1997 (cited in note 116), p. 7, plates 5 and 6. They also appear on a chair in *Before* and *After* (a pair; paintings coll. J. Paul Getty Museum, Malibu; repr. Paulson 1971, plates 87–8; for the engravings of 1736 see Paulson 1989, cat. nos 141–2, repr.). Hogarth included seven 'profiles' of stays in the ornamental border of Plate 1 of *The Analysis of Beauty* (*c*.1753); see Paulson 1989, cat. no. 195, repr.

180. See D.C. Browning, *Dictionary of Quotations and Proverbs*, London 1951, p. 479, no. 8106 as '16th cent.'

181. The broken-off right hand of the figure of Actaeon in Scene 4, among the junk the Countess purchased in an auction sale, may presage this inability to defend himself.

182. For a double-page colour detail of the Countess's face in close-up, see Webster 1978, pp. 116–17.

183. See Bomford and Roy 1982, pp. 45–67.

184. See ibid., pp. 56–7 and fig. 16, an X-ray mosaic of the scene.

185. The latter scene, as staged in David Lingelbach's popular comedy *Pretended Virtue Exposed* (1687), was depicted in 1734 and again in 1739 by Hogarth's Dutch contemporary Cornelis Troost (1696–1750), who was closely involved with the theatre of his day. See *Cornelis Troost and the Theatre of his Time*, exh. cat., Mauritshuis, The Hague 1993 (cat. nos. 8 and 9, both repr.).

186. Hogarth's first version of *The Beggar's Opera* is coll. Tate Gallery.

187. Hazlitt 1824, edn 1843, p. 147.

188. Paulson 1971, p. 486. Paulson continues: 'Hogarth must have taken the count's pose straight from a painting, probably Flemish, seen in France on his 1743 tour, not even adjusting for the absence of the man supporting Christ's body under the arms.' See also Paulson 1989, p. 122: source still untraced, but 'it does appear to be a Flemish, and not an Italian, paradigm'. The nearest possible source for Paulson's hypothesis which this compiler has been able to find is Federico Barocci, *The Deposition*, *c*.1566–9, the Duomo, Perugia; repr. Harold Olsen, *Federico Barocci*, Copenhagen 1962, plate 27, engr. 1606. Hogarth may have had the idea of a deposition in his mind; but the exaggerated awkwardness of the Earl's pose would seem to make any direct borrowing from a painting unlikely.

189. See Cowley 1983, p. 126.

190. See *Thomas Hudson*, exh. cat., 1979 (cited in note 162), e.g. *Mary Carew*, engraving, ? 1741 (cat. no. 10, repr.). Sir Godfrey Kneller (1646–1723) painted *Lady Midleton as a Shepherdess*, see Millar 1963, cat. no. 357, plate 158.

191. Samuel McPherson was the most active of a group of soldiers of a Highland Regiment who, being stationed at Highgate, refused to obey orders to march northwards, fearing that they would be compelled to take action against their fellow-countrymen. With three others, he was sentenced to death for desertion, and shot at the Tower of London on 18 July 1743. The engraving published in 1743 is by George Bickham junior; in it, the large dirk hanging vertically from McPherson's waistband may perhaps have suggested to Hogarth the object dangling from the hand of the painted lady above. The subject was later engraved by George Cruikshank. The compiler is indebted to Robin Nicholson, Curator, Collection of the Drambuie Liqueur Company, for help over the Bickham engraving.

192. Watteau's painting is lost. Cochin's engraving after it is repr. in Levey 1993 (cited in note 29), p. 30, fig. 25.

193. See Paulson 1989, pp. 129–39, cat. nos. 168–79, repr. pp. 350–62; Plate 11, *The Idle 'Prentice Executed at Tyburn*, is repr. p. 361.

194. Fielding parodied *Pamela* in *Shamela*, fully titled *An Apology for the Life of Mrs Shamela Andrews*, published anonymously in 1741.

195. *Gnomologia* 1732 (cited in note 72), no. 2952.

Fig. 20 Paul Sandby (1731–1809), *Wife of Mr Lane who purchased first the pictures by Hogarth of Marriage Alamode*, *c*.1760. Red and black chalk on paper, 22.5 × 17.5 cm. Windsor, Royal Collection.

NG 1162

The Shrimp Girl

*c.*1740–5

Oil on canvas, 63.5 × 52.5 cm (25 × 20¾ in.)

Provenance

Remained in Hogarth's studio, and with his widow until her death in 1789; Mrs Hogarth's sale by Mr Greenwood at the Golden Head, Leicester Square, 24 April 1790 (51, as 'The shrimp girl, a sketch'), bt Mathew Mitchell, and in his sale after his death, Christie's 8 March 1819 (31, 'An Oyster Woman, a Sketch'), bt Seguier £15 4s. 6d.; George Watson Taylor, Erlestoke Park, Wiltshire, where sold by George Robins, 14th day, 24 July 1832 (47, 42 guineas); Sir William Miles, Leigh Court, near Bristol (by 1854), by descent to Sir Philip Miles, sold Christie's 28 June 1884 (31, 250 guineas), bt Agnew's for the National Gallery (Wheeler Fund).

Exhibited

London, South Kensington Museum, 1862 (40); RA Winter 1875 (31); Paris, Louvre, 1938 (68); Art Institute of Chicago and Toronto, Art Gallery, *Masterpieces of English Painting*, 1946–7 (4); Manchester, City Art Gallery, *William Hogarth*, 1954 (39); Tate Gallery 1971–2 (129); Munich, Haus der Kunst, *Zwei Jahrhunderte englische Malerei: Britische Kunste und Europa 1680 bis 1880*, 1988 (x); Leningrad and Moscow 1988 (no cat.); Tate Gallery, *Hogarth the Painter*, 1997 (8).

At the Tate Gallery 1960–1; 1963–4.

Literature

Nichols 1781, p. 59; Nichols and Steevens 1817, III, p. 270; R.B. Beckett, *Hogarth*, London 1949, p. 72; Davies 1959, p. 68; Frederick Antal, *Hogarth and his Place in European Art*, London 1962, pp. 116–17; Robert Raines, *Marcellus Laroon*, London 1967, p. 14; Paulson 1971, I, p. 203; II, p. 246; Jack Lindsay, *Hogarth: His Art and his World*, London 1977, pp. 134–5; Webster 1978, pp. 119, 122.

Engraved

in stipple, and in reverse, by Bartolozzi, (1) first state, before title, *Engravd from an Original Sketch in Oil in the possession of Mrs Hogarth, published Dec.24, 1781*, by R. Livesay; (2) lettered 'Shrimps!', published 25 March 1782 by Jane Hogarth and R[ichar]d Livesay, Leicester Fields: repr. John Ireland and John Nichols, *Hogarth's Works*, 3rd series, London n.d., following p. 268.

Technical Notes

Cleaned and relined in 1966. In very good condition, though thinly painted, with ground visible in many places. The paint has become slightly lighter in a strip about 5 cm wide at both sides, roughly corresponding to the width of the stretcher bars.

The picture is painted on a white ground (several layers as in the *Marriage A-la-Mode* series), composed of lead white mixed with chalk. The ground is now rather grey through discoloration. This priming layer is left unpainted in parts of the composition, for example in the light-coloured patch beneath the girl's 'sou'wester', to the left side of her face.

The sou'wester, presumably made of oilskin, is intended to be a dark bluish grey since the paint contains traces of Prussian blue (mixed with black pigment, white and a little yellow ochre).

The earliest record of the picture appears to be in 1781, when John Nichols listed 'a most spirited sketch in oil of a young fishwoman' among works which remained in Mrs Hogarth's possession nearly two decades after Hogarth's death.[1] The title 'Shrimps!' lettered on Bartolozzi's engraving of the subject, published in 1782, must have been intended to suggest the girl's street cry; but it is Bartolozzi's title rather than Hogarth's. The title *The Shrimp Girl* first appears in Christie's 1790 sale catalogue of works remaining in Hogarth's studio after Mrs Hogarth's death; and apart from Mathew Mitchell's sale in 1819 in which the picture was called 'An Oyster Woman', it has been used ever since.

Hogarth probably knew Marcellus Lauron's *Cryes of the City of London, Drawne after the Life*, published in various editions between 1688 and 1733.[2] Raines (1967) suggests that *The Shrimp Girl* has something of the feeling of Lauron's *Six pence a pound fair Cherryes*; the subject has even stronger affinities with *Buy my Dish of Great Eeles* (fig. 1).[3] But it is unlikely that Hogarth needed inspiration from Lauron (or any other artist[4]) to paint a 'fishwoman' whom he could have observed at first hand as she cried her wares in the London streets.

For at least a century before and a century after Hogarth painted *The Shrimp Girl*, most of the itinerant sellers of shell-fish in London were women, usually the daughters or wives of fishmongers in the markets. Donald Lupton describes them in 1632[5] as 'crying, wandering and travelling creatures [who] carry their shops on their heads, and their store is ordinarily *Billingsgate*... They set up every morning their trade afresh. They are easily set up and furnished, get some-thing and spend it jovially and merrily. Five shillings, a basket and a good cry, is a large stock for one of them...' By the 1850s, Henry Mayhew observed that most fishmongers worked from stalls or pitches in the streets; but 'the females in the shrimp line' still went through the streets, especially in wet weather, 'when people prefer buying at their doors'; their cry, he noted, was 'A penny half-pint, fine fresh s'rimps'.[6] Hogarth sketches in a half-pint measure in the basket balanced on his 'Shrimp Girl's' head; a few darker shells suggest that she sells mussels (? and cockles) as well as shrimps. She wears what Mayhew was later to describe as the shrimp-seller's customary garb – 'a hybrid sort of cloak, half a man's and half a woman's garment'[7] – somewhat greasy, and perhaps made of oilskin. But nothing can dim her vitality. Showing the picture to visitors after Hogarth's death, with a wealth of contempt for some critics' attempts

Figs. 1 and 2 Marcellus Lauron (*c.*1648/9–1701/2), *Buy my Dish of Great Eeles* and *Crab Crab any Crab*. Engravings, published in his *Cryes of the City of London*, *c.*1680.

to demote him to a mere caricaturist, Mrs Hogarth reputedly liked to remark: 'They say he could not paint flesh and blood. There's flesh and blood for you: – them!'[8]

There can be no doubt that this sketch is from life; and although Hogarth may never have known the girl's name, Paulson is surely right in calling this 'a portrait'.[9] Compared with the 'fancy pictures' of pretty street vendors which became popular some fifty years later, such as John Hoppner's *Girl with Sallad*, exhibited at the Royal Academy in 1782 (fig. 3, for which the sitter was in fact the artist's wife Phoebe),[10] or with the still more prettified girls crying *Two bunches a penny primroses* or *Sweet China Oranges* in Francis Wheatley's *Itinerant Trades of London* (engraved 1793–5, and frequently copied),[11] Hogarth's image is direct and wholly unpatronising. This painter recognises that the 'Shrimp Girl' is an individual in her own right, and does not presume to tidy her up. It is difficult to agree with Antal that this is 'not a work on its own account' but was 'intended for a figure in one of Hogarth's finished compositions',[12] and equally difficult to agree with Webster that Hogarth 'must have intended to work it up to a much smoother finish'.[13]

Beckett (1949) considered *The Shrimp Girl* to be 'not datable, but fairly late';[14] since no pointers to a precise date have emerged, 'circa 1740–5', as suggested by Webster (1978), remains the likeliest approximation to its date. No comparable single-figure oil sketches by Hogarth are known. Oil sketches of groups such as *The Dance*, of about 1745 (one of three surviving sketches for an unfinished series to have been called 'The Happy Marriage'),[15] show a similar brilliance of rapid handling, but *The Shrimp Girl* appears to be unique in being painted from life, spontaneously, and for its own sake.

The Shrimp Girl remained in Hogarth's studio during the remaining twenty years or so of his life. He did not add a single brushstroke to her image. He was no doubt well aware that his *Shrimp Girl* triumphantly illustrated his own dictum that 'if a thing is good, the action and the passion may be more truly and distinctly conveyed by a coarse bold stroke than the most delicate finishing'.

In the early 1850s Dr Waagen, Director of the Berlin Gallery, went to see Sir William Miles's collection at Leigh Court, near Bristol. He went chiefly to see the revered Altieri Claudes in the Saloon; he was delighted to come across *The Shrimp Girl*, 'animatedly conceived and sketched with the utmost freedom', hanging less obtrusively in the Little Dining-Room.[16]

Fig. 3 John Hoppner, *Girl with Sallad*, exhibited 1782. Oil on canvas, 88.9 × 68.6 cm. Waterville, Maine, Colby College Art Museum.

NOTES

1. Nichols 1781, p. 59.

2. See Raines 1967, pp. 14–39; and see also Sean Shesgreen, *The Criers and Hawkers of London: Engravings and Drawings by Marcellus Laroon*, Aldershot 1990, p. 92.

3. See Raines 1967: *Six pence a pound fair Cherryes* is no. 46, repr. p. 32, *Buy my Dish of Great Eeles* is no. 9, repr. p. 21, and *Crab Crab any Crab* is no. 21, repr. p. 24.

4. Antal 1962, p. 116, suggested a parallel between Hogarth's *Shrimp Girl* and Frans Hals's *Fisher Girl* (Cincinnati Art Museum); see also Paulson 1975, p. 69.

5. Donald Lupton [d.1676], *London and the Countrey Carbonadoed and quartred into severall characters*, London 1632, no. 23, 'Fish-women'; ed. Thomas Park, reprinted in *Harleian Miscellany*, London 1812, vol. IX, p. 310.

6. *London Labour and the London Poor* [1851], 1864 edn, vol. I, p. 76. Mayhew adds 'I heard them called nothing but "s'rimps" by the street-dealers.'

7. Ibid.

8. Possibly apocryphal; much quoted, with some variations, e.g. by Lindsay 1977, p. 134; Webster 1978, p. 119. Paulson 1971, I, p. 203, alone gives a source, an undated clipping in the Forster Collection (V&A, F.10 E.3 No. 1874, undated).

9. Paulson 1971, II, p. 246.

10. Colby College Art Museum, Waterville, Maine (no. 62-p31); engraved by William Ward. See John H. Wilson, 'The Life and Art of John Hoppner RA', unpublished PhD thesis, Courtauld Institute, London 1972, I, pp. 124–6.

11. See Mary Webster, *Francis Wheatley*, London 1970, pp. 173 ff.

12. Antal 1962, p. 116–17: 'It is not, as is customarily concluded, a work on its own account, but in terms of the first half of the 18th century was intended for a figure in one of Hogarth's finished compositions – either for the milkmaid in his engraving *The Enraged Musician* (1741) or the fisherwoman in the engraving *Beer Street* (1751).'

13. Webster 1978, p. 122.

14. Beckett 1949, p. 72.

15. Tate Gallery, London; see [Elizabeth Einberg], Einberg and Egerton 1988, pp. 118–22, plates 105–6.

16. Waagen 1854, III, p. 186.

Thomas Jones

1742–1803

Born 26 September 1742 at Trefonnen manor house, Radnorshire, Wales, second son of Thomas Jones, landowner. Educated at a nearby grammar school; went up to Oxford (Jesus College) but left without taking a degree; attended Shipley's art school 1761, and St Martin's Lane Academy 1762. Accepted by Richard Wilson as a pupil for two years 1763–5. Exhibited regularly at the Society of Artists from 1765, showing classical landscapes in Wilson's manner (*A Land-storm, with the Story of Dido and Æneas*, exh. 1769, purchased for Catherine the Great, is now in the Hermitage Museum, St Petersburg), views in Wales and some paired subjects (e.g. 'A sunset'; 'An evening'), now untraced. Worked in watercolour as well as oil. From about 1770, began to paint oil studies from nature, with an instinctive and entirely unconventional directness of approach, working in this way occasionally, for his own pleasure, with no thought of exhibiting or selling such studies.

Spent seven years in Italy 1776–83, chiefly in Rome and Naples. To support himself, painted views and classical landscapes in Wilson's manner, sometimes on a large scale; acquired some patrons, notably the Earl-Bishop of Derry, but failed to please conventional Grand Tourists. In Naples during 1782–3, renewed his practice of making oil studies direct from nature. His small oil studies of buildings in Naples observed from rooftops or windows, rediscovered in 1956, are now acknowledged to be his most original works.

The deaths of his father and elder brother recalled him to England, and the unexpected role of a man of property. Lived for a few years in London; exhibited nine works at RA 1784–9; but by 1789 had retired to his 'paternal estate', Pencerrig, Radnorshire, painting and sketching occasionally, and compiling (from journals kept at the time, and from recollection) the highly entertaining *Memoirs* which are the chief source of information about his work, his friendships and his personality.

References

Ed. A.P. Oppé, 'Memoirs of Thomas Jones, Penkerrig, Radnorshire, 1803', *Walpole Society 1946–1948*, vol. XXXII, London 1951; Ralph Edwards, *Thomas Jones*, Marble Hill House, Twickenham, and National Museum of Wales, Cardiff, exh. cat. 1970. For Jones's years in Italy, see Ingamells 1997, pp. 561–4.

NG 6544

A Wall in Naples

? 1782

Oil on paper laid on canvas, 11.4 × 16 cm (4½ × 6 5/16 in.)

Provenance

After the artist's death, passed to his younger daughter Elizabeth Francesca who, having married Captain John Dale, died in 1806 leaving no surviving children; passed to Captain Dale,[1] then by descent through Rose Adams (his daughter by his second marriage) to his great-grandson Dr Adams, by whose widow[2] sold Christie's 28 July 1955 (as 'An Italian house', one of three in lot 6, £14), bt Agnew's; purchased from Agnew's by Lady Ashton (Madge Garland, Royal College of Art, Department of Fashion and Design) December 1955; sold by her, Christie's 23 March 1979 (88, £5500), bt Appleby Brothers for Mrs Jane Evan-Thomas, widow of Commander Charles Evan-Thomas DSO, RN, of Pencerrig;[3] purchased from Mrs Evan-Thomas through Agnew's by the National Gallery 1993.

Exhibited

London, Marble Hill House, and Cardiff, National Museum of Wales, *Thomas Jones*, 1970 (65, as 'Window in Naples'); New York, Museum of Modern Art (touring to Joslyn Art Museum, Omaha, Nebraska, Frederick S. Wight Art Gallery, University of California, Los Angeles, and Art Institute of Chicago), *Before Photography: Painting and the Invention of Photography*, 1981–2 (27, repr. on cover of catalogue); Manchester, Whitworth Art Gallery, *Travels in Italy 1776–1783, based on the Memoirs of Thomas Jones*, 1988 (105); Washington, National Gallery of Art (touring to Brooklyn Museum, New York, and St Louis Art Museum), *In the Light of Italy: Corot and Early Open-Air Painting*, 1996–7 (10, repr. with colour detail p. 123).

Literature

J.A. Gere, 'An Oil-Sketch by Thomas Jones', *British Museum Quarterly*, XXI, no. 4, 1959, pp. 93–4; J.A. Gere, 'Thomas Jones: An Eighteenth-Century Conundrum', *Apollo*, XCI, 1970, p. 470, fig. 4; Lawrence Gowing, *The Originality of Thomas Jones*, London 1985, pp. 47, 63; Francis Hawcroft, *Travels in Italy 1776–1783, based on the Memoirs of Thomas Jones*, exh. cat., Whitworth Art Gallery, Manchester 1988, particularly pp. 89–92; Peter Galassi, *Corot in Italy: Open-Air Painting and the Classical-Landscape Tradition*, New Haven and London 1991, p. 34, plate 35.

Technical Notes

Cleaned and restored on acquisition. The support is buff-coloured paper which has been laid down onto hardboard.

Technical Notes

Cleaned in 1960. In good condition apart from a tear in the distant landscape. The impasto has been crushed by lining. The X-radiograph, reproduced here as fig. 1, shows some change in the outline of the hair. There are also alterations in the background above and to both sides of the head.

Painted at the age of twenty. Oliver Millar 1969 describes this as 'one of the most brilliant of all royal portraits, the only portrait of the Queen worthy to hang in company with Gainsborough's'. Yet it failed to please either the Queen or the King, and remained on Lawrence's hands.

Queen Charlotte (1744–1818), born and brought up in the small North German duchy of Mecklenburg-Strelitz, had been selected as the most suitable bride for the newly succeeded George III by his mother's agent, who toured 'various little Protestant courts' before awarding 'the golden apple' to the Princess Charlotte Sophia of Mecklenburg-Strelitz. She arrived in England the day before her marriage to George III (8 September 1761) and was jointly crowned with him on 22 September 1761. Horace Walpole observed that she was 'sensible and quick' in understanding, had 'great good nature' and 'much grace in her manner'; but neither he nor anyone else pretended that she had good looks. 'She is not tall, nor a beauty; pale, and very thin, but looks sensible and is genteel. Her hair is darkish and fine, her forehead low, her nose very well, except the nostrils spreading too wide; her mouth has the same fault, but her teeth are good...'[3] Four years later, the Earl of Chesterfield summed her up as 'a good woman, a good wife, a tender mother, and an unmeddling Queen'.[4] She had a passion for music,[5] and an interest in botany. Her devotion to the King was absolute, despite many trials; and she bore him fifteen children, all but two surviving infancy.

By 1789 Queen Charlotte had already sat to Ramsay, Zoffany, Cotes, Angelica Kauffmann, West, Reynolds and Gainsborough.[6] Their portraits, Lawrence's and later portraits of the Queen are the subject of Michael Levey's illuminating essay *A Royal Subject*, 1977.

An account of the circumstances in which Lawrence's portrait was painted, compiled some forty years later, is given in the *Journals* of Charlotte Papendiek. Mrs Papendiek in 1789 was the young wife of one of the Queen's German gentleman-pages; she herself had a small place in the Queen's household, in time becoming Assistant Keeper of the Wardrobe.[7] She was only a few years older than Lawrence, and was evidently sympathetic to him.

Lawrence painted Queen Charlotte in Windsor Castle. The portrait was not positively commissioned. It seems that the initiative in suggesting that Lawrence should paint the Queen, and in securing permission for him to visit Windsor for this purpose, was taken by the American-born Lady Cremorne, 'a universal encourager of merit',[8] and then one of the Queen's ladies-in-waiting. She was one of Lawrence's first sitters; his stately portrait of Lady Cremorne[9] (his first full-length) had been exhibited in the spring of 1789 at the Royal Academy, where the Queen could have seen it. Some time in September 1789, Lawrence received a letter from Mr Compton, one of the Queen's pages, desiring him to 'come down to Windsor' on 27 September and to 'bring your painting apparatus with you'; the Queen would sit to him the following Monday. This letter (quoted in full below[10]), though undoubtedly encouraging, was not a formal commission; yet, as Levey notes, Lawrence had for some months believed that he would be given an opportunity to paint her,[11] and now seized this chance.

Lawrence arrived at Windsor, as instructed, on 27 September. There was no certainty that the Queen would sit to him. When Lady Cremorne brought Lawrence before the Queen the next day, she was reluctant to sit, saying (presumably to Lady Cremorne rather than to the unknown young man) 'that she had not recovered sufficiently from all the trouble and anxiety she had gone through to give so young an artist a fair chance, more particularly as he saw her for the first time'.[12] That 'trouble and anxiety' refers of course to George III's protracted mental illness over the last year; deep concern for him, and anxiety also over his crown and her own position combined to age her prematurely. A diary entry for 5 November 1788 by Fanny Burney, then Assistant Keeper of the Queen's Wardrobe, paints a sad picture which should contribute to our understanding of Lawrence's image of her, painted ten months later: '...pale, ghastly pale she looked; she was seated to be undressed, and attended by Lady Elizabeth Waldegrave and Miss Goldsworth; her whole frame was disordered, yet she was still and quiet ... I gave her some camphor julep, which had been ordered her by Sir George Baker. "How cold I am" she said, and put her hand on mine; marble it felt! and went to my heart's core!'[13] Though the King's recovery was publicly celebrated in a Thanksgiving Service in St Paul's Cathedral on St George's Day 1789, there could be no certainty that it was permanent. Mrs Papendiek observed after this that the Queen was 'much changed; her hair quite grey, and her spirits sadly depressed'.[14] Queen Charlotte may also, as Levey suggests, have been perturbed by political events in France.[15] She was in no mood to sit for yet another portrait.

When she eventually agreed to sit to Lawrence, she did so with ill grace, her initial concern for 'so young an artist' rapidly evaporating. The sitting on 28 September is the only documented sitting, and was probably the only one she gave. It proceeded under difficulties. The Queen chose to sit in a dove-coloured dress which, Mrs Papendiek noted, 'with her sallowish complexion was most unbecoming'. Lawrence contrived to paint it as pale lavender; he gave a minutely sparkling edge to the gossamer-like apron and converted the lace falling below the sleeves into exquisite cascades. The Queen had arrived to sit wearing a bonnet; since Lawrence objected to the bonnet and her proposed alternatives, a cap or a hat, she decided to sit to him bare-headed.[16] In this she knew exactly what she was doing. She was perfectly aware that she was a plain woman; she also knew that (as Mrs Papendiek records) her hair was 'really beautiful'. Her favourite hairdresser Sonardi had evolved a style of dressing her hair in a manner

Fig. 1 *Queen Charlotte*, X-radiograph detail

Fig. 2 *Queen Charlotte*, detail

which was kind to her face; and she sat to Lawrence with her hair thus dressed, piled high over a false hair-piece which Mrs Papendiek calls a 'toupet' (and the English a rat),[17] adorned with tiny black bows. This, as she knew well (and Levey's illustrations of more frumpish portraits of her in bonnets and caps prove her right), was becoming to her; and although Lawrence's portrait of her bare-headed reputedly 'disgusted' George III,[18] her 'Sonardi' style as later displayed in Lawrence's studio set something of a fashion, at least among Lawrence's sitters.[19]

As the sitting wore on, the Queen became increasingly dour, her spirits not lifted by the fact that one of her daughters read to her. Lawrence suggested that she should 'converse now and then with the Princesses, to give animation to the countenance'; the Queen considered the suggestion 'rather presuming'.[20] Perhaps someone should have thought of sending for one of the musicians usually in attendance at Windsor; but she may have been too careworn even for the solace of music. Levey demonstrates, with infra-red and X-ray photographs of the head (the latter reproduced here, fig. 1), that Lawrence had to use all his skill to animate the Queen's unyielding features (fig. 2). The interruption of the sitting by Benjamin West, Historical Painter to George III since 1772, did not help matters; Mrs Papendiek sensed that West 'did not care to encourage too many of his own art about the King'.[21] West's suggestion that 'a light scarf' should be thrown over the Queen's shoulders to break the plainness of her gown seems, however, to have been adopted.

Eventually the Queen refused to give Lawrence any further sittings, on the pretext that only Sonardi could dress her hair, that he was away and that it would be 'troublesome' to send for him.[22] Lawrence 'implored' the Queen for one more brief sitting so that he might paint the ornaments she had worn: 'by just putting on the ornaments as her Majesty wished to have them for a few minutes, he could sketch in their outline and finish them afterwards'. These 'ornaments' included several items from the casket of jewels which the King had given her as a wedding present in 1761, and which had assumed a deep symbolic importance to her. Pre-eminent among them were a pair of six-stranded pearl bracelets (each pearl 'as large as a full pea'); each bracelet fastened with a large, diamond-studded asymmetrical clasp, one clasp inset with a miniature portrait of the King by Jeremiah Meyer (in profile, facing left and wearing a crimson coat), the other with his monogram GR outlined in diamonds on strands of his hair. She wears the bracelets (Levey perceives that there is 'an aspect of manacles' about them, 'for all that they are made of diamond and pearl'[23]) in other portraits, sometimes with only the strands of pearls visible, occasionally with one or both clasps showing. Zoffany's *Queen Charlotte* of 1771 shows the miniature on her right bracelet clearly;[24] but only in Lawrence's portrait do the bracelets play such a significant role, as if the Queen were resolutely displaying the King's portrait over her right wrist (fig. 3) and his royal cipher over her left to demonstrate her unwavering loyalty amid his trials. The gold and diamond ring worn on the little finger of

Fig. 3 *Queen Charlotte*, detail

her left hand in Lawrence's portrait is likely to be the ring inset with a smaller version of Jeremiah Meyer's miniature of the King, also his present to her, which the Queen wore on her wedding day.[25] The brooch holding her muslin scarf has not been identified.

Lawrence had not failed during the Queen's sitting to sense the importance she attached to the bracelets. Although his request for one more sitting so that he could paint the ornaments 'as she wished to have them' was refused, the Queen nevertheless made what must, for her, have been the huge concession of allowing Mrs Papendiek to put on the bracelets and the brooch holding the scarf as a 'model' for Lawrence.[26] In the finished picture, and from a close viewpoint , the 'ornaments' display the intricate craftsmanship of the clasps and ring as well as the brilliant sparkle suggested by minute touches of impasto. But looking at the picture as a whole, one can see that the bracelets have more than an ornamental role to play in Lawrence's composition. The tiny black bows in the Queen's piled-up hair lead the eye downwards on a pyramidal course, through the black scarf over the shoulders to the darkly sparkling clasps of the bracelets on the Queen's widely spread wrists, and finally to a pattern of dark lozenges on the carpet. Thus elegance is lent to but not forced upon the Queen's dumpy figure.

All chances of finishing the portrait from life were then over. Lawrence was permitted to remain at Windsor (with board and lodging) until the New Year, 'working up the picture and finishing it off'.[27] There was the background to paint. In Levey's phrase, Lawrence turned the Queen's plain chair 'into a symbolic throne, suggesting a baldacchino by the sweep of heavily tasselled curtain, and associating her with the tradition of royal, pious benefaction by the distant glimpse of "holy Henry's" Eton College chapel amid the autumnal trees'.[28] At some point during his stay at Windsor, he painted a small (23¼ × 17¼ in.) portrait of the youngest of the royal family, the six-year-old Princess Amelia, for which he received fifteen guineas.[29] He also made a chalk study of Mrs Papendiek and her young son.[30] Otherwise he whiled away his time playing whist in the pages' room, and attending the Papendieks' musical evenings.[31]

The Queen's portrait was finished, presumably by the New Year; but it failed to please either the Queen or the King. Lawrence received no payment: Mrs Papendiek states clearly that 'No money was paid'.[32] The King told Lawrence to remove the portrait to London and have it engraved: 'when that was done, the portrait was to be sent to Hanover, and then the King proposed to pay.'[33] The royal decision to despatch the portrait to the King's relatives abroad instead of keeping it for the royal collection at home anticipates, as Lawrence later learnt, that 'the Queen had considered her portrait a failure'.[34] Lawrence's shortage of money saved the portrait from export; since he could not afford to carry out the careless royal injunction to have the portrait engraved, it remained in his studio.

The chagrin Lawrence no doubt felt at Windsor in 1789 was to some extent mitigated by the acclaim given to the portrait when he exhibited it at the Royal Academy the following year. Lawrence sent eleven pictures to the exhibition of 1790 (only the second year in which he had exhibited), including his portraits of the Queen and the Princess Amelia.[35] His eleven exhibits together made his name, reviewers dubbing him 'the future Sir Joshua'.[36] Reynolds himself, realising the difference between his own *Mrs Billington as Cecilia* (no. 181 in the exhibition) and Lawrence's work, is said to have remarked to Lawrence: 'In you, sir, the world will expect to see accomplished all that I have failed to achieve.'[37] The chief sensation in the exhibition was undoubtedly Lawrence's *Portrait of an Actress* (Elizabeth Farren, infinitely seductive in fur-trimmed white satin):[38] 'completely Miss Farren: arch, careless, spirited, elegant and engaging.' But the Queen was not far behind – perhaps fourth, by *The World*'s rating: it considered that 'the best portraits in the Room' are 'Sir Joshua's Lady & Dog, Lawrence's Head of Mr Locke, Miss Farren, and the Queen';[39] the latter portrait, it declared, was 'a performance of which VANDYKE would have been proud'.[40] Several reviewers commented on the 'strong resemblance'[41] or 'most perfect likeness'.[42] The *English Chronicle and Universal Morning Post* declared that 'The QUEEN, by this young artist, is an admirable portrait, and, independent of the strong likeness, has a multitude of beauties. Even the background has a powerful effect. Criticism could scarcely point out a fault in this picture: true, her Majesty's nose, indeed, appears sore from taking snuff; but that is not the fault of the painter.'[43]

The King and Queen paid at least two visits to the exhibition at the Royal Academy. The King suggested to

Reynolds that Lawrence should be elected ARA; but this was interpreted by the academicians as royal interference, and they did not elect Lawrence until the following year.[44] On Reynolds's death in 1792, Lawrence was appointed Principal Painter to the King. He portrayed the King twice,[45] and dutifully made copies of Reynolds's portraits of Their Majesties for official distribution;[46] but the Queen did not sit to him again, nor was there ever any hint that either the King or the Queen wished to recall the portrait of 1789 which they had rejected.

That portrait remained in Lawrence's studio during his lifetime. After his death in 1831, it took its turn (lot 133) at Christie's in his studio sale, which also included (as part of lot 130) a study for the head of the Queen (untraced: perhaps, Garlick suggests, the 'tasteful sketch' of the Queen with a scarf thrown over her shoulders mentioned by Mrs Papendiek).

For Lawrence NG 6370 and NG 129, see pp. 358–69.

NOTES

1. ML (Michael Levey), *The Thames and Hudson Encyclopaedia of British Art*, London 1985, p. 145.

2. Andrew Wilton, *Turner in his Time*, London 1987, p. 136, repr. in colour, fig. 189.

3. Walpole to Horace Mann, 10 September 1761; *Walpole Correspondence*, vol. XX, p. 529.

4. Earl of Chesterfield to his son, 2 July 1765, published in ed. Lord Mahon, *Letters of ... Philip Dormer Stanhope, Earl of Chesterfield*, 1892, vol. IV, p. 426.

5. See Papendiek 1887, *passim*; Levey 1977, p. 5.

6. For details, see *NPG Dictionary*, II, p. 42; this omits the portrait by Angelica Kauffmann, but includes drawings and miniatures. Portraits by Beechey and Stroehling are later than Lawrence's.

7. Mrs Charlotte Louisa Henrietta Papendiek, born in England in 1765, was the daughter of Frederick Albert, who accompanied Queen Charlotte to England as a gentleman-page. In 1783 she married Christopher Papendiek, another German gentleman-page. According to Mrs Delves-Broughton, her granddaughter and editor, Mrs Papendiek began her Journals in 1833, continuing until her death in 1839; thus her account of Lawrence's work on Queen Charlotte's portrait in 1789 must be largely recollection, and may not be wholly reliable. Mrs Papendiek is usually stated to have been Assistant Keeper of the Wardrobe at the time of Lawrence's visit in 1789; but that post was then held by Fanny Burney (Mme d'Arblay). Mrs Papendiek was appointed to the post in 1797 or 1798 (and later to the post of Reader to the Queen). In 1789 she was aged 24.

8. Papendiek 1887, II, p. 132.

9. Exh. RA 1789 (100), coll. Tate Gallery; Garlick 1989, no. 220, p. 174, repr. in colour plate 1.

10. H. Compton to Thomas Lawrence [September 1789]; published in ed. George Somes Layard, *Sir Thomas Lawrence's Letter-Bag*, London 1906, p. 10: 'SIR, – I am commanded by Her Majesty to desire you will come down to Windsor and bring your painting apparatus with you./ Her Majesty wishes you to come down on Sunday next the 27th ins[t]: to be ready for Her to sit to you on Monday morning./ She likewise desires you will bring some of your pictures with you in crayons and in oil. – I am, Sir, your most obedient humble Servant, H. COMPTON/ Friday noon. – Bring some primed cloths with you. When you arrive, enquire for me at the Queen's Lodge./ Mr. LAWRENCE,/ Portrait Painter,/ (No. 41) Jermyn Street, St. James's,/ near St. James's Church.'

11. Levey 1977 notes that he was quoted in *The World* of 17 July 1789 as including the Queen among his portraits 'yet to come'.

12. Papendiek 1887, II, p. 133.

13. Ed. Austin Dobson, *Diary and Letters of Madame D'Arblay*, IV, London 1905, p. 133.

14. Papendiek 1887, p. 16.

15. Levey 1977, p. 15.

16. Papendiek 1887, II, pp. 133–4.

17. Ibid., I, p. 9.

18. Ibid., II, p. 134.

19. Two sitters of *c.*1789 with hair dressed in Queen Charlotte's manner are Martha Carr (Garlick 1989, no. 169, repr. p. 165) and Maria Louisa Lennox (Garlick 1989, no. 483, repr. p. 223).

20. Papendiek 1887, II, p. 134.

21. Ibid., II, p. 134. In I, p. 232, Mrs Papendiek calls West 'the friend of no one who might possibly interfere with his success'.

22. Papendiek 1887, II, p. 142.

23. Levey 1977, p. 5.

24. Repr. Millar 1969, plate 25 (cat. no. 1196). Zoffany shows it even more clearly in his *Queen Charlotte* of *c.*1766 (Holburne Museum, Bath).

25. The pearl bracelet with Jeremiah Meyer's miniature of George III is repr. by Richard Walker, *The Eighteenth and Nineteenth Century Miniatures in the Collection of Her Majesty The Queen*, Cambridge 1992, p. lxxvi, from an old photograph in the Royal Library, Windsor Castle; both bracelets appear to be untraced, and may have been broken up. For the gold and diamond ring with Jeremiah Meyer's miniature portrait of George III, see Walker 1992, p. 127, no. 250, repr.; dispersed from the Royal Collection, it was acquired again in 1909 and given by the Prince and Princess of Wales to Edward VII as a birthday present in 1909.

26. Lawrence's chalk study of Mrs Papendiek, made at this time (Metropolitan Museum of Art, New York), effectively disposes of legends that Lawrence had completed the figure of the Queen from Mrs Papendiek: the wasp-waisted young woman in Lawrence's drawing in no way resembles the Queen.

27. Papendiek 1887, II, p. 142.

28. Levey 1977, p. 16. Glimpses of Eton College chapel recur in Lawrence's portrait of *Arthur Atherley*, 1791–2 (Garlick 1989, no. 50, plate 10) and in *George III*, *c.*1809 (Garlick 1989, no. 324b, repr. p. 193).

29. Millar 1969, no. 881 (for the painting's history), plate 186.

30. Now coll. Metropolitan Museum of Art, New York; exh. NPG 1979–80 (55), repr. p. 89; also repr. Papendiek 1887, II, facing p. 1.

31. Ibid., p. 145.

32. Ibid., p. 142.

33. Ibid.

34. Ibid., p. 181: Lawrence told Mrs Papendiek *c.*1828 that the Duke of Gloucester had told him 'that the Queen had considered her portrait a failure'.

35. His other exhibits in 1790 were portraits of William Lock, of Norbury (19); Princess Amelia (26); General Paterson (103); Mrs Carter (145); The Hon. Thomas and the Hon. John Moreton (151); Miss Farren (171); The Children of Lord George Cavendish (212); Lord Paisley (219); Revd Andrew Lawrence [the artist's brother] (260); Captain John Tasker (268); and Lady Harriet Hamilton (275).

36. *The World*, 16 April 1790 [p. 3].

37. Quoted by Levey, exh. cat., NPG 1979, p. 16.

38. No. 171 in the exhibition. Coll. Metropolitan Museum of Art, New York; Garlick 1989, cat. no. 294, colour plate 5.

39. *The World*, 28 April 1790 [p. 3].

40. *The World*, 29 April 1790 [p. 3].

41. *St James's Chronicle*, 1 May 1790.

42. *London Chronicle*, 27–29 April 1790.

43. 1 May 1790 [p. 4].

44. See Whitley 1928, II, pp. 131–2.

45. Garlick 1989, nos. 324 a and b, repr.

46. Millar 1969, p. 59.

Sir Joshua Reynolds PRA

1723–1792

Born 16 July 1723 in Plympton, near Plymouth, Devon, seventh child of the Revd Samuel Reynolds, master of the Free Grammar School at Plympton, where he was educated. Apprenticed in 1740 to Thomas Hudson, portraitist in London; left Hudson in 1743, and began portrait-painting, at first in Plymouth, then in London. In 1749, seized the chance to sail with Commodore Keppel to Algiers, then spent two years in Italy, chiefly in Rome, 1750–2, studying, sketching, copying, collecting prints and drawings and above all accumulating ideas for portraiture.

By 1753, established his portrait-painting practice in London, first in St Martin's Lane, then in Great Newport Street. He was from the first successful, his portraits much in demand; many of them engraved. He seemed to have an inexhaustible variety of ideas not only for poses but for classical allusions, while at the same time understanding the social milieu in which his sitters moved: *Lady Cockburn* (NG 2077, pp. 210–17) exemplifies this. Employed studio assistants (e.g. James Northcote, pupil and assistant 1771–5). Principal Painter to the King 1784–92.

Founder-member and first President of the Royal Academy from 1768 (knighted 1769) until his death. Between 1769 and 1790, delivered a series of fifteen *Discourses* to students and members of the Royal Academy, at first annually (on the occasion of prize-giving), then every other year. While constantly reiterating that 'There is no easy method of becoming a good Painter' ('Labour is the only price of solid fame'), Reynolds's *Discourses*, first published in 1779, often reprinted, helped to endow the new Academy with a sense of purpose and dignity, while also revealing much about Reynolds's own methods of composing a picture. Exhibited SA 1760–8; RA 1769–90.

Did not marry but was gregarious, and with Dr Johnson founded 'The Club' (which continues). Eyesight failing from mid-1789; nearly blind by the end of 1791. Died 23 February 1792.

References

Ed. Robert R. Wark, *Sir Joshua Reynolds: Discourses on Art*, New Haven and London, 1975; E.K. Waterhouse, *Reynolds*, London 1941; ed. Nicholas Penny, *Reynolds*, exh. cat. Royal Academy 1986.

NG 1259

Anne, 2nd Countess of Albemarle

completed 1760

Oil on canvas, 126.5 × 101 cm (49¾ × 39¾ in.)

Provenance

Presumably commissioned by the sitter's eldest son, 3rd Earl of Albemarle (d. 1772), whose executor paid for it in December 1773; by descent to the 7th Earl of Albemarle, by whom sold to Agnew's May 1888; two months later, purchased from Agnew's out of the Lewis Fund by the National Gallery.

Exhibited

RA Winter 1873 (77); London, Grosvenor Gallery, *Sir Joshua Reynolds*, 1883–4 (67); Moscow and Leningrad 1960; Birmingham 1961 (25); Paris, *Reynolds*, 1985–6 (17, repr. p. 149); RA, *Reynolds*, 1986 (33, repr. p. 194 and in colour p. 92).

At the Tate Gallery 1963–4.

Literature

Graves and Cronin, I, 1899, pp. 11–12, II (under Lennox), pp. 578–9; Steegmann 1933, p. 32; Waterhouse 1941, p. 43, plate 56; Davies 1946, pp. 123–4; Davies 1959, pp. 83–4; Cormack 1970, pp. 108, 144; Potterton 1976, pp. 21, 24–6, plate 17; Penny 1986, pp. 194–5.

Copy

A copy recorded in the Albemarle collection at Quidenham Hall in 1907 is believed to remain (elsewhere) in the family collection.[1]

Technical Notes

In good condition, with comparatively minor cracking and wrinkling of the paint. The layer structure is less complex than in many of Reynolds's paintings, and lacks the intermediate non-drying layers found elsewhere in his work. Cleaned in 1959.

The face of the sitter, almost dead-white, has been judged to have faded, although no direct evidence for this colour change had been available. A recent cross-section from the cheek, however, shows clearly that the original colour must have been a good deal warmer. The flesh paint appears to comprise a single layer of white, tinted with red lake pigment (see below), but the red has been bleached from the paint layer by the action of light. A trace of pink survives at the base of the layer, where the fugitive lake is most protected from light. It is difficult to be certain whether the face ever had a final pink glaze, since it is likely that all colour now would have been lost.

There is further evidence of fading in the picture. A strip of protected paint of the curtain to the left, under the frame, is a deeper, more saturated plum colour than the exposed area. This is demonstrated in cross-sections as well as on the picture. The curtain is painted in a number of layers of red lake interspersed with layers containing lead white mixed with lake. There is a final pure red-lake glaze, evidently faded, where it is beyond the frame's protection. Similarly, the pinkish-plum colour of the chair-back shows some fading. The red lake of the curtain has been shown to derive from cochineal dyestuff.

A sample was taken from Lady Albemarle's left forearm, where the flesh in shadow is depicted as a curious grey-green. In cross-section, a scumble of Naples yellow is worked over a series of dark pinkish-mauve layers containing red lake, black pigment and white. This unusual colour effect seems to have been intended, since there is no evidence of colour change in the surface paint.

The principal colour of Lady Albemarle's dress has been identified as Prussian blue mixed with white in various concentrations. The layer structure is complicated. There is a greyer-blue undermodelling containing some black pigment in addition to the blue.

Overall, the layer structure seems less complex than, for example, in *Colonel Tarleton* (NG 5985) or *Lord Heathfield* (NG 111). It is not so heavily worked as either, and *Lady Albemarle* lacks the non-drying intermediate layers present in those pictures. The state of preservation is therefore better.

The sitter, born 24 June 1703 and styled Lady Anne Lennox before her marriage, was the younger daughter of Charles Lennox, 1st Duke of Richmond (1672–1723);[2] he, the illegitimate son of Charles II and Louise de Kerouaille, was as personable as his father but reputedly unprincipled.[3]

Lady Anne Lennox married, on 21 February 1722 (1723 old style), William-Anne Keppel, 2nd Earl of Albemarle, courtier, Colonel of the Coldstream Guards, Knight of the Garter and Groom of the Stole. Ten years later she sat to John Vanderbank, for an unremarkable portrait signed and dated 1732.[4] Lady Albemarle became a Lady of the Bedchamber to Queen Caroline and a favourite of George II; in 1743 she escorted their youngest daughter Princess Louisa to Denmark to be married.[5] Her husband the 2nd Earl ('charming Albemarle'[6]) was famously extravagant, squandering his own fortune of £90,000 as well as his wife's dowry of £25,000. Of their fifteen children, only four sons and two daughters survived childhood. In 1749 Albemarle was appointed ambassador to Paris where, on 22 December 1754, he died 'suddenly, in his coach, after supper'.[7] George II thereupon awarded Lady Albemarle a pension of £1200 a year.[8] She was to live for another 35 years.

This portrait was presumably commissioned by her eldest son George, 3rd Earl of Albemarle (it was eventually paid for by his executor in 1773); but the suggestion that Lady Albemarle should sit to Reynolds almost certainly came from her second son, Augustus Keppel RN (1725–86). His long friendship with Reynolds began in 1749 when he (then Commodore of the *Centurion*) offered Reynolds a passage to Italy. Reynolds was to portray Keppel at least seven times.[9] It was Reynolds's second dynamic full-length portrait of Keppel, painted in 1752–4 (fig. 1),[10] which made his name. The earlier portraits of Keppel (before he grew corpulent and double-chinned) are of some relevance to *Lady Albemarle*, since they suggest that Reynolds caught a family likeness between the dark-haired, dark-eyed son and the mother whose complexion as we now see it is so faded. Reynolds's long friendship with Keppel must primarily account for his readiness to paint not only seven portraits of Keppel and one of his illegitimate daughter,[11] but at least twelve portraits of other members of the family. These include portraits of his two military brothers, General George Keppel, 3rd Earl of Albemarle,[12] the hero of Havana (painted in 1755 and 1765–6), and Lieut.-General the Hon. William Keppel (painted in 1758–9 and 1762–4, the latter a post-victory portrait which in some ways anticipates *Lord Heathfield*, NG 111, pp. 228–33).[13] The youngest brother who went into the Church (and became Bishop of Exeter) was not, seemingly, considered worthy of Reynolds's attention.[14] Both Lady Albemarle's daughters, Lady Caroline[15] and Lady Elizabeth Keppel,[16] were portrayed more than once by Reynolds; the portrait of Lady Elizabeth Keppel as a bridesmaid (at the wedding of George III and Queen Charlotte) also shows a likeness to her mother. Within Lady Albemarle's lifetime, Reynolds painted her young grandson William Charles Keppel, 4th Earl of Albemarle;[17] thus he painted three generations of her family.[18]

Reynolds's pocket-books record eleven appointments for Lady Albemarle to sit between 26 September 1757 and 28 June 1759 (as well as several cancelled appointments). Penny 1986 observes that there are enough recorded sittings for two different portraits, but only one is known.[19] After the first three sittings on 26, 27 and 29 September 1757, two appointments (28 December 1757 and 2 January 1758) were cancelled. Nineteen months lapsed before Lady Albemarle began sitting to Reynolds again, in the spring of 1759; thereafter progress appears to have been steady, with eight sittings between April and June 1759 (she sat on 28 April, 8, 19 and 26 May and 9, 19, 23 and 28 June; she cancelled appointments on 5 May and 7 and 8 June). The portrait was presumably finished by 18 November 1760, when Reynolds entered the price in his ledger ('Novr 18th Lady Albemarle 42': i.e. 42 guineas); under the same date he noted 'Lady Albemarle' in his pocket-book, perhaps indicating that the portrait was finished and ready for despatch. But he had to wait over twelve years for payment for it. After the death of her eldest son the 3rd Lord Albemarle, his executor finally – on 13 December 1773 – settled Reynolds's account for Albemarle's own portrait of 1765–6 and paid for Lady Albemarle's portrait of 1760.[20]

Lady Albemarle is portrayed as she approaches the age of 60. Aileen Ribeiro notes[21] that the material of her dress, probably a damask, 'has a swirling rococo design which was

Fig. 1 *Commodore Augustus Keppel*, 1752–4. Oil on canvas, 233 × 146 cm. Greenwich, National Maritime Museum.

slightly old-fashioned by the end of the 1750s (but there was often a gap between the buying of expensive silks and their making up)',[22] and that the black spotted silk pelerine or shoulder-mantle also reflects an earlier fashion, in this case French.[23] Long drifts of fine white lace emerge from it to flow over Lady Albemarle's arms.

Reynolds depicts her engaged in knotting – or in pretending to knot. It was precisely because knotting gave the illusion of useful activity – seeming to show what Mme de Genlis declared to be 'the aversion which all females ought to have to complete idleness'[24] – that it had long been fashionable. Little or no skill was required, other than the ability to form a loop of thread over one hand, pass a shuttle of thread through it with the other, then draw it into a knot. Advanced knotters like Mrs Delaney could produce raised knots called 'sugar plums'; most ladies simply produced evenly knotted cords which could then be sewn on to fabrics in decorative patterns. Seeming to be prettily preoccupied with one's 'work' was also a useful female gambit in conversation, especially with suitors; here knotting (a rudimentary pastime) was less prone to error than the higher skill of embroidery.[25] Sidley's 'Knotting Song', set to music by Purcell in the 1690s, proved lastingly popular; at each refrain, a frustrated lover sighs as 'Phillis, without Frown or Smile/ Sat and knotted all the while'.[26] The popularity of knotting lasted well into the eighteenth century. Addison devoted most of one of his *Spectator* letters to it in 1712, pointing to its advantages in leaving 'the Eyes at full liberty to be employed ... as also the Thoughts, and the Tongue'; he suggested that men 'in want of Business' might equally take it up.[27] Dr Johnson attempted it, but could not master it ('I once tried knotting. Dempster's sister undertook to teach me; but I could not learn it'[28]).

Knotting was a godsend to the portraitist, since it offered a solution (at least in the case of the female sex) to the perennial question of what a sitter should do with her hands. Reynolds may well have seized on the knotting motif (without

Fig. 2 *Elizabeth Sandby*, engraved in mezzotint by James McArdell after Francis Cotes, published in 1756.

observing it too closely) from Francis Cotes's portrait of Elizabeth Sandby (fig. 2), painted in 1755, engraved in mezzotint and published in 1756.[29] He used it, rather stiffly, in a smaller portrait of Jean, Countess of Hyndford, 1757.[30] Reynolds's treatment of Lady Albemarle's knotting is comparatively perfunctory: probably neither he nor Lady Albemarle is seriously interested in it. Whereas Elizabeth Sandby's thread is closely knotted, not a single knot is visible in Lady Albemarle's.[31]

Was Lady Albemarle an habitual knotter, or is the pose in which Reynolds casts her his own idea of how 'Keppel's mother' ought to appear? Reynolds allotted the roles; his sitters complied. By 1760 Lady Albemarle was too old to be portrayed as goddess or nymph. She (in 1760) and Mary, Countess of Bute, in 1778, were perhaps the oldest of all his female sitters;[32] Reynolds allotted the Countess of Bute an umbrella, and the Countess of Albemarle a knotting-shuttle. Whether she knew how to use it is as unanswerable a question as whether the small mahogany work-table depicted beside her came from her house in Spring Gardens or from Reynolds's studio (or, as Potterton 1976 suggests, from one of the designs in Thomas Chippendale's *The Gentleman and Cabinet-Maker's Director*, first published in 1754). The scissors lying on her work-table have been construed as the artist's reference to 'the classical Fates cutting the threads of life' and as appropriate to Lady Albemarle's 'recent widowhood'.[33] Perhaps, but scissors were also indispensable for cutting the more prosaic threads with which to knot; and in any case Lady Albemarle had already been a widow for five or six years, and evidently a merrier one than the now faded, almost dead-white colour of her face suggests.

Lady Albemarle's later life is fragmentarily but vividly reflected in the correspondence of Horace Walpole, who was fond of her; his niece Laura (the natural daughter of Sir Edward Walpole) had married her youngest son Frederick.[34] Walpole could do no more than nod to Lady Albemarle at the coronation of George III and Queen Charlotte in September 1761 ('Oh! the buzz, the prattle, the crowds, the noise, the hurry!!'), but noted that she looked 'very genteel' among the 'ancient peeresses'.[35] Each of her three eldest sons won distinction in the siege and capture of Havana in 1762: George, 3rd Earl of Albemarle, as commander-in-chief, Commodore Augustus Keppel as second-in-command of the fleet and Lieut.-General William Keppel, 56th Foot, as leader of the assault on Fort Moro. When the victory at Havana was announced at Court in October 1762, Walpole reported that the Duke of Cumberland 'stepped across the room to Lady Albemarle and said "If it was not in the Drawing-Room, I would kiss you."' Walpole added: 'Lady Albemarle; there is a happy mother! Honours military and ecclesiastic raining upon her children!'[36] The 'Honours ecclesiastic' which rained (and continued to rain) upon Lady Albemarle's youngest son Frederick included his consecration as Bishop of Exeter in November 1762.

Lady Albemarle's daughters were less reliable: she was 'in a furious passion' in 1759 when her elder daughter Caroline eloped with Robert Adair, a surgeon;[37] her niece Lady Caroline Fox, reporting this affair, began 'A most vexatious affair has happened in the family', and concluded 'There is certainly something nasty in the idea of a woman of fashion falling in love with her surgeon.'[38] She was better pleased when her second daughter Elizabeth married the Marquess of Tavistock in 1764. A robust spirit, Lady Albemarle stared down two muggings, the first in 1750, when nine men ambushed and robbed her in Great Russell Street,[39] and the second in June 1780, during the Gordon Riots, when she was set upon at midnight as she left her daughter-in-law's house in Pall Mall.[40] Earlier that year, Lady Sarah Lennox had reported her to be 'as well as ever, and the better for being electrified, which agrees very well with her'.[41]

By 1786 Lady Albemarle had outlived all her children; but she was no recluse. On 22 December 1782, at a party at Lady Ailesbury's, she was overheard to say that 'old as she was she could not resist temptation, and made her words good for she eat a large quantity of cold partridge pie and drank champagne' – two glasses of champagne, according to Walpole, who noted that she 'stayed till past one in as good spirits as ever I saw her'.[42] Seven years later, Walpole reported that she 'has her senses and spirits as well as ever'.[43] Lady Albemarle died the following month, on 10 October 1789, at the age of 86, in her house in New Street, Spring Gardens.

NOTES

1. Ed. Duleep Singh, *Norfolk Houses*, Norwich 1907, II, Quidenham, no. 12, p. 148.

2. By his wife Anne, widow of Lord (Henry) Bellasis and daughter of Francis, Lord Brudenell.

3. Portraits of him by Kneller are at Goodwood (*c.*1705) and NPG (Kit-Cat Club, *c.*1710). See J. Douglas Stewart, *Sir Godfrey Kneller and the English Baroque Portrait*, Oxford 1983, p. 16, no. 610 and p. 125, no. 609 (NPG 3321).

4. Sold Christie's 20 April 1990 (17), repr. in colour. A pair of portraits by Thomas Hudson *c.*1755–60, presented in 1948 to Exeter Museum and Art Gallery as of the (? 2nd) Earl and Countess of Albemarle, are too late to be portraits of them.

5. A letter from Lady Albemarle to the Duke of Newcastle, written from Altona, 8 November 1743, reports on the happy conclusion of her mission (BL, Add.MSS 32,701 f.248); she writes a good letter. Other letters from her to the Duke of Newcastle 1740–67 are in Add.MS 32,695-33,071.

6. Horace Mann's phrase, used sardonically of a man who relied on 'charm' to cover up his debts (*Walpole Correspondence*, vol. XX, p. 269).

7. Quoted in *GEC* 1910, I, p. 94.

8. According to Horace Walpole, Lady Albemarle was a 'great favourite' with George II. On 31 January 1750 he related to Horace Mann, 'My Lady Albemarle was robbed t'other night in Great Russell Street by nine men: the king gave her a gold watch and chain the next day...' (*Walpole Correspondence*, vol. XX, p. 111).

9. Seven known portraits: (i) 1749, NMM, no. 2821; (ii) 1752, as Reynolds claimed, or 1753–4, the best-known, NMM no. 2823 (fig. 1 above); (iii) 1759, coll. Duke of Bedford, Woburn Abbey; (iv) 1762–4, ? replica, NMM; (v) 1779, NPG no. 179; (vi) 1780, Tate Gallery (N 00886); (vii) 1785, Her Majesty The Queen, Millar 1969, cat. no. 1024.

10. Steegmann 1933, pp. 29–31. For full discussion of this portrait (and the mezzotint of 1759), see ed. Penny 1986, pp. 181–3. Penny notes that Augustus Keppel remained a lifelong friend of Reynolds, who portrayed him, at various stages of his career from Commodore to Admiral, at least seven times between 1749 and 1785.

11. Miss Keppel (later Mrs Thomas Meyrick), Augustus Keppel's illegitimate daughter, coll. Ashmolean Museum, Waterhouse 1941, p. 74, plate 236.

12. General George Keppel, 3rd Lord Albemarle (1724–72), sat twice:
(i) in 1755–6, see Waterhouse 1968, p. 141; (ii) in 1765–6, in armour, in honour of his victory at Havana, at Quidenham 1907 (Singh 1907, cited in note 1, II, Quidenham no. 31, repr. facing p. 148). Replica, without the shield of Saint George, sold Christie's 20 April 1990 (28, repr.).

13. Two portraits: (i) 1758–9, Waterhouse 1941, p. 44 (Singh 1907, II, Quidenham, no. 48, repr. facing p. 160); (ii) 1762–4, Waterhouse 1941, p. 52, Earl of Rosebery sale, 5 May 1939 (115, repr.), replica at Quidenham in 1907, no. 48, repr. Singh 1907, II, p. 157.

14. No portrait by Reynolds of Lady Albemarle's youngest son Revd the Hon. Frederick Keppel is known, though an entry in Reynolds's ledgers, 23 January 1764, suggests that his brother Augustus commissioned either a portrait of Frederick or a replica of one of his own portraits for him. The entry reads 'General Keppell in full/ for his own two Pictures & the Bishop/ of Exeter 117.0' (Cormack 1970, p. 126). Pastel portraits by Cotes of Revd the Hon. Frederick Keppel, Bishop of Exeter, and his wife Laura (Horace Walpole's niece) were at Quidenham in 1907 (Singh 1907, II, Quidenham, nos 49 and 27). A portrait of the Bishop by anon. is said to be in the Bishop's Palace, Exeter.

15. Two portraits of Lady Caroline Keppel: (i) 1755–7, coll. Duke of Bedford, Woburn Abbey, Waterhouse 1941, p. 40; (ii) 1757–9, coll. Earl of Iveagh, Waterhouse 1941, p. 43, plate 47.

16. Three portraits of Lady Elizabeth Keppel: (i) 1755–7, coll. Duke of Bedford, Woburn Abbey, Waterhouse 1941, p. 40; (ii) 1757–9, coll. Anthony de Rothschild, Ascott (NT), Waterhouse 1941, p. 43, plate 46; (iii) 1761–2, in the dress worn as a bridesmaid at the wedding of George III and Queen Charlotte, exh. SA 1762 (87), coll. Duke of Bedford, Woburn Abbey, Waterhouse 1941, p. 50, plate 76.

17. Portrayed at the age of about nine, private collection, Waterhouse 1941, p. 74, plate 115.

18. Only Francis Cotes RA (1726–70) came near to finding such favour with the the Keppels, executing at least six pastel portraits of them between 1752 and 1764 (Singh 1907, II, Quidenham nos. 21, 26–9, 49); a pastel portrait of similar size of 'Anne, Countess of Albemarle ... Age 50' listed at Quidenham (no. 10), though not given to Cotes, may also be by him. A small portrait of her aged 65 ($8\frac{3}{4} \times 7\frac{1}{2}$ in.) by anon. (formerly at Quidenham) is now untraced.

19. If a 'first' portrait had indeed been completed and paid for by 1759, it would predate the earliest surviving ledger. Conceivably, Reynolds began a portrait in 1757, did not finish it and later discarded it. There is no evidence that NG 1259 has been reworked.

20. Both debts had been carried over to Reynolds's second ledger, to be cancelled at last by a line drawn through 'Lady Albemarle 42. 0. not paid' and 'Lord Albemarle 36. 15', and a marginal note reading 'paid Dec 13 1773 by the Executor of Lord Alb'.

21. In correspondence with the compiler.

22. Potterton 1976, plate 21, illustrates a detail of an English silk of the mid-1750s with a 'spot and sprig' pattern (coll. V&A).

23. In ed. Penny 1986, p. 195.

24. Mme de Genlis, *Dictionary of Court Ceremonial*, quoted by Sylvia Groves, *The History of Needlework Tools and Accessories*, London 1966, p. 86.

25. A telling contrast between the two is offered by two facing colour plates in ed. Penny 1986 (pp. 92–3): while Lady Albemarle is perfunctorily knotting, her niece Lady Caroline Fox employs her skills in more elaborate crewel embroidery.

26. See Olive Baldwin and Thelma Wilson, 'Purcell's Knotting Song', *Musical Times*, July 1987, pp. 379–81. As they note (p. 380 n. 6), 'The Knotting Song' was often performed by Benjamin Britten and Peter Pears, and was the final song in the Purcell group in the last recital they gave together, at Snape Maltings in September 1972.

27. No. 536, 14 November 1812; the quotation is from *The Spectator*, Everyman edn, 4 vols, London 1946, vol. IV, p. 189.

28. Ed. G.B. Hill, *Boswell's Life of Johnson*, 6 vols, Oxford 1934, 7 April 1778, III, p. 242.

29. The original portrait is repr. in William Sandby, *Thomas and Paul Sandby*, 1892, facing p. 176 (the sitter was the second wife of Thomas Sandby), but is now untraced. The mezzotint by James McArdell, lettered *F Cotes Pinxt 1755*, was published 1756 (Chaloner Smith, II, p. 894, no. 162; see also Edward Mead Johnson, *Francis Cotes*, Oxford 1976, p. 58, no. 58).

30. Graves and Cronin, II, p. 504; engr. by J. McArdell, 1759. Sold Christie's 14 July 1994 (22, repr. in colour).

31. Could John Singleton Copley have seen Reynolds's *Lady Albemarle*, some time after his arrival in England in 1772? His *Portrait of a Lady* (? Mrs Seymour Fort: repr. Prown 1966, II, fig. 363, sitter's identity uncertain) of 1778 is perhaps based on *Lady Albemarle*, though the virtuous industry of Copley's bourgeois sitter is very different.

32. *Mary, Countess of Bute* is repr. ed. Penny 1986 (121).

33. Dillian Gordon, *The National Gallery School of Painting: British Paintings*, London 1986, p. 36.

34. Walpole to Horace Mann, 28 October 1762, *Walpole Correspondence*, vol. XXII, p. 94.

35. Walpole to George Montagu, *Walpole Correspondence*, vol. IX, p. 387.

36. Walpole to Horace Mann, 28 October 1762, *Walpole Correspondence*, vol. XXII, p. 94.

37. Possibly the 'Mr Adair' who sat to Reynolds for a portrait evidently completed in 1754, but now untraced. Robert Adair, surgeon (?1710–90) married Lady Caroline Keppel in 1759.

38. Letter from Lady Caroline Fox to the Countess of Kildare, 21 February 1759, ed. B. Fitzgerald, *Correspondence of Emily Duchess of Leinster*, 3 vols, Dublin 1949–53, I, p. 197.

39. Walpole to Horace Mann, 31 January 1750, *Walpole Correspondence*, vol. XX, p. 111.

40. Walpole to William Mason, 9 June 1780, *Walpole Correspondence*, vol. XXIX, p. 59 (also reported to Harcourt, 10 June 1780, vol. XXXV, p. 505).

41. Letter to William Ogilvie, from Goodwood, 1 February 1780, Fitzgerald 1949–53 (cited in note 38), II, p. 309.

42. Coke, MS Journals, quoted in *Walpole Correspondence*, vol. XXXIII, p. 387 n. 15; Walpole to Lady Ossory, 8 February 1783, ibid., p. 387.

43. Walpole to Lady Ossory, 13 September 1789, *Walpole Correspondence*, vol. XXXIV, p. 63.

NG 681

Captain Robert Orme

1756

Oil on canvas, 239 × 147 cm (94⅛ × 57⅞ in.)

Inscribed *J. Reynolds pinxit 1756* in red lower right

Provenance

Evidently not commissioned by the sitter or his relatives, but painted as a speculation; remained in Reynolds's studio until purchased 1 December 1777 by 5th Earl of Inchiquin, then by descent through the issue of his first marriage (to Mary, Countess of Orkney in her own right)[1] to his great-grandson, 5th Earl of Orkney, by whom sold Christie's 10 May 1863 (62), bt Sir Charles Eastlake for the National Gallery.

Exhibited

SA 1761 (84, as 'Ditto [whole-length] of a gentleman'); BI 1860 (119); Washington, National Museum of American History, Smithsonian Institution, *George Washington: A Figure upon the Stage*, 1982 (no cat. nos, fig. 82, pp. 128–9); Paris, *Reynolds*, 1985–6 (12, repr. p. 139); RA, *Reynolds*, 1986 (26, repr. pp. 86, 188).

At the Tate Gallery 1963–4.

Literature

Reynolds's Ledgers, 1 December 1777 (Cormack 1970, p. 156); Walpole, *Notes...on Exhibitions 1760–91*, p. 75; Northcote 1818, pp. 65–6; Graves and Cronin, II, 1899–1901, pp. 711–12; Whitley 1928, I, p. 175; Waterhouse 1941, p. 41, plate 37; Davies 1959, pp. 81–2; Waterhouse 1973, pp. 18, 37, plates 14 and 15 (detail); Homan Potterton, 'Reynolds's Portrait of Captain Robert Orme in the National Gallery', *Burlington Magazine*, 106, 1976, p. 106, figs. 67–9; Potterton 1976, p. 20, plates 14–16; Penny 1986, pp. 187–8.

? Copy

Graves and Cronin, III, 1899, p. 1091, identify a small (21 × 15 in.) 'Portrait of an Officer' (then coll. A. Parrish) as of Captain Robert Orme.

Technical Notes

Cleaned in 1960. In good condition, with no significant loss or damage. There is some cracking and wrinkling of the paint in the darks, but this condition is less severe than in many of Reynolds's paintings. A paint sample of the red of the coat, taken from near the lower of the two fastened buttons, shows an admixture of coarse and fine vermilion with a deep red lake and a minor proportion of red earth.

The sitter is Captain Robert Orme (1725–90), portrayed at the age of 31 during the war against the French for supremacy in the North American colonies. First commissioned as ensign in the 34th Foot, he transferred to the Coldstream Guards on 16 September 1745 and was promoted lieutenant on 24 April 1751.[2] When General Edward Braddock of the Coldstream Guards was appointed commander-in-chief of the British forces in America, he selected Orme as his aide-de-camp, giving him the acting rank of captain. With two battalions of a force of 6000 men which had been voted for the prosecution of the war, they arrived in Virginia on 20 February 1755. Orme retains a place in American history because of his brief friendship with the young George Washington. Washington in 1755 was aged 23; he had been Colonel of a Virginian regiment, but in May 1755 volunteered to serve under General Braddock. Like Orme, Washington became one of Braddock's aides-de-camp, and he and Orme became friends.[3]

Waterhouse describes NG 681 as 'a heroic military portrait of a soldier of no particular consequence'.[4] In the Society of Artists exhibition in 1761, it was described simply as 'Portrait of a gentleman'; an annotation by Horace Walpole in his copy of the exhibition catalogue identifies it as 'Captain Orme with a horse'.[5] Orme's portrait (84 in the exhibition) hung next to Reynolds's portrait (85, see p. 246, fig. 4) of *General Lord Ligonier*,[6] undoubtedly a soldier of far greater 'consequence' than Captain Orme. Yet while the *Ligonier* is in a grander manner (and on an even grander scale) than Orme's portrait, it is more conventional and less personal. An unidentified young officer whose father had asked him to report on the exhibition dutifully admired the portrait of General Lord Ligonier ('...little inferior to some of the greatest masters of the ancients'), but of *Captain Orme* he was moved to write: 'There is an officer of the Guards with a letter in his hand, ready to mount his horse with all that fire mixed with rage that war and the love of his country can give.'[7] 'In the background', he noted, 'a view of a skirmish.'

That 'skirmish' in the background (not easy to read) almost certainly represents the episode of 9 July 1755, disastrous for the British but famous in American history as 'Braddock's Defeat'. On that day, General Braddock, accompanied by Orme and the rest of his staff, advanced with a large force of British and provincial troops towards the French garrison of Fort Du Quesne[8] on the Ohio River. Having crossed the Monongahela River, they had to pass through a forest ravine: and there they were ambushed by French and Indian riflemen hidden above the cliffs. British cannon-fire was almost useless against the invisible enemy. Braddock's troops were virtually massacred; a survivor reckoned the number of men 'killed, wounded or left on the Field' to be 896.[9] Only George Washington, whom Orme described as conspicuous that day for 'the greatest courage and resolution', seemed to be under 'the miraculous care of Providence'.[10] Braddock was mortally wounded; Orme, himself wounded, cried out that he would give 60 guineas to anyone who would convey his general out of the range of fire. Braddock survived only a few days, his last words allegedly being 'Next time we shall know how to deal with them'.[11]

The despatch in Orme's hand is illegible: possibly he is carrying the news of Braddock's death to headquarters. Orme's own wounds (unspecified) cannot have been grave; by September 1755, said to be 'nearly recovered', he sailed

Fig. 1 *Captain Robert Orme*, detail

for England, charged with 'explaining American affairs to the Duke [of Cumberland]' and other military authorities.[12] The manuscript journal which Orme kept as Braddock's ADC survives;[13] in correct military style, it is factual and impersonal, imparting less about Orme's American experience than is conveyed by the urgent, almost haunted look which Reynolds captured in his portrait (fig. 1).

Orme probably sat to Reynolds late in 1755, soon after his return to England. Reynolds's sitter book for that year is missing, but the portrait is dated 1756. Orme sat for it in his campaign (i.e. not full dress) uniform as an officer of the Coldstream Guards: scarlet frock-coat with blue lapels and cuffs over a grey waistcoat, all trimmed with broad gold lace, buff breeches and black gaiters over buckled shoes. Only the hilt and the tip of his sword show, since the sword-belt is worn, correctly, under the coat; his long hair is tied behind his neck, and a blue and gold sash is looped over his horse's saddle.

Orme does not appear to have commissioned his portrait; certainly he never owned it. Perhaps Reynolds took the initiative in asking Orme (who may have been a Devonshire man,[14] like himself) to sit. At this stage in his rise to fame, Reynolds was keen to keep heroic full-length portraits on display in his studio, so that (in Waterhouse's words) 'sitters who came with more moderate intentions could see what possibilities of immortality were available'.[15] Reynolds could have read accounts of Orme's role in 'Braddock's Defeat' in London newspapers and in the *Gentleman's Magazine* for August 1755.[16] He may also have hoped that the portrait of a military hero would attract an engraver, and thereby increase his own fame. That there was likely to be a demand for such engravings is suggested by the comments of the young officer whose admiration for Orme's portrait has already been quoted: he added that he hoped that Mr Reynolds would 'oblige the world' with prints of both *Captain Orme* and *Lord Ligonier*: 'if he does he will have military subscribers enough.' But *Captain Orme* was never engraved. Given the demand for engravings after Reynolds, this is puzzling.

James Northcote, who joined Reynolds's studio in the mid-1770s, later recalled that the portrait attracted much notice in Reynolds's studio 'by its boldness and singularity'.[17] Captain Orme was painted on the same scale as *Commodore Keppel* (reproduced on p. 203, fig. 1), which Reynolds had painted in 1753–4 but managed to retain for several years on view in his studio: displayed together, they must have presented an impressive appearance. *Captain Orme* does not have the same qualities which make *Commodore Keppel* a great work, but to different degrees, both are in Northcote's category of portraits which 'assume the rank of history'.[18] *Captain Orme* remained on Reynolds's hands until 1771, when it was purchased, apparently simply as a fine example of Reynolds's work, by the newly succeeded 5th Earl of Inchiquin (no relation of the sitter, and not yet connected by marriage to the artist).

As Homan Potterton demonstrated in 1976,[19] Reynolds derived the pose of both Orme and his horse from a detail in one of the lunette frescoes by Jacopo Ligozzi (fig. 2) in the Cloister of the Ognissanti in Florence; he made a sketch of it on the spot in 1752 (fig. 3), no doubt anticipating that it might be useful for some future portrait involving a sitter and a horse (the latter never his strong point). Ligozzi's figure holds his horse's reins and is evidently about to swing himself up into the saddle, thus turning his back to the spectator. For *Captain Orme*, Reynolds reversed the composition. Orme stands, momentarily paused, and facing the spectator. Reynolds cannot be said to have dealt entirely successfully with the ensuing problem of how to represent his right arm: it holds the reins, more or less as Ligozzi's figure does, but is not convincingly articulated to the shoulder, instead extended like a bolster upon his horse's back.[20] Nevertheless, his sketch of the Ligozzi served him well. He was sufficiently pleased with the poses of Captain Orme and his horse to repeat them three years later (and exactly, down to the horse's markings) in his portrait of Cornet Nehemiah Winter, 11th Dragoons,[21] and in 1782 he adapted the pose of Orme's horse for his portrait of Colonel George Coussmaker,[22] this time with variations (unlike the preoccupied Captain Orme, Colonel Coussmaker is portrayed at leisure).

Noting Reynolds's reverence throughout his career for 'the ancestral images of British seventeenth-century nobility, as defined for eternity by Van Dyck', Robert Rosenblum suggests that Captain Orme's pose (and presumably that of his horse) is 'an allusion to the portrait of Charles I' (Louvre);[23] but it is an allusion, not a direct borrowing.

Orme resigned from the Army in October 1756. The rest of his life is fairly obscure. In or about 1756 he married Audrey, daughter of the 3rd Viscount Townshend of Raynham, Hertfordshire; the marriage was contrary to the

Fig. 2 Jacopo Ligozzi (1547–1627), detail from *Saint Francis embracing a Sick Man*, one of the *Life of Saint Francis* series of lunette frescoes in the cloister of the Ognissanti, Florence.

Fig. 3 Reynolds's sketch of 1752 of the horse and rider in Ligozzi's fresco (fig. 2), made in leadpoint in his Italian sketchbook, page size 18.5 × 123.2 cm. London, British Museum.

wishes of her parents (they had intended her to marry Lord George Lennox), and the couple reputedly eloped.[24] They lived at first in Hertford, but when Orme made his will in 1771, he was living at Topsham in Devon, where he may have inherited property, and where he constructed a mansion which came to be known as 'The Retreat'.[25] In 1778 Orme's son, on admission to his Cambridge college, gave his father's address as 'of Devonshire, and of Bergham, Brabant, Netherlands',[26] the latter address ominously suggesting a refuge from creditors. Orme died on 17 June 1790 'at Mr Bourchier's house, in Queen-Street, Mayfair'.[27]

NOTES

1. She died 1791; Lord Inchiquin (later Marquess of Thomond) later married Mary Palmer, Reynolds's niece and heiress, but that future connection can hardly have influenced this purchase from Reynolds in 1777.

2. See D. Mackinnon, *Origins and Services of the Coldstream Guards*, London 1833, II, pp. 484–5.

3. The friendship between Orme and Washington is well-documented; see, for instance, D.S. Freeman, *George Washington*, 2 vols, London 1948, II, pp. 13, 17, 18, 19, 37. On returning to England Orme wrote to Washington: ' [not] Distance Absence nor change of Circumstances shall ever alter the Sincere Friendship and Affection which I shall ever have for you' (quoted in L.M. Sears, *George Washington*, New York 1932, p. 24).

4. 1973, p. 18.

5. Walpole, *Notes ... on Exhibitions*, p. 75.

6. Coll. Tate Gallery (N 00143), Waterhouse 1941, cat no. 143, plate 61.

7. Quoted in Whitley 1928, I, pp. 174–5: Whitley describes his source as 'a letter written in May 1761, by a young officer who had been asked by his father to send him descriptions of some of the pictures'.

8. On the site of what developed as Pittsburgh. The ambush took place about seven miles to the south.

9. Braddock had sent his engineers ahead to prepare a road through the ravine: presumably they were seen and heard by the enemy, who then lay in wait. Contemporary verdicts on Braddock were harsh. The journal of an unidentified survivor censures him for failing to have 'the least suspicion of falling into an ambush, although he was in a country, of all the Globe, the most adapted for one to encounter an enemy whose mode of fighting is confined to that method' (p. 360). Officers killed or wounded are listed on pp. 360–5. Horace Mann was more summary: 'An ambuscade in a wood is too old a trick for any general of common prudence to be caught by' (letter of 20 September 1755 to Horace Walpole, *Walpole Correspondence*, vol. XX, pp. 496–7. For a detailed account of Braddock's Defeat, see Winthrop Sargent, 'History of the Expedition against Fort Du Quesne in 1755', in *Memoirs of the Historical Society of Pennsylvania*, publishing the unidentified survivor's journal, pp. 358–9, Philadelphia 1855, V, *passim*; also Freeman 1948 (cited in note 3), pp. 64–102.

10. Quoted by Freeman 1948, p. 73.

11. Widely reported; e.g. see undated MS letter from Lady Charlotte Watson-Wentworth to her brother the Marquis of Rockingham, Sheffield Record Office, R1-69.

12. Governor Morris to Captain Shirley, 5 September 1755: 'Captain Orme is going to England and will put the affair of the western campaign in a true light. You know his situation and abilities gave him great opportunities of knowing everything that has passed in the army or in the colony, relative to military matters, and I am sure he will be of great use to the Ministry in the measures that may be considered for the future safety and defence of these provinces' (quoted in Sargent 1855, cited in note 9, p. 284).

13. Orme's journal, 20 February–13 July 1755, MS., BL (King's MSS. 212), was published by Sargent 1855 (cited in note 9), pp. 281–357.

14. Efforts by the compiler and by the Devon Record Office to trace Orme's birthplace have been unsuccessful.

15. Waterhouse 1983, p. 18.

16. pp. 378–80.

17. Northcote 1818, I, pp. 65–6.

18. Northcote 1818, II, p. 306.

19. Potterton 1976.

20. See David Mannings, 'Reynolds's "Captain Orme"', *Burlington Magazine*, 106, 1976, p. 650 (letter), for the suggestion that while the composition of the figure with the horse seems to derive from the Ognissanti fresco, the pose of Orme himself is derived (like Commodore Keppel's) from the Apollo Belvedere: 'the Apollo is ingeniously combined with the Ognissanti horse'.

21. Coll. Southampton Art Gallery; 113.5 × 137.5 cm, exh. *Pictures from Southampton*, Wildenstein, London 1970 (18, repr.); the landscape format allows more space for a battle scene in the background (left). The suggestion in the *Reynolds* exh. cat., Birmingham 1961(28), that Reynolds may have begun Winter's portrait in the same year (1756) that he was painting Orme's ignores the fact that Winter's commission as Cornet, 11th Dragoons, is dated 1 March 1758 (Army List).

22. Repr. ed. Penny 1986, p. 154.

23. Repr. Christopher Brown, *Van Dyck*, Oxford 1982, plate 170.

24. See Erroll Sherson, *The Lively Lady Townshend and her Friends*, London 1926.

25. Orme's will, PRO, PROB 11/1197/f.476, refers to a house and land in the parish of Topsham, Devon, 'where I now dwell'. His house is described in N. Pevsner and B. Cherry, *Devon*, 1989, p. 825, as 'a tall handsome house ... converted from a sugar warehouse into a mansion by Capt. Robert Orme (before 1775). Later substantially remodelled.'

26. *Al. Cantab.* 1752–1900, IV, p. 599.

27. *Gentleman's Magazine*, 1790, p. 577.

NG 2077

Lady Cockburn and her Three Eldest Sons

1773

Oil on canvas, 141.5 × 113 cm (55¾ × 44½ in.)
Inscribed 'J REYNOLDS:PINX' in gold lower centre, above the fur-trimmed edge of Lady Cockburn's mantle, and '1773' in gold lower left

Provenance

Commissioned by Sir James Cockburn, 8th Bt of Langton, Co. Berwick, the principal sitter's husband (d.1804); by descent to their eldest son General Sir James Cockburn, 9th Bt (d.1852), and then to his only child Marianna Augusta, wife of Sir James John Hamilton, Bt; as a bequest from Lady Hamilton, first entered the National Gallery in 1892 as NG 1365, but after the legality of the bequest was challenged by six co-heiresses,[1] was deaccessioned and delivered to the co-heiresses 8 April 1900; sold by them the next day to Agnew's and Asher Wertheimer; purchased 11 April 1900 from Wertheimer by Alfred Beit, by whom bequeathed to the National Gallery 1906.

Exhibited

RA 1774 (220, as 'Ditto [Portrait] of a lady with three children'; BI 1813 (128, with sitters identified); BI Winter 1843 (16); RA Winter 1878 (89).

At the Tate Gallery 1960–1; 1963–4.

Literature

Reynolds's Sitter Book, 1773; Reynolds's Ledgers, II, f.10 r. Northcote 1818, II, pp. 29–30; Graves and Cronin, I, 1899–1901, pp. 181–2, II, p. 1283; Wilhelm Bode, *The Art Collection of Mr Alfred Beit at ... 26 Park Lane, London*, London 1904, p. 60 (as 'Portrait of Lady Cockburn as Caritas'); Edgar Wind, 'Charity, The Case History of a Pattern', *JWCI*, I, 1937–8, pp. 322–30 (on NG 2077, pp. 326–7); Waterhouse 1941, p. 64, plate 155; Davies 1946, pp. 125–6; Davies 1959, pp. 84–5; ed. Penny 1986, p. 259, under no. 88; Shawe-Taylor 1990, pp. 186–8, repr. p. 187; Giovanna Perini, 'On Reynolds's art of borrowing: two more Italian sources', *Burlington Magazine*, CXXXVI, 1994, pp. 27–9, figs. 32–3.

Engraved

(1) in stipple, by Charles Wilkin (Hamilton 1874, p. 91): two states (i) before title, published 1 December 1791 by C. Wilkin: the BM impression of this was exh. RA, *Reynolds*, 1986 (88), repr. p. 260; (ii) lettered *CORNELIA and her CHILDREN*, published 2 January 1792 by C. Wilkin; lettered left of title (repeated in French on the right) with a passage beginning 'Cornelia, after the death of her Husband, applied herself to the care of her family with a wisdom and Prudence that acquired her great esteem... – Hook's Roman History'; (2) Reduced version by S.W. Reynolds after Wilkin, mezzotint (6 × 4¾ in.).

Copy

by Henry Pierce Bone, in enamel on copper (33 × 25 cm), dated 1842, Wallace Collection; see Graham Reynolds, *Wallace Collection: Catalogue of Miniatures*, London 1980, no. 311, pp. 317–18, repr.; exh. *Reynolds* 1980 (311, repr.).

Technical Notes

Cleaned in 1985. In good condition, with no significant loss or damage. Most of the lighter paint has wrinkled, particularly in Lady Cockburn's costume, in her left hand and in the flesh of the eldest and youngest of the three children.

Shrinkage cracks have affected most of the darks, but less severely than in many other paintings by Reynolds. The X-radiograph shows some changes in the curtain in the upper right corner.

This is one of the few paintings where medium analysis has confirmed the use of bitumen. A sample from the shadow of the red curtain, top right, showed the main component to be linseed oil with traces of pine resin and of tripertanes indicative of the use of bitumen. Walnut oil and poppy oil were identified in samples from elsewhere in the picture.

This portrait of a real flesh and blood woman of 1773, with her three all too fleshy infants, largely derives from Van Dyck's allegory *Charity*, a painting of about 1627–8 of which there are two versions; one entered the National Gallery's collection in 1984 (fig. 4).[2] With Faith and Hope, Charity is one of the three theological virtues. The personification of Charity as a mother-figure selflessly caring for (and often suckling) infants goes back several centuries before Van Dyck. Wind 1937–8 traced its antecedents back to Michelangelo (then forward to Raphael, and thence to a bewildering variety of Bolognese painters); but the concept is found in Tuscan sculpture over a century earlier than Michelangelo (fig. 1).[3]

As Potterton suggests, Reynolds has not 'copied wholeheartedly any particular prototype; rather, the design is probably composed of various elements from different sources'.[4] The 'invention' of a picture from a variety of undisclosed sources was characteristic of Reynolds's practice, and has been much discussed;[5] he himself (in one of his lectures to Royal Academy prize-winners) drew a fairly fine distinction between plagiarism and 'borrowing a particular thought, an action, attitude or figure, and transplanting it into your own work', thereby (he believed) improving both.

It has long been recognised that Van Dyck's *Charity* (as we see it in fig. 4) was Reynolds's principal source for his Cockburn group. At some unknown date, Reynolds made a small, incomplete oil sketch of the upper part of the composition (fig. 3),[6] evidently working not from the Van Dyck itself but from the engraving of it made shortly after Van Dyck's death by Cornelis van Caukercken, which reverses (as Reynolds's oil sketch does) the direction of Van Dyck's painting. It is unlikely that Reynolds made this oil sketch with

Fig. 1 Tino di Camaino (*c.*1285–1337), *La Carità*, ?1320s. Marble, height 136 cm. Florence, Bardini Museum.

Fig. 2 Attributed to Giuseppe Maria Crespi (1665–1747) (although signed Ludovico Mattioli) after Anthony van Dyck, *La Balia Favorita*. Etching, 26.7 × 21.8 cm. Hamburg, Kunsthalle.

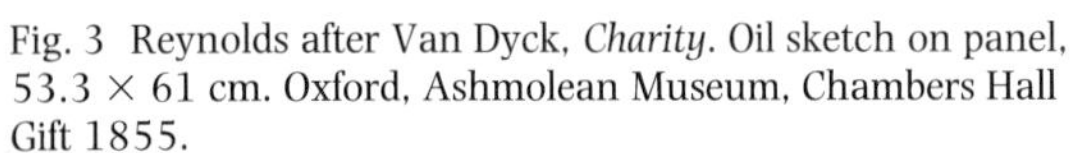

Fig. 3 Reynolds after Van Dyck, *Charity*. Oil sketch on panel, 53.3 × 61 cm. Oxford, Ashmolean Museum, Chambers Hall Gift 1855.

the Cockburn portrait group in mind: however sketchy, it is reasonably faithful to Van Dyck, and was probably made as an *aide-mémoire* which he might at some time adapt to a particular commission. Reynolds's vast print collection served as a continual mine for ideas; it was particularly rich in engravings after Van Dyck, and may well have included an impression of Van Caukercken's engraving. Recently, Giovanna Perini has detected another borrowing in the Cockburn picture,[7] this time from a different, now lost version of Van Dyck's *Charity*. Perini notes that although the painting itself was certainly in the Sampieri collection in Bologna when Reynolds visited the city in 1752, it is unlikely that Reynolds could have seen it; but he presumably knew the etching (fig. 2), a rather coarse work bearing the name of Ludovico Mattioli (? but by Giuseppe Maria Crespi), popularly known as *La Balia* or *The Wet Nurse*. The etching translates a lofty abstract virtue into earthier, contemporary reality, as Reynolds was himself to do in the Cockburn group. Perini points to a telling detail virtually proving that Reynolds must have known the engraving of *The Wet Nurse*: the large macaw perched incongruously beside the window-sill in his Cockburn picture (further discussed below) is first cousin to *The Wet Nurse*'s parrot.

The commission in 1773 to paint Lady Cockburn with three infants all under the age of three presented Reynolds with an ideal opportunity to adapt Van Dyck's allegory to a contemporary portrait group. Comparison of Van Dyck's *Charity* (fig. 4) and the Cockburn group reveals the skill with which he converted an abstraction of Charity and her orphans into Augusta, James, George and William Cockburn. By altering the pose and expression of the mother-figure, he combines a portrait of an individual with the personification of a Virtue. Lady Cockburn is portrayed in a manner which no doubt made her easily recognisable to her family and friends, and her hair is dressed in contemporary fashion. Her preoccupations are specifically with her own children, rather than (like Charity's) with the world's waifs. Shawe-Taylor notes that her youngest child 'clings, in an obviously suckling position to his mother's breast, covered for modesty, but in a suggestive creamy-white'; tirelessly giving suck is a mode in which Charity was frequently represented, and was in reality Lady Cockburn's lot for many years. But Reynolds elevates her above the earthy demands of the little Cockburns by swathing her in a mantle of old gold, and of Michelangel-esque capacity; this brings an aura of allegory into the otherwise almost palpably moist atmosphere of the nursery, and must have come out of Reynolds's property box rather than Lady Cockburn's wardrobe.

For the pose of the elder boy, Reynolds adapts the pose of Cupid in Velázquez's *Toilet of Venus*. This must be one of the most adroit of all Reynolds's borrowings, from a source

Fig. 4 Sir Anthony van Dyck, *Charity*, *c.*1627–8. Oil on oak panel, 148.2 × 107.5 cm. London, National Gallery.

Fig. 5 Detail from *Lady Cockburn and her Three Eldest Sons*

Fig. 6 Richard Cooper after Velázquez, *The Toilet of Venus* (NG 2057), *c.*1767–9. Pencil on paper, squared in brown ink, the verso chalked for transfer, in a sketchbook, page size 32.1 × 43.4 cm. Edinburgh, National Gallery of Scotland.

then almost unknown in England. Seen in profile, his right leg kneeling, both arms held forward to expose his childishly swelling belly, his vestigial garment an echo of Cupid's sash and his brown hair falling over his face, James Cockburn echoes the pose of Velázquez's Cupid closely; but Reynolds has worked this pose so skilfully into the Cockburn trio of infants that his borrowing has hitherto remained unrecognised. Precisely what source he used is not entirely certain. Though Reynolds is known to have greatly admired Velázquez, he could not have seen *The Toilet of Venus* itself since it remained in private Spanish collections until 1813,[8] known to few foreign artists (Mengs might have seen it, but is not known to have drawn it) and it is not known to have been engraved. The link between Reynolds and *The Toilet of Venus* was almost certainly the highly finished and squared drawing by Richard Cooper reproduced here as fig. 6. Having trained as an engraver,[9] Cooper worked abroad for about a decade (? from about 1764). Writing in 1767 to Lord Cardross, newly appointed British Ambassador to Madrid, he hoped for introductions to Spanish collections, as 'My chief views in going abroad, was to make a collection of Drawings from the most proper pictures for Prints, that I shou'd meet with; for which purpose among many other places, I in particular fully resolv'd going to Spain...'[10]

A full account of Cooper's success, probably in 1767, in obtaining permission to study and make copy-drawings of works in the Duke of Alba's collection in Madrid, is given by Duncan Bull and Enriqueta Harris in their illuminating *Burlington Magazine* article, 'The Companion of Velasquez's Rokeby Venus and a source for Goya's Naked Maja',[11] to which annotated copy-drawings by Cooper provide an essential source; they publish Cooper's highly finished pencil drawing of *The Toilet of Venus*: squared in brown ink and chalked verso for transfer,[12] it must have been intended for engraving. But it was not engraved, unlike his copy-drawing of Correggio's *Venus with Mercury and Cupid* or '*The School of Love*' (now NG 10), also from the Duke of Alba's collection in Madrid. Cooper had exhibited both a drawing and an engraving after Correggio at the Society of Artists in 1764; he showed his *Venus with Mercury and Cupid* drawing after Correggio (with others after Titian, Procaccini and Albano) at the Royal Academy in 1778. Perhaps the subject matter of *The Toilet of Venus* inhibited Cooper (a Scot) from exhibiting his drawing of it, and from proceeding to engrave it. Apart from the silent witness of the elder child in the Cockburn group, there is no evidence that Reynolds saw Cooper's drawing of the Velázquez; but it seems likely that he was shown or requested to see drawings by a respected draughtsman of paintings in Spanish collections which he had been unable to see for himself.[13] Reynolds was sufficiently pleased with the result to repeat the elder Cockburn child's pose in 1788 (down to the detail of the way the child's hair falls over his face) for the portrait of the six-year-old Lord Grantham, in *Lord Grantham and his Two Brothers*.[14]

Reynolds does not appear to have made any figure studies specifically for this portrait. Studies of infants and of mother and child groups in earlier sketchbooks may have helped (with Van Dyck's *Charity*) to suggest poses (three are reproduced in Potterton[15]); but by 1773 he had, after all, painted numerous well-born (and a few holy) mother and child groups. The child looking over Lady Cockburn's shoulder was believed by a Chicago paediatrician in 1924 to be typically mongoloid; he revised his opinion only on learning that this child became (in 1851) Admiral of the Fleet.[16] The hefty baby was in fact only nine months old when the picture was exhibited.

The portrait was commissioned by Lady Cockburn's husband, Sir James Cockburn. Reynolds's Sitter Book for 1773 notes appointments for Lady Cockburn to sit on 1, 8 and 9 September 1773; then, after Reynolds's return from a West Country trip, appointments for 'Master Cockburn' (these may be for both elder boys) were made for 13, 20, 21 (cancelled), 22 and 27 October and 11, 12, 23 and 24 November; the latter appointment included Sir James Cockburn, who may have wished to approve the nearly final work. Lady Cockburn had a final sitting, perhaps with her baby ('Chi...' follows her name in the Sitter Book) on 8 December 1773. In March 1774 Sir James Cockburn paid Reynolds's bill of £183 15. 0., which included the frame.

Reynolds appears to have embarked confidently enough upon the group of figures, for there are no indications of second thoughts there (the changes in the upper right corner noted under Technical Notes do not extend to the middle child). Northcote (at that time Reynolds's studio assistant) observed that 'the whole group of figures was so placed on the canvas, as to throw all the principal light too much on one side of the composition, which gave it a very awkward appearance'. After 'much consideration' and 'many trials', Reynolds 'illumined the vacant space in the canvas behind the figures, by an opening of most exquisitely coloured landscape in the background'; in front of this he added a red curtain and 'the gay plumage of a macaw'.[17] Evidence that Reynolds did make changes in the area of the curtain is noted under Technical Notes above. The background 'opening' and the glimpse of rich blue sky which it admits also follow Van Dyck; but Reynolds's 'exquisitely coloured landscape' otherwise consists of little more than a shrubbery and two cypresses. The macaw perched on the pillar's base, seemingly an incongruous addition, may acknowledge Reynolds's borrowing from *The Wet Nurse* after Van Dyck, as Perini (see above) has suggested; but the bird was painted from life. Reynolds owned a macaw, hated by his housemaid but tame enough to perch on Dr Johnson's wrist, where Hannah More observed it in about 1774.[18] The Cockburn macaw is an adult male, whose bright plumage and sharp beak provide a welcome counterpoint in this superfecund scene. Averting its gaze from the virtuous group, it appears to be at large, and might at any point misbehave. Reynolds's macaw was to reappear in his portrait of the Countess of Derby, 1777: the oil was destroyed, but a detail of the macaw from William Dickinson's mezzotint engraving of 1780 is reproduced by Potterton.[19]

Northcote notes that on completing Lady Cockburn's portrait, Reynolds 'marked his name within the embroidered edge of her garment, in the same manner as on the portrait of Mrs Siddons; and these two are the only pictures in which he has ever done so'. Northcote also records that when the Cockburn group arrived at the Royal Academy for the exhibition of 1774, 'all the painters then present were so

Fig. 7 *Charity*, *c*.1778–9. Oil on canvas, 173 × 69 cm.
A study for the central light in the window of New College, Oxford.
Oxford, Ashmolean Museum, Chambers Hall Gift 1855.

struck with its extraordinary splendour and excellence, that they testified their approbation of it by suddenly clapping with their hands.'[20] In the discreetly impersonal fashion of the day, it was exhibited as 'Portrait of a lady with three children'. The *Public Advertiser*'s reviewer was wholeheartedly enthusiastic, particularly admiring 'the Flesh Parts, which are judiciously collected in the Middle of the Picture, and form one great Mass of Light'; he declared the children to be 'sprightly and natural', deemed the macaw 'happily introduced' and concluded that the picture 'is undoubtedly one of the best performances of this excellent Artist, and in Richness and Harmony of Colouring seems to vie with the most celebrated Works of the Flemish and Venetian Schools'.[21] But a later critic in the same newspaper, while admiring 'all the Faces', considered that 'the Design is crouded, unnatural and inconsistent'.[22]

In 1777 Reynolds adapted his – or Van Dyck's – theme, freely and to a tall upright format, for one of the twelve subjects he designed for the west window of New College Chapel, Oxford. The seven lower lights in this window represent the seven virtues (Justice, Fortitude, Prudence and Temperance, the four cardinal virtues, and Faith, Hope and Charity, the three theological virtues).[23] Reynolds exhibited his designs for the window at the Royal Academy: *Faith, Hope* and *Charity* were exhibited in 1779. In the painted window, *Charity* (fig. 7) is placed centrally among the virtues. She turns her head in the same direction as Lady Cockburn,[24] but her gaze is lowered; and the tall narrow design of the space she has to occupy compels her forever to stand, supporting the weight of three (older) children.

Lady Cockburn, born in 1749[25] and christened Augusta Anne, was the daughter of Revd Francis Ayscough DD and his wife Anne, daughter of Sir Thomas Lyttelton, 4th Bt, of Hagley Hall. Her father had been tutor to the future George III and his brother Edward, Duke of York (Richard Wilson portrayed him with his two royal pupils, in about 1749–50[26]), and was later rewarded with the Deanery of Bristol. On 10 July 1769, at the age of twenty, Augusta Ayscough married (as his second wife) Sir James Cockburn, 8th Bt of Langton, Berwickshire,[27] twenty years older than herself.

If Lady Cockburn looks somewhat harassed in Reynolds's picture, the importunities of the three infants are not wholly to blame. She also had three young stepdaughters to look after; and she herself was to bear three more children. Her marriage was to have severe financial trials. Cockburn, the son of a Scottish merchant, had unexpectedly succeeded a cousin to a bankrupt baronetcy; determined to buy back its former estates and restore its prestige, he went into commerce, where he speculated increasingly wildly, and into Parliament where (as MP for Linlithgow Burghs, 1772–84) he was a time-server, his support for Government rewarded by such pickings as the contract (in 1776) to supply rum to the troops in America and the agency for collecting Scottish land tax.[28] When he commissioned Reynolds to portray his wife and three children, he was comparatively affluent; but by 1778 he was hopelessly in debt, chiefly through a highly speculative loan to the Nawab of Arcot. Lord North arranged a secret service pension of £600 per annum, to be paid in Lady Cockburn's name; but in 1781 Cockburn was declared bankrupt. Learning of this, George III granted Lady Cockburn a private pension, 'on account of her distress and the former connexions of her father with his Majesty and the Royal Family'. But the Cockburns continued to be in desperate financial straits, dogged by creditors until the late 1790s when their elder sons (the infants in Reynolds's picture) began, with Lady Cockburn's Lyttelton relations helping to promote their interests, to achieve professional success.

Each of the three sons in the Cockburn group was to have a creditable career in (respectively) the Army, the Navy and the Church. James, the eldest, born on 21 March 1771 and portrayed here on the left, became a Major-General; on his father's death in 1804, he succeeded as 9th Baronet. George, the second and most eminent son, born 22 April 1772 and portrayed on the right, became Admiral of the Fleet, briefly succeeding his elder brother as 10th Baronet in 1852 before his own death in 1853. William, the baby in the picture, born 2 June 1773, became Dean of York and 11th Baronet, dying in 1858. Lady Cockburn survived her husband by over thirty years, dying at the age of 88 on 14 November 1837, five months after Queen Victoria's accession.

The picture's continuing fame is shown by the fact that in 1791, eighteen years after the painting was exhibited, it was engraved by Charles Wilkin. It is said that the first proofs were lettered *Lady Cockburn and her children*, but that Sir James Cockburn objected to his wife being thus publicly identified, whereupon Wilkin burnished out that title and substituted *Cornelia and her Children* (with the passage from *Hook's Roman History* quoted under Engraved).[29] This is unlikely; Wilkin would have discussed his proposed engraving and its title with Sir James before being permitted to borrow the painting for engraving, and no proof bearing Lady Cockburn's name has been traced. The title *Cornelia and her Children* adroitly fuses the 'Charity' of Christian theology with a famous anecdote from Roman history: Cornelia, mother of the Gracchi, indifferent to personal ornament, called her children her 'jewels'.

NOTES

1. Lady Hamilton bequeathed a total of twenty family portraits to the NG (all of members of the Ayscough, Lyttelton and Cockburn families). Accessioned by the NG in 1892–3 as nos. 1354–73, they appear in NG catalogues 1893–1900. The six co-heiresses who challenged Lady Hamilton's bequest (Miss Phelips, Mrs Bankes, Mrs Fortescue, Mrs Benyon, Miss Astley and Mrs Hood) claimed that she had no power to give away family portraits. They did not have to take their case to court; on the advice of the Treasury Solicitor that a judgement would almost certainly go against the NG (Board Minutes, vol. 7, pp. 83, 87, 108), the NG delivered all the works in Lady Hamilton's bequest to the co-heiresses on 6 April 1900. They sold the Reynolds the next day, and the other nineteen portraits at Christie's, 25 June 1900 (1–19). After the deaccessioning of works in Lady Hamilton's bequest the numbers formerly allocated to them were reused for later accessions: when *Lady Cockburn* re-entered the NG in 1906, it was renumbered NG 2077.

2. NG 6494, oil on panel, 148.2 × 107.5 cm, purchased 1984: see *NG Report 1982–4*, pp. 34–5, repr., and Christopher Brown, *Flemish Paintings*, London 1987, p. 82, colour plate 35. A second version, on canvas, was formerly in the Methuen collection at Corsham Court, Wiltshire.

3. Repr. Raimond van Marle, *Iconographie de L'Art Profane au Moyen-Age et à la Renaissance*, New York 1971, p. 59, fig. 70. The compiler has not attempted an exhaustive search for the image.

4. H. Potterton, *Reynolds and Gainsborough*, London 1986, p. 34.

5. For example, by E.H. Gombrich, 'Reynolds's Theory and Practice of Imitation', *Burlington Magazine*, LXXX, 1942, pp. 40–5, and J. Newman, 'Reynolds and Hone – The Conjuror Unmasked', in ed. Penny 1986, pp. 344–54.

6. It entered the Ashmolean Museum in 1855 as by Van Dyck, but see Francis Broun, 'Sir Joshua Reynolds's Collection of Paintings', PhD dissertation, Princeton University, New Jersey 1987, pp. 100–2. Broun's attribution of the sketch to Reynolds is well argued and now generally accepted.

7. Perini 1994, pp. 28–9.

8. For the history of NG 2057, see MacLaren/Braham 1970.

9. This Richard Cooper (1740–1814) trained as an engraver under his father, Richard Cooper the elder (d.1764) and under Le Bas in Paris.

10. Quoted by Duncan Bull and Enriqueta Harris, *Burlington Magazine*, CXXVIII, 1986, p. 646.

11. Ibid., pp. 643–54: Cooper's squared drawing is repr. fig. 8 and discussed on p. 647.

12. The drawing is D4823/11/9 in the second of two albums of Cooper's copy-drawings presented by one of his descendants to the National Gallery of Scotland in 1959. One of the albums is labelled 'Drawings from Original Pictures done for the finished Drawings of the same by Richard Cooper – to be kept – R.C.'. They are described by Bull and Harris (cited in note 10), p. 647.

13. Reynolds probably knew Cooper's father, Richard Cooper the elder, a prolific portrait engraver, who had made a soft-ground etching of Reynolds's portrait of Boswell.

14. Private collection; repr. Waterhouse 1941, plate 287.

15. 1986, plates 28–30.

16. Isador Harrison Tumpeer MD, 'The Ease of Erring in the Diagnosis of Mongolism from Premedical Portraits', *Bulletin of the Society of Medical History of Chicago*, vol. I, 1937, pp. 10–17.

17. Northcote 1818, II, p. 30.

18. William Roberts, *Memoirs of the Life and Correspondence of Mrs Hannah More*, 4 vols, 2nd edn, London 1834, I, p. 48.

19. 1986, p. 35, plate 33.

20. Northcote 1818, II, p. 29.

21. 28 April 1774 [p. 2].

22. 3 May 1774 [p. 2].

23. See ed. Penny 1986, pp. 290–1 and p. 32, fig. 18: The West Window of the Chapel, New College, Oxford, painted on glass by Jervaise after Reynolds, engraved by Richard Earlom. Reynolds's designs are discussed by Max Roldit, 'The Collection of Pictures of the Earl of Normanton, at Somerley, Hampshire', *Burlington Magazine*, II, 1903, pp. 211–13; Reynolds's paintings of *Charity*, *Faith* and *Hope*, exhibited RA 1779, are repr. facing p. 211, and by Postle 1995, pp. 168–91, 177–9, fig. 71.

24. Having painted NG 2077, and with his earlier 'mother and child' drawings at hand, it seems unlikely that Reynolds needed another model for his New College design. There appears to be no evidence for the statement in Roldit 1903, p. 212, followed by Postle 1995, p. 179, that his model for it was Mrs Sheridan; this may be a confusion with the fact that Mrs Sheridan sat for the figure of the Virgin in the large *Nativity* designed for the upper lights in the New College window (and for *Saint Cecilia*, 1775); see ed. Penny 1986, pp. 265–7.

25. Her father was then Rector of Northchurch, Hertfordshire, but she was not baptised there. The compiler is grateful to the County Archivist of Hertfordshire for examining the registers.

26. Coll. NPG (1165), Kerslake 1977, pp. 9–11, plates 38–9.

27. His career is traced in ed. Namier and Brooke 1964, II, pp. 229–30. See also Sir Robert Cockburn, Bt and Harry A. Cockburn, *The Records of the Cockburn Family*, London and Edinburgh 1913, pp. 53ff., which lists the six children of the marriage.

28. Cockburn was a partner of Henry Douglas, a wealthy Scots-West Indian merchant, whose daughter Mary he firstly married (she d.1766). In the 1760s Cockburn was successively a commissary of supply to the army in Germany, a speculator in plantations in Dominica, a partner in the Colebrooke Bay Co. and a director of the East India Co.

29. Graves and Cronin, I, p. 182.

to Parliament 5 December 1782, and finally ratified by the Treaty of Paris, signed 3 September 1783 (Richard Oswald, see under NG 4931, being one of the British signatories).

16. Tarleton and many others left America nearly two years before the Treaty of Paris was signed.

17. Quoted in Bass 1958, p. 8.

18. Letter to his brother, 2 February 1782, quoted in Lewis Bettany, *Edward Jerningham and his Friends*, London 1919, p. 25.

19. *c.*1812; private collection, Scotland, repr. *Painting in Scotland*, exh. cat. Talbot Rice Gallery, Edinburgh 1986, and Tate Gallery, London 1987 (110), p. 132, plate 57. A smaller (single) portrait of Dundas by Raeburn is in the same coll. Dundas also sat to Downman and Daniel Gardner.

20. In the collection of the Oriental Club, there called '19thc. English School'.

21. 1814, Royal Collection. An anon. miniature of Lake *c.*1800 is repr. as frontispiece to H. Pearse, *Memoir of the Life and Military Service of Viscount Lake, Baron Lake of Delhi and Laswaree, 1744–1808*, London 1908.

22. See ed. Thorne 1986, p. 332, and Bass 1958, p. 170.

23. Delivered 11 December 1769; reprinted in Wark 1981, quotations taken from p. 27.

24. The subject is from the Apocrypha, Book of Tobit, 6, i–v (ii: 'And when the young man went down to wash himself, a fish leaped out of the river, and would have devoured him'). The drawing bears (bottom right) Reynolds's collector's mark (Lugt 2364), and was probably one of the 49 Rembrandt drawings (titles not given) in his posthumous sale of 26 May 1794, conducted from the house of A.C. de Poggi. It is now in the Louvre. See Otto Benesch, *The Drawings of Rembrandt*, vol. V, London 1957, no. 908, fig. 1119; Benesch records the Grosvenor Gallery catalogue's observation.

25. *Winter Exhibition*, Grosvenor Gallery, London 1877–8 (1181). The catalogue note may have been made by Sir Coutts Lindsay, proprietor of the Gallery, or by J. Comyns Carr, noted in the preface as in the course of preparing lengthier notes. In either case, the observation was probably made from the engraving of Colonel Tarleton, which was well known, rather than from the painting, then in Admiral Tarleton's private collection.

26. It is not mentioned in Davies 1959, nor in ed. Penny 1986.

27. Stewart 1988, p. 261.

28. Ed. Penny 1986, p. 301. For the antique sculpture, see Haskell and Penny 1981, pp. 182–4, repr. p. 183.

29. Joseph Baretti, *A Guide through the Royal Academy*, London 1781, p. 20, notes that the cast was placed in the First Room of the Academy of the Antique.

30. Stewart 1988, p. 263, and *passim*. Pigalle presented his *Mercury* to the French Academy in 1744. According to Michael Levey ('The Pose of Pigalle's "Mercury"', *Burlington Magazine*, 106, 1964, p. 462), 'The Mercury became, and probably has remained, one of the most famous pieces of sculpture executed in eighteenth-century France.' Reynolds could have seen it in Paris in 1752; it was also engraved.

31. It is not known when Reynolds acquired it. See Perini 1994, p. 26 and n. 11, for the suggestion that the version owned by Reynolds (offered for sale in 1791, sold in 1795) is the picture now on loan to the Shipley Art Gallery, Gateshead.

32. Coll. National Gallery of Ireland; repr. ed. Penny 1986, p. 343, cat. no. 173, repr.

33. *Lyric Odes to the Royal Academicians for MDCCLXXXII*, in *The Works of Peter Pindar, Esq*r., I, 1794, pp. 16–17.

34. The evidence in Reynolds's pocket-books for Tarleton's sittings is summarised in ed. Penny 1986, p. 300.

35. Published 1 April 1782.

36. Carman 1984 (cited in note 5), pp. 129–30.

37. The suggestion in ed. Penny 1986, p. 301, that appointments reading simply 'horse' in Reynolds's pocket-book early in 1782 may have been for Tarleton's rather than Colonel Coussmaker's horse seems most unlikely. Only the horses' heads are visible in Tarleton's picture; it seems unlikely that Reynolds would have made an appointment with a horse just to paint its head; and even supposing the heads to have been painted from life, Tarleton could not (in the rapid exit from America after Yorktown) have brought his own chargers with him.

38. 30 April 1782.

39. 2 May 1782. 'An Angel' is coll. Duke of Portland, Welbeck Abbey.

40. Quoted in Graves and Cronin 1899.

41. 200 guineas = £210, Reynolds's usual charge for a full-length in the period 1782–91; see M. Kirby Talley Jr on Reynolds's practice and studio in ed. Penny 1986, p. 58.

42. First established in 1774 but disbanded in 1775, it was reconstituted in 1783, with Henry Blundell Ince as President and Roscoe as Vice-President.

The compiler is very grateful to Alex Kidson, Walker Art Gallery, Liverpool, for communicating two letters from Reynolds to Roscoe (relevant extracts only given here). (1) Letter of 2 October 1784: '...I am very glad to hear of the success of your Exhibition, I shall allways wish to contribute to it, to the best of my power' (MS, Roscoe Papers, Liverpool Record Office, 920.ROS.3112); (2) Letter of 16 October 1784 (Yale Center for British Art, Reynolds MS no. 15). Other RAs who lent to the 1784 Liverpool exhibition included Paul Sandby, George Barret and Henry Fuseli.

43. The full entry, undated (Ledgers, Cormack 1970, p. 165), reads: 'Col. Tarlton. Sent to his Mother, near Liverpool (to Exors) 210.0.0.' This compiler suggests that the entry 'Col. Tarlton 210.0.0.' was made on or soon after 10 July 1792 (the date of the immediately preceding entry); that Reynolds added 'Sent to his Mother, near Liverpool' some time after the close of the Liverpool exhibition, autumn 1784; and that '(to Exors)' refers to eventual payment made in 1791, but perhaps not cleared until after Reynolds's death.

44. Presumably his elder brother Thomas Tarleton, head of the family business.

45. Many Parker family portraits, including a pair by Hamlet Winstanley of Banastre Tarleton's maternal grandparents Banastre Parker and his wife (96), were in the sale of the late R.A. Tatton of Cuerden Hall, Christie's, 28 February 1947 (lots 43–106). This sale included eight portraits by (or attr. to) Wright of Derby of the Parker and related Clayton and Townley families (lots 102–6). Several Parker and Townley portraits are now on public view at Astley Hall, Chorley, Lancs. Wright's portrait of 'Mrs Sarah Clayton' (102) is now coll. Fitchburg Art Museum, US, exh. *Wright of Derby*, Tate Gallery 1990 (26, repr.). Wright's portraits of 'John Tarleton' and 'Jane Tarleton' (a copy of the latter is noted in Wright's Account Book 1769; both in a descendant's private collection, England, in 1958) are repr. in Bass 1958, facing p. 182. Below, on the same page, and in the same collection, is repr. a portrait of 'Cornet Banastre Tarleton' as a young man, his right hand on a sword hilt, presumably painted soon after his purchase of a commission in 1775: stated to be by Allan Ramsay, but Ramsay was no longer painting at this date, and the portrait appears (in repr.) to be hardly fine enough to be by him.

46. See Bass 1958 (cited in note 5), *passim*, particularly pp. 211–18.

47. See ed. Penny 1986, p. 299.

48. It is the chief subject in Bass 1958 (cited in note 5, *passim*). For a well-illustrated short account chiefly from 'Perdita's' angle, see John Ingamells, *Mrs Robinson and her Portraits* (Wallace Collection Monographs no. 1), 1978, *passim*.

49. See F.G. Stephens and Dorothy M. George, *Catalogue of Pol. and Pers. Satires*, vol. V, 1935. In this Gillray's *The Thunderer* is cat. no. 6116.

50. Walpole to Revd William Mason, *Walpole Correspondence*, vol. XXIX, 1955, p. 189.

51. See Bass 1958, pp. 258ff.

52. Notably a series of 'Strictures on Lieutenant-Colonel Tarleton's "History", 1787, from Lieutenant Roderick Mackenzie', published in the *Morning Post*: 'Lieutenant Colonel Tarleton landed in America in the year 1777, with the rank of Cornet of Dragoons, and in the beginning of January 1781, we find him the *primum mobile*, the master spring which puts the whole machinery of the army in motion!'

53. John Tarleton to his mother, early in 1782: 'The picture of my Brother at Gainsborough's will not measure with the frame less than 12 feet 6 inches': Tarleton family papers, quoted by Bass 1958, p. 196.

54. BM 1875-8-14-1305, n.d.; in this Tarleton is turned to the right, bare-headed, apparently in a different uniform with epaulettes.

NG 111

Lord Heathfield of Gibraltar

exhibited 1788
Oil on canvas, 142 × 113.5 cm (56 × 44¾ in.)

Provenance
Commissioned by Alderman John Boydell and presented by him to the Corporation of the City of London 1794; removed from Guildhall in 1809 by his nephew Josiah Boydell, replaced with a copy and offered for sale first privately, then from 31 May 1809 at the European Museum, Pall Mall, where purchased by [Sir] Thomas Lawrence RA 7 June 1809; presumably mortgaged or sold by Lawrence at some unknown date to John Julius Angerstein;[1] purchased with the Angerstein collection for the National Gallery 1824.

Exhibited
RA 1788 (115, as 'Portrait of a nobleman, half length'); on public display in the Common Council Chamber, Guildhall, City of London, from 1794 to mid-1809; Paris, Louvre, 1938 (112); Ottawa, National Gallery of Canada, *Masterpieces of European Painting, 1490–1840*, 1960 (22, repr. in colour on cover); Tate Gallery 1992–3 (38, repr. in colour).

At the Tate Gallery 1960–1; 1963–4.

Literature
Reynolds's Sitter Books 1787; Reynolds's Ledgers II, f.32v., October 1787, ed. Cormack 1970, p.155; *St James's Chronicle*, issue of 20–29 April 1787 [p. 4]; Alderman John Boydell, *A Description of Several Pictures Presented to the Corporation of the City of London by John Boydell, Alderman of the Ward of Cheap, and Placed in the Common-Council Chamber of the City…*, London 1794, p. 24, no. XX; James Barry, *Works*, London 1809, I, p. 553; Northcote 1818, II, p. 235; Cunningham 1830–3, I, p. 310, VI, pp. 244–5; Passavant 1836, I, p. 54; Waagen 1854, I, p. 365; Shee 1860, pp. 107–8; Leslie and Taylor 1865, II, p. 517; Graves and Cronin, II, 1899, pp. 455–6; IV, pp. 1337, 1480; Waterhouse 1941, p. 79, plate 281; Davies 1946, pp. 114–15; Davies 1959, pp. 80–1; Haydon, *Diary*, vol. III, 1963, p. 486; Waterhouse 1973, p. 33, plate 107; Potterton 1976, pp. 43, 48, repr. p. 46; Hermann Arnold Bruntjen, *John Boydell (1719–1804). A Study of Art Patronage and Publishing in Georgian London*, PhD thesis published in facsimile, Ann Arbor, Michigan 1985, pp. 212, 266, 273–6; Vivien Knight, *The Works of Art of the Corporation of London*, Cambridge 1986, pp. 12–13 [239]; Shawe-Taylor 1990, p. 49.

Engraved
by Richard Earlom, 16⅝ × 13¼ in., published 1 November 1788 by John & Josiah Boydell, Cheapside (Hamilton 1874, p. 36). For later versions see Graves and Cronin, II, p. 456.

Copies (numerous) include
(1) 65 × 44 in. by anon, commissioned by Josiah Boydell *c.*1808–9 and 'openly made' to replace Reynolds's portrait in Guildhall, coll. Guildhall Art Gallery (on long loan to the Royal Military College, Shrivenham), repr. Knight 1986, p. 239; (2) by Samuel Lane, presented 1851 to United Service Club, Pall Mall (now coll. Crown Estates Commissioners); (3) small (6½ × 5 in.) enamel by Henry Bone, in his sale, Christie's 20 July 1832 (17), now untraced.

Technical Notes
This picture displays many of the defects of Reynolds's technique. Notes in the Gallery's archives record that in 1859 *Lord Heathfield* was 'very bitumen cracked throughout' and that in 1867 'some repaints were removed from the background' and that it was 'repaired and re-varnished'. Since then, the picture has been surface cleaned, and some shrinkage cracks in the red coat were touched out in 1986. These cracks seem to have become more prominent than they had been in a photograph of 1931, suggesting that the paint was still contracting and exposing a brighter underlayer of red paint.

The red coat is a mixture of coarse and fine vermilion enhanced in colour by the addition of a deep red-purple lake and a small proportion of red earth. The upper surface of a paint sample shows that the colour is muted by dirt and old varnish, suggesting that the coat was originally a brighter red.

The appearance of the background is marred by very wide and deep shrinkage cracks which have been filled and painted out. There is much retouching disguising cracks elsewhere, and the yellow varnish has a mottled appearance, especially on the face.

General George Augustus Eliott, later Lord Heathfield (1717–90),[2] was acclaimed as a national hero for his defence of Gibraltar against a long siege by the Spanish and their French allies, ended at last on 13 September 1782. Hearing of his triumph, Horace Walpole dubbed him 'Rock-Eliott'.[3] Britain had won Gibraltar from Spain in 1704, British possession of the Rock being ratified by the Treaty of Utrecht in 1713. Gibraltar was regarded by the British people as a key possession. Lord Townshend had stated in 1728 that 'the bare mention of a proposal, which carried the most distant appearance of laying England under an obligation of ever parting with that place, would be sufficient to put the whole nation in a flame',[4] though as Horace Walpole was to remark nearly sixty years later, 'There are many, I believe, who think it is in the parish of St Martin in the Fields, and would as easily have relinquished the Isle of Wight.'[5]

General Eliott took up his command as Governor of Gibraltar in 1777, at the age of 60. Within two years, Spain declared war on Britain. The Spanish had never been reconciled to the loss of Gibraltar. In June 1779, calculating that Britain's naval and military forces would be so heavily deployed in the War of American Independence that she would be unable to defend the Rock, the Spanish and their French allies began a siege and blockade of Gibraltar. The ordeals endured by the British garrison during a siege which lasted three years, seven months and twelve days are recounted by

Fig. 1 G.F. Koehler, *General Eliott directing Fire on the Spanish Batteries from the King's Bastion at Gibraltar, 13 September 1782, assisted by his Aide-de-camp Lt. G.F. Koehler*. Engraving.

Captain John Drinkwater of the 72nd Regiment, in *A History of the Siege of Gibraltar*.[6] Here only the episode which inspired Reynolds's portrait can be outlined. Having failed to starve the British garrison into surrender, the Spanish devised a new form of offensive: bombardment from 'floating batteries' or 'battering-ships', vaunted throughout Europe as '*impregnable* and *incombustible*'.[7] On the morning of 13 September 1782, ten such ships, laden with enough ammunition to pound the British defences to destruction, anchored close to the sea-wall of the Rock and opened fire.

'Unawed by the impending storm',[8] General Eliott directed return fire from the King's Bastion on the Rock. This is the background Reynolds economically suggests with two small cannon and a little crenellation; it is elaborated in the engraving after a drawing made by Eliott's aide-de-camp, Lieutenant G.F. Koehler (fig. 1). The British cannon fired red-hot shot with such accuracy that the allegedly '*incombustible*' floating batteries burst successively into flames, each serving to illuminate the next as a target. By midnight the entire harbour seemed ablaze. The Spanish attack had failed – spectacularly. The following month a British fleet under Lord Howe pierced the Spanish and French blockade. The siege was over;[9] Gibraltar remained British. Peace terms were agreed on 20 January 1783.

Drinkwater described the scene of the destruction of the Spanish floating batteries as one 'of mingled sublimity and terror'.[10] Such descriptions, aided by the sketches of eyewitnesses[11] and newspaper reports,[12] inspired many British painters and popular print-publishers to seize upon the subject while it was still topical.[13] William Hamilton, Thomas Whitcombe and James Jefferys and George Carter all exhibited paintings of the subject at the Royal Academy the following year, 1783; others already had pictures in the hands of engravers. Joseph Wright of Derby, having hoped to be quick off the mark (on 13 January 1783 he wrote that there was 'no time to be lost, as the subject is ... already in the hands of several & will soon be a hackney'd one'[14]), took over two years to complete his picture, finally exhibiting it as the star turn in his one-man exhibition in 1785 (it is now untraced).[15] George Carter, who had worked since 1783 on a large picture of *General Eliott and his Officers observing the Destruction of the Floating Batteries, Gibraltar, September 1782* (exhibited in his own one-man show in Pall Mall in 1785),[16] missed the chance to secure a commission from Boydell for the subject; it went instead to his friend John Singleton Copley, who took eight years to complete a vast canvas (211 × 298 in.),[17] first exhibited by the artist in a tent in Green Park in 1791, and later in Guildhall (removed from Guildhall in 1941, and recently restored, it will return to public display in the new Guildhall Art Gallery, scheduled to open in 1998).[18]

Paintings and prints thus kept the drama of the end of the siege of Gibraltar fresh in the public memory during the five years which passed until Reynolds could portray the hero of that hour. General Eliott had repelled the enemy; but his term of service as Governor of Gibraltar still had several years to run. On St George's Day 1783, on his own parade-ground at Gibraltar, he was invested with the Order of the Bath: Reynolds's depiction of the Star of that Order on the breast of his still-embattled hero is several months premature. General Eliott KB returned from Gibraltar in 1787, to a hero's welcome, a parliamentary pension for life and a peerage. On 6 July 1787 he was created Lord Heathfield of Gibraltar. On 27 August he had his first sitting to Reynolds.

Heathfield's portrait was commissioned by Alderman John Boydell (1718–1804), who paid for it in October 1787 (£105). Boydell, a staunch patron of British artists[19] as well as an Alderman of the City of London (he was Lord Mayor in 1790), determined to establish in Guildhall a gallery of paintings depicting 'great and glorious actions', believing that such works would have a 'moral effect' upon his fellow-citizens. Boydell records Heathfield's 'affability ... and readiness' to sit for his portrait as part of this patriotic scheme.[20]

When he sat to Reynolds on 27 August 1787 (the first of seven sittings),[21] Heathfield was aged 70. Five years had passed since his ordeal and triumph at Gibraltar. It is the moment of trial before that triumph which Reynolds recaptures. Heathfield is portrayed battle-stained, in his uniform as an officer of the 15th Light Dragoons ('The King's Own'): short red coat 'lapelled and turned up with dark green', white waistcoat and white linen breeches – a uniform virtually unchanged since that regiment had been formed (as the 1st Light Horse) under Heathfield's command in 1759.[22] The red of his coat has faded; this faded colour, for which one might otherwise have blamed Reynolds's pigments, may allude to the general's five years' service on the Rock. George Carter's picture also shows Heathfield's coat as of a faded red, in striking contrast to the pristine uniforms of officers surrounding him. Farington records that Lawrence later remarked on 'the Colour of the Scarlet Coat, so unlike what either Hoppner or any other painter obtains', but in what way the 'scarlet' of Heathfield's coat was 'unlike' the colour used by other artists for regimental coats is not recorded.[23]

Heathfield's portrait was exhibited at the Royal Academy as 'Portrait of a nobleman...' in 1787 (115), but the sitter was instantly identified by the *St James's Chronicle*: 'No. 115. A fine Portrait of Lord Heathfield; with the Key of the Fort of Gibraltar in his Hand.' Boydell, a print publisher, commissioned Richard Earlom to engrave it;[24] to boost sales of the engraving (published in 1788, at one guinea), he displayed the painted portrait beside the engraving in his gallery in Pall Mall, declaring it to be 'the most Capital Portrait ever Painted by this Master'. The young Martin Archer Shee saw 'Lord Heathfield' there on 7 November 1788, and acclaimed it as 'one of the finest portraits Sir Joshua ever painted'.[25]

Probably Reynolds 'got a likeness'. Heathfield's features closely resemble those in the head and shoulders portrait by Mather Brown (fig. 2), painted at much the same time,[26] and are recognisably the same in portraits (or larger Gibraltar scenes) by George Carter, Antonio Poggi (1783)[27] and Copley (noted above); but Copley's study of Heathfield's head exaggerates the imperiousness of the sitter's profile, as well as his 'in-jawed' appearance' (an eighteenth-century euphemism for loss of teeth).[28] Lord Heathfield died in 1790. More than forty years after his defence of Gibraltar, the country commemorated him with a marble monument by J.C.F. Rossi RA in St Paul's Cathedral. Life-size and vigilant, Heathfield stands in the south transept, directly opposite the statue later erected in honour of J.M.W. Turner.[29]

It is Heathfield's indomitable expression which has justly preserved the fame of this portrait; and for this it has always been revered, particularly by other artists. Contemporaries especially admired the manner in which Heathfield holds the so-called 'key of Gibraltar' in his hands. James Barry remarked in 1809 that 'He grasps the key of Gibraltar in his hand, and seems to say, amid the volleying smoke and fire, "This rock shall melt and run into the Mediterranean before I yield thee".'[30] Heathfield's grasp of the key similarly impressed Constable, who noted '...the chain of the massive key of the fortress twice passed round his hand, as to secure it in his grasp. He seems to say, "I have you, and will keep you!"'[31] Reynolds depicts an unreally huge key, whose function in his portrait is chiefly symbolic; this is not wholly a product of his imagination, but a brilliant example of his instinct to rise above detail. As Governor of Gibraltar, Heathfield would have used a bunch of about fifteen keys of various shapes and sizes for the daily ceremonial of locking the fortress gates;[32] possibly he described this ceremonial to Reynolds. Reynolds, well aware that a bunch of miscellaneous keys would have had little pictorial impact, replaces them with one massive key; and that key, heavy in Heathfield's hands, becomes a symbol not only of his responsibility for the fate of Gibraltar, but also of Gibraltar itself, long known by such names as 'The Key', 'The Lock', 'The Gate' or 'The Keeper'.[33] Reynolds's general study of Van Dyck's *Iconography* underlies much of his portraiture. In this case, noting Heathfield's 'intense gaze, past the spectator, to some distant prospect', Potterton 1976 suggests that the engraving after Van Dyck's portrait of *Paul de Vos* (which Reynolds would certainly have known, and which Potterton reproduces, p. 46) might have stimulated ideas for his *Lord Heathfield*.

Within twenty years of its execution, *Lord Heathfield* was reputedly already in poor condition. Farington reports a conversation at Charles Long's dinner table on 10 June 1809, when 'Pictures painted by Sir Joshua Reynolds were spoken of. Mr. Knight sd. His fine portrait of John Hunter [exh. 1786] is utterly gone by cracking &c. West sd. the same of His portrait of Lord Heathfield';[34] two days later Farington reported similar observations from Lord Lonsdale ('a few small pieces' had 'come out' of his *Infant Hercules*) and the Duke of Rutland (his *Nativity* was in a 'bad state' and 'the eye of one of the Heads had fallen out').[35] During the previous year, Josiah Boydell, nephew and business heir of the late Alderman John Boydell, had managed to remove the Reynolds from Guildhall on the grounds that it 'wd. have perished had it remained hung upon a damp wall';[36] but though damp had affected some paintings in Guildhall, neither contemporary nor present evidence indicates that damp, rather than Reynolds's faulty technique, caused the picture's deterioration. Josiah Boydell paid for a copy (by an unidentified artist)[37] to be hung in its place, and (probably in March 1808) offered Reynolds's original portrait for sale at 350 guineas. It found no takers over the next year, largely because Boydell's legal title to it was uncertain. Farington noted that 'Should the City claim it it would have to be given up';[38] but the City made no claim.

There was one man, himself a portraitist, and perhaps the best man in England to appreciate *Lord Heathfield*'s qualities, who wanted it for what he could learn from it. Thomas Lawrence RA talked several times to Farington about his desire to possess *Lord Heathfield*.[39] When (on 31 May 1809) Josiah Boydell placed the portrait openly for sale in the European Museum, where 'all the eminent artists, military officers & foreigners of distinction' went to see it,[40] Lawrence (rarely

Fig. 2 Mather Brown (1761–1831), *Lord Heathfield*, 1788. Oil on canvas, 76.2 × 63.5 cm. Detroit Institute of Art. Photo courtesy Leger Galleries.

financially stable) was forced into a decision. On 7 June he spoke to Farington 'of the advantage it wd. be to him, to have that picture to be a guide to him. He said there is in it a total absence of manner, & a compleat whole in effect without any part being sacrificed'.[41] Farington, as so often an intermediary (this time between Lawrence and Boydell), replied characteristically 'that it certainly is an admirable picture for an able artist to regulate His pictures by'; he then arranged for Lawrence to buy the portrait for £300, to be paid over seven months.[42] *Lord Heathfield* was delivered to Farington's house the next day. Lawrence called; elated, he declared that 'He thought it the best of Sir Joshua's pictures of men & equal to that of Mrs Siddons', adding that 'He felt he should learn much from it, particularly in *breadth of colour*'.[43] Lawrence bought the *Lord Heathfield* in a mood of rising self-confidence; he told Farington 'that He found himself firmly fixed in reputation in His Art, and now had many persons desirous to sit to Him, whenever He shall name the time'. But Lawrence never learnt how to manage money, despite repeated advice and generous help from John Julius Angerstein (see under NG 6370, pp. 358–65). It may have been Angerstein who in fact paid for (or helped substantially with) Lawrence's acquisition of *Lord Heathfield*, the picture reverting to him later; it was purchased for the National Gallery in 1824 as part of the Angerstein collection.

Lawrence's admiration for *Lord Heathfield* found swift expression in his own portrait of *Lt.-General Sir Thomas Graham, later 1st Baron Lynedoch*, painted about 1810–11 (fig. 3).[44] Graham's portrait is painted in direct emulation of *Lord Heathfield*; the pose, the turn of the head, the battle-rent background and (providentially) the uniform are closely similar; but Lawrence cannot resist painting such details as a golden medal, a silken cummerbund and a prominent trouser-button which distract attention. Comparison between the two enables us to appreciate the fact that it is the almost imperceptibly upward tilt of Heathfield's head which confirms his resoluteness, combined with the supremely judged simplicity of the manner in which he holds (and will never release) the key.

Fig. 3 Sir Thomas Lawrence, *Lt.-General Sir Thomas Graham, later 1st Baron Lynedoch*, *c*.1810–11. Oil on canvas, 144.2 × 113 cm. Private collection. Photo courtesy Christie's.

The last word must go to Benjamin Robert Haydon, generally no friend of academicians. After seeing the portrait of Lord Heathfield on 18 May 1824, shortly after its acquisition for the new National Gallery, he wrote in his diary: 'It affected me like the explosion of a bomb! It is an honour to the country.'[45]

NOTES

1. Angerstein's help to Lawrence in his financial difficulties is noted on p. 358.

2. He was educated at Leyden University and the military college of La Fere. His army career, beginning as a volunteer in the Prussian Army in 1735 and including service at Dettingen and Fontenoy, at Havana and as commander-in-chief in Ireland (1774–5), is outlined in *DNB*. Past experience served him well in sustaining the Siege of Gibraltar: he had trained at Woolwich as a field engineer, he had long schooled himself to austerity (and a diet of vegetables and water) and he was famous in the army for his concern for the welfare of his troops, never overlooking such practical matters as rearing chickens or growing carrots within a garrison. Heathfield died on 6 July 1790, three years after sitting to Reynolds, at his château at Aix-la-Chapelle.

3. Letter to Horace Mann, 23 January 1783, *Walpole Correspondence*, vol. XXV, p. 357.

4. 3rd Lord Townshend, statesman and negotiator with France and Spain, to Stephen Poyntz, 3–14 June 1728, quoted in G. Hills, *Rock of Contention: A History of Gibraltar*, London 1974, p. 97.

5. Letter to Horace Mann, 23 January 1783, *Walpole Correspondence*, vol. XXV, p. 357.

6. Drinkwater's *A History of the Siege of Gibraltar*, London 1785, went into four editions by 1790.

7. Ibid., p. 116. General Eliott's report of the action, dated 15 September 1782 and published in the *Annual Register* for 1782, pp. 238ff., uses the term 'battering ships', though artists and engravers mostly title them 'floating batteries'. Hills 1974 reproduces an Austrian engraving (facing p. 337) showing the Spanish 'batteries' as they moved into position before Gibraltar on 13 September 1782, and gives an account of the combat on pp. 333–44; see also Prown 1966, pp. 322–36.

8. The phrase is Drinkwater's 1785, p. 116.

9. A report of the end of the siege reached Horace Walpole at Strawberry Hill on 3 November 1782: he passed on the news the same day to Lady Ossory with the comment 'Well, Madam, is not this General Eliott the Old Man of the Mountain who destroyed enemies with his *feu grégeois*?' (*Walpole Correspondence*, vol. XXX, p. 358).

10. Drinkwater 1785, p. 137.

11. In particular, Admiral Sir Roger Curtis, who took part in the action, made 'Drawings of the general effect & of all the particular parts – as of the Rock, Batteries, Gun Boats, Falucas &c &c'. He made these available to artists. Joseph Wright of Derby asked William Hayley to obtain Sir Roger Curtis's permission for 'some good draftsman in Town' to copy details from Curtis's sketches and send them to him (Wright to Hayley, 3 January 1783, Inglefield MSS, Derby).

12. For example, the *London Gazette*, November 1782, *Annual Register*, 1782, pp. 238ff.; *Gentleman's Magazine*, 1782, pp. 511–12, 545–6, etc.

13. Paintings of 'The Destruction of the Spanish Floating Batteries' (or variants of that title) include: (i) Thomas Whitcombe, 1782, exh. RA 1783 (173), NMM, repr. NMM 1988, p. 434; (ii) Dominic Serres (unlocated), engr. F. Jukes, published 10 February 1783; (iii) James Jefferys, exh. RA 1783 (241), Maidstone Museum, engr. W. Woollett & J. Emes, published 1789; (iv) William Hamilton, exh. RA 1783 (228), unlocated, engr. Archibald Robertson, published 25 March 1783; (v) John Keyse Sherwin, engr. by himself, published 14 September 1784; (vi) Wright of Derby, shown in his one-man exh., Mr Robins's Rooms, 1785 (24), and in the Manchester *Art Treasures* exhibition, 1857 (D, 81), but since then untraced: see note 15; (vii) George Carter, a large picture, in his one-man exhibition 1785, NAM, with a preliminary oil sketch, coll. NPG, repr. NPG cat., 1981, p. 653: see note 16; (viii) John Singleton Copley, commissioned by the Corporation of London 1783: a vast work finished in 1791, coll. Guildhall, repr. Prown 1966, fig. 489; (ix–xii) Richard Paton, four large canvases commissioned by Alderman John Boydell and presented to the Corporation of the City of London 1792, repr. Knight 1986, pp. 228–9.

14. Wright to Hayley, see note 11.

15. *View of Gibraltar during the destruction of the Spanish Floating Batteries, 13th September 1782*, exhibited by Wright at Mr Robins's Rooms, 1785 (24); bt by John Milnes for 420 guineas, it was the most expensive (? and the largest) picture Wright painted, but has been untraced since 1857 (see Nicolson 1968, pp. 16, 159–60, 248, and Egerton 1990, p. 69). The picture in Milwaukee Art Museum, identified as the lost Wright in the *Burlington Magazine*, CXVI, 1974, pp. 270–2, fig. 50, and studied by the compiler and others since then, is generally agreed to be not by Wright.

16. Carter's picture was purchased between 1785 and 1795 by General Lord Balcarres, 10th Earl of Balcarres; later on long loan to the National Army Museum, it entered its permanent collection in 1996. The compiler is indebted for information about it to Michael Ball, National Army Museum.

17. For Copley's picture and the various pencil and oil studies made for it, see Prown 1966, ch. XVI, pp. 322–36.

18. Information kindly contributed by Gill Leighton, Conservator, Guildhall Art Gallery.

19. See Bruntjen 1985, *passim*.

20. Boydell 1794, quoted in Knight 1986, p. [12]. Paintings presented by Boydell to the Corporation of London 1792–8 are discussed and catalogued by Bruntjen 1985, pp. 197–228, 257–68, and repr. (small size) by Knight 1986. They included portraits of *Lord Howe* (by Northcote), *Lord Duncan of Camperdown* (by Hoppner), *Lord Cornwallis* (by Copley), *Lord Nelson* and *Earl St Vincent* (both by Beechey); and four paintings by Richard Paton depicting the destruction of the Spanish floating batteries (see note 13), in the centre of which Boydell hung *Lord Heathfield*.

21. Reynolds's Sitter Book for 1787 records eight appointments for sittings: 27 August and 5, 7, 10, 12, 15, 18 and 21 September, but the last appointment was cancelled. Select reporters were presumably admitted to Reynolds's studio: the *Morning Herald* of 20 September 1787 reported on the progress of the portrait: 'The face is rubbed in, and a stronger likeness was never seen from the pencil of Sir Joshua.'

22. For the uniform, see Revd Percy Sumner, 'Morier Paintings at Wilton', *Journal of the Society for Army Historical Research*, XIX, London 1940, p. 70.

23. Farington, *Diary*, 7 June 1809, vol. IX, p. 3481.

24. Published 1788.

25. Letter from Shee to his brother, 7 November 1788, in Shee 1860, I, pp. 107–8.

26. Two portraits: (i) full-length, commissioned ? by the sitter 1788; exh. RA 1791 (138, as 'Portrait of Lord Heathfield, Designed for Heathfield Park'); coll. East Sussex Council, Pelham House, Lewes, East Sussex, repr. Dorinda Evans, *Mather Brown*, Middletown, Conn. 1982, p. 80, fig. 64; (ii) coll. Detroit Institute of Arts, Michigan (fig. 2 above).

27. Poggi's small (17¼ × 13¾ in.) oil, three-quarter-length, was reputedly painted at Gibraltar in 1783; engr. Bartolozzi 1788. Sold Sotheby's 23 November 1966 (57), repr. Waterhouse 1981, p. 287. A small chalk study for the head is coll. SNPG.

28. Coll. NPG (170). Compare Farington's description of Stubbs's appearance at the age of 80 as 'very in-jawed and shrunk': *Diary*, 25 January 1804, vol. VI, p. 2225.

29. Rossi exhibited the bas-relief for 'Lord Heathfield's monument ordered by Government' at the RA in 1824 (991). A 'Committee of Taste' appointed by the Treasury had from 1802 taken over from the RA the commissioning of naval and military monuments for St Paul's; its members included Sir Charles Long and Sir George Beaumont. Rossi's St Paul's monument is a mediocre work. Far finer is the monument to Heathfield of 1795 by John Bacon the elder at Buckland Monachorum (there because Heathfield married the daughter of Sir Francis Henry Drake of Buckland Abbey); described by N. Pevsner, *The Buildings of England, South Devon*, Harmondsworth 1952, p. 72.

30. Barry 1809, I, p. 553.

31. Quoted in Leslie and Taylor 1865, II, p. 517.

32. The compiler is indebted to Bob Richards, her colleague at the NG, for discussing this, and to the present Governor of Gibraltar, HE Admiral Sir Derek Reffell KCB, for further information, in correspondence.

33. Wilbur C. Abbott, *Documents relating to the International Status of Gibraltar 1704–1934*, New York 1934, pp. 3–4: 'Standing as it [Gibraltar] does at one of the great crossroads of the world, its very nicknames – the Gate, the Key, the Lock, the Keeper, the Watchdog, the Guardian, the Sentinel of the Mediterranean – reveal the reasons for that concern.'

34. Farington, *Diary*, 10 June 1809, vol. IX, p. 3483.

35. Ibid., 12 June 1809, p. 3485.

36. For Josiah Boydell and his business partnership with his uncle John Boydell, see Bruntjen 1985, p. 67. The Boydell Shakespeare Gallery failed in 1804, the last year of John Boydell's life, and Josiah Boydell evidently (see Farington, *Diary*, 16 June 1809) needed money. He had succeeded his uncle as Alderman of the Ward of Cheap in 1805. It is not clear how he persuaded the Corporation of the City of London that Reynolds's *Lord Heathfield* was in such a bad state that they would be better off with a copy. He alleged that damp would have destroyed the Reynolds: damp was said to have destroyed earlier pictures (see Knight 1986, pp. 4–5), and more recently, Northcote's portrait of Lord Howe, commissioned by John Boydell at the same time as *Lord Heathfield*, was said to have been so 'destroyed' that it was replaced (? *c*.1800) with a copy after Gainsborough Dupont (Knight 1986, p. 12). But Josiah Boydell had trained as an artist (under Benjamin West), and would have understood the true condition of the Reynolds. He asked Farington's help in selling *Lord Heathfield* as early as 26 March 1808 (*Diary*, pp. 3246–7), after offering it unsuccessfully to the Marquess of Stafford and to William Smith. Presumably he had by then removed *Lord Heathfield* from Guildhall and replaced it with a copy: Farington adds that the day after doing so, Josiah Boydell 'resigned his Alderman's gown'. Josiah's actions provoked 'accusation', but he insisted that the copy had been 'openly made' and the original 'openly' sent for sale (Farington, *Diary*, 6 June and 29 June 1809, vol. IX, pp. 3480, 3499).

37. Perhaps a Northcote pupil; evidently working in the manner of Northcote, who had been commissioned by John Boydell to execute portraits for the Guildhall.

38. Farington, *Diary*, 29 June 1809; vol. IX, p. 3499.

39. Not yet knighted; that honour was bestowed in 1815.

40. *Morning Post*, 5 June 1809. The European Museum occupied the premises in Pall Mall which had been the RA's first home (until its move to Somerset House); it functioned as a showroom for works (including the Orléans collection) offered for sale by private contract.

41. Farington, *Diary*, vol. IX, p. 3481.

42. Plus £15 commission to the Keeper of the European Museum.

43. Farington, *Diary*, 8 June 1809, vol. IX, p. 3482.

44. Garlick 1989 cat. no. 521 (a), as untraced (stipple engraving of 1811 repr. p. 231); sold Christie's 16 November 1996 (35, repr. in colour). Lawrence did not exhibit this portrait, though he showed two later and very different portraits of Lord Lynedoch in 1813 and 1817.

45. *Diary*, vol. III, p. 486.

Fig. 1 *Lord Ribblesdale in the dress of Master of the Queen's Buckhounds*, c.1892. Photograph, taken by a Windsor and Eton photographer. National Portrait Gallery Archives.

The sitter is Thomas Lister, 4th Baron Ribblesdale of Gisburne Park, near Skipton, Yorkshire, and Green Street, Grosvenor Square. Born at Fontainebleau on 29 October 1854, he was the eldest son of the 3rd Baron Ribblesdale and the great-grandson of Thomas Lister, 1st Baron Ribblesdale, whom Reynolds had portrayed in 1764 as a boy in brown satin (the so-called 'Brown Boy').[2] He grew up in France, his father's gambling debts having compelled his father to mortgage the Gisburne estate and let the house to tenants; he was sent home to school at Harrow, then served in the Army from 1873 to 1886.[3]

Having succeeded his father (a suicide) in 1876, at the age of 22, the 4th Lord Ribblesdale took his seat the following year in the House of Lords, where he was an active member, and a consistent Liberal. In 1877 he married Charlotte,[4] one of the sixteen children of the rich Glasgow industrialist Sir Charles Tennant; but Ribblesdale himself was never wealthy. In order to help to free Gisburne Park from its mortgage and its tenants, he had to sell the Reynolds to a richer Lister relation ('We have sold the boy!', wrote his wife in 1889[5]); and it was only with help from his father-in-law (on many of whose City boards he now sat) that he also acquired a town house in Green Street, Mayfair. Both Lord Ribblesdale ('Tommy') and his wife ('Charty') became members of the well-bred coterie known as the Souls, 'that unconventional, highbrow and alarming set of Edwardian kindred spirits'[6] formed around Lord Curzon, and including Arthur Balfour and 'Charty' Ribblesdale's sister, Margot Asquith. Ribblesdale seems effortlessly to have fulfilled an uncommon variety of roles: Lord-in-Waiting to Queen Victoria 1880–5 and 1886, Master of the Royal Buckhounds 1892–5,[7] Liberal Whip in the House of Lords 1896–1907, Alderman of London County Council 1898–1904, Trustee of the National Portrait Gallery 1895–1923 and Trustee of the National Gallery 1909–23. But he was happiest when hunting in the Ribble valley with his own pack of hounds or with the Craven and Pendle Forest harriers.

Ribblesdale's daughter Lady Wilson records that 'it was when he was making an after-dinner speech for the Artists' Benevolent Fund that Sargent first saw him and determined to paint him'. That was in 1894,[8] but the portrait was not begun until about five years later. Sargent, near the peak of his fame in the mid-1890s, had an abundance of work on hand, and from 1898 was particularly burdened by the commissions for nine family portraits heaped upon him by the picture dealer Asher Wertheimer: he described himself in 1898 as in a state of 'chronic Wertheimerism'.[9] In the late summer of 1899, after visiting the Sitwells at Renishaw,[10] Sargent went on to stay with Lord Ribblesdale at Gisburne Park. There the projected portrait was discussed. In particular, Sargent wanted to decide on the dress in which he was to portray Lord Ribblesdale: Ormond notes that Sargent 'regarded the choice of costume as entirely his prerogative'.[11]

If seeing Ribblesdale in London in evening-dress had initially made Sargent determined to paint him, seeing him at Gisburne in hunting-dress was enough to convince him that that was how he must portray this lean attenuated figure. Sargent first considered painting Ribblesdale in his livery as Master of the Queen's Buckhounds – dark green coat, green and gold embroidered shoulder-belt, white leather breeches and black boots with champagne tops. Photographs of Ribblesdale thus attired were produced; from one of them (fig. 1)[12] Sargent made a preliminary oil sketch,[13] then discarded the idea, for it was abundantly clear that the livery, however prestigious, was aesthetically hideous: in particular, the contrast between the green coat and white breeches interrupted the long line of his sitter's body.

Whether it was Sargent's decision or his own, happily Ribblesdale sat to Sargent in the idiosyncratic hunting garb he had evolved for himself. Although the portrait is frequently described as 'dandified',[14] it might rather be described as a portrait of a man in 'ratcatcher', the Edwardian slang term for unconventional hunting-dress. Ribblesdale himself uses the term elsewhere, averring that he had no objection to the Queen's field riding 'in ratcatcher',[15] and his daughter noted that Ribblesdale 'always wore mufti when hunting'.[16] Never a man for swagger, he disliked scarlet coats, buckskin breeches and boots with 'champagne tops' in the hunting-field. Ribblesdale was a fastidious man, but never a dandy. He dressed habitually in clothes which suited him, disdaining changes in fashion. Efforts to find orders from Lord Ribblesdale to fashionable London tailors, hatters and bootmakers have failed. His preference for his own style of unfashionably plain dress became so well-known that a *Vanity Fair* portrait of him by 'Spy', published 11 June 1881, needed only the caption 'Mufti' to identify him. In the last year of the Boer War, when his elder son Thomas was serving in South Africa with the 10th Hussars, Lord Ribblesdale was permitted to visit him and to trek with the regiment over the veldt, 'having no other uniform than a veteran covert-coat, and no other weapon than an umbrella'.[17]

Ribblesdale particularly disliked red coats in the hunting-field, for the aesthetic reason that they brought an unnaturally gaudy note into the beauty of the countryside. To ask, as Richard Dorment does, 'Why did Sargent throw away the chance' to paint Ribblesdale in a 'scarlet hunting coat?'[18] is to ignore the fact that Ribblesdale would have declined to sit in one, even for Sargent; it also underrates Sargent's perception of his sitter's individuality. When Ribblesdale sat to Sargent, it was in his own habitual style of hunting-dress, which Sargent had quickly recognised as individual to him: pale yellow waistcoat, drab jacket (almost invisible in the portrait), box-cloth breeches, possibly inherited from his father, and well-cleaned butcher boots, all set off by the hat and its angle.[19] He was, in his own phrase, 'a stickler for the tall hat' ('It looks the best, and in every way is the best for riding of all kinds, which includes falling'[20]). The black silk muffler, which one might have supposed to be Sargent's flamboyant addition, was the one Lord Ribblesdale habitually knotted over his riding-tie; at Gisburne he kept it on a hall table, with a covert coat and a riding-whip or two.[21] The black velvet-collared topcoat casually thrown over his hunting attire, almost certainly part of his London wardrobe, is likely to have been donned at Sargent's request; Sargent had already proved himself a master of the painted overcoat in his portrait of the young W. Graham Robertson (fig. 2).[22] The austere colours of Ribblesdale's *ensemble* enabled Sargent to suggest the aesthete within the hunting-dress.[23]

Sittings, probably during 1901 (dates unrecorded), were almost certainly in Sargent's studio in Tite Street (Sir George Sitwell had observed that Sargent 'will only paint in his own studio in London'[24]). The two men, of much the same age – in 1902, when the portrait was exhibited, Ribblesdale was 47, and Sargent 45 – got on well together. Lady Ribblesdale attended one or two early sittings, but had to be asked to stay away since her 'passionate keenness for the success of the portrait' made progress difficult.[25] Sargent first thought of setting the figure against stonework columns of the daunting

Fig. 2 *W. Graham Robertson*, 1894. Oil on canvas, 230.5 × 118.7 cm. London, Tate Gallery, presented by W. Graham Robertson 1940.

kind he favoured for backgrounds at this time; he and Lady Ribblesdale 'clambered ... over the roofs and terraces of Somerset House, searching for grey pilasters that might come in well'.[26] In the preliminary oil sketch noted above, the figure is posed on stone steps between massive columns, but Sargent eventually decided to paint the background from the panelling of his own studio:[27] wisely, in Ormond's opinion, since that panelling provides 'no more than a decorative pattern, a geometrical grid, against which Sargent's characterisation is projected with uninterrupted force'.[28]

That characterisation was evidently true to life. As his contemporaries observed, Lord Ribblesdale had a faintly archaic air. Edward VII nicknamed him 'The Ancestor';[29] the sobriquet catches the flavour of this portrait. L.E. Jones wrote

Fig. 3 *'The Ancestor': Lord Ribblesdale*. Photograph by Walter Stoneman, published in *The Graphic*, 9 September 1902. National Portrait Gallery Archives.

of Ribblesdale that 'for patrician good looks, expressing intelligence and sensibility, I have never seen his equal'. Another friend considered that 'the famous portrait ... hardly exaggerates his individuality'.[30] Sargent seems almost to convey the manner in which Ribblesdale, 'a master of light and quizzical table-talk',[31] will converse when the sitting is over, 'rolling his rrrs and betraying the barest suggestion of a lisp'.[32] His three books of memoirs are elegantly written, but reticent.[33] Perhaps surprisingly, he had a gift for drawing caricatures;[34] less surprisingly, he is the subject of several caricatures by Max Beerbohm, including a sketch of the 'Annual Meeting of Mr Stirling Stuart-Crawford, Mr Augustus John and Lord Ribblesdale, to protest against the fashions for the coming spring', 1909.[35] By temperament he was hardy and stoical. His daughter notes his frugality, and 'a great simplicity in his possessions': with no appetite for luxury, he preferred '*pot-au-feu* life – poached eggs and a cup of strong tea for dinner, a pair of bedroom slippers on his feet, and an open book on his lap'.[36]

Sargent exhibited the portrait at the Royal Academy in 1902, with seven other portraits or portrait-groups.[37] The *Magazine of Art* observed that Ribblesdale's portrait was 'infused with that quaint old-world spirit in dress and manners which informs the noble lord'.[38] The *Academy* reviewer ('C.L.H.') found his eye straying from the grandeur of Sargent's huge Reynolds-like group *The Acheson Sisters* (89) to 'the quiet power and unaffected humility of the Ribblesdale portrait. This has character. It makes no effort to be impressive. It is content to be itself. It waits, ready to give, when you are ready.'[39] The *Art Journal* gave the most positive verdict, pronouncing that 'Sargent's most masterly portrait of the year is Lord Ribblesdale... As a pictorial presence, firmly and sympathetically knit, complete and unmannered, he dominates the central gallery.'[40] But as *The Times* noted, *Lord Ribblesdale* was so badly hung that the head was 'practically invisible'.[41]

The portrait was shown to better advantage two years later in Paris, at the 'New Salon'. The *Art Journal* redoubled its praise, declaring that 'there is nothing in either Salon to compare for a moment with the magnificent Sargent, "Portrait of Lord Ribblesdale" ... [which] dominates the whole exhibition by its superb dignity and individuality'.[42] Ribblesdale himself visited the Salon exhibition, where he was instantly recognised; he wrote to his mother that Sargent's portrait 'has forced a greatness on me which is quite embarrassing ... wherever I go, I am recognised, and much *chuchotement* and pointing out to friends goes on ... Sargent will be gratified, and I am writing him a line'.[43] His daughter later recalled that 'people were nudging each other as they recognised the subject of the picture and whispering, "Ce grand diable de milord anglais" '.[44]

Lord Ribblesdale's first wife died in 1911. Both their sons were killed in action, the elder in Somaliland 1904 and the younger at Gallipoli 1915. The 4th and now inevitably last Lord Ribblesdale commented stoically that 'the span of life must be measured, not by its length, but by its excellence';[45] but his old life was shattered. In 1915 he presented his portrait by Sargent to the National Gallery, in memory of his wife and his sons. He then sold his London house and most of his furniture, and moved into the Cavendish Hotel for several years, becoming (with no impropriety) the star paying guest of its Cockney proprietress, Rosa Lewis.[46] His manner with people of all classes had always been easy and unaffected, and he was now happy to open the annual servants' ball at the Cavendish by leading out the head cook. Rosa Lewis was displeased when Lord Ribblesdale left the Cavendish in 1919 to marry (secondly) Ava Willing, widow of John Jacob Astor. Before he left, he is said to have given Rosa a large coloured photograph of the Sargent portrait: this (or a replica) hangs still above the staircase in the Cavendish.

Lord Ribblesdale remained a Trustee of the National Gallery until the end of 1923.[47] He died on 21 October 1925, six months after Sargent. Such was the lasting impact of Sargent's image of him that *The Times* the next day reproduced Sargent's portrait of 1902 rather than a recent photograph, and discussed the portrait before recounting the career of its sitter. It concluded that the portrait of Lord Ribblesdale reflected 'the traditions of a time and of manners that are not of today, and were not wholly of 1902', and it added 'He looked an Old Master'.[48]

NOTES

The compiler is particularly grateful to the Rt Hon. James Ramsden PC for advice on hunting and hunting-dress.

1. Ribblesdale's offer of the portrait to his fellow Trustees of the National Gallery was gratefully accepted at the meeting of 23 November 1915 (Board Minutes, vol. 8, p. 286). The accompanying wording was drawn up by Lord Ribblesdale. See *NG Report 1915*, p. 3.

2. Bradford City Art Galleries and Museum; exh. *Reynolds*, 1976 (53, repr. in colour p. 105).

3. Joined 64th Foot November 1873; exchanged into Rifle Brigade January 1874; later seconded for Parliamentary duties; retired as Major, Rifle Brigade, 1886.

4. A photograph of her inscribed 'your Angel Queen' is repr. in ed. Beatrix Lister, *Emma, Lady Ribblesdale, Letters and Diaries*, London 1930, facing p. 56.

5. Sold for 9500 guineas through Agnew's 1889 to Samuel Cunliffe-Lister, later 1st Lord Masham. Charlotte Ribblesdale wrote to her mother-in-law (n.d.): 'We have sold the boy! It is very sad though in some ways a great relief. I felt a pang of grief when I saw the poor dear being walked down the stair' (quoted in Lister 1930, p. 89). For his earlier sale to the NG of James Ward's *Gordale Scar*, see Introduction, p. 12.

6. Julian Fane [the sitter's grandson], *Memories of My Mother*, London 1987, p. 8. See Jane Abdy and Charlotte Gere, *The Souls*, London 1984, particularly pp. 14, 19, 35 (quoting Algernon Cecil's pithy account of 'the Souls', from his *DNB* notice of Arthur Balfour) and 136.

7. The Mastership of the Royal Buckhounds (or 'The Queen's Hounds') was a political appointment: Lord Ribblesdale was Mr Gladstone's nominee. As the buckhounds were kennelled near Ascot, it had become the Master's responsibility to issue tickets for the Royal Enclosure on Ascot Cup Day, an invidious task. The Master of the Buckhounds also led the royal procession up the course on the first day of the Ascot Meeting; presumably this accounts for the number of photographs of Ribblesdale in his livery.

8. See her Preface to Ribblesdale 1927, p. xxviii. The compiler is indebted to the Secretary of the Artists' Benevolent Fund for tracing (in the Stewards' Books) the date of the Anniversary Dinner at which Lord Ribblesdale spoke.

9. Charteris 1927, p. 164.

10. See Stanley Olson, *John Singer Sargent*, 1986, p. 221. Renishaw, in north Derbyshire, is not far from Gisburne. Sargent's group portrait *The Sitwell Family* was in progress (exh. RA 1901; Ormond 1970, pp. 251–2, plate 91).

11. Ormond 1970, p. 63.

12. Two such photographs in the NPG Archives are stamped verso by Hills & Saunders, of Windsor and Eton. See reprs in Lord Ribblesdale, *The Queen's Hounds and Stag-Hunting Recollections*, London 1897, facing p. 189; Lister 1930 (cited in note 4), facing p. 110, and (signed) on a page in the Taplow Court Visitors' Book (private collection), repr. Abdy and Gere 1984 (cited in note 6), p. 14.

13. Though Ribblesdale's figure is very sketchy, the costume and pose, with one leg raised on a stone step, is unmistakably taken from one of the Buckhounds photographs. The sketch (34¼ × 24 in.), of which there is a photograph in the Tate Gallery archives, was in Sargent's studio sale, Christie's, 24 July 1925 (92), bt Arthur Bendir, who presented it to Lady Wilson (Ribblesdale 1927, p. xvi).

14. For example, Albert Boime and others, 'Sargent in Paris and London', in *John Singer Sargent*, exh. cat., Whitney Museum of American Art, New York and Chicago 1986, p. 104: '...a dandified hunting costume ... Lord Ribblesdale, who measured his friends by their fashions and was fastidious about his own clothing, actually recedes behind his outfit. The accumulation of riding accessories imparts an absurd almost caricatural, look...'

15. Ribblesdale 1897, p. 156.

16. Ribblesdale 1927, p. xxviii.

17. Ibid., p. xxix.

18. *NG News*, October 1994.

19. 'Given the tall hat, properly put on box-cloth breeches and well-cleaned butcher boots look a great deal better than the buckskins and tops' (Ribblesdale 1897, p. 157).

20. Ibid.

21. Lady Wilson, in Ribblesdale 1927, p. x.

22. Tate Gallery; see Ormond 1970, p. 248.

23. Dorment in the *NG News* (October 1994) observes that 'Sargent certainly knew Whistler's full-length portrait of the American millionaire George Vanderbilt in riding costume (NGA, Washington) and may even have based Ribblesdale's pose on it'; but, as he adds, Whistler's pose is 'more a study in subtle tonal relationships than an exploration of the sitter's character'. But did Whistler paint George Vanderbilt 'in riding costume'? His sitter appears to be dressed in a dark suit, and holding a cane rather than a riding whip. Whistler's *Portrait of George W. Vanderbilt*, painted 1897–1903, is repr. A. McLaren Young et al., *The Paintings of James McNeill Whistler*, New Haven and London 1980, plate 310 (cat. no. 481).

24. See Ormond 1970, p. 252.

25. Lady Wilson, in Ribblesdale 1927, p. xxviii.

26. Ibid.

27. A photograph of the Tite Street studio showing part of the panelling is repr. Ormond 1970, fig. 25, facing p. 58.

28. Ibid., p. 58. Dorment 1994 maintained that a small detail in the picture shows that Sargent was 'certainly 'thinking of Whistler when he painted this portrait... On the wall behind Ribblesdale at the left, clear as day, he has painted a stylised butterfly logo, the symbol with which Whistler signed all his works.' Close scrutiny shows that the 'butterfly' is in fact a lightly sketched decorative motif or rosette in the panelling.

29. *The Times*, 22 October 1925.

30. 'O', writing in *The Times*, 24 October 1925, p. 17.

31. L.E. Jones, *An Edwardian Youth*, London 1956, p. 235.

32. Iris Tree, quoted by Daphne Fielding, *The Duchess of Jermyn Street. The Life and Times of Rosa Lewis of the Cavendish Hotel*, London 1964, p. 59.

33. His chief publications are: (i) *The Queen's Hounds and Stag-Hunting Recollections*, London 1897; (ii) *Charles Lister: Letters and Recollections*, London 1917; (iii) *Impressions and Memories*; with Preface by his daughter Lady Wilson, London 1927.

34. Some repr. in Ribblesdale 1897 and Ribblesdale 1927. As a boy in France, he may have had some tuition from Edouard Detaille, whom he quoted as saying 'Dessinez, dessinez! Il faut dessiner les bons-hommes dans la rue' (Ribblesdale 1927, Preface, p. xiv).

35. Reproduced in Michael Holroyd, *Augustus John*, London 1975, between pp. 142–3. For others, see Rupert Hart-Davis, *Catalogue of the Caricatures of Max Beerbohm*, London 1972, p. 115, nos. 1218–21.

36. Lady Wilson, in Ribblesdale 1927, pp. x–xi.

37. 'The Ladies Alexandra, Mary and Theo Acherson' (89); 'Mrs Endicott' (148); 'Alfred Wertheimer Esq.' (157); 'The Misses Hunter' (229); 'The Duchess of Portland' (323); 'Mrs Leopold Hirsch' (681); 'Lady Meysey Thompson' (688).

38. 1902, p. 358.

39. *The Academy*, LXII, 10 May 1902, p. 488. *The Acheson Sisters* is repr. NPG exh. cat. 1978, colour plate X.

40. *Art Journal*, 1902, p. 210.

41. 3 May 1902, p. 16. Elaborating its first point the reviewer wrote: 'The hangers have followed the pernicious old rule which forbids a full-length to be hung on the line – the rule which made Gainsborough refuse to exhibit and makes the head in a tall picture practically invisible.'

42. *Art Journal*, 1904, p. 212, repr. facing p. 213.

43. Quoted in Lister 1930 (cited in note 4), p. 182.

44. Lady Wilson in Ribblesdale 1927, pp. xvi–xvii.

45. Lady Wilson in Ribblesdale 1927, p. xxix.

46. See Fielding 1964 (cited in note 32), *passim*, particularly pp. 553–9, 118.

47. His letter of resignation because of ill-health was accepted by the Trustees at their meeting on 9 January 1924. Sir Robert Witt was appointed a Trustee in his place.

48. 22 October 1925; obituary p. 14.

George Stubbs ARA

1724–1806

Born in Liverpool, the son of a currier. Worked briefly (aged about fourteen) under Hamlet Winstanley copying old masters at Knowlsey Hall; otherwise self-taught, both as painter and engraver. Neither his life nor his work is well documented (no account books survive, and very little correspondence); Ozias Humphry's MS Memoir (Liverpool City Libraries), compiled from Stubbs's recollections in the 1790s, is largely anecdotal, and unreliable. Apart from a brief visit to Rome in 1754, Stubbs remained until the late 1750s in the north of England, painting portraits (few now known) while studying anatomy. Worked at York Hospital *c.*1745–51, and taught himself to engrave in order to illustrate Dr Burton's *Midwifery* treatise, 1751. In Lincolnshire during 1756–8, devoted eighteen months to the study of the anatomy of the horse, tirelessly dissecting and delineating every stage of his dissections; 42 drawings survive (coll. Royal Academy), from which Stubbs engraved a series of fastidiously beautiful plates, published in 1766 as *The Anatomy of the Horse*.

Stubbs did not fully emerge as a painter until he was nearly 35, and had moved (? in 1758) to London. His reputation was quickly established among a circle of noblemen to whom the breeding of thoroughbred horses (and the attendant pleasures of racing and gambling) was all-important. In the 1760s Stubbs's genius blossomed, prolifically. For his noble patrons, he painted their brood mares and foals, their stallions, their racehorses, grooms and jockeys. For those interested in wild or exotic animals he painted the zebra, tiger, cheetah and kangaroo; and he returned, repeatedly and in various media, to an obsessive theme of his own: the horse in a state of nature, first attacked and finally devoured by a lion. His incidental portraits of grooms and jockeys, and his occasional conversation pieces (such as NG 6429, pp. 248–55) reveal him as a perceptive portraitist of human beings at different levels of society. Exhibited from 1761 to 1774 at the Society of Artists (President, 1772) and later at the Royal Academy; elected ARA 1780 and RA 1781, but refusal to comply with a new rule requiring deposit of a diploma work disqualified him from status as a full Academician.

Stubbs experimented constantly in all media. In engraving, he perfected a mixed-method technique which places work such as *Hay-makers* and *Labourers* or his three small foxhound prints among the greatest achievements of English print-making. Working first on copper and then on earthenware supports specially made for him by Josiah Wedgwood, he translated many of his subjects into enamel paintings. In oils, his occasional use of wax underlayers (particularly when working on panels), until recently not comprehended by restorers, means that much of his later work has not been retained in its original condition. Began work on comparative anatomy in 1795, then aged over seventy. His last great paintings, such as *The Prince of Wales's Phaeton* (coll. Her Majesty The Queen), 1793, or the monumental *Hambletonian, Rubbing Down*, 1800 (National Trust, Mountstewart), demonstrate that Stubbs's powers remained undiminished to the end.

References

Basil Taylor, *Stubbs*, London 1971; Bruce Tattersall, *Stubbs & Wedgwood* (with an introduction by Basil Taylor), exh. cat., Tate Gallery 1974; Terence Doherty, *The Anatomical Works of George Stubbs*, London 1974; Judy Egerton, *George Stubbs, Anatomist and Animal Painter*, exh. cat., Tate Gallery 1976; Judy Egerton, *George Stubbs*, exh. cat., Tate Gallery 1984; Christopher Lennox-Boyd, Rob Dixon and Tim Clayton, *George Stubbs: The Complete Engraved Works*, London 1989.

For discussion of the medium in paintings by Stubbs, see John Mills and Raymond White, 'Research Note', *NG Technical Bulletin*, 4, 1980, p. 64, and 9, 1985, pp. 60–4. Stubbs's use of unusual painting materials, particularly on panels, is discussed by Robert Shepherd in Egerton, *George Stubbs*, exh. cat., 1984, pp. 20–1.

NG 6569

Whistlejacket

? 1762

Oil on canvas, 292 × 246.4 cm (115 × 97 in.)

Provenance

Commissioned by Charles Watson Wentworth, 2nd Marquess of Rockingham (d.s.p. 1782); his nephew and principal heir, William Wentworth-Fitzwilliam, 2nd Earl Fitzwilliam, then by descent to the 10th Earl Fitzwilliam (d.1979); Trustees of the Rt. Hon. Olive, Countess Fitzwilliam's Chattels Settlement, from whom purchased with the support of the Heritage Lottery Fund and private donations by the National Gallery 1997.

Exhibited

On long loan to Kenwood House, London, 1971–81, and the centrepiece of a small exhibition there in 1971 (no cat.); Tate Gallery, 1984–5 (34); on loan to the National Gallery from April 1996 until its purchase by the Gallery in 1997.

Literature

Horace Walpole, MS journal, 1772, published in ed. Paget Toynbee, 'Horace Walpole's Journals of Visits to Country Seats', *Walpole Society*, XVI, 1928, p. 71; Ozias Humphry, 'Particulars of the Life of Mr Stubbs... given to the author ... by himself and committed from his own relation', MS compiled *c.*1790–7, Picton Collection, Liverpool City Libraries; Waagen 1854, III, p. 339; Christopher Hussey, 'Wentworth Woodhouse, Yorkshire', *English Country Houses: Early Georgian 1715–1760*, London 1955, p. 154 and fig. 252; H.F. Constantine, 'Lord Rockingham and Stubbs; Some New Documents', *Burlington Magazine*, XCV, 1953, pp. 236–8; Parker 1971, pp. 56, 65; Taylor 1971, pp. 29, 205–6; Egerton 1984, cat. no. 34, p. 60.

Engraved

Etching and stipple, in reverse direction, image 8.6 × 10.2 cm, with etched inscription across lower corners *GS RA* (left) and *BK* (right); a sketchy view of Wentworth Woodhouse and some rocky cliffs added as background. This etching (of which only one impression is known) is assumed to have been made by Benjamin Killingbeck while working for the Marquess of Rockingham *c.*1781 (repr. Christopher Lennox-Boyd, Rob Dixon and Tim Clayton, *George Stubbs: The Complete Engraved Works*, London 1989, p. 175, no. 61).

Technical Notes

In very good condition. The picture was lined, cleaned and restored a few years before its acquisition. The canvas support has a vertical seam 64 cm from the left edge. There are numerous small splashes of original grey/brown paint scattered over the background.

Stubbs arrived in London in or around 1758, bringing with him a portfolio of drawings made during eighteen months' dissection and intensive study of the anatomy of the horse (see Biography). His arduous anatomical research was undertaken primarily because, as a painter of horses, he wanted fully to understand what lay beneath the skin, how the bone structure governed movement and how the relationship of muscle to bone shaped bodily contours. He emphasised that his dissections were limited to 'as much as I thought necessary for the study of Painting'; he did not explore 'the internal parts of a Horse'.[1]

To those who were interested in breeding and racing horses – and for many noblemen and gentlemen, this was their chief interest – the truth to nature displayed in Stubbs's anatomical drawings was a revelation, dramatically exposing the horse paintings of such hitherto popular artists as John Wootton (1682–1764) and James Seymour (*c.*1702–52) as deficient in fundamental knowledge. Stubbs quickly attracted the attention of a circle of aristocratic patrons, with the 3rd Duke of Richmond taking the lead in commissioning the three large canvases still at Goodwood House,[2] and the Dukes of Ancaster, Grafton and Portland, the Viscounts Torrington and Bolingbroke and Lord Grosvenor offering numerous commissions.[3] He painted their racehorses and jockeys, their stallions and grooms and their dogs. In particular, he painted the brood mares and foals of their stud farms, in a sequence of at least ten variations, chiefly painted during the 1760s. To the general eye, Stubbs's paintings of mares and foals offer a lyrical glimpse of the English countryside, enhanced by the most graceful and least menacing of its creatures. But those who commissioned such paintings wanted (and got, from Stubbs) accurate portraiture of their own animals. Much thought and considerable expense would have gone into selecting a stallion to cover a mare, and among the foals, future racing winners and good breeders would be looked for. For the moment, however, the mares and foals are seen as if in a state of nature, free from the bridles, saddles and spurs of the racecourse.

Charles Watson-Wentworth, 2nd Marquess of Rockingham (1730–82), was to commission twelve works from Stubbs, almost as many as Stubbs's most constant patron, the 1st Earl Grosvenor. For both men, Stubbs produced some of his finest work (for the *Grosvenor Hunt* and Lord Grosvenor's *Mares and Foals* must surely be counted among the finest).[4] But for Rockingham – and largely as a direct result of Rockingham's particular aesthetic sensibilities – Stubbs produced certain works which transcend all previously accepted traditions of horse painting by dispensing with backgrounds, allowing the subject alone to command attention. The finest of these are *Whistlejacket* and *Mares and Foals without a background* (fig. 1). No correspondence between the patron and the painter has survived to indicate how such a decision was reached, but given the fact that Lord Rockingham had formed the larger part of his collection of classical sculpture before commissioning work from Stubbs, it is likely to have been chiefly his decision to let the noblest of Stubbs's paintings of his horses stand out, almost like bronzes, against plain backgrounds.

It is the privilege of the art historian largely to ignore the public life of a patron (or to relegate it to an endnote[5]), unless it affects the work he commissioned. Here the only facts relating to Lord Rockingham's political career which need be mentioned are that by 1761 he had become (with some reluctance for the role) leader of the Whig opposition to George III's favourite, Lord Bute, that he formed a short-lived ministry in 1765, and that he became Prime Minister again in 1782, the year of his death. He sat at least three times to Reynolds.[6] For Rockingham himself, being in the public eye meant that he had less time to indulge his two private, seemingly disparate passions, collecting sculpture and breeding racehorses.

Rockingham was one of the richest men in England, having inherited (in 1750) vast properties in Ireland, Northamptonshire and Yorkshire, including coal mines and quarries. His principal seat was Wentworth House, Yorkshire (now known as Wentworth Woodhouse); rebuilt by his father on a huge scale,[7] it offered vast scope for the display of sculpture, its Great Hall in particular having been designed for

Fig. 1 *Mares and Foals without a background*, 1762. Oil on canvas, 99 × 190.5 cm. Trustees of the Rt. Hon. Olive, Countess Fitzwilliam's Chattels Settlement and Lady Juliet Tadgell.

statues in niches.[8] In Italy in 1748–50, on the Grand Tour, Rockingham (then still bearing the junior title of Lord Malton) commissioned for the Great Hall eight six-foot-high marble copies of the Farnese *Callipygian Venus*, the Capitoline *Flora*, *Germanicus* and *Antinous*, the *Dancing Faun* in the Tribuna of the Uffizi, the *Queen of Sweden's Faun* and the *Medici Venus* and *Apollino*.[9] His most important purchase (from the sculptor) was Foggini's marble group *Samson and the Philistines* (now coll. V&A). He also began the collection of medals and small bronzes which were to be shown both at Wentworth and in his London house in Grosvenor Square. The bronzes bought in Italy included 'a horse' and 'a running horse' by Giambologna.[10] There was ample room at Wentworth House for large paintings as well as for a sculpture collection. In 1749, while Rockingham was in Florence, his father had asked him to look for two large pictures for the dining room; he reported that he had seen two large hunting pictures which might do, but they were £100 each, 'above my venturing at'.[11]

Rockingham loved sport, particularly racing. Whenever cares of state permitted, he went to Newmarket, where he kept a string of racehorses, and gambled heavily. In this he shared a passion common to his class; Horace Walpole observed that 'half the nobility and half the money of England' went to Newmarket.[12] Rockingham's wife resignedly hoped that he would restrict his gambling to 'just upon *the turf*, for there is always a possibility of some sort of pleasure in that; but not the smallest in other sorts'.[13] He took equal pleasure in racing at York, where his donation of a grandstand in 1755 transformed the former fairly disorderly meetings on the Knavesmire into an orderly spectator sport. At Wentworth he bred thoroughbred horses, his stud farm there including some two hundred horses. The letters he received from Joshua Cobb, his head groom, must have been a welcome relief from his despatch-boxes, and he preserved several of them, including one dated 9 April 1769 which reads: 'My Lord, Cloudy foal'd Wednesday morning the 8 day of April and as got a Colt foal a bay small star and the near hind leg white – She foaled about three of the clock in the morning...'[14]

Rockingham was quick to recognise that Stubbs was the ideal painter to do justice to his horses. Evidently he invited Stubbs to spend some months in the first half of 1762 at Wentworth. The first five works he commissioned from the artist are entered in his account book under the heading 1762 as follows: 'Aug. 15th – to Mr Stubbs Horse Painter, a picture of Brood Mares – Stallions – Hounds – and Scrub and [illegible] – £194.5.' Stubbs's receipt for this payment gives fuller details:[15]

> August Yth 1762 Recd of the Most Honble ye Marquis of Rockingham, the sum of one Hundred and ninty four pounds five shillings in full for a picture of five brood-Mares and two foles one picture of three Stallions and one figure and one picture of a figure on Horseback and a picture of five Dogs and another of one Dog with one Single Horse.

These documents establish that the first works Stubbs painted for Rockingham were those now known as *Mares and Foals without a background* (fig. 1), *Joshua (or Simon) Cobb with Whistlejacket and two other Stallions* (fig. 2),[16] *Scrub with John Singleton up*,[17] *Foxhounds in a Landscape* and a now untraced painting of a single horse with a dog. Rockingham is likely to have admired Stubbs's exact and elegant depiction of a group of his mares and foals so much that he asked Stubbs to leave them as they were, like a classical frieze, without

Fig. 2 *Joshua (or Simon) Cobb with Whistlejacket and two other Stallions*, 1762. Oil on canvas, 99 × 187 cm. Trustees of the Rt. Hon. Olive, Countess Fitzwilliam's Chattels Settlement and Lady Juliet Tadgell.

adding a background. *Foxhounds in a Landscape* (fig. 3) perhaps suggests the sort of Yorkshire background which Stubbs might have added. *Joshua (or Simon) Cobb with Whistlejacket and two other Stallions* was also left without a background. In these decisions, Rockingham's feeling for the supremacy of sculpted forms without scenery is likely to have been uppermost. As a breeder of horses, he also valued exact portraiture of specific animals, their conformation and their individual characteristics (down to the 'small star' and the markings of a hind leg, such as his head groom had reported of a newborn colt). Earlier artists had painted 'horses'. No artist before Stubbs had combined powers of general anatomical knowledge with specific observation of particular animals.

Whistlejacket's beauty as represented in the painting reproduced here as fig. 2 must have inspired Rockingham to commission the larger portrait in which Whistlejacket is the sole, monumental figure. Art historians have generally shuddered at attempts to relate the word 'beauty' to the word 'horse' (especially after Ellis Waterhouse opined that admiration for lesser horse painters merely confused 'the history of art with praising famous horses'[18]); but the Marquess of Rockingham and George Stubbs prove them to be blinkered. Rockingham asked Stubbs to paint Whistlejacket on a canvas nearly twelve feet high not because he was a 'famous horse' but because he was a supremely beautiful specimen of the pure-bred Arabian horse at its finest.

Whistlejacket, foaled in 1749, was bred at Sir William Middleton's stud farm at Belsay Castle, Northumberland. The finest Arabian blood available in England flowed through his veins. His sire was Mogul, a son of the Godolphin Arabian, one of the three Arabian stallions imported into England which provided the male line for the development of the thoroughbred horse through some thirty generations to the present day.[19] Whistlejacket's (unnamed) dam was also high-bred, for she was a daughter of the Hampton Court Chestnut Arabian, from the stud founded by Cromwell and enriched by Charles II's imports of Arabian horses.[20] Paintings (however conjectural) of famous sires were of particular interest to breeders of thoroughbreds, and formed one of the specialities of John Wootton. Versions of Wootton's *The Bloody-Shouldered Arabian* and *The Hampton Court Arabian*, perhaps acquired by Rockingham's father, were already at Wentworth;[21] with their angular shoulders, spindly legs, spade-shaped heads and bulging eyes, they are likely immediately to have looked out of date when Stubbs's work was hung.

Whistlejacket's career as a racehorse was only moderately successful. Between 1753 and 1755, he won various races and matches in the North of England (Stockton, Morpeth, Newcastle, York, Lincoln, etc.), but on his first appearance at Newmarket in 1756, lost two of his three races; whereupon Sir William Middleton sold him to Lord Rockingham. Whistlejacket's most celebrated victory was at York races in August 1759, in a match for 2000 guineas against Mr Turner's Brutus. Whistlejacket, ridden by Rockingham's favourite jockey John Singleton,[22] won by a length in a finish so exciting that the *Public Advertiser*'s reporter called it the finest match ever seen (hardly a rare phrase in racing news). Whistlejacket was by then ten years old. He did not race again. Instead, Rockingham retired him to stud at Wentworth, where Horace Walpole (visiting Wentworth Park in 1766) could have observed him but probably did not; disappointed in the landscaping of the park, Walpole commented sourly: 'This lord loves nothing but horses, and the enclosures for them take place of everything.'[23] Whistlejacket was averagely successful at stud;[24] presumably he died there some time before Lord Rockingham's death in 1782 and the ensuing sale of the stud, in which his name is not listed. Compared with racehorses and stallions such as Eclipse, Gimcrack or Mambrino (all 'sitters' to Stubbs), Whistlejacket has small claim to fame, and is not even mentioned in the annals of northern racing history.[25] Without Stubbs, his name might have been remembered only as a passing echo in Goldsmith's line (in *She Stoops to Conquer*) about plans for an elopement: 'I have got you a pair of horses that will fly like Whistlejacket.'[26]

White hope of the Whigs though he continued to be, racegoer and gambler at Newmarket though he occasionally was, the 2nd Marquess of Rockingham was eminently capable of recognising beauty when he saw it. He would have been fully aware that in Whistlejacket he owned a creature which exemplified the finest characteristics of the Arabian breed. In colour, Whistlejacket was a rich coppery chestnut, his tail and mane lightening to white, reputedly the colouring of the original wild horses of Arabia. His head was small and tapering, very broad in the forehead, the ears delicately modelled in an exquisite curve; his nostrils very large and wide, thin-edged and mobile; his profile concave, like a gazelle's, with the head joining the neck in a beautifully arched curve. The arch of the neck swells in stallions into a crest of potency, as Whistlejacket's clearly does. The shoulders are long and sloping, the chest broad and deep, the back short and level, the legs 'hard as iron, the back tendons like steel bars'. If this reads like a purple passage, it should be stated that it is drawn from the standard definition of the ideal characteristics of the Arabian horse,[27] which are displayed by Whistlejacket to perfection.

Rockingham also knew when to let a good thing alone. That Whistlejacket remains as Stubbs painted him must primarily have been the Marquess's decision. Contemporaries were so astonished that a single horse should command a huge canvas that legends quickly developed that the Marquess's original intention was that Whistlejacket should be simply the subordinate steed in a picture originally conceived as an equestrian portrait of George III. Such a belief was noted by Horace Walpole, as he passed through Wentworth Woodhouse on his Yorkshire tour of August 1772. He noted 'Many pictures of horses by Stubbs, well done. One large as life, fine, no ground done; it was to have had a figure of George 3d until Lord Rockingham went into opposition'.[28] Walpole was visiting the house, not the Marquess, and is likely to have been shown round it by the housekeeper, who may not have been as well-informed as Mrs Garnett, housekeeper at Kedleston between 1766 and 1809.[29] Ozias Humphry's MS Memoir repeats the story; but nothing else confirms it. The small etching already noted (? made by Benjamin Killingbeck while he was working for Rockingham in about 1781) adds a sketchy view of Wentworth House in the background; it does not presume to add a rider.

Large equestrian portraits in a heroic tradition had of course been regularly commissioned over the centuries, from sculptors (as in the Colleoni Monument[30]) as well as painters. Rubens had portrayed the Cardinal-Infante Ferdinand on a heavy horse.[31] More fulsomely, Charles II had been portrayed on Pegasus, no less.[32] Velázquez had portrayed Philip IV of Spain and his son Prince Balthasar Carlos mounted on great horses, and kept an oil sketch of a horse in his studio, ready to be 'mounted' by whichever personage might aspire to such elevation.[33] But by the 1760s the convention was largely outworn, and by 1800, when David used it for his portrait of *Napoleon crossing the Alps*,[34] faintly absurd. That the Marquess of Rockingham should seek to ingratiate himself with George III by commissioning his portrait astride Whistlejacket seems completely out of character; even more out of character is the notion that if he conceived such an idea, he was then mean-spirited enough to cancel it out of pique because he was (temporarily) out of office. The notion that Whistlejacket was designed to bear a rider is likely to have arisen only in the minds of those to whom the idea of a horse as sole hero of a huge canvas was unprecedented.

Fig. 3 *Foxhounds in a Landscape*, 1762. Oil on canvas, 101.5 × 127 cm. Trustees of the Rt. Hon. Olive, Countess Fitzwilliam's Chattels Settlement and Lady Juliet Tadgell.

Some idea of what Stubbs's picture might have looked like if a rider had been added is offered by Reynolds's equestrian portrait of Lord Ligonier (fig. 4). In this, the horse may in fact have been painted for Reynolds by Stubbs. Humphry records that Stubbs's first commission in London was to paint a 'war horse' for Reynolds;[35] and certainly Lord Ligonier's horse is beyond Reynolds's own capabilities. The essential aspect of the horse in equestrian portraits of heroic figures – monarchs, military commanders, or anyone else depicted for propaganda purposes – was that the horse should be seen to be a magnificent yet wholly subordinate animal, as submissive to the rider's reins as (by inference) were the subjects of a kingdom to a monarch's rule, or the soldiers of an army to their commander's orders. In such equestrian portraits, the horse is often depicted in a rearing position, akin to that of the *levade* of *haute école*; but it invariably faces straight ahead, controlled by a fierce bit which would break its jaw if it dared to disobey.[36]

Whistlejacket, by contrast, is portrayed as a free spirit. Apart from the fact that he is shod, he is depicted as if in a state of nature. No bridle, saddle or reins curtail his freedom; he could be a stallion prancing at liberty, his mane untrimmed, his tail undocked. Even Dr Waagen, who in general forebore to comment on paintings of horses, was impressed by Whistlejacket; visiting Wentworth in the early 1850s, he noted 'A brown horse, size of life; of great animation'.[37] His head is turned towards the painter, as if startled, or resentful of the painter's intrusion on his privacy. Humphry's Memoir includes anecdotes about Whistlejacket's nervousness, his intractability, his need to be soothed by a groom before 'sitting' to the painter; but these are a townee's imaginings of the horse painter's difficulties.

The Wentworth Woodhouse archives, though unusually comprehensive, contain no clear reference to the commission to paint *Whistlejacket*. The receipt from Stubbs dated 30 December 1762 (quoted above) records 'Eighty guineas for one Picture of a Lion and another of a Horse Large as Life'; the second item has been assumed to refer to Whistlejacket,[38] but the conjunction of those two pictures probably refers to the pair of large pictures now known as *Lion attacking a Horse* and *Lion attacking a Stag* painted for Lord Rockingham's London house.[39] Possibly the commission for the life-size *Whistlejacket*, likely to have been given in or about 1762, was also given and paid for in London, its documentation not preserved among the Wentworth Woodhouse Muniments.

Fig. 4 Sir Joshua Reynolds, *General Lord Ligonier*, 1760. Oil on canvas, 279.4 × 238.8 cm. Presented by William IV to the National Gallery, 1836. London, Tate Gallery.

The next recorded payments by Rockingham to Stubbs are on 31 August 1764, when Stubbs received £70.15.0. for two pictures (now known as *Sampson in Three Positions* and *The Marquess of Rockingham's Arabian Stallion led by a Groom at Creswell Crags*).[40] In 1766 Rockingham commissioned Stubbs to paint his victorious racehorse *Bay Malton with John Singleton* (a fairly conventional profile portrait). Stubbs also painted two later racehorse portraits for him, in which another artist (? Benjamin Killingbeck) appears to have completed the backgrounds.[41]

Some time after Rockingham's death (in 1782), a 'Whistlejacket Room' was created at Wentworth House.[42] There, set into the white plasterwork of a room 40-foot square, Whistlejacket enjoyed the luxury of space. Only two family portraits kept him company: Reynolds's portrait of the 2nd Marquess as a child, and Lawrence's portrait of his eventual heir, the 2nd Earl Fitzwilliam.

NOTES

An exceptionally large and well-preserved collection of papers relating to the 2nd Marquess of Rockingham and to Wentworth Woodhouse has survived and, fully calendared, is in the care of Sheffield Archives. References below to Wentworth Woodhouse Muniments are to papers in this collection.

1. In a letter of 17 October 1771 to Peter Camper, Professor of Anatomy at Gröningen, who had written to him praising *The Anatomy of the Horse* and hoping that Stubbs would deepen his anatomical research, Stubbs wrote: 'What you have seen is all I meant to do, it being as much as I thought necessary for the study of Painting, and being too well employ'd in my Profession of Painting to spare the time, if I had been qualify'd, but I look'd very little into the internal parts of a Horse, my search there being only a matter of curiosity' (Bibliothecaris der Rijksuniversiteit, Leiden).

2. *The 3rd Duke of Richmond with the Charlton Hunt*, ? 1759; *Henry Fox and the Earl of Albemarle shooting at Goodwood*, ? 1759; *The Duchess of Richmond and Lady Louisa Lennox watching the Duke's Racehorses at Exercise*,

? 1760: all coll. Trustees of the Goodwood Collection, Goodwood House, Chichester; Egerton 1984, cat. nos. 28, 30, 31, all repr.

3. The index in Egerton 1984 will offer pointers to examples of Stubbs's work for all these noblemen except the Duke of Portland; Stubbs's work for him was not available for the 1984 exhibition, but an example is repr. in Taylor 1971, fig. 37.

4. For Stubbs's work for Lord Grosvenor, see Judy Egerton, 'The Painter and the Peer: Stubbs and the Patronage of the 1st Lord Grosvenor', *Country Life*, 22 November 1979, pp. 1892–3. For *The Grosvenor Hunt* and Lord Grosvenor's *Mares and Foals*, see Egerton 1984, cat. nos. 39 and 90, both repr.

5. See *DNB*; also Ross J.S. Hoffman, *The Marquis: A Study of Lord Rockingham, 1730–82*, New York 1973, *passim*.

6. First at the age of four, noted on p. 246. The prime version of Reynolds's full-length portrait of him in Garter robes, 1768, is coll. Trustees of the Rt. Hon. Olive, Countess Fitzwilliam's Chattels Settlement; several replicas (including one coll. Her Majesty The Queen, Millar 1969, cat. no. 1045) and reduced versions. Reynolds's double portrait *Lord Rockingham and his Secretary, Edmund Burke* (coll. Fitzwilliam Museum, Cambridge; repr. ed. Penny 1986, cat. no. 70, pp. 236–8, and in colour p. 117) carries deliberate echoes of the double portrait in Rockingham's collection of the Earl of Strafford with his secretary, Sir Philip Mainwaring.

7. For the building and reconstruction of Wentworth Woodhouse, see Hussey 1955, pp. 147–54. Fig. 242 reproduces a photograph of its east front, 660 ft long (the façade of the National Gallery is 462 ft long). See also H. Avery Tipping, 'Wentworth Woodhouse', *Country Life*, 1924: Part I, 20 September, pp. 438–44; Part II, 27 September, pp. 476–83; Part III, 4 October, pp. 512–19; Part IV, 11 October, pp. 554–62.

8. For photographs of the display of sculpture in the Great Hall and elsewhere at Wentworth, see Hussey 1955, fig. 246; Penny 1991 (cited in note 9) *passim*.

9. For a most informative and well-illustrated account of Rockingham as a collector of sculpture, see Nicholas Penny, 'Lord Rockingham's Sculpture Collection and *The Judgment of Paris* by Nollekens', *J. Paul Getty Museum Journal*, 19, 1991, pp. 5–34. For Rockingham's Grand Tour see Ingamells 1997, pp. 631–3.

10. See Penny 1991 (cited above) pp. 18–19. Two of the Giambologna bronzes can be seen on top of the chimneypiece in the library at Wentworth in a photograph repr. Penny, p. 18, fig. 16.

11. Quoted in Ingamells 1997, p. 632.

12. Walpole to Mann, 27 April 1755, *Walpole Correspondence*, vol. XX, p. 373.

13. Quoted by Hoffmann 1973 (cited in note 5), p. 14.

14. Wentworth Woodhouse Muniments, R1-776.

15. The Marquess of Rockingham's Account Book and Stubbs's receipts for payments are Wentworth Woodhouse Muniments (A/1000).

16. The groom's name has long been given as Simon Cobb. Rockingham's correspondence over his horses is with Joshua Cobb, but there may have been two Cobbs (? father and son, or brothers) in his employ.

17. Coll. Trustees of the Rt. Hon. Olive, Countess Fitzwilliam's Chattels Settlement; see Egerton 1984, cat. no. 35, repr. p. 62.

18. Waterhouse 1953, p. 205.

19. The Godolphin Arabian, foaled in the Yemen in 1724 and imported into England soon afterwards, was so-called after entering the 2nd Earl of Godolphin's stud at Newmarket. He died in 1753. Stubbs's posthumous portrait of him (based on a print by David Morier) was included in his series of notable horses engraved by George Townly Stubbs, 1794, and published in *A Review of the Turf* (repr. Lennox-Boyd, Dixon and Clayton 1989, cited under Engraved, p. 236). The other two most famous Arabian imports were the Byerley Turk (captured by Captain (later Colonel) Byerley at Buda in 1688, and brought to England) and the Darley Arabian (foaled in 1700, imported to join Mr Darley's stud in Yorkshire). See Roger Longrigg, *The History of Horse Racing*, London 1972, pp. 57–61.

20. Whistlejacket's pedigree is given in William Pick, *The Turf Register and Sportsman and Breeder's Stud-Book*, 1803, I, pp. 154–5. The compiler is indebted to Lorraine Moran of Weatherbys for this information. See also *An Authentic Historical Racing Calendar of all the Plates, Sweepstakes, Matches &c. run for at York, from...1709,...to 1785, in which is also given pedigrees and performances of the most celebrated racehorses, that have appeared on the English turf*, York [1785].

21. In the Wentworth Inventory made after the 2nd Marquess's death in 1782, these are nos 133 and 136; no. 131 is a portrait of a horse and jockey by Wootton. All three have remained in the collection of his heirs.

22. Rockingham commissioned two portraits of John Singleton from Stubbs: *Scrub with John Singleton up*, 1762, and *Bay Malton with John Singleton up*, *c*.1765; both coll. Trustees of the Rt. Hon. Olive, Countess Fitzwilliam's Chattels Settlement.

23. Horace Walpole to Richard Bentley, August 1766; *Walpole Correspondence*, vol. XXXV, p. 267.

24. Whistlejacket's progeny, listed by Pick (cited in note 20), include Mr Pigott's Coriolanus and Roscius, Lord Grosvenor's Scoles, Lord Rockingham's Rambler and Lord Ossory's Laura, the latter (the most successful racehorse got by Whistlejacket) painted by Stubbs in 1771, with a jockey and stable-lad (exh. Whitechapel Art Gallery, *George Stubbs*, 1957, no. 20).

25. Whistlejacket is not even mentioned in J. Fairfax Blakeborough, *Northern Turf History*, 3 vols, York 1950.

26. Act IV; the play was first produced in 1773.

27. See ed. Stella Walker, *Summerhays' Encyclopaedia for Horsemen*, 6th edn, London 1975, pp. 13–14.

28. Ed. Paget Toynbee, p. 71. Walpole had previously visited Wentworth Woodhouse in August 1766; writing to Richard Bentley that month, he describes the grounds and the 'modern front', but mentions only a few pictures (none by Stubbs), and may not have seen much of the interior on that occasion (*Walpole Correspondence*, vol. XXXV, p. 267).

29. See Laing 1995, p. 14, describing her role ('It was an important part of the business of house servants – and generally of the housekeeper – to show respectable visitors around notable houses') and her portrait by Thomas Barber (cat. no. 1, repr.).

30. The equestrian monument to Bartolomeo Colleoni, modelled by Andrea Verrocchio and cast in bronze after his death; erected in the Campo Scuola di San Marco, Venice, and unveiled in 1496.

31. Coll. Prado, Madrid; see Hans Vlieghe, *Rubens Portraits, Corpus Rubenianum*, Part xix, II, cat no. 93, plate 76. This is perhaps the best-known of Rubens's equestrian portraits.

32. By Abraham van Diepenbeeck, engraved by Caukercken, published in William Cavendish, Duke of Newcastle, *A General System of Horsemanship* (Antwerp 1658), London 1743, facsimile edn New York 1970.

33. See José Lópes-Rey, *Velázquez*, London 1963, cat. nos. 187, 199, 220; plates 83, 85, 95.

34. Coll. Louvre, Versailles; repr. Anita Brookner, *Jacques-Louis David*, London 1980, plate 74.

35. MS Memoir, n.p.

36. Brian Sewell, in an article on *Whistle-jacket*'s arrival in the NG ('The Stallion that stands alone in Greatness', *Evening Standard*, 27 June 1996, pp. 28–9), reproduces a page of sketches by Leonardo da Vinci for a monument to Gian Giacomo Trivulzio. In these, the horse's head is turned towards the spectator, but at the command of the rider, who is putting him through a movement to the right.

37. Waagen 1854, III, p. 339.

38. Constantine 1953, p. 237.

39. Coll. Yale Center; repr. Egerton 1984, pp. 92–3, cat. nos. 60–1.

40. Both coll. Trustees of the Rt. Hon. Olive, Countess Fitzwilliam's Chattels Settlement. *Sampson*, originally left without a background, is repr. Constantine 1953, with a background added by ? George Barrett, recently painted over (but not ineradicably) at the owners' request. The *Arabian at Creswell Crags* is repr. Egerton 1984, cat. no. 72, repr. pp. 72–3.

41. See Constantine 1953, p. 238.

42. A photograph of the room, showing *Whistlejacket in situ*, is repr. Hussey 1955, fig. 252.

NG 6429

The Milbanke and Melbourne Families

? exhibited 1770
Oil on canvas, 97.2 × 147.3 cm (38¼ × 58 in.)

Provenance
Presumably commissioned by Peniston Lamb, later 1st Viscount Melbourne; by descent to his daughter Emily Lamb, who married 5th Earl Cowper, and thence by descent in the female line through the Fane and Desborough families until inherited by the Hon. Julian Salmond, by whom sold in 1975 to Marlborough Fine Art Ltd, from whom, after an export licence had been refused by the Reviewing Committee, purchased by the National Gallery 1975.

Exhibited
Probably SA 1770 (133, 'A Conversation'); RA Winter 1881 (2); London, Whitechapel Art Gallery, *Animals in Art*, 1907 (37); London, Grosvenor Gallery, *Woman and Child in Art*, 1913–14 (81); London, 25 Park Lane, *18th-Century English Conversation Pieces*, 1930 (5); RA 1934 (401; *Commemorative Catalogue* no. 166); Paris, Orangerie, *Le Paysage Anglais de Gainsborough à Turner*, 1953 (66); RA, *European Masters of the Eighteenth Century*, 1954–5 (110); Whitechapel Art Gallery, *George Stubbs*, 1957 (5); Canada and USA, 1957–8 (68); Tate Gallery and Yale Center for British Art, *George Stubbs*, 1984–5 (110).

Literature
J.H. Anderdon, MS annotation *c.*1840 to SA exhibition catalogue of 1770, Whitley Papers; Mary Louisa Boyle, *Biographical Catalogue of the Portraits at Panshanger, the Seat of Earl Cowper, KG*, London 1885, cat. no. 11, p. 322; Sitwell 1936, p. 59; Waterhouse 1953, p. 209; Constance-Anne Parker, *Mr Stubbs the Horse Painter*, London 1971, p. 163; Taylor 1971, pp. 37–8, 209; Egerton, *George Stubbs*, exh. cat., London and New Haven 1984, pp. 150–1; Judy Egerton, *Stubbs: Portraits in Detail*, London 1984, pp. 30, 32 (two details repr. pp. 31, 33).

Copy
by John Best (1750–92),[1] 39 × 59 in., signed by him and dated 1770, formerly collection of Sir Walter Gilbey (his sale 12 May 1910, lot 155); ? the picture sold by Mrs Alfred Morrison, Christie's 19 November 1920 (73, as by Stubbs), bt Mason, now untraced.

[Not engraved in Stubbs's lifetime; engraved in mezzotint by H. Macbeth Raeburn (who exhibited other work at the RA 1881–1904).]

Technical Notes
Cleaned on acquisition in 1975. In good condition except for a fine network of cracks in the darkest part of the paint.

The ground of the picture is a pale fawn colour. Prussian blue is used extensively throughout. A very light tint of Prussian blue mixed with white and traces of red ochre and black is used in the sky, where there has almost certainly been some fading of colour (as so often with very pale tints of Prussian blue in eighteenth-century pictures). The dark grey-blue of Peniston Lamb's coat is a mixture of Prussian blue, white and a little fine-grained black pigment; John Milbanke's lighter coloured coat is painted with more white added to the blue, and with a thin veil of grey paint over the grey-blue under-layer. For the dark blue-green of the spokes of the carriage-wheel, the main pigment is Prussian blue of a rather greenish tone (as it sometimes is in eighteenth-century examples), mixed with some yellow earth and possibly also yellow lake. The greenest leaves of the tree are painted in Prussian blue, black, some earth pigment and probably yellow lake.

Analysis of a paint sample from the white cloud (top right) suggests that the medium was based on walnut oil, with no inclusion of resin, while a sample of the dark green indicated linseed oil, with no addition of resin or wax (and no suggestion of heat pre-polymerisation in either sample).

The Milbanke and Melbourne Families is almost certainly the picture which Stubbs exhibited at the Society of Artists in 1770 as 'A conversation', the only occasion upon which he exhibited a picture with such a title.[2] The only other possible candidate for it at that date is the Pocklington group (fig. 1) now in Washington,[3] which is dated 1769, but has never (so far as is known) been associated with the exhibition of 1770. The identification of *The Milbanke and Melbourne Families* as Stubbs's 'Conversation' of 1770 seems first to have been recorded by J.H. Anderdon in about 1840, during his systematic and usually reliable annotations to Society of Artists and Royal Academy exhibition catalogues; no contemporary notice of the picture which might prove (or disprove) the identification has so far been found.

Reading from left to right, the sitters are Elizabeth, née Milbanke; her father, Sir Ralph Milbanke MP, 5th Bt, of Halnaby Hall in the North Riding of Yorkshire;[4] her younger brother, John Milbanke; and her husband, Sir Peniston Lamb, 2nd Bt, of Brocket Hall, Hertfordshire.[5] On 13 April 1769, Elizabeth Milbanke, aged sixteen, had married Peniston Lamb, aged twenty-four.[6] Just over a year later, on 3 May 1770, their first child was born; and on 8 June 1770 Peniston Lamb was given an Irish peerage. He chose to call himself Lord Melbourne, after his mother's family home, Melbourne Hall, Derbyshire.[7] Thus from 8 June 1770, while this family group was still on view at the Society of Artists, the young couple became Lord and Lady Melbourne. Their new rank is customarily (and only slightly prematurely) used in the title *The Milbanke and Melbourne Families* by which the picture has become known.

It was as Lady Melbourne that the only woman in Stubbs's picture achieved fame, or notoriety. She was to sit to

NOTES

1. John Mills and Raymond White, *NG Technical Bulletin*, 1980, 4, p. 64, and 1985, 9, pp. 60–4.

2. See Marylian Watney, *The Elegant Carriage*, London 1961, p. 18, reproducing a coach builder's design for a high Crane-Neck phaeton *c.*1790.

3. The comparison is with Stubbs's drawing of the skeleton of a fowl in his *Comparative Anatomy* of about 1795. In this compiler's *George Stubbs* exh. cat. (132, Tate Gallery, 1984–5) the unfortunate omission of the Literature (and Exhibited) sections during printing meant that Constance-Anne Parker's work was not cited; fortunately there is an opportunity to cite it here.

Fig. 1 *Phaeton with a Pair of Cream Ponies in charge of a Stable-Lad*, *c.*1780–5. Oil on panel, 89.5 × 136 cm. New Haven, Yale Center for British Art, Paul Mellon Collection.

Fig. 2 *A Gentleman driving a Lady in a Phaeton*, detail of the carriage mechanism

Joseph Mallord William Turner RA

1775–1851

Born in London 23 April 1775, son of a barber. Largely self-taught, working first in watercolour; early employment as assistant to the architectural draughtsman Thomas Malton consolidated his grasp of structure and perspective. Entered the Royal Academy Schools 1789; first exhibited at the Royal Academy in 1790 (a watercolour), showing his first oil (a marine) there in 1796. Elected ARA 1799 and RA in 1802, at the uniquely early age of 26, recognised by then as a painter of huge potential with an ambition to rival the old masters.

Turner's output in both watercolour and oils was vast, and his choice of subjects – landscape, classical literature and history, modern poetry and contemporary life – extraordinarily wide. He exhibited regularly at the RA up to 1850. The Academy itself, which he served loyally, became the sheet-anchor in his otherwise largely solitary, unsociable life. Travelled widely, both in Britain and (when peace allowed) abroad, frequently commissioned by print-publishers to paint topographical watercolours, engraved for such series as *Picturesque Views in England and Wales* (1827–38) and *Wanderings by the Seine (Turner's Annual Tour, 1834)*; during the 1830s, also painted vignette illustrations to the works of Thomas Campbell, Samuel Rogers, Byron, Sir Walter Scott and Thomas Moore.

After sitting next to Turner at an RA dinner in 1813, Constable noted 'he is uncouth but has a wonderfull range of mind'. That 'range of mind', combined with deeply poetic imagery and frequently idiosyncratic technique, baffled and exasperated contemporary reviewers, who often mocked his work. Turner never lacked patrons, and discerning collectors were ready to pay very high prices for his work. But Turner, who had earned a fortune – and with it, complete independence – began during the 1820s to retain major works, sometimes, as with *Sun rising through Vapour* (NG 479), buying them back in the saleroom, for eventual bequest to the nation. The incomplete realisation of Turner's intentions was largely due to the fact that his will was contested by relatives. Litigation was finally resolved by an out-of-court settlement confirmed by a Court of Chancery decree (19 March 1856), whereby the nation (in effect the National Gallery) was deemed to be the heir of all paintings and drawings by Turner which had remained with him at his death on 19 December 1851, whether finished or unfinished. Thus 100 'finished pictures', 182 'unfinished pictures' and 19,049 'drawings and sketches in colour and in pencil' entered the National Gallery's collection.

After the foundation in 1897 of the Tate Gallery as the national collection of British art, the larger part of what is now known as the Turner Bequest was gradually transferred to the Tate Gallery, the National Gallery retaining ten of the oil paintings.

References

Martin Butlin and Evelyn Joll, *The Paintings of J.M.W. Turner*, 2 vols, text and plates, London 1977, revised edn 1984; Andrew Wilton, *The Life and Work of J.M.W. Turner* (including a catalogue of over 1600 watercolours), London 1979; ed. John Gage, *Collected Correspondence of J.M.W. Turner*, Oxford 1980.

The literature on Turner is voluminous. For particular aspects of his work, see the Tate Gallery's continuing series of studious exhibition catalogues; see also *Turner Studies*, published by the Tate Gallery (11 vols, 1981–91).

NG 472

Calais Pier, with French Poissards preparing for Sea: an English Packet arriving

exhibited 1803

Oil on canvas, 172 × 240 cm (67¾ × 94½ in.)

Provenance

Turner Bequest 1856.

Exhibited

RA 1803 (46); Tate Gallery 1931 (19); Paris, Louvre, 1938 (140); New York, Chicago, Toronto and London, Tate Gallery, 1946–7 (45); Moscow and Leningrad 1960 (51); RA 1974–5 (75); Tate Gallery, *Turner's Holland*, 1994 (2).

At the Tate Gallery 1910–19; 1949–56; 1961–8; and for the opening of the Clore Gallery, April 1987, for six months.

Literature

Farington, *Diary*, vol. VI, pp. 2013, 2023–4, 2030, 2287–8; Ruskin 1851, vol. XII, p. 378 and note 1; Ruskin 1857, vol. XIII, pp. 105–7, 111 n.; Whitley 1928, pp. 58–9; Davies 1946, p. 147; Davies 1959, pp. 94–5; Finberg 1961, pp. 81–2, 97–101, 171; Ziff 1963, p. 320; Gowing 1966, p. 10, with detail of sea; Gage 1969, p. 40; Wilton 1979, pp. 82–3, 219; A.G.H. Bachrach, 'Turner, Ruisdael and the Dutch', *Turner Studies*, I, no. 1 [1981], pp. 22–5, with three details, figs. 7–9; Wilton 1982, pp. 11–12; Butlin and Joll 1984, pp. 37–8 (with exhaustive bibliography to 1984), cat. no. 48, plate 58; Gage 1987, p. 66; Wilton 1987, pp. 64–6, 85, fig. 89; Shanes 1990, pp. 121–2; A.G.H. Bachrach, *Turner's Holland*, exh. cat., Tate Gallery 1994, pp. 13–14, 28–9.

Engraved
by J. Cousen for *The Turner Gallery*, 1859 (Rawlinson 692), republished *The Art Journal*, New Series, vol. VII, 1861, facing p. 48.

Technical Notes
In very good condition. As with *Sun rising through Vapour* (NG 479), Turner used a double thickness of canvas. An unprimed canvas was attached to the stretcher before the second canvas on which the picture was to be painted. In this instance, it appears that the second canvas was sized and primed after it had been stretched – some of the ground has penetrated through to the first canvas. Both canvases are loosely woven and have threads of very variable thickness. Many of the thicker vertical threads of the second canvas have left ridges on the paint surface.

The picture was surface cleaned and varnished in 1890. By 1954, the varnish had become very discoloured and the tacking edges of both canvases had split, and the picture was cleaned and lined.

Fig. 1 *Our Landing at Calais – nearly swampt*, 1802. Black and white chalk on grey paper, drawn across two of the pages, each 43.5 × 27.3 cm, of the 'Calais Pier' sketchbook (TB LXXXI-58–9), and inscribed as title. London, Tate Gallery.

Calais Pier was included in the first public display of 34 oils and 102 watercolours from Turner's bequest to the nation, selected by Ruskin and presented from February 1857 as 'The Turner Gallery' in Marlborough House, then the only additional space available to the National Gallery. Ruskin's account of the oils, entitled *Notes on the Turner Gallery 1856* and published in a paper-covered booklet (price one shilling), provided most people with their first guide to Turner's works, ordered (with long-unchallenged authority) into 'periods'. In these *Notes*, Ruskin pronounced *Calais Pier* to be 'the first' picture to bear the signs of 'Turner's colossal power'.[1]

Calais Pier, Ruskin added, was 'the richest, wildest and most difficult composition'. 'What actually happens' in this complex picture is expertly explained by A.G.H. Bachrach (1981).[2] Turner's title specifies an 'English packet arriving'; this is the regular cross-channel ferry-boat on the left, dark-sailed and cutter-rigged, which has arrived in the outer harbour. Passengers crowd her deck to watch a near-collision as a large French fishing-boat with light-coloured sails makes for the open sea.[3] From the piers on both sides of the harbour, small fishing-boats are trying to put out to sea. On the right, and most conspicuously, a small ketch is 'frantically trying to get ... away from the pier on which she threatens to be smashed by the violent on-shore wind'. Bachrach draws attention to Turner's placing of a similar ketch on the left, which has succeeded in putting out from the further pier, and is now in a position to make sail and follow the big fishing-boat in the centre on her way to the open sea: this is exactly the course that the ketch still at the pier hopes to follow. Bachrach observes that 'For a sail-conscious public such implied diagonals would have been perfectly obvious'. The packet-boat flies a British flag; all the fishing-boats appear to be local. Turner dubs them 'French poissards' in his title; this appears to be an idiosyncratic adaptation of the feminine word 'poissarde', denoting a fish-wife (in a 'low' or 'Billingsgate' sense).[4]

A strong on-shore wind bedevils all manoeuvres. But for all the risks in the air, this is not a scene of grave danger, like *Dutch Boats in a Gale: Fishermen endeavouring to put their Fish on Board*, the so-called 'Bridgewater Seapiece', which Turner had exhibited in 1801 (on long loan to the National Gallery since 1987).[5] In that picture, collision is imminent, and dark clouds contribute to the sense of danger. In *Calais Pier*, Ruskin remarked, 'It is very squally and windy; but the fishing-boats are going out to sea, and the packet is coming in in her usual way, and the flat fish are a topic of principal interest on the pier. Nobody is frightened, and there is no danger.'[6] While Ruskin is perhaps unaware of the potential danger, he is surely right to stress that this is not a scene of 'violent storm'. The fishwives on the pier itself, stolidly getting on with the gutting and scaling, assure us of that, as do the blue sky above the wind, and the band of sunlight on the horizon.

The air of excitement which hangs over the picture is largely an echo of Turner's own feelings. *Calais Pier* is based on his own observations on arriving at Calais the previous year. On his first trip abroad, at the age of 27, and taking advantage of the Peace of Amiens, Turner had crossed from Dover to Calais on 15 July 1802, in this or a similar 'English packet'. Farington, who followed him to France the next month, records that the crossing from Dover to the point of landing at Calais pier took 'three Hours & 35 minutes' (and cost ten shillings and sixpence, plus a shilling and threepence to the captain).[7] Turner's 'Calais Pier' sketchbook (TB LXXXI) contains many pen and ink and chalk studies of shipping, some used in the sea pictures with which Turner made his name in this decade, as well as ideas for historical or mythological paintings such as *Hero and Leander* (NG 521, pp. 296–305), painted much later.

A study inscribed 'Calais Pier' (fig. 2) provided the essential idea for the painting, indicating a passenger-boat on the left, a smallish fishing-boat nearby and another trying to put out from the pier on the right. Turner developed this, with much additional drama, into the principal elements of his finished painting; but in the painting, the central fishing-boat becomes a larger, light-sailed trawler, derived from another of his 'Calais Pier' sketchbook studies (LXXXI-151), and its proximity to the ferry-boat is developed into a drama of near-collision. In *Fishing Boats entering Calais Harbour*,[8] probably painted about 1803, or soon after *Calais Pier*, Turner depicts another risk of collision taken by two French fishing-boats in what Professor Bachrach calls 'another hair-raising manoeuvre',[9] also in a strong wind; this time the scene is set outside the piers, with the town of Calais in the background.

Several studies in the 'Calais Pier' sketchbook record Turner's own arrival in France; most of them are reproduced in the exhibition catalogue *Turner en France*.[10] A study inscribed 'Our Landing at Calais – nearly swampt' (fig. 1)[11] is often taken as evidence that Turner himself landed in the same high wind that he depicts in *Calais Pier*; but as Professor Bachrach points out, if the ferry-boat had to make a tide-stop off Calais, passengers eager to land could have themselves rowed ashore, and in fact such sketches show a landing from just such a rowing-boat, more liable to be 'nearly swampt'. Farington, by 1802 aged 55 and temperamentally less adventurous, waited to disembark from the ferry until 'we were placed against the Pier in the harbour of Calais, and landed by ladder'.[12]

Calais Pier was one of five paintings which Turner exhibited at the Royal Academy in 1803.[13] Farington records comments on it from several Royal Academicians, most of whom had not hesitated to praise Turner's *Dutch Boats in a Gale*, exhibited two years earlier, particularly for its emulation of the younger Van de Velde. Now full exposure to Turner's own 'manner' rather floored them. West considered that 'the "Harbour of Calais", by Turner was clever in his manner but would have been better had more time been employed upon

Fig. 2 *Calais Pier*, 1802. Black and white chalk on grey paper, drawn across two of the pages, each 43.5 × 27.3 cm, of the 'Calais Pier' sketchbook (TB LXXXI-102–3), and inscribed as title. London, Tate Gallery.

it'.[14] Fuseli 'commended both the "Calais Harbour" and the large Landscape [*The Festival upon the Opening of the Vintage of Macon*, no. 110 in the 1803 exhibition], thinking they shewed great power of mind, but perhaps the foregrounds too little attended to';[15] but on the same day Farington added that 'Garvey said to me today that this praise of such crudeness was extravagant, a Humbug'. Sir George Beaumont considered that 'Turner finishes his distances & middle distances upon a scale that requires *universal precission* throughout his pictures, – but his foregrounds are comparatively *blots*, & faces of figures witht. a feature being expressed'.[16] Constable, making a general comment on Turner's five exhibits, thought 'that Turner becomes more and more extravagant and less attentive to nature'.[17] It should be remembered that Turner in 1803 was regarded as a rather uncouth prodigy, *capable de tout*, but at no point beyond criticism. He had been elected a Royal Academician (on 12 February 1802, at the astonishingly early age of 26) only a year before exhibiting *Calais Pier*. Neither his works nor his behaviour conformed to the standards to which most Royal Academicians aspired. In short, Turner baffled his elders. Talking about him to Farington in May 1803, shortly after Turner's election to the Council of the Academy, Ozias Humphry remarked on his 'arrogant manners ... more like those of a groom than anything else: no respect to persons or circumstances'.[18]

Fig. 3 *Calais Pier*, detail

The sea in *Calais Pier* came in for heavy and continued criticism. Farington noted that Beaumont thought 'the Water in Turner's Sea Piece (Calais Harbour) like the veins of a marble Slab';[19] nearly a year later, he recorded Thomas Hearne's remark that in 'Calais Pier' the sea 'appeared like batter'.[20] A harsh review in the *Sun* declared 'The sea looks like soap and chalk, smoke, and many other things', while the sky 'is a heap of marble mountains'; it considered that the picture demonstrated 'a lamentable proof of genius losing itself in affectation and absurdity', concluding that 'the boards of the Pier are well painted, but what an inferior object that is for an artist who has bolder points in view!'[21]

Ruskin detected 'the first indication of colour, properly so called, in the fish' lying on the boards of the pier (fig. 3); they appear to be mostly skate, whose rosy-coloured wedge shapes have attracted painters from Chardin to Ensor (they reappear on the sands in *Sun rising through Vapour* (NG 479, see p. 267)).[22] He recounts that while the engraver Thomas Lupton was at work on a mezzotint of *Calais Pier* (eventually unfinished, as noted below), Turner called to examine his progress, and also saw his own painting for the first time for several years.[23] 'In the foreground was a little piece of luxury, a pearly fish wrought into hues like those of an opal. He stood before the picture for some moments; then laughed, and pointed joyously to the fish; – "They say that Turner can't colour!" and turned away.'[24]

Calais Pier was based on Turner's own observations; but his decision to paint it may have been stimulated by seeing, towards the end of his first trip abroad, Jacob van Ruisdael's *Une tempête sur le bord des Digues de la Hollande* in the Louvre,[25] a very different composition, but one with a stormy sea and dark sky relieved by a band of light along the horizon. Returning from the tour of Switzerland which had been the chief purpose of his trip, Turner arrived in Paris around 27 September 1802; he appears to have devoted the next week or more to making the sketches and memoranda of paintings in the Louvre which densely fill his 'Studies in the Louvre' sketchbook (TB LXXII).[26] Turner's pencil sketch of Ruisdael's *Tempest* is on page 81 of this sketchbook; his notes on the picture are given in full below.[27] Turner criticised Ruisdael for '*His* inattention of the forms which waves make upon a lee shore', though Bachrach (1981, p. 22) argues that Turner's comment was not based on knowledge of Dutch shallows and shores. Turner's own picture is too different to be 'in part a private competition' with Ruisdael's *Tempest*, as suggested by Ziff 1963, though his notes indicate that he studied it carefully, and no doubt he learned much from it.

Farington records on 13 May 1803 that 'Lord Gower asked the price of "Calais Harbour", and Turner signified that it must be more than that for which He sold a picture to the Duke of Bridgewater' (i.e. more than the 250 guineas for which he had painted *Dutch Boats in a Gale*, the so-called 'Bridgewater Seapiece', for Lord Gower's great-uncle the 3rd and last Duke of Bridgewater in 1801). *Calais Pier* remained in Turner's possession. In a note of about 1810 in his 'Finance' sketchbook (CXXII-36), Turner set a figure of £400 against 'Calais' (but see Finberg 1961, p. 171).

A mezzotint of the subject was begun by Turner's friend the engraver Thomas Lupton. W.B. Cooke saw 'Turner's grand picture of Calais Pier' in Lupton's studio on 20 February 1835,[28] and according to Ruskin's 'fish' story quoted above the painting was there for several years. The engraving was never completed. Turner was continually dissatisfied with its progress, believing that in reducing the scale of his picture to that of the plate Lupton had misjudged the relative proportions of the shipping, and demanding so many alterations that Lupton refused to proceed. Rawlinson describes it as a 'fine plate', and records several engraver's proofs, but no impressions were published.[29]

Turner's *Calais Pier* made the subject popular. As Mary Bennett and Edward Morris suggest,[30] it is likely to have directly inspired the oil of *Calais Pier*, dated 1844–5, made by David Cox (1783–1859), chiefly a watercolourist. Cox is known to have admired Turner's work. He himself visited Calais in 1826 and again in 1829, when he spent a week sketching there, exhibiting his first *Calais Pier*, a watercolour, in 1829. His oil of *Calais Pier* of 1844–5 appears to be his only oil painting of a continental subject,[31] and although the composition is his own, the Turneresque qualities of Cox's view of the pier crowded with fishwives and sailors (a brisk sea in this case to the right) strongly suggest that he is likely to have seen Turner's picture, either in Turner's house or in the studio of the engraver Thomas Lupton.

NOTES

1. *Notes on the Turner Gallery at Marlborough House 1856*, London 1857, pp. 8–9 (reprinted in Ruskin, *Works*, vol. XIII, see pp. 105–7).

2. 1981, p. 22. The compiler is indebted to Professor Bachrach (scholar and sailor) for discussing the picture and allowing her to draw so heavily on his knowledge.

3. Shanes 1990, p. 122, suggests that in depicting the near-collision of the French fishing-boat and the English packet Turner wanted to demonstrate 'what bad sailors the French could be'.

4. *Harrap's New Standard French and English Dictionary*, London 1972, p. 69.

5. Private collection; B & J, cat. no. 14, plate 11. See Bachrach 1994, pp. 28–9.

6. *Notes on the Turner Gallery*, p. 9.

7. Farington, *Diary*, including the journal of his visit to Paris, beginning 27 August 1802, vol. V, pp. 1810, 1916.

8. Frick Collection, New York; B & J, cat. no. 142, plate 147.

9. In correspondence with the compiler.

10. Centre Culturel du Marais, Paris 1981–2. Pages 58–9, 71, 74–5 and 78–9 are repr., figs. 159, 160, 161, 163; but disregard the perversity whereby the grey pages of Turner's sketchbook are reproduced as blue or even bright green.

11. TB LXXXI-58–9.

12. Farington, *Diary*, journal as cited in note 7, vol. V, p. 1810.

13. His four other RA exhibits in oils in 1803 were *Bonneville, Savoy, with Mont Blanc* (24; B & J, cat. no. 46), *The Festival upon the Opening of the Vintage at Macon* (110; B & J, cat. no. 47); *Holy Family* (156; B & J, cat. no. 49); and *Chateau de St Michael, Bonneville, Savoy* (337; B & J, cat. no. 50); he also showed two ambitious watercolours, *St Huges denouncing Vengeance of the Shepherd of Cormayer, in the Valley of d'Aoust* (384; W 364) and *Glacier and Source of the Arveron, going up to Mer de Glace* (396; W 364). As Wilton notes (1987, p. 85), many of these subjects and others of the period were planned in the 'Calais Pier' sketchbook (TB LXXXI).

14. Farington, *Diary*, 17 April 1803, vol. VI, p. 2013.

15. Ibid., 2 May 1803, vol. VI, p. 2023.

16. Ibid., 3 May 1803, vol. VI, p. 2023.

17. Ibid., 17 May 1803, vol. VI, p. 2031. Constable may have been thinking chiefly of Turner's other exhibits; he continued 'His views in Switzerland fine subjects but treated in such a way that the objects appear as if made of some brittle material.'

18. Farington, *Diary*, 15 May 1803, vol. VI, p. 2031.

19. Ibid., 3 May 1803, vol. VI, p. 2024.

20. Ibid., April 1804, vol. VI, p. 2288.

21. Quoted by Whitley 1928, p. 59. Butlin and Joll 1984 quote a more favourable review (probably by John Britton) in the *British Press*, 9 May 1803, which found more to praise but criticised the clouds as 'too material and opake; they have all the body and consistency of terrestrial objects, more than fleeting vapours of insubstantial air'.

22. Ruskin 1851, p. 378. By 'first indication of colour' Ruskin perhaps means the selection of objects for the sake of their colour, as distinct from the rendering of facts.

23. In relating this anecdote in 1851 (pp. 51–2), Ruskin wrote 'several months', correcting himself in 1857 (p. 472, n.) to 'several years'. The longer interval presumably reflects Lupton's account of the length of time spent in trying to produce a plate which would satisfy Turner. Rawlinson dated the mezzotint to 1827. As Butlin and Joll 1984 note (p. 38), John Gage has traced a reference in the Cooke papers to W.B. Cooke seeing 'Turner's grand picture of Calais Pier' at Lupton's on 20 February 1835.

24. John Ruskin, *Pre-Raphaelitism*, London 1857, p. 51. Ruskin does not state here that the picture was *Calais Pier*, but his *Academy Notes*, 1857, p. 472 establish it.

25. Inv. 2558; repr. Bachrach 1981, fig. 5.

26. Catalogued by Finberg 1909, I, pp. 181–94; see also Finberg 1961, pp. 85–91.

27. TB LXXII, p. 23: 'a Brown picture, which pervades thro' the waters so as to check the idea of it being liquid, altho' finely pencild the introducing of the House on the embankment destroys all the dignity of the left – an Offing with Ship moring in strip of Weather happily disposed and color'd and a heavy sombre grey sky with warm lights (the half tints this leaf) – the chief light is upon the surge in the foreground – but too much is made to suffer: so that it is artificial – and shows the brown in a more glaring point of view and His inattention of the forms which waves make upon a lee shore Embanked (the ships all in shadow).' Turner's sketch of Ruisdael's *Tempest* deliberately omits 'the House on the embankment'. TB LXXII-81 is Turner's sketch of Ruisdael's *Coup de Soleil*, also in the Louvre; his comments on it are on p. 22a.

28. See note 23.

29. See Rawlinson 1913, II, p. 381, no. 791. The copperplate remained in Turner's possession until his death; it was later sold, and presented to the Artists' General Benevolent Institution.

30. *The Emma Holt Bequest, Sudley: Illustrated Catalogue*, Liverpool 1971, pp. 21–2, plate 34. Bennett and Morris note that 'during his first residence in London, 1804–14, he [Cox] studied Turner's pictures at the Royal Academy with particular care and then or later he may have seen Turner's *Calais Pier* which remained with the artist'.

31. Stephen Wildman, *David Cox*, exh. cat., Birmingham Museums and Art Gallery and V&A, London 1983–4, p. 82, repr. (A copy of *The Emma Holt Bequest* catalogue, cited above, annotated by the authors (Walker Art Gallery, Liverpool) notes that Cox painted two oil versions of his *Calais Pier*.)

NG 479

Sun rising through Vapour: Fishermen cleaning and selling Fish

exhibited 1807
Oil on canvas, 134 × 179.5 cm (52¾ × 70⅝ in.)

Provenance

Purchased from the artist in December 1818 by Sir John Fleming Leicester, 5th Bt (cr. 1st Baron de Tabley of Tabley House, co. Chester, 10 July 1826, d.18 June 1827), by whose executors sold Christie's 7 July 1827 (46), bt by Turner himself; with *Dido building Carthage*, specifically bequeathed by Turner to the National Gallery, to be 'placed by the side of Claude's "Seaport" and "Mill"', on condition that they were accepted and so placed by the Gallery within twelve months of Turner's death on 18 December 1851; by agreement with Turner's executors,[1] placed in the National Gallery in accordance with Turner's wishes, formally entering the Collection upon the Court of Chancery's decree settling litigation over Turner's will, 19 March 1856.

Exhibited

RA 1807 (162); BI 1809 (269, as 'Sun-rising through vapour, with fishermen landing and cleaning their fish'); Turner's Gallery 1810 (1, as 'Dutch Boats'[2]); Sir John Leicester's Gallery *c.*1819–25 (7, first as 'Sun-Rise, through a Mist' and later as 'Dutch Fishing Boats; the sun rising through vapour'; Paris, Louvre, 1938 (141); New York, Chicago, Toronto and London, Tate Gallery, 1946–7 (46); Moscow and Leningrad 1960 (52); Tate Gallery, *Turner's Holland*, 1994 (5).

Literature

Farington, *Diary*, 7 April, 11 May, 19 June 1807 and 16 January 1819; William Carey, *A Descriptive Catalogue of Paintings by British Artists in the Possession of Sir John Fleming Leicester, Bart.*, London 1819, no. 7, pp. 21–5; John Young, *A Catalogue of Pictures by British Artists in the Possession of Sir John Fleming Leicester, Bart., with Etchings from the whole collection ...* London 1821, reprinted 1825, no. 7, p. 3; Hamerton 1879, pp. 98–100, 306–10; Whitley 1928, pp. 120–1; Whitley 1930, pp. 136–7, 282–3; Davies 1946 pp. 147–8; Hilda F. Finberg, 'Turner's Gallery in 1810', *Burlington Magazine*, XCIII, 1951, pp. 384–5; Davies 1959, pp. 95–6; Finberg 1961, pp. 134–6, 172–3, 255, 302, 321, 331, 441, 468 no. 111, 478 no. 202, 512 nos 149a and 157a; ed. Douglas Hall, 'The Tabley House Papers', *Walpole Society 1960–62*, vol. XXXVIII, 1962, pp. 93, 120; Rothenstein and Butlin 1964, pp. 10, 22, 26; John Gage, 'Turner and the Picturesque', *Burlington Magazine*, CVII, 1965, pp. 18 n. 12, 23; Wilton 1979, p. 121, and n. 20 (p. 133); Gage 1980, pp. 4, 44–5, 75; Michael Kitson, 'Turner and Claude', *Turner Studies*, 2, no. 2, 1983, pp. 7–8; Butlin and Joll 1984, cat. no. 69, pp. 53–4 (including a more exhaustive bibliography to 1984), plate 79; Selby Whittingham, 'A Most Liberal Patron: Sir John Fleming Leicester, Bart., 1st Baron de Tabley, 1762–1827', *Turner Studies*, vol. 6, no. 2, 1986; Fred G.H. Bachrach, *Turner's Holland*, exh. cat., Tate Gallery 1994, pp. 14–15, cat. no. 5, pp. 34–5, repr. with detail and three other figs. p. 35.

Engraved

Small outline etchings by John Young of this (no. 7) and other pictures in the collection were published in his *Catalogue of Pictures ... in the Possession of Sir John Fleming Leicester, Bart.*, 1821.

Technical Notes

Cleaned in 1968. In good condition apart from some abrasion in the sky. The original construction of the support was similar to that of *Calais Pier* (NG 472), that is, an unprimed canvas was stretched underneath the primed canvas on which the picture was to be painted. Although some repairs to the tacking edges of the painted canvas had been necessary, the support remained in its original state until 1986, when malicious damage by a visitor to the Gallery necessitated lining.

Turner's essential idea for this picture, a black and white chalk drawing inscribed 'Study/ Calm' in his 'Calais Pier' sketchbook (fig. 1), appears to have come spontaneously: the shipping, the sun ascending through 'vapour' or mist, its reflection in the shallows and the line of the shore are all present in this study and were only slightly modified in the finished picture. Turner used his 'Calais Pier' sketchbook, made up of large (45 × 27.3 cm) grey pages, for working drawings for most of his pictures painted between 1802 and 1805, including, of course, *Calais Pier* itself (NG 472, pp. 260–5), and for *Hannibal crossing the Alps*, 1812.[3] Another page from the sketchbook (TB LXXXI-56), shows that the number of boats was reduced (see also pp. 26 and 34). The mood of 'Calm' was linked to human bustle by extending the composition to the right to include a beached fishing-smack and a knot of figures cleaning and selling the catch – skate, sole, whiting, dabs. Page 20 of the 'Calais Pier' sketchbook is a rapid idea for this extension of the scene.[4] For the pier-head, Turner may have recalled one of the blue-grey studies of boats at Dover he had made about 1793–5 in Dr Monro's 'Academy', in Girtin's company, from 'outlines' by John Henderson;[5] it may have suggested other details, including the figure of the man with his back to us, though he was by now familiar with many shores and boats.

'Calm', the key word inscribed on the first study for this picture, was a new ingredient in Turner's marine paintings, compared with the wind-tossed seas in such previously exhibited pictures as *Calais Pier* (1803), *Boats carrying out Anchors and Cables to Dutch Men of War*[6] (1804) and *Shipwreck*[7] (1805). Hamerton 1879 described *Sun rising through Vapour* as 'the first decided expression on an important scale of Turner's master-passion in his art, the love of light and mystery in combination'. It is likely to have been primarily for the quality

Fig. 1 *Study/ Calm*, *c.*1802–5. Black and white chalk on grey paper, 27.3 × 43.5 cm, drawn in the 'Calais Pier' sketchbook (LXXXI-40), and inscribed as title. London, Tate Gallery.

of the light that this picture was to retain a special place in Turner's estimate of his own work. When shown at the Royal Academy in 1807 it made no great stir. Farington, as usual collecting various artists' opinions, reported that Richard Westall RA thought it 'inferior to His [Turner's] former productions', and that Benjamin West PRA considered that 'Turner has greatly fallen off in a large Sea piece'.[8] Robert Smirke RA thought 'Turner's picture of Boats, & his Blacksmith's Shop ... excellent'.[9] The 'Blacksmith's Shop', the second of Turner's 1807 Royal Academy exhibits, was *A Country Blacksmith disputing upon the Price of Iron, and the Price charged to the Butcher for shoeing his Poney*, painted to show that he could rival Wilkie's success in low-life genre; the same impulse may have inspired the Teniers-like intensity with which the fishing folk on the right of *Sun rising* go about their business. But it was Wilkie's *The Blind Fiddler* which attracted chief attention in the 1807 exhibition: Smirke told Farington that 'The crowd prevented His approaching Wilkie's picture'.[10]

Sun rising through Vapour was re-exhibited at the British Institution in 1809. In the spring of 1810, Turner included it in an exhibition of seventeen works in the gallery of his house in Harley Street (open free of charge, to those who obtained tickets, while the Royal Academy exhibition was on). A printed list[11] shows that this time he gave the picture the short title of 'Dutch Boats'. A more descriptive handlist also seems to have been available for visitors; this must have been what Turner himself referred to when he later told Sir John Leicester that 'The description of the Picture was as follows. Dutch Boats and Fish Market – Sun Rising thro' Vapour'.[12] For the time being, and perhaps because the picture had not so far found a purchaser, Turner chose to draw attention to its 'Dutch' content before the quality of its atmosphere. Bachrach 1994 finds 'strong Dutch echoes' in the picture: 'The boats on the left recall Van de Capelle, the man-of-war in the centre is pure Van de Velde, and the group of figures on the right ... is Teniers all over.' After the picture's acquisition by Sir John Leicester, William Carey's *Descriptive Catalogue* of his collection (1819) notes: 'This scene is supposed to represent a harbour on the coast of Holland; although the artist has not confined himself to the particulars of a local view. The shipping are built like those which were used by the Dutch towards the close of the sixteenth century.' Six years later, when John Young engraved the subject, it was with the title *Dutch Fishing Boats: The Sun rising through Vapour*, to which he adds 'Being a View of a Harbour on the Coast of Holland'. As Bachrach observes, 'Holland's North-Sea coast faces West, i.e. where the sun sets, and so the locality depicted for a "sun rising" from open sea could not really be a beach on the mainland': not that Turner himself, composing the picture in his studio, had ever made such a claim for it. He had not set out to paint a 'view' but 'A Calm', which was a favourite subject with Dutch marine painters; it is here, and in the sky above the calm, that 'Dutch echoes' from Cuyp and Van de Velde are most apparent.

A smaller picture now in the Barber Institute, Birmingham, is also known as *The Sun rising through Vapour.* The subject (but not the composition) is similar.[13] The Barber Institute catalogues suggest that it may have been one or other of the pictures shown in Turner's Gallery in 1810 as *Fishing Boats in a Calm*. Whatever Turner called it, it was bought by his friend and patron Walter Fawkes, and can be seen in Turner's watercolour of about 1818–19 of the drawing-room at Farnley, hanging as a pendant to *The Victory in Three Positions*, on either side of *Dort, or Dordrecht, the Dort Packet Boat from Rotterdam becalmed* of 1818.[14] Butlin and Joll suggest that Fawkes may have asked for a subject similar to the *Sun rising through Vapour* which Turner had exhibited in 1807 but which, evidently, he did not mean to sell except on advantageous terms.

On 12 December 1810 Turner answered an enquiry from Sir John Leicester, already one of his chief patrons, who had evidently asked what medium-size marine subjects were available for purchase. In reply, Turner drew sketches on four pictures[15] on one page (fig. 2) above a letter[16] which reads:

> Queen Ann St West Dece^r 12 1810
>
> Sir John
>
> Perhaps the above slight mem^m of the only four subjects I have near the size may lead your recollection in regard to their fitness or class, and if I knew when you would favour me with a call I would most certainly remain at home
>
> Your most truly obliged S^t
>
> J M W Turner

A sketch of *Sun rising through Vapour* appears lower right, under its alternative title 'Dutch Boats'; below the sketch Turner has written 'This (6 feet long) wants Cleaning', a fact he was to not to forget eight years later. Two 'hand signals' remind Sir John that this picture is 'now in S^r J Ls Gallery in Hill S^t' (that is, already in the prospective purchaser's gallery in his own house, presumably on approval). At this point, discreetly, Turner adds 'Pretium [price] 300 Gs –'. This was no doubt a carefully considered price and one which Turner was not prepared to lower.[17]

Eight years passed without a decision from Sir John Leicester. The picture may have remained in his gallery (not open to the public until 1818) in his house, 24 Hill Street, Mayfair, throughout those years. As Whittingham 1986 has shown, Leicester had been a good enough patron to Turner over the years (acquiring in all nine works, two of which were commissions to paint views of Tabley, his Cheshire seat) for Turner to oblige him by waiting patiently for a decision over *Sun rising*; it may also have suited him to have a painting hanging securely in Hill Street, perhaps drawing admiration from other possible patrons.

Leicester finally bought the picture at the end of 1818, for 350 guineas; in a letter of 16 December 1818, Turner thanked him for part payment of £100 of this sum and, not forgetting that the picture 'wants cleaning', asked him to 'have the goodness to send it to Mr Bigg's [William Redmore Bigg RA's studio in Russell Street] for cleaning'.[18] The spur for Leicester to purchase the picture was the fact that in January 1819 he was to re-open his gallery of modern British painting (first opened in his house in Mayfair the previous year), and wanted to increase the strength of the collection.[19] In 1819 he was to publish a catalogue of his collection, and discussed 'the description of the picture' with Turner once more. Turner's reply has already been quoted in part: 'The description of the Picture was as follows: Dutch Boats and Fish Market – Sun Rising thro' Vapour'; he then added: 'but if you think "dispelling the morning Haze" or "Mist" better, pray so name it.'[20] Turner may have sensed that Leicester did not care for the word 'Vapour'. In William Carey's *Descriptive Catalogue* of Leicester's collection, 1819, the title appears as 'Sun-Rise, Through a Mist'.

Leicester died on 18 June 1827, leaving his friend and executor T. L. Parker to discover 'that the state of affairs is so bad, that everything must be sold that can be, and the house and gallery the first.'[21] Within three weeks of his death, the pictures at Hill Street were sold in the gallery by Christie's. Turner attended the sale. He bought back *Sun rising through Vapour* for 490 guineas, prompting the following newspaper item:[22]

> The landscape of Dutch fishing boats with the sun rising through a morning vapour, by Mr. J.M.W. Turner, was purchased by the artist himself for four hundred and ninety guineas. This picture excited the admiration of the whole company, which was manifested by loud clappings of hands on its being brought forward. The biddings for it, which were most exciting, also produced great applause, and Mr. Turner, on becoming the purchaser, received the congratulations of his friends.

The presence of *Sun rising through Vapour* in Leicester's gallery had made it well-known. W.F. Witherington's painting *A Modern Picture Gallery*,[23] exhibited at the Royal Academy in 1824, depicts an imaginary or ideal collection of British paintings, rather like P.C. Wonder's *Imaginary Picture Gallery* of old masters;[24] in this, *Sun rising through Vapour* is clearly depicted on the left wall. In reality, *Sun rising through Vapour* had returned to Turner's house for his lifetime. The collector Elhanan Bicknell (1788–1861), who bought six paintings from Turner's studio in March 1844,[25] reputedly offered him £1600 for *Sun Rising through Vapour*;[26] but well before then, Turner had reserved it in his mind for the National Gallery.

His wish to bequeath two specific paintings 'to be placed by the side of Claude's "Sea Port" and "Mill" that is to hang on the same line same height from the ground and continue in perpetuity to hang' had been formed by 29 September 1829, the day after his father's funeral, and the day on which he signed and sealed his first will. The idea that two of his pictures should hang forever beside the two Claudes which he always calls 'The Sea Port' and 'The Mill' (NG 14 and NG 12, both of which he had known ever since John Julius Angerstein bought them) did not change, nor did his wish that *Dido building Carthage* (NG 498, pp. 272–81) should be one of them; but over the second picture he changed his mind. His first will of 1829 specifies *The Decline of Carthage*[27] as the second of the pictures to hang as a quartet with the

Fig. 2 Letter from J.M.W. Turner to Sir John Leicester, 12 December 1810, with sketches of four marine paintings offered for purchase, noting that *Sun rising through Vapour* (lower left) 'wants cleaning'. University of Manchester (Tabley House Collection).

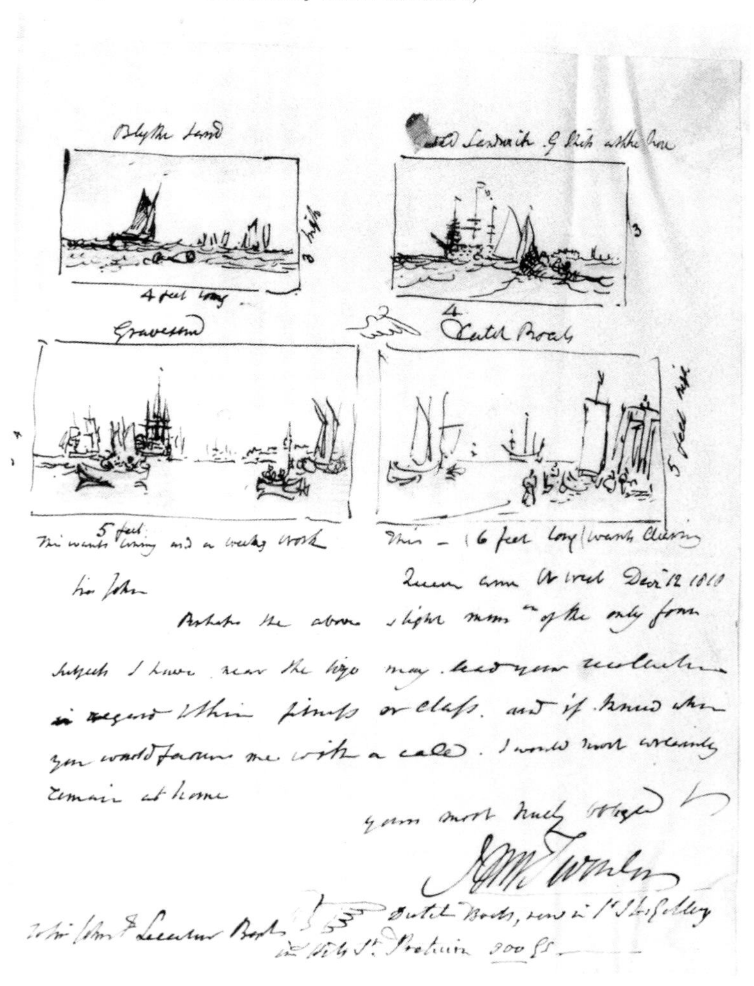

Blythe Sand

Gravesend

Dutch Boats

Sir John

Queen Anne St West Decr 12 1810

Perhaps the above slight mem of the only four subjects I have near the size may lead your resolution in regard to their size or class. and if I knew when you would favour me with a call. I would most certainly remain at home

Your most truly obliged

JMW Turner

two Claudes. His second will, signed and sealed on 10 June 1831, introduces the condition that the two pictures must be accepted within twelve months and 'placed as directed'; and it substitutes *Sun rising through Vapour* for *The Decline of Carthage*. The reasons for this change of mind were not stated, and are unlikely to have been discussed with the Trustees of the National Gallery or with anyone else. Turner may have felt that as the two Claudes were different from each other in subject and in mood, so the two he selected to hang in their company should be different from each other; he may also have felt that two ancient seaport subjects might suggest too close an emulation of Claude. Or, perhaps, looking at *Sun rising through Vapour*, hanging in his dark house since he had succeeded in buying it back in 1827, he knew that in its sky alone he had achieved effects which could hold their own with Claude.

Fig. 3 *Sun rising through Vapour*, detail

NOTES

1. For the background to this, see Finberg 1961, pp. 441–2. Briefly, Turner's will had been contested by his next of kin on the ground that the testator was of unsound mind and incapable of making a legal will. Turner's bequest to the National Gallery of the two specific pictures (now NG 479 and NG 498) to hang next to two of the Angerstein Claudes (NG 14 and NG 12) was conditional upon his two pictures being accepted and hung within twelve months. The National Gallery Trustees were 'extremely anxious' to obtain the pictures; but Turner's will (having already been the subject of a case in the Prerogative Court) had later in 1852 gone to the Court of Chancery, whose delays were notorious.
Finberg recounts the solution: 'An agreement was drawn up with Turner's executors in which they consented to deliver the two pictures to the gallery on condition that they would be returned to them if the Court should order this to be done. The solicitor to the Treasury sanctioned this agreement, and the pictures were discharged from the suit on November 12. The time-limit expired on December 18, 1852.' There was no time to clean the pictures properly. They were hung between the Angerstein Claudes on [?or by] 9 December 1852.

2. This title appears in a printed list of seventeen exhibits at Turner's Gallery, 1810, found by F.J.B. Watson (later Sir Francis Watson) and communicated to Hilda Finberg, who published the list (pp. 512–13), with other new material, as a Supplement to the Appendix of the second (1961) edition of her husband A.J. Finberg's *Life and Work of J.M.W. Turner*.

3. It is described in Gerald Wilkinson, *The Sketches of Turner R.A.*, London 1974, p. 57.

4. Repr. Wilkinson 1974, p. 58.

5. Sold Christie's, 17 November 1992 (62, repr.). For Dr Thomas Monro's employment of the young Turner and Girtin (and others) to copy drawings, see Andrew Wilton, 'The "Monro School" Question: Some Answers', *Turner Studies*, 4, no. 2, 1984, pp. 8–23; for the Dover views after John Henderson, see particularly pp. 20–2. The 'Monro School' drawings remained with Dr Monro. Turner bought many back in Monro's sales in 1833.

6. B & J, cat. no. 52, plate 62.

7. B & J, cat. no. 54, plate 64.

8. Farington, *Diary*, 7 April 1807, vol. VIII, quoting Westall p. 3006, West p. 3007: West added 'He seems to have run wild with conceit', but this may have been a comment on Turner's other exhibit at the RA that year, *A Country Blacksmith disputing upon the Price of Iron, and the Price charged to the Butcher for shoeing his Poney*, B & J, cat. no. 68, plate 78.

9. Farington, *Diary*, 19 June 1807, vol. VIII, p. 3071.

10. Accusations by Allan Cunningham 1843 that Turner's two paintings were deliberately hung next to Wilkie's *Blind Fiddler* so that 'their "unmitigated splendour" should fling it into eclipse', and assertions by Peter Cunningham in 1852 that Turner tried to 'redden the sun' on Varnishing Day for the same purpose, are effectively countered by Finberg 1961, pp. 15–16, and B & J, p. 54.

11. The list is on a small white card, published in facsimile by Hilda Finberg, 1951, p. 384. Mrs Finberg added these titles to a Supplement to Finberg 1961, pp. 512–13; in this, *Dutch Boats* is no. 157a.

12. Turner to Sir John Leicester 16 December 1818: see note 18.

13. Coll. The Barber Institute of Fine Arts, University of Birmingham, 60.9 × 102 cm; B & J, cat. no. 95, plate 103.

14. See David Hill, 'Turner at Farnley Hall', in *Turner's Birds*, exh. cat., Leeds City Art Gallery 1988, pp. 9–24; *Farnley Hall, the Drawing Room* is repr, in colour plate 2, p. 11.

15. The other three are of: upper left, *Fishing upon the Blythe-Sand, Tide setting in*, exh. 1809, B & J, cat. no. 87, plate 97; upper right, *Guardship at the Great Nore, Sheerness*, exh. 1809, B & J, cat. no. 91 plate 101; lower left, the now untraced 'Gravesend', *c.*1807–10, B & J, cat. no. 206.

16. Gage 1980, no. 36, pp. 44–5, transcribes the letter. The whole page was reproduced in facsimile by Bachrach 1994, p. 35.

17. See Finberg 1961, p. 172, for the suggestion that in his estimates of the value of various assets in his 'Finance' sketchbook (TB CXXII) in 1810, Turner had *Sun rising through Vapour* in mind when he put £300 against 'Picture of last year', since *Sun rising through Vapour* had been re-exhibited in 1809.

18. Gage 1980, no. 78, p. 75. This letter also arranges for the cleaning of the picture by 'Mr. Bigg' (Farington, *Diary*, 16 January 1819: 'Bigg called ... He told me He had cleaned a picture painted by Turner, & now bought by Sir John Leicester from Turner for 350 guineas. The subject "A Dutch Sea-port"'.) It also discusses the 'description of the Picture'.

19. For a full discussion of Sir John Leicester's ownership of works by Turner, his collection as a whole and his ambitions for it, see Whittingham 1986.

20. In the same letter of 16 December 1818 as cited in note 18.

21. Quoted by Hall 1962, p. 61.

22. Unidentified newspaper quoted by Whitley 1930, p. 135.

23. Coll. National Trust, Wimpole Hall, Cambridgeshire; repr. Whittingham 1986, p. 27.

24. Coll. NPG (1595).

25. *Calder Bridge* (B & J, cat. no. 106); *Ivy Bridge Mill* (B & J, cat. no. 122); *Port Ruysdael* (B & J, cat. no. 237); *Palestrina* (B & J, cat. no. 295); *Wreckers – Coast of Northumberland* (B & J, cat. no. 357); *Ehrenbreitstein* (B & J, cat. no. 361).

26. Robertson 1978, p. 206; Peter Bicknell with Helen Guiterman, 'The Turner Collector: Elhanan Bicknell', *Turner Studies*, vol. 7, no. 1, 1987, p. 38, and *passim*, pp. 34–44.

27. *Decline of the Carthaginian Empire ....* Turner Bequest 1856, now coll. Tate Gallery (N 00499): B & J, cat. no. 135, plate 137.

NG 498

Dido building Carthage; or the Rise of the Carthaginian Empire

exhibited 1815
Oil on canvas, 155.5 × 230 cm (61¼ × 91¼ in.)
Inscribed DIDO / BUILDING / CARTHAGE / OR / THE / RISE / of the / CARTHAGINIAN / EMPIRE / JMW Turner / 1815 on wall at extreme left and SICHÆO as if carved on a stone tablet on curved wall of tomb at right

Provenance
Specifically bequeathed by Turner to the National Gallery, with *Sun rising through Vapour*, to be 'placed by the side of Claude's "Seaport" and "Mill" ', on condition that they were accepted and so placed by the Gallery within twelve months of Turner's death on 18 December 1851; by agreement with Turner's executors,[1] placed in the National Gallery in accordance with Turner's wishes, formally entering the Collection upon the Court of Chancery's decree settling litigation over Turner's will, 19 March 1856.

Exhibited
RA 1815 (158); London, NG, *Second Sight: Claude: The Embarkation of the Queen of Sheba; Turner: Dido building Carthage*, 1980.

Literature
Farington, *Diary*, 4–5 June 1815, 5 June 1816; Ruskin 1843, vol. III, pp. 113, 241, 267, 297; Anon., 'Turner and Claude', *Art Journal*, New Series, V, 1853, p. 74; Ruskin 1857, vol. XIII, p. 124; Whitley 1928, pp. 241–4; Whitley 1930, pp. 282–3; Davies 1946, pp. 149–50; Davies 1959, p. 96; Finberg 1961, pp. 218–20, 229, 330, 340, 414, 441, 476 no. 189; Reynolds 1969, pp. 94–6; Gage 1974, pp. 75–8; Wilton 1979, pp. 156–9; Gage 1980, pp. 4, 64, 88, 244, 258; Michael Wilson, *Second Sight: Claude, The Embarkation of the Queen of Sheba: Turner, Dido building Carthage*, exh. cat., National Gallery 1980, pp. 2–23, detail p. 11; Wilton 1980, pp. 75–6; Michael Kitson, 'Turner and Claude', *Turner Studies*, vol. 2, no. 3, 1983, pp. 2–15; Butlin and Joll 1984, cat. no. 131, pp. 94–6 (with an exhaustive bibliography to 1984), plate 133; Wilton 1987, pp. 111, 142, 220; Nicholson 1990, pp. 103–5, 108, 237, 281, detail fig. 48; Shanes 1990, pp. 191–203, 213–15, with three colour details plates 126–8.

Copy
153.7 × 229.2 cm, Christie's 11 November 1983 (45); Sotheby's 8 April 1992 (223).

Technical Notes
This is the least well preserved of the Turners in the National Gallery collection. It was evidently in a poor state not much more than twenty-five years after it had been painted as several visitors to Turner's gallery recorded (see page 279). The future Lady Eastlake noted in her journal, 20 May 1846, 'The great "rise of Carthage" all mildewed and flaking off...'[2] In 1855 the condition was described as 'surface much cracked, the cracks in part projecting; the state of the picture, for example in the water and in portions of the sky is consequently dangerous. The canvas requires lining. Parts of the stretching frame wanting.'[3] The lining was done in 1860 and the picture was varnished. John Bentley, the restorer chosen for the task because he was acknowledged to be the best person to deal with damaged Turners, was given 'the strictest instructions to do no more than is necessary for the preservation of the picture'.[4]

Though Turner may have been led towards an unwise choice of materials by his desire to imitate Claude's effects, it is more likely that the flaking paint was due to the picture having been exposed to damp than to defects of technique. The tendency of the sky paint in particular to flake away from the canvas has continued until the present day. Treatment of the flaking paint has always been complicated by the very low melting point of the glazes in the sky. Much of Turner's final glazing and scumbling over the sky may have been lost in the lining of 1860, and in the frequent sessions of blister-laying since. Comparisons with the companion picture *The Decline of the Carthaginian Empire* (Tate Gallery N 00499) and with other works painted in emulation of Claude suggest that Turner probably intended more dramatic and colourful effects than are now seen. A combination of the low melting point and vulnerability to solvents of the medium, and possibly the use of fugitive pigments, have detracted from Turner's intentions.

In 1961 the picture was lined again in an attempt to remedy the flaking, and in 1965 it was marouflaged to a solid support. Some discoloured varnish was removed and the old flake losses were retouched. The remainder of the paint surface is in better condition, though its texture has suffered a little from wrinkling and from shrinkage cracks.

Turner exhibited the picture at the Royal Academy in 1815 with a catalogue note giving his source as '1st book of Virgil's Æneid'. He is most likely to have used John Dryden's celebrated verse translation of the *Æneid* (1697), which was on his shelves in volume XII of his set of Robert Anderson's *Works of the British Poets*:[5] indeed he had already quoted four lines from Dryden's *Æneis* the previous year, when exhibiting *Dido and Æneas*,[6] the first of his paintings on a Carthaginian theme. He is also likely to have read Dryden's translation of Ovid's *Epistle from Dido to Æneas*, which includes lines that seem to anticipate the vision of a Claudian seaport:

> To foreign countries I removed my fate,
> And here, a suppliant, from the natives' hands
> I bought the ground on which my city stands,
> With all the coast that stretches to the sea,
> E'en to the friendly port that sheltered thee;
> Then raised these walls, which mount into the air...

Fig. 1 First idea for a *Ulysses and Polyphemus* subject, *c.*1807. Pen and ink and sepia wash, 11.5 × 18.3 cm, inscribed *Ullissi Poly*, from the 'Wey, Guildford' sketchbook (TB XCVIII 5). London, Tate Gallery.

with him Giulio Romano's 'noble figure' of Polyphemus in the Palazzo del Te.[10] Turner's Polyphemus was to bear no likeness to Giulio Romano's upright, near-Herculean seated figure with pipes and club;[11] nevertheless, as Gage suggests, Eastlake's description, combined with his otherwise derogatory comments on Giulio Romano, may well have provided both a stimulus and a challenge to Turner to take up his own Polythemus theme once more.

Probably in the next few months (before leaving Rome on 3 January 1829), Turner painted an oil sketch for *Ulysses deriding Polyphemus* (fig. 3),[12] working on the first section of a roll of canvas (uncut at the time) which eventually held seven oil sketches;[13] the evidence of tacking holes shows that Turner attached each section of the roll to a support while he worked on it. The colouring in this sketch is mostly sombre; the glorious dawn of the final painting has yet to break. Polyphemus sprawls across a cliff-top, in a pose close to the final one, facing left. A vaporous blue-grey mass hovers behind him, and there is an outbreak of fire (? or burning lava) below him on the sea; a smoking volcano nearby on the left suggests that Turner was aware of the tradition (noted in Pope's commentary to Homer, and observed by Claude in his 'Acis and Galatea' drawings) that Polyphemus dwelt in Sicily, near or even under Mount Etna. Below Polyphemus' cliff, Ulysses' unadorned and as yet unrigged ship rides on a dark sea. Ulysses is already in his taunting attitude, both arms upraised.

Butlin and Joll describe this as the 'only one of this group of sketches with so specific a relationship to a finished work'. But other oil sketches evidently made in Rome in 1828 suggest that Turner's thoughts were tending towards classical subjects in which voyaging is endangered by deep emerald-blue seas and perilous rocks. The next oil sketch on the large roll, known as *Italian Bay*,[14] has a massive rocky arch on the right; an oil sketch from a smaller roll is known as *Rocky Bay*.[15] They are usually thought to be recollections of the Naples coast from Turner's visit in 1819, and may be partly made of such recollections. But while neither of them is 'specifically related' to *Ulysses and Polyphemus*,[16] the fact that they were painted at a time when Turner was meditating about that picture suggests that they may have been conceived as imaginative ideas of the perilous seas through which Ulysses voyaged. Both sketches have the air of being settings for some story rather than being seascapes in their own right.

Turner returned to London early in February 1829. Probably he had already decided to include *Ulysses deriding Polyphemus* in the forthcoming Royal Academy exhibition, opening in May. He had three months in which to paint it; and its completion became more urgent as three of the pictures he had also planned to show – works which he had exhibited in Rome in 1828 and sent home by sea – failed to appear. 'I begin to be figgitty about them', he wrote to Eastlake in mid-February, and with good reason, for they did not arrive until July, too late for the exhibition.

Imagination triumphed over anxiety. Butlin and Joll note that Turner may not have had the oil study in front of him as he worked (that is, if he had sent the canvas roll back with the three slow-travelling pictures);[17] but he hardly needed it. Retaining the essential composition of both the drawing and the oil sketch, he proceeded to embellish the design with inventive detail and miraculous colour, ranging from inkiest deep-water blue to 'paradisaical pinks, purples, yellows and greens'.[18]

The greatest change in the finished work was in Ulysses' flagship, transformed from the dark endangered craft of the oil sketch into an extravagantly ornate vessel, symbolic of the bliss of liberty. Its general shape was perhaps derived from a Claudian ship, such as the central vessel in the *Coast Scene with the Trojan Women setting fire to their own Fleet*,[19] but Turner's own imagination quickly took over. Flags and pennants flutter, some as salutes to Ulysses: a crimson flag flies above his head, a red and gold pennant near the top of the mainsail is lettered 'ΟΔΥΣΣΕ' ('Odysse'), and below it a painted flag depicts his most famous ruse with the Trojan horse. Every surface that could be painted is painted, in colours of old gold, green and coral; even the anchor is the colour of old gold. A carved swan above the prow may or may not have some significance; it appears (or re-appears) in *Regulus* (1828), a scene from ancient Carthage, one of the three slow-travelling pictures he had intended to exhibit at the same time as *Ulysses*, and which he reworked in 1837. In depicting the ship's crew, Turner seems to have thrown all his considerable knowledge of shipping to the winds. The oarsmen are impossibly high above the water. The masts will hardly support the numerous sailors swarming up to unfurl the sails; but the pictorial purpose here was perhaps to bend the masts under the sailors' weight so that they seem to echo the angle of the sun's rays as it rises in salute to Ulysses. Ruskin, whose occasional devastatingly sarcastic remarks about details in Turner add salt to his general admiration for the artist,[20] summed up the ship as 'a composition of the Lord Mayor's procession with a piece of ballet-scenery'.[21]

The oarsmen and the wind have carried Ulysses' ship out of close range of Polyphemus' missiles; but since Ulysses persists in taunting the giant, the ship is still at risk. In Pope's version of Homer's phrase (which Turner faithfully follows), they are now 'in the shallows clear'. Sea-nymphs sport about the prow, preceded by flying fish. Both the nymphs and the fish are luminous, and many of the nymphs have stars at their foreheads. The effect is enchanting but, as Gage has brilliantly shown,[22] Turner is also demonstrating his interest in the phenomenon of phosphorescence. Gage traces Turner's source to Joseph Priestley's *History and Present State of Discoveries Relating to Vision, Light and Colours* (1772), which Turner is known to have used in his lectures on perspective. Priestley showed that phosphorescence was caused by putrescent particles in the sea, usually in the wake of a ship; that did not deter Turner from depicting the sea-nymphs and flying fish around the prow as phosphorescent or, in Erasmus Darwin's phrase (quoted by Gage 1969, p. 131), 'like bodies electrified in the dark'. It is generally assumed that the sea-nymphs round Ulysses' ship are nereids, and probably they are; but although beguiling, they are not certainly benign.[23] They may have streamed out of the nearby volcanic cave in response to Poseidon's orders to delay Ulysses' return home: who knows what the chain of command from Poseidon to the nereids may be?

In the landscape of the finished painting, the prominence given to Ulysses' ship obscures part of Polyphemus' cliff, and also the vaporous mass emanating from it. The distinct volcano of the sketch has been replaced by a range of mountains, some snow-covered; one of these, from which white smoke issues, may be volcanic. The fire on the water in the sketch does not appear in the final painting; instead, fire burns in the depths of a sea-cavern to the left. Gage 1969 suggests that this may be Turner's visualisation of Erasmus Darwin's idea that volcanoes were created by the rush of sea-water into the burning caverns of the earth.

The two great rocky arches guarding the straits through which Ulysses' ship must sail towards the sunlight in the finished picture appear to have been freely adapted from Jacques Callot's etching *The Large Rock* (fig. 2);[24] he may

Fig. 2 Jacques Callot (1592–1635), *Le Grand Rocher (The Large Rock)*, *c.*1630. Etching, 11.7 × 25.2 cm.

Fig. 3 Oil sketch for *Ulysses deriding Polyphemus*, 1828. Canvas, 60 × 89 cm. London, Tate Gallery.

already have had this in mind when making the two oil sketches noted above. The purpose of the two arches may chiefly be to act as markers along a course, anticipating the route Ulysses' ship will take as it passes them on the left and heads straight into the sunrise. The further one is reminiscent of the arch in Claude's *Coast Scene with Perseus ('The Finding of Coral')*. On the right, where the rest of Ulysses' fleet waits (he had taken one ship only on his adventure to Polyphemus' island), one vaguely Phoenician prow seems designed to echo but reverse the angle of the foremost rock arch, thereby adding to the sense of a predestined route which Ulysses' ship will take.

The sun itself is drawn upwards by the four horses of Apollo's chariot (fig. 5). Turner sketches their snorting profiles in delicate silhouette, as if reluctant to make them too obtrusive. The motif is adapted from the four sculptured horses' heads which originally occupied a corner of the eastern pediment of the Parthenon frieze. The two foremost heads were among the Elgin Marbles which entered the British Museum in 1817.[25] Lord Elgin gave Turner a very early preview of his 'marbles'; Turner thanked him on 7 August 1806 for the chance to see 'perhaps the last [collection] that will be made of the most brilliant period of human nature'. Gage suggests[26] that Turner may have drawn on one of the plates in Stuart and Revett's *Antiquities of Athens* which depicted the heads *in situ*. But as one might expect, Turner's representation of the four horses' heads in the dawn sky is fairly free. In the Parthenon frieze, the horses' heads are close together, as if in a closely harnessed team. Turner's horses are wilder – 'leaping up into the sky and shaking their crests out', in Ruskin's phrase – and so far apart as to present problems to any charioteer. The romantic artist has put his own gloss on the classical image.

Chubb[27] notes and illustrates a strong similarity between Turner's rendering of the horses of the sun and that of Poussin in *Cephalus and Aurora* (NG 65, bequeathed to the Gallery in 1831), which Turner could have seen when it was exhibited at the British Institution in 1819 and 1821. A characteristically absurd comment by Thornbury alleges that Apollo himself had once been depicted in the picture, but had 'vanished ... due to sugar of lead';[28] no trace of Apollo in fact appears, and given the acute angle at which the horses are ascending, Apollo and his chariot would in any case have been invisible below the horizon.

Reviewers who saw the picture at the Royal Academy in 1829 were mostly enthusiastic. *The Times* on 11 May declared that there was 'no other artist living who can exercise any thing like the magical power which Mr. Turner wields with so much ease'. The *Gentleman's Magazine*, June 1829, considered that Turner had considerably extended his art 'by an invention of prismatic colours, and a singularly overpowering display of them', but warned that the success of 'this over-gorgeous school' might set a bad example to the young. What John Gage describes as 'the paradisaical pinks, purples, yellows and greens' of the picture were to the *Morning Herald*'s reviewer in 1829, '*colouring run mad* – positive vermilion, positive indigo, and all the most glaring tints of green, yellow and purple contend for mastery on the canvas with all the vehement contrasts of a kaleidescope or Persian carpet'.[30] The *Athenaeum* reviewer on 13 May admired 'the poetical feeling which pervades the whole composition, the ease and boldness with which the effects are produced, the hardihood which dared to make the attempt...'

Writing in 1856, when *Ulysses deriding Polyphemus* was first displayed to the public in Marlborough House, Ruskin pronounced it to be 'the *central picture* in Turner's career'. 'The burnished glow upon the sea, and the breezy stir in the blue darkness about the base of the cliffs, and the noble space of receding sky, vaulted with its bars of cloudy gold ... are all as perfect and as great as human work can be.' Then, he considered the sky to be 'beyond comparison the finest that exists in Turner's oil paintings'. Later he perceived foreboding in the sky, listing the picture in *Modern Painters* IV as among works in which the sky is 'the colour of blood'.

Fig. 4 *Ulysses deriding Polyphemus*, detail

NOTES

1. Gage 1981, p. 24 n. 14, notes that Turner took lessons in Greek from his friend Revd Henry Scott Trimmer, and transcribed many Greek inscriptions into his *Vatican Fragments* sketchbook (TB CLXXX).

2. Turner may have used Alexander Pope's translation in rhyming couplets (1725: many later editions) or William Cowper's blank verse translation (1791).

3. Nicholson 1977, p. 364.

4. Ruskin 1857, pp. 44–5: 'He [Turner] had been himself shut up by one-eyed people, in a cave "darkened with laurels" (getting no good, but only evil, from the fame of the great of long ago) – he had seen his companions eaten in the cave by the one-eyed people – (many a painter of good promise had fallen by Turner's side in those early toils of his); at last, when his own time had like to have come, he thrust the rugged pine-trunk – all a-blaze – (rough nature, and the light of it) – into the faces of the one-eyed people, left them tearing their hair in the cloud-banks – got out of the cave in a humble way, under a sheep's belly – (helped by the lowliness and gentleness of nature, as well as by her ruggedness and flame) – and got away to open sea as the dawn broke over the Enchanted Islands.'

5. See Pigler 1956, vol. II, pp. 9–10.

6. For Annibale Carracci's frescoes in the Farnese Palace, see Charles Dempsey in André Chastel et al., *Le Palais Farnèse*, I, Rome 1981, pp. 269–311, and fig. 15. Turner's Polyphemus also suggests a debt to Agostino Carracci's lounging figure of *Pluto* (the drawing, coll. Her Majesty The Queen, is repr. by Babette Bohn, 'Malvasia and the Study of Carracci Drawings', *Master Drawings*, vol. 30, no. 4, 1992, p. 403, fig. 8, above his oval painting of the subject (Modena, Galleria Estense), fig. 9). For Poussin see below, note 7. Claude's *Coast Scene with Acis and Galatea* (Gemäldegalerie,

Dresden) is Roethlisberger fig. 236. Baudet's engraving after Watteau's *Acis et Galathe* is repr. Marianne Roland Michel, *Watteau*, Paris 1984, p. 150.

7. Anthony Blunt, *The Paintings of Nicolas Poussin*, London 1966, p. 125, no. 175; coll. Hermitage, St Petersburg. Engraved by Etienne Baudet (in same direction) by 1701 (G. Wildenstein, 'Les Graveurs de Poussin au XVIIe siècle', *Gazette des Beaux-Arts*, XLVI, 1955, pp. 316–17, no. 178, repr. p. 316).

8. The comment in B & J, p. 184, that 'there is no connection in composition' between TB XCVIII-5 and the finished painting is puzzling. Nicholson's comment (1977, p. 359) that 'the finished oil of twenty years later was not significantly different in conception' to the study in TB XCVIII-5 is more apt.

9. John Gage, 'Turner's academic friendships: C.L. Eastlake', *Burlington Magazine*, CX, 1968, p. 679.

10. Lady Eastlake, in Sir Charles Eastlake, *Contributions to the Literature of the Fine Arts*, 2nd edn, London 1870, p. 128. Eastlake refers to 'the great Polyphemus ... (a noble figure)'.

11. East wall of Sala di Psiche, Palazzo del Te, Mantua; repr. Ernst Gombrich et al., *Giulio Romano*, exh. cat., Milan 1989, p. 346; the whole east wall is repr. Egon Verheyen, *The Palazzo del Te in Mantua*, Baltimore 1977, p. 88, fig. 339 (Polyphemus also appears, with Cerberus, Diana of Ephesus and two cupids, in a lunette on the west wall of the Sala delle Aquile).

12. Coll. Tate Gallery (N 02958); B & J, cat. no. 302, plate 305.

13. The seven oil sketches originally on the roll were separated at the National Gallery in 1913–14, and are now B & J, cat. nos 302–8. The original canvas is sometimes referred to as Turner's 'travelling roll'. Cecilia Powell observes (in correspondence) that it would have been too bulky for Turner easily to have carried with him; and in fact he sent it back to England by ship, while he continued his travels overland. She suggests that possibly this canvas roll was given to (or bought from) Eastlake in Rome.

14. Coll. Tate Gallery (N 02959); B & J, cat. no. 303, plate 306.

15. Coll. Tate Gallery (N 03380); B & J, cat. no. 309, plate 312.

16. A tower on the left in *Rocky Bay*, with a sketchy terrace in the foreground, suggests that alternatively this may be an idea for *Hero and Leander* (NG 521: pp. 296–305), a picture completed in 1837, but seemingly never wholly out of Turner's thoughts since his first sketch for it in the 'Calais Pier' sketchbook.

17. See B & J, p. 176: Turner sent the pictures he had exhibited in Rome 1828–9 back by sea, and they did not reach London until after the opening of the RA exhibition in May 1829. The canvas roll probably accompanied them.

18. Gage 1969, p. 96.

19. LV 71.

20. A similarly sarcastic comment about the river in *Dido building Carthage* (NG 498) is quoted on p. 278.

21. Dennis Farr, *William Etty*, 1958, p. 141, suggests that Turner's ship may owe a debt to Etty's *Cleopatra's Arrival in Cilicia* [in a golden barge], exhibited RA 1821 (261); while there is nothing in common between the two vessels, Etty's water-nymphs may have helped to inspire Turner's nereids.

22. Gage 1969, pp. 129–31.

23. Nicholson 1990, p. 274, does well to reminds us that in the *Æneid*, a source at least partly familiar to Turner, Æneas's ship is surrounded by 'a choir of nereids': 'They know him from afar, and in a ring / Inclose the ship that bore the Trojan king.' They do not mean well.

24. Callot's drawing of this is coll. Trustees of the Chatsworth Settlement. Etched for the series *Diverse Vedute Designate in Fiorenza* of *c.*1618–20. See H. Diane Russell, *Jacques Callot: Prints and Related Drawings*, exh. cat., NGA, Washington 1975, p. 294, no. 240, repr.

25. Two of these heads were left *in situ* in the pediment.

26. 1969, p. 131; 1981, p. 24 n. 5.

27. See Chubb 1981, p. 31, figs. 10 and 11.

28. Thornbury 1877, p. 445.

29. Gage 1969, p. 96.

30. Quoted by Gage 1969, p. 123.

Fig. 5 *Ulysses deriding Polyphemus*, detail, showing the heads of the four horses drawing up the chariot of the sun

NG 1991

The Evening Star

? *c.*1830
Oil on canvas, 91.1 × 122.6 cm (35¾ × 48¼ in.)

Provenance
Turner Bequest 1856.

Exhibited
Paris, Louvre, 1938 (144); Arts Council tour, Bristol City Art Gallery; Cardiff, National Museum of Wales; Derby Museum and Art Gallery; Harrogate Public Library and Art Gallery; Hull, Ferens Art Gallery; Leeds, Temple Newsam House, *English Romantic Art*, 1947 (25); London, Whitechapel Art Gallery, *J.M.W. Turner R.A.*, 1953 (86); Rotterdam, Museum Boymans van Beuningen, *English Landscape Painting 1740–1850*, 1955 (56); Canada and USA, 1956–7 (114); London, Tate Gallery, 1959 (352); Berlin, Gemäldegalerie, *J.M.W. Turner*, 1987 (11); Leningrad and Moscow 1988 (no cat.); Vienna, Österreichische Galerie, Vienna, as a loan exchange for two paintings by Caspar David Friedrich,[1] 1990; Canberra, National Gallery of Australia, and Melbourne, National Gallery of Victoria, *Turner*, 1996 (14).

At the Tate Gallery 1906–14; 1919–31; 1960–1; and for the opening of the Clore Gallery, April 1987, for six months.

Literature
A.J. Finberg, *The National Gallery: A Complete Inventory of the Drawings in the Turner Bequest*, London 1909, vol. II, p. 736; MacColl 1920, p. 31; Davies 1946, p. 154; Davies 1959, p. 100; Rothenstein and Butlin 1964, pp. 12, 48; Gage 1969, p. 144; Butlin and Joll 1984, cat. no. 453, plate 454; Andrew Wilton, 'J.M.W. Turner: The Parting of Hero and Leander', *Apollo*, CXXXIX, 1989, pp. 46–7; John Golding, 'Turner's Last Journey', in ed. Michael Lloyd, *Turner*, exh. cat., National Gallery of Australia, 1996, p. 175, repr. p. 164 with detail p. 165.

Technical Notes
Lined, and surface dirt removed, in 1956. There is no record of this picture having been cleaned since its arrival in the Gallery with the Turner Bequest of 1856. The hull of a boat, reddish in colour, shows through the sea and horizon to the right of centre. A smaller, darker shape shows through the paint just below the horizon near the right edge. The ground is a warm buff colour.

The right-hand part of the sky has a thick and pastose consistency. The paint of the figure, the star and its reflection, the light pink paint of the sunset just above the horizon and the stones (? or shells) lower right are also thickly applied, perhaps showing the use of a palette knife in places. The remainder of the paint is more thinly applied, the sea on the left for instance consisting of semi-transparent grey washes over a darker grey underpaint.

The title is unlikely to be Turner's. In the original (1854) schedule of 'finished' and 'unfinished' works listed by Turner's executors and the National Gallery Trustees, this canvas was untitled (like most of the 'unfinished' works); it was identified only by the number '117', chalked on the back of the canvas (and still there). With other untitled and 'unfinished' works, it was listed simply as '4 ft by 3 ft'. While those paintings which Turner had exhibited and which remained in reasonably good condition went on display almost as soon as the Turner Bequest was received, it took decades to sort out the 'unfinished' pictures.

Like *Margate (?), from the Sea* (NG 1984, pp. 293–5), NG 1991 was among paintings in the Turner Bequest of 1856 which were long thought to be unexhibitable 'on account of their unfinished or wrecked condition'.[2] Reconsideration in 1905 led to the selection of 22 pictures, including both NG 1984 and NG 1991, for conservation treatment, which in most cases (and in this case) involved only surface-cleaning. Only after that were they given inventory numbers and titles; they were then despatched in relays to hang in the National Gallery of British Art at Millbank, later known as the Tate Gallery. NG 1984 went to Millbank in 1905; NG 1991 was one of 23 Turners[3] transferred to Millbank during 1906.

The date of the picture is generally thought to be *c.*1830, but it is a difficult picture to date, and could be several years later. The apt title *The Evening Star* appears to have been invented for it in 1906,[4] and may have been an inspired suggestion on the part of A.J. Finberg, then engaged in an inventory of the Turner Bequest. In Turner's 'Worcester and Shrewsbury' sketchbook, used about 1829–30, Finberg found some lines of verse scribbled in Turner's hand; he transcribed some of them as follows:

> 'Where is the star which shone at ...Eve'
>
> 'The gleaming star of Ever...' [or Eve]
>
> 'The first pale Star of Eve ere Twylight comes
> Struggles with...'

Given the disjointed nature of the lines and the scrawl with which Turner jotted them down, it is difficult to improve on Finberg's transcription; but it should be noted that there are in fact eleven lines (of which Finberg quotes only the first, part of the fifth, the tenth and part of the eleventh), and that in these Turner makes one attempt after another to find poetic expression for an inevitable sequence common enough in nature: the sequence in which the 'pale' evening star appears with its 'mild' light (if 'mild' is indeed decipherable) at twilight, and briefly 'gleams' before its light is overtaken by the 'powerful ray' of (presumably) the moon. Turner was deeply interested in such transitional moments, later quoting a paraphrase of Byron ('The moon is up and yet it is not night/ The sun as yet divides the day with her') when exhibiting *Modern Rome* in 1838. The sketchbook lines are characteristic of his longing to find poetic expression for what he had, perhaps at the same time, perfectly caught in paint: on the canvas of this picture, the evening star appears, unassertively, as hardly more than a small impastoed point in a fading

From his friend Henry Howard's picture, he appears to have borrowed the idea of Cupid holding the torch traditionally associated with the story; but Howard's hovering putto-esque Cupid and Turner's muscular youth are very different. Howard places Leander in the centre of his picture, arriving ardently at Sestos, to be embraced by Hero, with Cupid lighting the lovers' way up the turret stair. Turner depicts them at the moment of farewell, though they cannot know that this will be their final parting.

The Parting of Hero and Leander is a superlative example of Turner's ability to study various sources, literary and visual, and then transcend them by bringing the full force of his own imagination to bear on his subject. His finished picture shows that whatever alternative ideas he may have tried out in later sketchbooks, for the basic composition he chiefly referred back to the early sketch in his 'Calais Pier' sketchbook. But he rethought the position of the doomed lovers. In the study they are prominently placed, descending the palace or temple steps. The works of Hamilton and Etty may have made him aware that this depiction had become a cliché. Instead, defying the conventions of history painting by which the protagonists are expected to be in or near the centre, registering conspicuous emotion, Turner depicts the lovers in his finished picture at the water's very edge, and in the shadows, where their emotions are private. The lovers' former places are in a pictorial sense taken by Cupid and Hymen on the terrace above, who seem to light the way as 'the deep salt wave breaks in above / Those marble steps below' (Tennyson's phrase).

The lofty architecture in the sketch is elaborated in the painting into a mysterious sequence of temples and towers. The topmost temple recalls that in *The Temple of Jupiter Panhellenius Restored*, 1816.[48] Wilton 1989 notes, within 'a perspective of classical buildings of a grandeur even Turner rarely matched', a watchtower like that which used to stand on the Acropolis at Athens and 'a screen borrowed from the Arch of Hadrian as published by Athenian Stuart'. Inlaid in the pavement is a mosaic picture, described by Wilton as a classical scene of Turner's own devising, but not easy to interpret at that angle.[49] Throughout, the aura of Greece is mingled with more exotic elements, and with awareness that at Sestos Hero dwells on the very edge of the Grecian world, with only the Hellespont (its narrow straits suggested here by huge rocks on either side) dividing it from Asia. The dark tower which looms in the shadows above the rocks on the left of the straits represents Sestos – Musæus refers to 'yon high tower, which close to Sestos stands / And all the roaring Hellespont commands'[50] – while opposite it, half hidden in shadows, is a more 'Moorish' tower representing Abydos, the point to which Leander must swim.

The tiers of temples remind us that Sestos is dedicated to the worship of Aphrodite, and that Hero is no ordinary love-struck girl but one of Aphrodite's priestesses. Probably she took vows of chastity; now she is in love with Leander. While living 'each night a woman, and each day a maid'[51] has its compensations, it is dangerous, and the affair must be conducted clandestinely, under cover of darkness, nuptials openly blessed by Hymen out of the question.[52] Goddesses do not suffer erring vestals gladly (as Callisto found out[53]). Leander must arrive by night, and depart by dawn. It is not just night but danger which fills Turner's stage with uneasy shadows. It is a stage on which Hero and Leander can trust nobody. Even the role of the gods Cupid and Hymen is ambivalent. Ruskin considered that the pavement and the steps leading from it were a supreme example of the fact that Turner's effects of light depend on his mastery of '*shadows*': 'the pavement on the left of the Hero and Leander, is about the most thorough piece of this kind of sorcery that I remember in art.'[54]

Mysterious swirls of greenish blue, too amorphous to be wrack from the sea, drift about the side of the terrace floor; even Hymen's wings are touched with this colour. These eerie drifts may be what the reviewer of *Blackwood's Magazine* had in mind when he complained of 'stone-blue ... daubed about in dreadful and dreamy disorder' (more fully quoted below).[55] The drifts of blue may allude to the belief that Aphrodite (Venus Anadyomene), the goddess whom Hero serves and of whose temple this is perhaps the threshold, was born from the foam;[56] such an allusion would also explain the presence of the (?) dolphin, one of Aphrodite's attributes, lying in the foreground on the marble floor, out of his own element but (as is proper to the dolphin in his emblematic role) with a fish in his mouth.

Night is ending; but 'love yet lingers' (Turner's phrase). Cupid and Hymen watch from the terrace, with perhaps Hero's 'attending damsel'[57] partly seen behind them (in dark red). Both Cupid and Hymen have chaplets of flowers in their hair; but which is which is more difficult to determine. Is Cupid the winged figure holding aloft a lamp and a torch whose flames are thickly impastoed in pure orange, having flung down his bow and quiver of flame-tipped darts on the terrace behind him, and Hymen the slighter, curly-haired sprite beside him? The latter's effeminate appearance conforms to Attic notions about this somewhat unreliable god of marriage.[58] Turner has depicted him in the manner of Thomas Stothard, with whom he had collaborated in illustrating Samuel Rogers's *Italy, A Poem* (1830).[59] Turner's verse seems to tell us that it is Hymen who 'upholds' the torch and failing lamp; but the lines read disjointedly at this point. It is possible that one line (between Turner's third and fourth lines) was inadvertently omitted by the printers of the Royal Academy catalogue,[60] and that it might have read something like this:

> [Where Cupid flinging down his bow and darts]
> Upholds young Hymen's torch and failing lamp.

Whatever the case, Cupid and Hymen seem penitent, doing their bit to help the lovers; but you can never be sure with the gods, and these two (especially Hymen, reputedly a son of Aphrodite) may be carrying out orders to seal the fate of the lovers. Musæus tells us that 'Love must submit to what the fates ordain'.[61] Cupid started all this: but on 'the night of stormy water', as Byron reminds us, 'Love, who sent, forgot to save' Leander. Other, mortal figures on the terrace drowse;

after all, they have seen Leander come and go many times, and at this stage have no cause for concern.

But there is a storm in the heavens. According to Musæus, it is now 'relentless winter', when 'blustering terrors fly/ Rage o'er the main, and battle in the sky'.[62] The weather forecast for Leander in *The Bride of Abydos* may also have been in Turner's mind:

> ...rising gale, and breaking foam
> And shrieking sea-birds warn'd him home;
> And clouds aloft and tides below,
> With signs and sounds, forbade to go...[63]

A swarm of nereids wait in the wild spume on the right of the picture. There is no authority for them in Musæus, though Ovid's Leander recounts that sea-nymphs (and tritons) watch him as he swims. Though Junoesque sea-nymphs dominate the paintings by Rubens and Fetti mentioned above, it is unlikely that Turner could have seen either picture. But in a sense he did not need to. He had depicted nereids disporting around Ulysses' ship in *Ulysses deriding Polyphemus* of 1829 (see pp. 282–9); they are proper to myth. Under the waters, Nicholson notes 'a tiny Hymen-like figure, torch in hand, hovering just at the edge of an ominously dark arch piercing the rock formation' near 'what appears to be a sarcophagus', but this figure's role is ambiguous: does it parody Hero's role, or Hymen's?[64] Nereids are not in themselves malign, but they are under Neptune's orders; and without willing Leander's death, they will be glad to claim Hero's lover for their own.

Above all, Turner's painting is a representation of dawn. 'Now rose the morn, in russet veil array'd', recounts Musæus.[65] Turner's own phrase 'crimsoned blush' only inadequately describes the ravishing ivories, pinks and golds with which dawn breaks,[66] exploding the clouds of night but touching the towers of Sestos with exquisite delicacy, conjuring up Homer's supremely beautiful phrase 'rododaktylos Io' (rosy-fingered dawn). A crescent moon, veiled in a shadowy penumbra, still emits sufficient light to reflect on the water, though the sun is rising, demonstrating Turner's continuing interest in the moment which, in the paraphrase of Byron which he attached to his painting *Modern Rome – Campo Vaccino*,[67] exhibited in 1839, he defined as 'The moon is up and yet it is not night, / The sun as yet divides the day with her.'

The Royal Academy exhibition of 1837 was the first to be held in William Wilkins's new building in Trafalgar Square, shared (until 1868) by the National Gallery and the Royal Academy. As well as *The Parting of Hero and Leander*, Turner showed his *Story of Apollo and Daphne* (sometimes thought to be a companion picture, but though Cupid appears in both, they are very different in size), *The Grand Canal, Venice*, and *Snow-storm, Avalanche and Inundation – a Scene in the Upper Part of Val d'Aouste, Piedmont*.[68] *Blackwood's Magazine* considered that together they constitute 'a bold attempt to insult the public taste. Whether we consider them as wholes, or examine their component parts, there is one equal defiance of common-sense, of nature, of art. White brimstone and stone-blue are daubed about in dreadful and dreamy disorder. The execution is as if done with the finger and the nail, as if he had taken a pet against brushes.' Discussing *The Parting of Hero and Leander*, the same reviewer declared that 'None but a genius could have been guilty of it; and what a pity is it that a genius should have perpetrated it. It is an indistinct dream, blending the ridiculous and the mysterious; yet there are in it the elements of a good picture. Go to a distance, and imagine it to be a sketch in chalk as a design, and you would expect something from it; but what all that white has to do in the picture, it would puzzle any one to find out.'[69] *The Athenaeum*'s reviewer was even less sympathetic. 'What shall we say of *The Parting of Hero and Leander*, with its masses of splendid architecture on the left, and on the right its masses of mist of all colours, in which are dimly huddled a company of water-sprites waiting for the lover, only less gross and deformed in their shapes than that lover himself...? The picture is full of imagination, but it is impudent imagination.' It was a relief for the *Athenaeum*'s reviewer to turn to Mr E. Landseer's *The Old Shepherd's Chief Mourner* (112), 'one of the most simply pathetic things in the Exhibition ... we looked upon it long and sadly'.[70] By 1837, Victorian art was hard on Turner's heels.

Hero and Leander remained in Turner's house, but seems not to have been shown in his gallery.[71] In 1844 he consulted his dealer Thomas Griffith about the condition of various works accumulating in his house:[72] 'The large Pictures I am rather fond of tho it is a pity they are subject to neglect and Dirt... If I could find a young man acquainted with Picture cleaning and would help *me* to clean accidental stains away, it would be a happiness to drag them from their dark abode.'[73] He mentions *Hero and Leander* indirectly as 'the Stormy Picture you said in the Parlour for Mr Foords *Hero* to advise with about cleaning and lining'; as Gage notes, this is probably a punning reference to an employee of Foord in Wardour Street, who was attending to Ruskin's Turners in 1844.

To National Gallery visitors, *The Parting of Hero and Leander* is probably the least known of all the works in the Turner Bequest, since it was on long loan for many decades, first to Glasgow and later to the Tate Gallery, where it still hangs.

NOTES

1. The name given in classical literature to the narrow strait between Europe and Asiatic Turkey, connecting the Sea of Marmora and the Aegean; now known as the Dardanelles.

2. One of the earliest English translations (or renderings) was by Christopher Marlowe, published in 1598 after his death (having been completed by George Chapman). For Marlowe's *Hero and Leander*, and also his *Tragedie of Dido Queene of Carthage*, see ed. Roma Gill, *The Complete Works of Christopher Marlowe*, Oxford 1987, vol. I, pp. 190–209; pp. 125–74.

3. See catalogue of translations in *Modern Language Notes*, XLIII, 1928, pp. 101–4. Virgil, *Georgics*, III, v. 258–63; Statius, *Thebaid*, VI, v. 542–7.

4. Ovid, *Heroides*, 18, 19; in Sir Samuel Garth's translation, published in Robert Anderson's *Poets of Great Britain*, vol. XIV, 1795, pp. 307–9.

5. 1720–77, poet and divine, considered by his contemporaries to be the best translator since Pope. The *DNB* gives 1760 as the date of his translation of Musæus, hereafter referred to as Musæus/Fawkes.

6. Musæus/Fawkes, pp. 235–9.

7. See John Gage, 'Turner and the Greek Spirit', *Turner Studies*, 1, no. 2, 1981, p. 24 n. 13.

8. It includes, for instance, a study (LXXXI-38, 39) for *Snow-Storm: Hannibal and his Army crossing the Alps*, exh. 1812; see B & J, cat. no. 126, p. 89.

9. Reproduced Nicholson 1990, p. 195, fig. 98, and described pp. 193, 197.

10. The sketch (pencil, 9.5 × 15.4 cm) is in the 'Yorkshire I' sketchbook, TB CXLIV-103a. Reproducing it as her fig. 99, Nicholson 1990, p. 197, considers that in this Turner 'revised the scene in a second sketch, refining its basic idea well enough that he needed to make only minor adjustments in subsequent drawings'. It seems to this compiler that if this is a sketch for a Hero and Leander subject, it is not a revision but a fresh idea.

11. TB CCCXLIV-427; 18.5 × 22.2 cm.

12. Wilton 1975, p. 119, cat. no. 189a, *Figures on a flight of steps in an architectural setting*, *c.*1832, noting that two pencil drawings in the *Mouth of the Thames* sketchbook of about 1832 (TB CCLXXVIII, ff. 1 verso, 2 recto), tentatively entitled by Finberg 'Hero and Leander', seem to be treatments of the same theme.

13. See Pigler 1956, vol. II, pp. 322–3, who lists works by or attributed to many artists, including Rubens, Jordaens and Rembrandt. Apart from the Rubens, discussed in the text, some of the other attributions seem doubtful, but not all have been checked by this compiler. A painting by or attributed to Van Dyck, sold in New York in 1978, appears to be the most unusual treatment of the theme, depicting Leander, having swum to Hero, tenderly wrapped by her in her cloak; see Erik Larsen, *L'Opera completa di Van Dyck*, Milan 1980, no. 180 (as *c.*1618), small repr.; it remains untraced.

14. Hollstein, vol. VIII, p. 35, H.159, 160, each repr., each 4.9 × 3.4 cm.

15. See John Rupert Martin, *The Farnese Gallery*, Princeton 1965, fig. 54. The ceiling also includes the (much larger) Polyphemus scenes (Martin 1965, figs. 61, 62). See p. 282 for the possibility that Turner saw the ceiling on his visit to Rome in 1828.

16. Michael Jaffé, who rediscovered the painting, discusses it in 'Rubens in Italy: Rediscovered Works', *Burlington Magazine*, C, 1958, pp. 415–22. Jaffé's rediscovery is of a smaller, earlier version of the picture first referred to in a letter of 1613 from Cavaliero Marino: 'Leandro morte tra le braccia delle Nereidi di Pietro Paolo Rubens'. A large version of this subject is in Dresden, having entered the archducal collection of Saxony in 1657. The smaller, earlier version (now coll. Yale University Art Gallery: see A.C. Ritchie and K.B. Neilson, *Selected Paintings and Sculpture from the Yale University Art Gallery*, New Haven and London 1972, no. 23, repr., and colour plate 6) appears to have been successively in the collections of Rembrandt (from 1637 to 1670), Pieter Six, Sir Peter Lely (sold in 1682 in London, bt Mr Creed), in a Venetian collection by 1684/5; in a Swedish collection by *c.*1950.

17. Anthony Blunt, *The Paintings of Nicolas Poussin: A Critical Catalogue*, London 1966, p. 163, listed among Poussin's 'Lost Paintings', with the caveat noted above.

18. Coll. Kunsthistorisches Museum, Vienna, inv. 160. See E.A. Safarik, *Fetti*, Milan 1990, cat. no. 113, pp. 247–55, repr. in colour pp. 254–5.

19. National Gallery of Victoria, Melbourne (3262/4); see Ursula Hoff, *European Paintings before 1800 in the National Gallery of Victoria*, 4th rev. edn, Melbourne 1995, pp. 227–8, repr. in colour.

20. Coll. Musée d'histoire et d'art du pays Blayais, Blaye. Exh. Paris, Salon, 1798 (383), and in Paris, Detroit and New York, *French Painting 1774–1830: The Age of Revolution*, 1975 (172).

21. J.P. Mouilleseaux, '"Léandre et Héro" de Taillasson: à propos d'un thème iconographique et littéraire', *Revue du Louvre*, 24, no. 6, 1974, pp. 411–16. The compiler is indebted to Richard Green, Curator, York City Art Gallery, for this reference.

22. Mouilleseaux 1974, n. 10 (Balthasard, untraced); n. 11, for Girodet: Dassy's lithograph of the work mentioned above is repr. p. 416, fig. 7, and Mouilleseaux notes a second lithograph, *Les adieux de Héro et Léandre*, and a drawing (Louvre) of Hero throwing herself from the tower.

23. J. Briant (1799), Debucourt (1801), L.P. Simon, Monsiau (1806), Ducis (1808), Delorme (1841), L.V. Pallière (1817) at Desene.

24. Coll. Musée Fabre, Montpellier; repr. Mouilleseaux 1974, p. 413, fig. 3.

25. Coll. City Art Gallery, Plymouth, The Cottonian Collection. Gouache, 25.4 × 37.8 cm. See Mary Peter, 'Four Drawings from the Cottonian Collection, Plymouth', *Apollo*, LXV, 1957, pp. 19–20, plate IV; she nicely characterises Loutherbourg's subject as 'respectably classical enough, but given a violent and dramatic treatment in keeping with a period of taste turning from the rational and reasonable to the operatic'. See Rüdiger Joppien, *Philippe Jacques de Loutherbourg RA*, exh. cat., The Iveagh Bequest, Kenwood House, London 1973 (57a, 57b). Also repr. Nicholson 1990, p. 194, fig. 97.

26. Mouilleseaux 1974, n. 21.

27. David Irwin, *John Flaxman 1735–1826*, London 1979, p. 91.

28. Present location unknown; 42.5 × 27.5 cm, sold Sotheby's 7 July 1977 (136); known to the compiler only from the reproduction in Sotheby's catalogue.

29. Exh. RA 1806 (230), with the quotation 'Till gain'd at last the Sestian shore he treads, etc.' Possibly a small oil sketch, such as Howard sometimes exhibited, rather than a finished painting.

30. Published in *The Gem*, London 1829, 9.5 × 7.4. cm, facing p. 145, on which is a short poem by Thomas Hood entitled *On a Picture of Hero and Leander*, mocking the subject and wondering why Leander did not come by boat. The same issue of *The Gem* published (p. 108) Keats's poem *On a Leander Gem...*, referred to on p. 300. Only four volumes of *The Gem* were published, 1828–31.

31. Henry Howard (1769–1847) was elected ARA 1801; RA 1808. See David Blayney Brown's succinct note on him, *Macmillan Dictionary of Art*, vol. 14, 1996, p. 810. For Howard's manner of treating classical and literary subjects, and for the probability that Turner learnt a great deal in this respect from this more learned friend, see Wilton 1979, p. 195. Thornbury 1877, pp. 119–22, quotes 'reminiscences of Turner' and his friendship with Howard recorded for him by Revd Henry Scott Trimmer.

32. Etty was elected RA 1828. His picture of 1827 was the first of four different and equally full-bodied variations on the theme. See Dennis Farr, *William Etty*, London 1958: (i) *The Parting of Hero and Leander*, exh. RA 1827 (438), coll. Tate Gallery, Farr cat. no. 77, plate 26; (ii) *Hero, having thrown herself from the Tower at the Sight of Leander drowned, dies on his body*, exh. RA 1829 (31), on permanent loan to York City Art Gallery since 1954, Farr cat. no. 62, plate 31; (iii) ? *Hero awaiting Leander*, *c.*1835; coll. V&A, Farr cat. no. 61; see R.D. Parkinson, *Victoria and Albert Museum, Catalogue of British Oil Paintings*, London 1990, p. 86, repr., for discussion of the subject; (iv) *Hero awaiting Leander*, *c.*1835, two versions, Williamson Art Gallery and Museum, Birkenhead and Public Library, Boston, Lincs., Farr cat. nos. 59, 60. 827.

33. Reynolds 1969, pp. 172–3, sees 'striking similarities' in Turner's picture to Etty's: in the lovers' posture on the steps, the moon shining through stormy clouds and its reflection in the sea'. In this he is followed by Butlin and Joll 1984, p. 221, and by Kathleen Nicholson, 'Style as Meaning: Turner's Late Mythological Landscapes', *Turner Studies*, 8, no. 2, 1988, p. 48, who goes so far as to say that Turner 'appropriated Etty's figures for his own composition' (see also Nicholson 1990, p. 197. Etty's figures in fact are closer to Hamilton's (see fig. 3, above) than Turner's are to Etty's, as Nicholson herself notes (1988, p. 53 n. 27).

34. *The Bride of Abydos*, Canto II, v. 1, in ed. F. Page and J. Jump, *Byron, The Poetical Works*, Oxford 1970, p. 269.

35. Byron to Robert Charles Dallas, from Constantinople, 23 June 1810, published in Leslie A. Marchand, *Byron's Letters and Journals*, vol. I, 'In my Hot Youth', London 1973, p. 248; see similar letters pp. 240, 242, 243, 246, 247–8, 250, 253, 255. See also Marchand, vol. VIII, 1978, pp. 80–3.

36. Byron to Henry Drury, 3 May 1810, from the *Salsette* frigate 'in the Dardanelles off Abydos', published in Marchand, vol. I, p. 237.

37. Page and Jump 1970, p. 59.

The last two of the five verses on Leander may give the flavour:

But since he cross'd the rapid tide
According to the doubtful story,
To woo – and Lord knows what beside,
And swam for Love, as I for glory;

'T were hard to say who fared the best:
Sad mortals! thus the gods still plague you!
He lost his labour, I my jest;
For he was drown'd, and I've the ague.

Controversy kept Byron's feat in the news, especially after William Turner, *Journal of a Tour to the Levant*, 1821, rather nastily observed that 'Lord Byron seems to have forgotten that Leander swam both ways with and against the tide, whereas he (Ld. B.) only performed the easiest part of the task by swimming with it from Europe to Asia'. See Marchand, vol. VIII, pp. 80–3. Stung, Byron wrote a long account of his exploit, published in *The Monthly Magazine* for April 1821 and in *The Traveller* for 3 April 1821.

38. Turner's illustrations to Byron are discussed in David Blayney Brown, *Turner and Byron* , exh. cat., Tate Gallery 1992, pp. 40–56, and by Jan Piggott, *Turner's Vignettes*, exh. cat., Tate Gallery 1993, pp. 44–9. For a catalogue of Turner's vignette illustrations to *Byron's Life and Works* 1832–4, see Piggott 1993, Appendix B, p. 99, nos. 59–75.

39. Two watercolour illustrations to *The Bride of Abydos* by Thomas Stothard and John Varley, repr. Brown 1992, cat. nos 16, 17 are to the main Zuleika/Selim part of the poem.

40. Cited in note 38.

41. Turner Bequest, Tate Gallery (N 00500); B & J, cat no. 138, plate 141. See Brown 1992, cat. no. 35, p. 92; repr. in colour p. 65. Exh. RA 1818 with lines adapted from Byron, *Childe Harold's Pilgrimage*, III, xxviii, the last line reading: 'Rider and horse – friend, foe, in one red burial blent!'.

42. Turner Bequest, Tate Gallery (N 00516); B & J, cat no. 342, plate 344. See Brown 1992, cat. no. 36, p. 93; repr in colour p. 65. Exh. RA 1832, with lines from *Childe Harold's Pilgrimage*, IV, iv. See Brown 1992, *passim*, for other works by Turner influenced by Byron.

43. Coll. The Earl of Rosebery, on loan to the National Gallery of Scotland; B & J, cat. no. 379, plate 383. See Brown 1992, cat. no. 37, p. 94; repr. in colour p. 69. Exh. RA 1839 with lines adapted from *Childe Harold's Pilgrimage*, IV, xxvii.

44. One of the series of paste reproductions of gems engraved with classical scenes produced by James Tassie (1735–99), repr. Ian Jack, *Keats and the Mirror of Art*, Oxford 1967, plate IXb. For Tassie, see James Holloway, *James Tassie*, Edinburgh 1986, with bibliography p. 31.

45. Reprinted in ed. Miriam Allott, *The Poems of John Keats*, London 1971, no. 50, p. 107. Keats concentrates on Leander as woman's victim, and on the moment of his death by drowning ('He's gone: up bubbles all his amorous breath!').

46. For Leigh Hunt's *Hero and Leander*, first published in 1819, see H.S. Mitford, *Poetical Works of Leigh Hunt*, Oxford 1923. Thomas Hood's long poem *Hero and Leander* (130 stanzas) was first published in his *The Plea of the Midsummer Fairies*, London 1827.

47. Ed. Christopher Ricks, *The Poems of Tennyson*, vol. I, London 1987, No. 95, pp. 250–1.

48. Private collection, New York; B & J, cat. no. 133, plate 138.

49. The subject is difficult to make out. Possibly it represents a figure in blue by a (?) tomb. Nicholson 1990 sees it as 'a Claudian seaport'.

50. Musæus/Fawkes, lines 273–4.

51. Musæus/Fawkes, line 412.

52. Musæus/Fawkes, lines 395–406:

No nuptial torch its golden lustre shed
Bright torch of love to grace the bridal bed!
No Iö Pæans musically rung;
No greeting parents Hymeneal sung
But all was gloom and silence all around...

53. Callisto, one of Diana's nymphs, became pregnant by Jupiter; Diana transformed her into a bear, and set her dogs on her, but she was saved by Jupiter. Deservedly the most famous treatment of the subject is by Titian, *Diana and Callisto* (Duke of Sutherland, on long loan to the National Gallery of Scotland); see also NG 4029, *Diana and Callisto*, now attributed to Paul Bril.

For a modern interpretation of the predicament of a vestal virgin in love, see Michael Levey, *An Affair on the Appian Way*, London 1984, *passim*.

54. Ruskin, *Works*, vol. III, p. 306; on p. 607 he observes that 'Any surveyor or engineer could have drawn the steps and balustrade in Hero and Leander, as well as Turner has; but there is no man living but himself who could have thrown the accidental shadows upon them'.

55. See note 69.

56. And from no ordinary foam, but from the foam of the genitals of the castrated Uranus when they were cast upon the sea.

57. Musæus/Fawkes, line 205.

58. See ed. William Smith, *Dictionary of Greek and Roman Biography and Mythology*, 1899, vol. II, pp. 536–7. Hymen, the god of marriage, is described in Attic legends as a youth of such delicate beauty that he might be taken for a girl. He is represented in works of art as a handsome youth, carrying in his hand a bridal torch.

59. For Stothard, see Shelley Bennett, *Thomas Stothard: The Mechanisms of Art Patronage in England circa 1800*, Columbia, Missouri 1988, p. 26. Bennett notes that in commissioning Turner and Stothard to design vignette illustrations for his *Italy*, 1830 (first published without illustrations in 1822), Rogers 'decided to assign the figural subjects to Stothard. Turner, who was considered weak in his treatment of figures, was given all the landscapes and architectural vignettes'. Bennett quotes Rogers as remarking to the Revd Alexander Dyce: 'sometimes I even put a figure by Stothard into one of Turner's landscapes.'

60. Omissions and errors in RA catalogues caused frequent grumbles among artists, who were often themselves partly to blame by submitting late or illegible copy.

61. Musæus/Fawkes, line 467.

62. Musæus/Fawkes, lines 454–5.

63. Canto II, v. 1, lines 8–11. Byron imagines Leander braving the storm to go to rather than depart from Hero.

64. Nicholson 1990, p. 204. On p. 197 she remarks that 'To narrate the story in the painting, Turner depicted each of its stages simultaneously, with characters reappearing as the event progresses in a left to right reading of its separate moments', which suggests that Turner depicts Leander drowning on the right, perhaps through the wiles of the 'tiny Hymen-like figure'.

65. Musæus/Fawkes, line 481.

66. Wilton's comparison of the colouring of the sky in this picture with that of *The Evening Star* (noted on p. 292) is illuminating. It may indicate that the two pictures are closer in date to each other than is usually supposed; indeed Finberg 1961 suggested that *Hero and Leander* (and *Apollo and Daphne*, which he saw as a 'companion' picture), 'had been in hand probably for some years', though Butlin and Joll 1984 do not support this suggestion.

67. (i) Coll. The Earl of Rosebery; B & J, cat. no. 379; (ii) coll. NGA, Washington; B & J, cat. no. 412. Byron's lines (from *Childe Harold's Pilgrimage*, IV, xxvii–iii) read :

The moon is up and yet it is not night,
Sunset divides the sky with her – a sea.

68. B & J, cat. nos 369 (110 × 199 cm), plate 371; 368, plate 373; 371, plate 375.

69. *Blackwood's Magazine*, XLII, no. CCLXIII, September 1837, pp. 335–6.

70. *Athenaeum*, 6 May 1837, p. 330.

71. See Whittingham 1986, pp. 8–11; he did not find *Hero and Leander* mentioned by visitors to the gallery.

72. Turner's letter to Thomas Griffith, from 47 Queen Ann Street, 1 February 1844, is published by Gage 1980, pp. 195–6; and see Gage 1969, p. 171.

73. It was probably for this purpose that Turner employed the young Margate painter Francis Sherrell as a studio assistant from 1848.

1834 exhibited at the British Institution in 1835[9] depicts Westminster Bridge in dramatically foreshortened perspective, slanting across the right half of the picture. *Juliet and her Nurse* (fig. 6),[10] exhibited in 1836, prefigures the composition of *Rain, Steam, and Speed* still more closely, the scenic differences between Venice and Maidenhead hardly obscuring the fact that in both pictures a bridge thrusts sharply into the bottom right corner of the picture and allows views on either side. Even closer in date to *Rain, Steam, and Speed* – in a sense almost a rehearsal for it – is *Bellinzona from the Road to Locarno* (fig. 1), a finished watercolour painted in 1843, based on a sample study of a year or so earlier. Here an 'unpicturesque' but impressive modern bridge thrusts across the river Ticino with much the same diagonal force as the Maidenhead Railway Bridge in *Rain, Steam, and Speed*, probably painted at about the same time. From Bellinzona to Berkshire was no great distance for Turner's imagination.

Whether Turner's picture was directly inspired by a recent journey on the Great Western Railway (GWR) must remain conjectural. By 1844, he could have been travelling on the GWR for six or seven years. He may (or may not) have been travelling to London on that line on a night of storm in June 1843. During the small hours of the next morning (according to an account written down at Ruskin's request some years later),[11] Jane O'Meara – then a young girl of about eighteen (later Mrs John Simon) – boarded the train, and found herself in a first-class carriage with two elderly gentlemen. One of them ('with the most wonderful eyes I ever saw, steadily, luminously, clairvoyantly, kindly, paternally looking at me') took a keen interest in the storm which was still raging when they reached Bristol; during a ten-minute stop there, he asked her permission to put down the window and leaned out of it for 'nearly nine minutes', regardless of being drenched by torrents of rain. As the train moved on, he 'leant back with closed eyes for I daresay ten minutes'. She remained unaware of his identity until, seeing *Rain, Steam, and Speed* in the next Royal Academy exhibition, she deduced that her fellow-passenger had been Turner.[12]

Her story is quoted, partially and sceptically, in almost every account of *Rain, Steam, and Speed*. It deserves fuller and fairer examination, if only because Ruskin was sufficiently convinced of its veracity to encourage Mrs Simon, whom he knew and trusted, to write down her recollection for him as fully as possible.[13] Ruskin calls it 'a sketch from life'; published in his *Dilecta* (correspondence etc. which he collected in 1886), it occupies three and a half closely printed pages, too long to be quoted here in full.[14] Mrs Simon does her best to recollect two different things: her journey, about which she is very clear, and Turner's picture, about which she is not clear. Each stage of her own journey on that stormy night in June 1843 is accurately related: she had been staying at Plymouth, intending to travel by boat to Southampton to

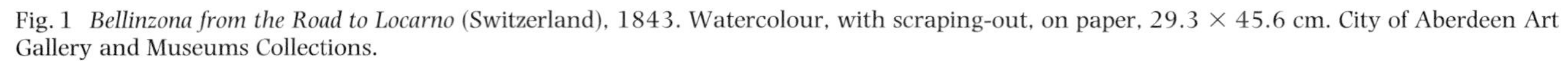
Fig. 1 *Bellinzona from the Road to Locarno* (Switzerland), 1843. Watercolour, with scraping-out, on paper, 29.3 × 45.6 cm. City of Aberdeen Art Gallery and Museums Collections.

meet her fiancé, but having missed the boat, took a horse-drawn coach to Exeter at 2pm, arriving there at 8pm; she continued in that coach as far as Beambridge (near Wellington), but by that time the storm was so fierce that coaching was unsafe, and she got out and waited in 'the shed which served as a station' for the next train.[15] When it arrived, she got into a first-class carriage, and there found 'Turner' and his companion, who had boarded the train (evidently not an express) at Exeter.[16] When 'Turner' gazed at the storm through a carriage-window, it was during a ten-minute stop at Bristol. By the time they reached Swindon, the storm was over; the train stopped there long enough for passengers to get out to buy refreshments ('My friend with the eyes said: "Tea! poor stuff; you should have had soup" '). After that her companions dozed, while she watched the dawn of a bright day. At 6am they 'steamed into Paddington station'.

These facts are clear enough. It is the disparity between her account of the storm which she and 'Turner' watched during the night ('torrents of rain' and 'a chaos of elemental and artificial lights and noises') and the picture which she saw the next year in the Royal Academy exhibition which has caused doubts about her story. She stood in front of Turner's picture in the Royal Academy exhibition and remarked: 'I was in the train that night, and it is perfectly and wonderfully true'; yet in Turner's picture passing showers alternate with gleams of sunlight. But what Turner chose to make of his picture need not have been tied to what any co-witness of that long journey saw and chiefly remembered about it.

If Mrs Simon's circumstantial account of her journey is of no other use, it serves as a reminder of how long-drawn out and uncertain travel could be in the 1840s. Travel by train did not abolish hazards and delays, but it diminished them. Turner had all his life been a traveller in search of fresh material. He had adapted from the 1820s to travelling by steamboats at home and abroad; he is unlikely to have ignored the advantages of locomotives. His choice of the Maidenhead stretch of the GWR for the setting was probably governed by the presence of the new yet noble bridge[17] which served as viaduct for the railway. The prefix *Great* in the name of the GWR may have influenced his choice, since it gave the picture's title additional force. Though the prefix *Great* was not peculiar to the GWR (it was also used in the names of the Great North of England Railway, and even of the Great Leinster & Munster Railway), the 'greatness' of the GWR was undisputed in 1844. A German visitor called it 'the most perfect and splendid railroad in Great Britain', with its 'roads and carriages ... of astonishing dimensions' and its 'gigantic locomotives'.[18] The Great Western Railway Company, though not the first to be formed, was foremost in 1844, having single ownership of the longest main line in the kingdom. It also had the advantage of the dynamic energies of Isambard Kingdom Brunel (1806–59), a prodigy who had been appointed engineer of the projected Great Western in 1833, at the age of 27, the same age at which Turner had been elected RA.[19] While the track was being constructed, using Brunel's pioneering broad gauge (7 ft), Brunel designed and built the Maidenhead Railway Bridge; built of brick, its two great arches each with a span of 128 feet were the largest and flattest that had (and possibly have) ever been constructed. The bridge was one of the wonders of the day.[20] The first London–Maidenhead section of the line opened to the public on 4 June 1838, with four trains running each way on weekdays and three on Sundays.[21] Queen Victoria herself took her first journey by train on the GWR in 1842, travelling from Slough (the nearest station to Windsor Castle) to Paddington, there to be greeted by 'deafening' demonstrations of loyalty, writing afterwards to her uncle Leopold, King of the Belgians, that she had arrived 'in half an hour, free from dust and crowd and heat', 'quite charmed' by the railway.[22] The line was steadily extended westwards, reaching Bristol in 1841 and Exeter in May 1844.

Fig. 2 *Ixion, from the Firefly class of broad-gauge engines designed for the GWR in 1841.* Detail from an engraving of 1841–2.

Turner's train is proceeding from London towards the West of England, along what in fact is a double track, though he chooses not to show it as double. The engine is one of the 'Firefly' class[23] designed for the Great Western Railway by Daniel Gooch, another prodigy, appointed locomotive engineer to the GWR at the age of 21. By 1844 there were 62 engines of the 'Firefly' class in operation on the GWR; 'unsurpassed for general excellence and economy of working',

Fig. 3 F.J. Dolbey, engraved by (?) E.T. Dolbey, *The Lickey Inclined Plane, on the Birmingham–Gloucester railway line*, c.1840. Lithograph.

each of them had a name suggestive of super-human power embossed in bold letters on a brass plate on its side.[24] Turner's (unidentified) engine would have looked more or less exactly like *Ixion*, 'Firefly' class of 1841 (fig. 2), built in Leeds. Turner has deliberately chosen to show his engine drawing a train of open-goods wagons, in which 'persons in the lower stations of life' were allowed, on sufferance, to travel at a cheap rate (those who could afford the first-class fare travelled in passenger coaches, and second-class passengers travelled in coaches which were roofed, though low-sided and open to the weather).[25] The average speed on the Great Western in 1844 was 33 mph, but on the long level stretch between Paddington and Swindon, on which the Maidenhead Railway Bridge is situated, the Great Western expresses could reach 55–60 mph.[26]

John Gage 1972 does well to remind us that 'as the title of the picture makes clear, Turner was painting not a view of the Great Western Railway, but an allegory of the forces of nature'.[27] *Rain* falls steadily through this picture, though not heavily enough wholly to obscure gleams of sunshine which fall on woods and fields on either side of the bridge. *Steam* is a minor yet (in vapourish form) pervasive element in the picture. The great heads of steam emitted by railway trains in popular prints were not attained by trains in 1844. Turner more accurately represents his 'Firefly' engine putting out three smallish and evenly spaced puffs of smoke, slightly discoloured now, but never as conspicuous as they are in Brandard's engraving (fig. 5). The progress of a typical train of the period was described by the engineer Sir Francis Head as 'marked by white steam meandering above it and by red-hot coals of different sizes occasionally falling from beneath it'.[28] *Speed* is primarily represented by the train itself, counterpointed by two small but telling details of unmechanised activity.

The first of these is a hare, running along the track ahead of the train. The hare was not part of the original conception of the picture. Lightly brushed in on top of the existing paint of the railway track, it was a late addition. Because its paint has sunk into the paint of the track beneath it, it has long been almost invisible, even photography under magnification producing only a blurred image of it.[29] It is Brandard's engraving of the picture (more fully discussed below) which has largely preserved the image of the hare in the collective memory. Brandard, carrying out a self-imposed duty of clarifying Turner's details, gave the hare firm definition and, for good measure, invented its shadow, which does not appear in the painting. In defining the hare, he seems (paradoxically) to have given it much the same shape as the hound coursing a hare in Turner's *Apollo and Daphne*,[30] which his younger brother and pupil Edward was engraving at the same date.

The hare is unlikely to be overtaken by its strange pursuer, nor does Turner intend that it should be. He was sufficiently familiar with Thomson's *The Seasons* to recognise the reproach in the line 'Poor is the triumph o'er the timid hare!'[31] Gage is surely right in believing that Turner painted in the hare 'jocularly as an emblem of speed', and in adding that 'no hare was likely to be outpaced by any locomotive of this period'.[32] Had Turner intended his picture to prompt thoughts of imminent danger to life of any sort (and there had been accidents enough on the GWR and other lines to warrant some such hint), he would surely have introduced a more forceful (and premeditated) symbol.[33]

The nine-year-old George Leslie (son of Charles Robert Leslie RA), who was allowed to watch Turner at work on Varnishing Day, 1844, recollected seventy years later that Turner 'talked to me every now and then, and pointed out the little hare running for its life in front of the locomotive on the viaduct'.[34] According to Leslie, it was 'the hare, and not the train' which Turner intended to represent the *Speed* of his title, and 'the word ["*Speed*"] must have been in his mind when he was painting the hare, for close to it, on the plain below the viaduct, he introduced the figure of a man ploughing, "Speed the plough" (the name of an old country dance) probably passing through his brain.'[35] The man driving a horse-drawn plough, a small but vivid detail in the foreground on the right, offers a second contrast to the train's mechanised progress. Here, knowing just what he wanted to achieve, Turner brushed in an image of strenuous effort which, even on a small scale, shows that the going is hard. Brandard translates this into a rustic vignette which might have been taken from W.H. Pyne's *Microcosm: or a Picturesque Delineation of the Arts, Agriculture, Manufactures &c of Great Britain*.[36]

Rain, Steam, and Speed is the work of a painter in his seventieth year who had never averted his eyes from contemporary life. Paintings such as *Staffa*, 1832; *The Burning of the Houses of Parliament*, 1834; *Keelmen heaving in Coals by Night*, 1835; *The Fighting Temeraire* (NG 524, pp. 306–15); *Snow Storm – Steamboat off a Harbour's Mouth*, 1842, and the *Whaling* pictures of 1845–6, all testify to his readiness (in Andrew Wilton's phrase) to 'make an entirely contemporary picture about the visual splendour of his own world'.[37] The assumption that because Turner was an artist he 'must have' deplored industrialisation is one which Ruskin repeatedly but wrongly made. As Gage observes, Ruskin could not bring himself to write one word about *Rain, Steam, and Speed*; when asked in conversation why Turner had chosen to paint a steam engine, he replied shortly 'To show what he could do even with an ugly subject.'[38] And yet, as Gage points out, 'there is nothing to suggest that Turner felt that the train and bridge were ugly'.[39] Others have construed *Rain, Steam, and Speed* as Turner's protest that the railway had invaded and must despoil the countryside.[40] It is true that Turner had known and painted this stretch of the Thames for forty years, exploring the river by boat as well as its hinterland by horse, once remarking that it could show finer scenery than any river in Italy. But at no point of his life was Turner a reactionary. The inclusion in his picture of the old thirteen-arch Maidenhead bridge, completed around 1780, and now

Fig. 4 *Rain, Steam, and Speed*, detail

receding in the background, may deliberately allude to the fact that nothing will turn the clock back. Nor does Turner – who had painted all aspects of travel, in Britain and on the Continent – suggest that this would be desirable. It is likely that he took to trains as he had taken to steamboats, relishing the fact that they made travel easier and quicker. Without a steamboat such as *The Maid of Morven*, could Turner have painted *Staffa?*[41] or so easily have explored the Seine?

Not everyone saw the railways as a form of progress. 'Hear ye that whistle?' Wordsworth asked prophetically, envisaging a 'long-linked Train' sweeping onwards to destroy the beauty and 'beloved retreats' of Britain; and in a series of communications to the Editor of the *Morning Post* during 1844 he opposed the projected Kendal and Windermere Railway.[42] Ruskin supported him, and (at his most young-fogeyish) wrote that 'Going by railway I do not consider as travel at all; it is merely being "sent" to a place, and very little different from becoming a parcel.'[43] Wordsworth, Ruskin and many others of the social class which they had attained were élitists, wanting to reserve the beauty of the countryside for 'the *meditative few* who have inherited by nature, or derived from education, a taste for the beautiful'.[44]

Dickens gave to Mr Dombey (in *Dombey and Son*, first published in instalments, 1846–8)[45] a tortured vision of the railway train as 'a type of the triumphant monster, Death'. Most of this hectic passage (with its reiterated 'Away, with a shriek, and a roar, and a rattle...') is too well-known to need quotation here. Attention should rather be drawn to one of its less sensational descriptions of the train, since it may be based on Dickens's recollection of Turner's picture: 'Breasting the wind and light, the shower and sunshine, away, and still away, it rolls and roars, fierce and rapid, smooth and certain, and great works and massive bridges crossing up above, fall like a beam of shadow an inch broad upon the eye, and then are lost...'

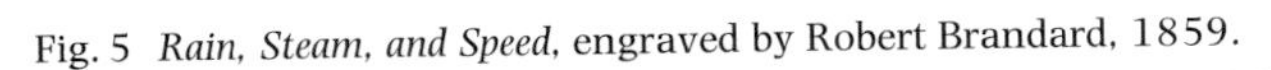

Fig. 5 *Rain, Steam, and Speed*, engraved by Robert Brandard, 1859.

The atmospheric effects diffused throughout the picture by rain, fitful sunlight and the vapour of steam mean that details are deliberately obscured. Brandard's engraving of 1859 (fig. 5) does its best to clarify them. During Turner's lifetime, Brandard had engraved many of his pictures, working under the artist's supervision and to his satisfaction.[46] After Turner's death, he was one of the 'Turner school' of engravers who were commissioned to engrave 60 plates for publication as *The Turner Gallery*, issued in sets between 1859 and 1861, with letterpress by Ralph Wornum, Keeper of the National Gallery (later reissues had different authors' texts).[47] Brandard was given eight pictures to engrave, including two of the most difficult (because most atmospheric) subjects: *Rain, Steam, and Speed* and *Snow Storm – Steam Boat off a Harbour's mouth, making signals in shallow water, and going by the lead. The author was in this storm on the night the Ariel left Harwich*.[48] In each case he took pains to define details which Turner (who once reputedly said 'Indistinctness is my forte') had deliberately left undefined.

In *Rain, Steam, and Speed*, almost every detail is indistinct except for the engine itself, whose forward rush is expressed, as Jack Lindsay observed,[49] by 'making the engine darker in tone and sharper in edge than any other object, so that it shoots out in aerial perspective ahead of its place in linear perspective'. This onrushing sensation is lessened by the engraving. Within the limits of monochrome, and with the artist's guidance no longer available, Brandard did his best; but he sharpens details in a manner which Turner may or may not have approved. In Turner's painting, the figures on the river-bank are indistinct, and have sometimes been thought to be locals, waving at the train, as if this spectacle was still quite novel; in the engraving, the figures (of which there are at least twelve) appear to be almost Claudian, and not waving but dancing,[50] and not one of them looks at the train. Turner's undulating golden mass behind the figures is interpreted in the engraving (probably correctly) as a thickly wooded hillside, from which a thin stream of smoke rises (roughly level with the centre of the train); a larger plume of smoke rises from the woods on the other side. Before Turner's picture became discoloured, this smoke rising on either side would have helped to balance the puffs of smoke from the engine. The engraver has seemingly edited out the 'persons' (or the illusion of persons) travelling in the wagons, which now appear to be full of coal. The structure of the 'old' bridge[51] has been clarified, and substantial houses have become visible behind it.

The bright flames generating energy within the engine's boiler contrast insistently with the soft drizzle outside. Robert K. Wallace 1988 observes that this contrast was to be powerfully echoed in *Whalers (boiling Blubber) Entangled in Flaw Ice*,[52] another contemporary subject exhibited two years later, in 1846; the detail he reproduces of the 'pure, lurid light of the red frontal flame' on the whaling ship's deck vividly recalls the 'Firefly' engine's fire. Whether or not Turner correctly located the fire seemingly occupying half his engine's boiler was to be disputed: the *Morning Chronicle* wondered 'how engine fires blaze where no one ever saw them blaze'.[53]

Turner showed seven pictures at the Royal Academy in 1844.[54] The *Morning Chronicle* of 8 May 1844 described *Rain, Steam, and Speed* as 'the most insane and the most magnificent' of them.[55] Writing under the pen-name 'Michael Angelo Titmarsh', Thackeray in *Fraser's Magazine* combines admiration with a mock-analysis of Turner's palette which parodies all 'Technical Notes':[56]

> As for Mr. Turner, he has out-prodigied almost all former prodigies. He has made a picture with real rain, behind which is real sunshine, and you expect a rainbow every minute. Meanwhile, there comes a train down upon you, really moving at the rate of fifty miles an hour, and which the reader had best make haste to see, lest it should dash out of the picture, and be away up Charing Cross through the wall opposite. All these wonders are performed with means not less wonderful than the effects are. The rain, in the astounding picture called 'Rain – Steam – Speed', is composed of dabs of dirty putty *slapped* on to the canvass with a trowel; the sunshine scintillates out of very thick, smeary lumps of chrome yellow. The shadows are produced by cool tones of crimson lake, and quiet glazings of vermilion. Although the fire in the steam-engine *looks* as if it were red, I am not prepared to say that it is not painted with cobalt and pea-green. And as for the manner in which the *Speed* is done, of that the less said the better, – only it is a positive fact that there is a steam-coach going fifty miles an hour. The world has never seen any thing like this picture.

Turner's 'railway picture' amazes us because of his choice of subject and his treatment of it. Railway travel itself was not new in 1844, but a representation of it hanging 'on the line' in the Royal Academy was. The public at large quickly grew accustomed to railways. Six years after Turner's painting was exhibited, the engineer and author Sir Francis Head wrote:[57]

> When railways were first established, every living being gazed at a passing train with astonishment and fear: ploughmen held their breath: the loose horse galloped from it, and then, suddenly stopping, turned round, stared at it, and at last snorted aloud. But the 'nine days' wonder' soon came to an end. As the train now flies through our verdant fields, the cattle grazing on each sides do not even turn their heads to look at it... It is the same with mankind. On entering a railway station, we merely mutter to a clerk in a box where we want to go – say '*How much?*' – see him horizontally poke a card into a little machine that pinches it – receive our ticket – take our place – read our newspaper – on reaching our terminus drive away perfectly careless of all or any of the innumerable arrangements necessary for the astonishing luxury we have enjoyed.

Sun, Wind and Rain, a large watercolour by David Cox, painted the year after Turner's picture was exhibited and now one of his best-known works, pays direct homage to Turner in its title and atmospheric effects, acknowledging the debt with the inclusion of a distant train.[58] A version in oil now known as *Rain, Wind and Sunshine*, dated 1845, is in Aberdeen Art Gallery. Cox's oil of *Calais Pier* painted in emulation of Turner is noted under NG 472 (p. 265). But as Gage observes, *Rain, Steam, and Speed* had a more significant effect after Turner's death, and in France. Claude Monet and Camille Pissarro would have seen it during their visit to London in 1870–1, and were perhaps thereby encouraged to paint similar subjects (see Gage 1972, figs. 45–7, 49–50), at first treated more realistically (Monet told a critic that Turner was 'antipathetic to him because of the exuberant romanticism of his fancy'[59]), later more atmospherically. In composition, Monet's *Railway Bridge at Argenteuil*,[60] painted in 1875, most evidently recalls Turner's picture; but the atmospheric legacy of *Rain, Steam, and Speed* is more potently expressed in his *Gare St Lazare*[61] of 1877. Paul Signac, who called his visit to London in 1898 a 'pilgrimage to Turner', made several visits to the National Gallery, including what he called in his diary for 29 March 1898 'a serious visit to Turner', noting that from 1834 'he frees himself from black and looks for the most beautiful colorations; colour for colour's sake'. Later, in a letter to his friend Angrand, he singled out a group of paintings by Turner in the National Gallery, including *Rain, Steam, and Speed*, the *Deluge* pair and *The Exile and the Rock Limpet*, for this comment: 'These are no longer pictures, but aggregations of colours (*polychromies*), quarries of precious stones, *painting* in the most beautiful sense of the word.'[62]

Fig. 6 *Juliet and her Nurse*, exhibited 1836. Oil on canvas, 92 × 123 cm. Private collection. Photo courtesy Agnew's.

NOTES

The compiler's debt to John Gage's Turner: Rain, Steam and Speed, *1972, will be evident from the extent to which she has drawn on it. She also had the privilege of reading (in proof) William S. Rodner's book* Turner: Romantic Painter of the Industrial Revolution, *published late in 1997, after her own book was in page-proofs. She did not think it proper to draw upon it before its publication, but would urge anyone interested in the picture to read it.*

1. McCoubrey 1986, p. 36.

2. Repr. Gage 1972, plate 1; also repr. McCoubrey 1986, p. 34, fig. 2.

3. Repr. McCoubrey 1986, p. 34, fig. 3. The lithograph is after a watercolour by F.L. Dolby (information kindly provided by Margaret Burns, Birmingham Local Studies and History Centre). Lickey, near Bromsgrove (Hereford and Worcester), is about fifteen miles south-west of Birmingham.

4. McCoubrey 1986, p. 36.

5. McCoubrey 1986, p. 34.

6. See Maurice Davies, *Turner as Professor: The Artist and Linear Perspective*, exh. cat., Tate Gallery 1992, pp. 64–5, 67–9. Davies's explanation (p. 64) of the 'perspective centre point' is invaluable here.

7. Quoted by Davies 1992, p. 68.

8. Wilton 1979 gives examples, particularly drawing attention (p. 221) to *Regulus* (coll. Tate Gallery, N 00519; B & J, cat. no. 294, plate 296), a sinister classical subject first shown in Rome in 1828, reworked and exhibited again at the BI in 1837, in which the 'ruled lines indicating the irradiation of the sunlight remind us of the lines of perspective in *Rain, Steam and Speed*'.

9. Coll. Philadelphia Museum of Art; B & J, cat. no. 359, plate 364. Another version of the subject is coll. Cleveland Museum of Art; B & J, cat. no. 364, plate 365.

10. Coll. Sra. Amalia Lacroze de Fortabat, Argentina; B & J, cat. no. 365, plate 369. As they note, Shakespeare's subject is set in Verona, Turner's in Venice.

11. Published in Ruskin's *Dilecta* (papers collected by him in 1886), *Works*, vol. XXV, pp. 598–601.

12. Her identification was by deduction only. It convinced Ruskin; but it should be noted that her fellow-passenger might have been David Cox, Anthony Vandyke Copley Fielding or any other man who enjoyed watching thunderstorms at night.

13. Ruskin gives some account of her in *Praeterita*, vol. II, p. 203. Jane O'Meara married John Simon, surgeon, in 1848; he was knighted in 1887. She was a friend of Burne-Jones and his wife, as well as the friend and confidante of Ruskin; thirteen letters from Ruskin to her variously dated between 1857 and 1869 are published in Ruskin, *Works*, vol. XXXVI.

14. For its publication as part of Ruskin's *Dilecta*, see note 11. A much abridged version, reputedly given to George Richmond RA, was published in A[nna] M[aria] W[ilhelmina] Stirling, *The Richmond Papers*, London 1926, pp. 55–6. Gage 1972, pp. 16–17, quotes the 'Richmond' version, considering it (p. 85 n. 4) 'far less open to objection than the one given to Ruskin'. In this the compiler cannot agree with him. Mrs Stirling, who had access to all Richmond's notes, states in her preface (p. v) that she compiled them from 'disjointed jottings written during his last illness'; it seems unlikely that she is quoting Lady Simon at first hand. Jack Simmons, *The Victorian Railway*, London 1991, p. 127, considers that Lady Simon's account as written for Ruskin 'has been impugned, quite unjustly', and believes that 'read carefully', her account of the journey can be accepted as 'simply and straightforwardly accurate'.

15. See D. St J. Thomas, *Regional History of the Railways of Great Britain*, vol. I, *The West Country*, Newton Abbot 1973, pp. 26–7. A Bristol–Exeter railway was under construction by an independent company (later to be taken over by the GWR). The Bristol–Beambridge section of the line opened on 1 May 1843, and Beambridge (on the main road west of Wellington) became, temporarily, the railhead and the point where coaches met the trains. (At this point the compiler must state that she is aware that railway history is an exact science in which she is no expert, and must apologise for any errors in piecing information together.)

16. Gage notes (1972, p. 85 n. 4) that the Bristol–Exeter extension of the GWR was not opened until 1 May 1844, only two days before the opening of the RA exhibition in which *Rain, Steam, and Speed* hung. Mrs Simon does not actually state that 'Turner' boarded the train at Exeter, but she may be thought to imply it in reporting the following exchange with 'Turner': 'He had not seen me at Exeter. "No, I got in at Plymouth." "Plymouth!!"' This compiler is not sufficiently informed to know whether, before the extension of the line to Exeter, a coach service may have operated to transport passengers from Exeter to the railway station at Bristol.

17. For the significance of bridges in Turner's work, see Adele M. Holcomb, 'The Bridge in the Middle Distance: Symbolic Elements in Romantic Landscape', *Art Quarterly*, XXXVII, 1974, pp. 31–58.

18. Johann George Kohl, *England and Wales*, 1844, reprinted New York 1968, p. 157.

19. See E.T. MacDermot, *History of the Great Western Railway*, London 1964, vol. I, much drawn on here, pp. 48ff.

20. Ibid., p. 48. J.C. Bourne's view of the bridge from the side, first published in his *History and Description of the Great Western Railway*, 1846, is repr. by Gage 1972, p. 24 fig. 12. Davies 1959 notes that another view of the bridge from the side may be found in George Measom, *The Official Illustrated Guide to the Great Western Railway*, 1860, p. 68 (and notes views of 1878, 1927, etc.).

21. See MacDermot 1964, p. 31, for a reproduction of the first timetable, published in *The Times*, 2 June 1838. He notes (p. 48) that the main-line station for Maidenhead was (until 1871) 'situated east of the Thames at Taplow, a long mile from the town'.

22. Quoted by John Pudney, *Brunel and his World*, London 1974, p. 59.

23. Gage 1972 reproduces a watercolour of one of the 'Firefly' class, p. 22, fig. 10.

24. MacDermot 1964, pp. 467–9, lists engines of the 'Firefly' class by name, with the dates each was delivered, rebuilt and ceased work; for his account of the 'Firefly' class see pp. 401–2, plates. The first 'Firefly' engines built in 1840 had 'fire' names (Firefly, Wildfire, Spitfire, etc.); later in 1840 the names of swift animals and birds were used (Tiger, Lynx, Vulture and, as Gage 1972 notes on p. 22, Greyhound). Legendary names mostly from the underworld (Cerberus, Pluto, Hecate, etc.) were followed by a group of 'heavenly' names (Castor, Orion, Pegasus, etc.) for the last of the 'Firefly' class to be built during 1841–2.

25. See MacDermot 1964, p. 50. When this stretch of the line opened in 1838, there were four sets of fares – posting carriage, first-class coach, second-class coach and second-class open carriages. MacDermot notes that second-class coaches were officially discontinued (? by 1839), offering a choice between travelling first and travelling in carriages which were roofed, but with doors and sides only about three feet high, the rest being open to the weather. By 1840, 'persons in the lower stations of life' had infiltrated into goods wagons: 'so, indirectly and by sufferance only, third-class passenger traffic on the Great Western began'. See MacDermot 1964, p. 335, for reforms under Gladstone's Railway Regulation Act, which came into force on 1 November 1844.

26. See Davies 1946, p. 99; Gage 1972, pp. 21–8; additional information kindly communicated by David Elliott, The Transport Trust, in correspondence. Daniel Gooch calculated in 1844 that in ideal conditions, 'from London to Bristol, stopping at Reading and Swindon for water or at Steventon alone, the trip could be performed in 2 h. 21 m.': see his Report to the GWR Directors on the special train which he and the directors took on the new London–Exeter run, published in D. St J. Thomas 1973, Appendix III, pp. 256–8.

27. Gage 1972, p. 19. Gage's insights into the picture are constantly illuminating, and are much drawn on here.

28. Anon. [Sir Francis Bond Head, 1793–1875], *Stokers and Pokers; or, The London and North-Western Railway*..., London 1850, p. 47.

29. The photograph repr. in Gage 1972, p. 17, fig. 4, comes as close as possible to catching the hare.

30. Coll. Tate Gallery (N 00520); B & J, cat. no. 369, plate 371. See Gage 1972, p. 21, fig. 9, for a detail of the hound and hare.

31. *The Poetical Works of James Thomson*, Aldine Press edn, London 1860: *The Seasons: Autumn*, line 401.

32. Gage 1972, writing of Turner's admiration for Rembrandt, suggests the influence of Rembrandt's *Landscape with a Coach* (Wallace Collection), which 'has a little figure running behind the coach, which might well have kindled his [Turner's] imagination when he was conceiving his figurative emblem of "speed"'; see his fig. 37 and detail, fig. 38.

In a note on the picture accompanying the publication of Brandard's engraving of it, a writer in *The Art Journal* (1860, p. 228) commented 'In advance of the huge machine is a hare, running for its life from the doom which seems inevitable. This incident is, we presume, the artist's illustration of "Speed". The "Rain and Steam" are significant enough. Looking at the length of rail which traverses the picture, and its elevation, it is difficult to understand how the scared animal could have found its way thither.' Similarly, in the 1878 edition of *The Turner Gallery* in which Brandard's engraving was published, Cosmo Monkhouse wrote of 'the terror of the poor hare, who will surely be overtaken and crushed in an instant'.

33. Gage 1972, pp. 57–9.

34. Leslie 1914, pp. 144–5. The author is George Dunlop Leslie RA (1835–1921), third son of Charles Robert Leslie RA.

35. Drawing attention to this as characteristic of the allusiveness of Turner's mind, Gage 1987 reproduces (plate 292) a watercolour of *Northampton*, *c.*1830, a crowded election scene in which Turner had included a prominent banner lettered *SPEED THE PLOUGH*, with a scene showing a similar scene of a ploughman driving a team of three.

36. Published in parts from 1802.

37. Wilton 1979, p. 220. For *Keelmen heaving in Coals by Night*, exh. RA 1835, see B & J, cat. no. 360, plate 363.

38. *Dilecta*, in *Works*, vol. XXXV, p. 601 n. 1.

39. Gage 1972, p. 33.

40. See Cosmo Monkhouse, *The Turner Gallery*, London 1878, vol. III, n. p.: facing the engraving of the subject: 'Some persons see a deeper meaning in this picture, something analogous to that of the *Temeraire* ... the old order changing, the easy-going past giving way to the quick-living future; and there is something in the contrast between the plough and the steam engine, the ugly form of the railway-bridge and train, and the beauty and peace of the old bridge and the landscape, which shows that some such thoughts were not absent from the painter's mind.'

See also (over a century later) David Hill, *Turner on the Thames*, London 1993, pp. 156–7: 'For one who had spent more or less his whole life in finding ways of structuring, detaining and retaining his experience of the world, and of travelling through it on foot or on horseback or by boat, the spectacle of the railway must have seemed the very negation of all that he had valued and stood for.'

41. Coll. Yale Center for British Art; B & J, cat. no. 347.

42. Wordsworth, *Miscellaneous Sonnets*, XLV: 'On the projected Kendal and Windermere Railway', in ed. E. de Selincourt and Helen Darbishire, *The Poetical Works of William Wordsworth*, Oxford 1954, pp. 61–2. Gage 1972, pp. 77–84, Appendix, publishes Wordsworth's communications to the London *Morning Post* on the projected railway.

43. Quoted by Gage 1972, p. 29.

44. A columnist in *Table-Talk*, 18 December 1844, quoted by Gage 1972, p. 84.

45. Published in monthly instalments October 1846–April 1848, and in one volume later in 1848. The quotation is from the first edition of the book, London 1848, p. 200.

46. See Luke Herrmann, *Turner Prints: The Engraved Work of J.M.W. Turner*, Oxford 1990, pp. 119, 168–9, 170, 173, 177, 196–7, 213, 226, 240; Frontispiece and plates 99, 134, 141, 157, 173.

47. For a clear, short summary of the various issues of *The Turner Gallery*, see Anne Lyles and Diane Perkins, *Colour into Line: Turner and the Art of Engraving*, exh. cat., Tate Gallery 1989, pp. 79–80. The plates are listed in Rawlinson, II, pp. 207–8, 357–9.

48. Coll. Tate Gallery (N 00530). Exh. RA 1842 (182); B & J, cat. no. 398.

49. *Turner: His Life and Work*, 1966, St Albans 1973, p. 267.

50. McCoubrey 1986, pp. 35, 38, describes the figures in the painting as fragile, white-gowned figures, perhaps Diana and her nymphs, surprised by *Actaeon* (the name of one of the GWR locomotives).

51. Designed by Sir Robert Taylor; begun in 1772 and nearly complete by 1775.

52. Coll. Tate Gallery (N 00547); B & J, cat. no. 426, plate 427. The full title is *Whalers (boiling Blubber) entangled in Flaw Ice, endeavouring to extricate themselves*. Wallace 1988, p. 28, notes similar contrasts in *Keelmen heaving in Coals by Night*, exh. 1835 (B & J, cat. no. 360), and *Peace – Burial at Sea*, exh. 1842 (B & J, cat. no. 399). His detail from *Whalers (boiling Blubber)* is repr. p. 28, fig. 13.

53. Issue of 8 May 1844; quoted by Butlin and Joll 1984, p. 257.

54. B & J, cat. nos. 407–413.

55. Quoted in B & J under cat. no. 409, p. 257. The (anonymous) reviewer was in fact Thackeray, as one can deduce on what art historians like to call 'stylistic grounds alone'; he wrote regularly for the *Morning Chronicle* until his resignation in 1846.

56. 'May Gambols; or, Titmarsh in the Picture Galleries', *Fraser's Magazine*, June 1844, pp. 712–13. The most quoted of all reviews of the picture, it largely (but more punchily) echoes a review in the *Morning Chronicle*, 8 May 1844 (see extract quoted in B & J, p. 257), of which Thackeray himself was the author. An obvious mistake in punctuation in the third sentence from the end has been silently corrected here.

57. [Head] 1850 (cited in note 28), pp. 8–9. As noted in *DNB*, this book is 'a clear and effective sketch of the difficulties attending the construction, maintenance and working of a great railway'.

58. Coll. Birmingham Museums and Art Gallery; see their exh. cat., *David Cox*, 1983, cat. no. 75 (including a note on the oil), repr. colour plate III. Repr. Gage 1972, p. 64.

59. Quoted by Gage 1972, p. 68. Théophile Gautier in his *History of Romanticism*, 1877, described Turner's engine as writhing 'like the Beast of the Apocalypse, opening its red glass eyes in the shadows, and dragging after it, in a huge tail, its vertebrae of carriages' (quoted by Gage, p. 33). But, as Gage has elsewhere shown (1973, p. 393), Gautier appears to have conflated his memory of the Turner with that of the mezzotint engraving of John Martin's *Last Judgement*.

60. Coll. Philadelphia Museum of Art; repr. Gage 1972, fig. 46.

61. Private collection, New York; repr. Gage 1972, fig. 49, one of several treatments of the subject; another is in the National Gallery, NG 6479.

62. Quoted by Gage 1972, p. 75. The other paintings Signac mentions are coll. Tate Gallery; B & J, cat. nos. 404, 443 and 400.

Magdeburg in 1650). Experiments were carried out by scientists all over Europe; among them was Constantijn Huygens, ambassador and 'philosopher', whose portrait by Thomas de Keyser in the National Gallery (NG 212) is justly well-known, and who, with Nicolas Papin, contributed a paper on the distillation of spirits of the air pump to the Royal Society's *Philosophical Transactions* in 1675.[22] The air pump was used for various experiments in pneumatic physics, to demonstrate the weight, pressure and elasticity of air.[23] It was first used for animal experiments in 1659, by Robert Boyle and Robert Hooke, who carried out experiments placing larks, sparrows, mice, frogs, kittens etc. in a receiver from which air was pumped out, with varying results (in many cases, death) caused by 'impeded respiration'. By the time Wright painted his picture, the air pump had become 'a common item in cabinets which included instruments of experimental philosophy'.[24] William Constable of Burton Constable in Yorkshire bought his (a 'neat double barrell Air Pump with all ye usual apparatus') from the instrument maker Benjamin Cole, Fleet Street, for £21 in 1757.[25] By the 1760s, engravings of scientific equipment had been published in dictionaries and encyclopaedias, with tiny figures or letters keyed to learned exposition. But the public at large probably encountered 'science' only in the form of demonstrations by travelling lecturers,[26] usually in town halls, but sometimes, as both *The Orrery* and *The Air Pump* suggest, privately, and by invitation.

One of the most solidly professional of the travelling lecturers was James Ferguson FRS, the London-based maker of astronomical and other scientific instruments, who had lectured on 'Popular Astronomy' in London and the provinces since 1749.[27] In about 1760 he decided that he would do better financially to extend the range of his lectures and to organise them into courses, inviting subscribers at one guinea each per course: minimum audience not less than twenty in London, not less than thirty within ten miles of London, and not less than sixty subscribers within a hundred miles of London.[28] The courses consisted of twelve lectures on 'the most interesting parts of Mechanics, Hydrostatics, Hydraulics, Pneumatics, Electricity and Astronomy'.[29] Ferguson travelled (presumably by wagon) with his own apparatus – at least fifty different pieces, including an air pump, an armillary sphere, an orrery and much other equipment. He gave his courses in various provincial towns – Bath, Liverpool, Newcastle among them. In 1762, on a Midlands tour, he gave them in Derby.[30]

Fig. 6 *A Philosopher giving that Lecture on the Orrery, in which a Lamp is put in place of the Sun*, exhibited 1766. Oil on canvas, 147.3 × 203.2 cm. Derby Art Gallery.

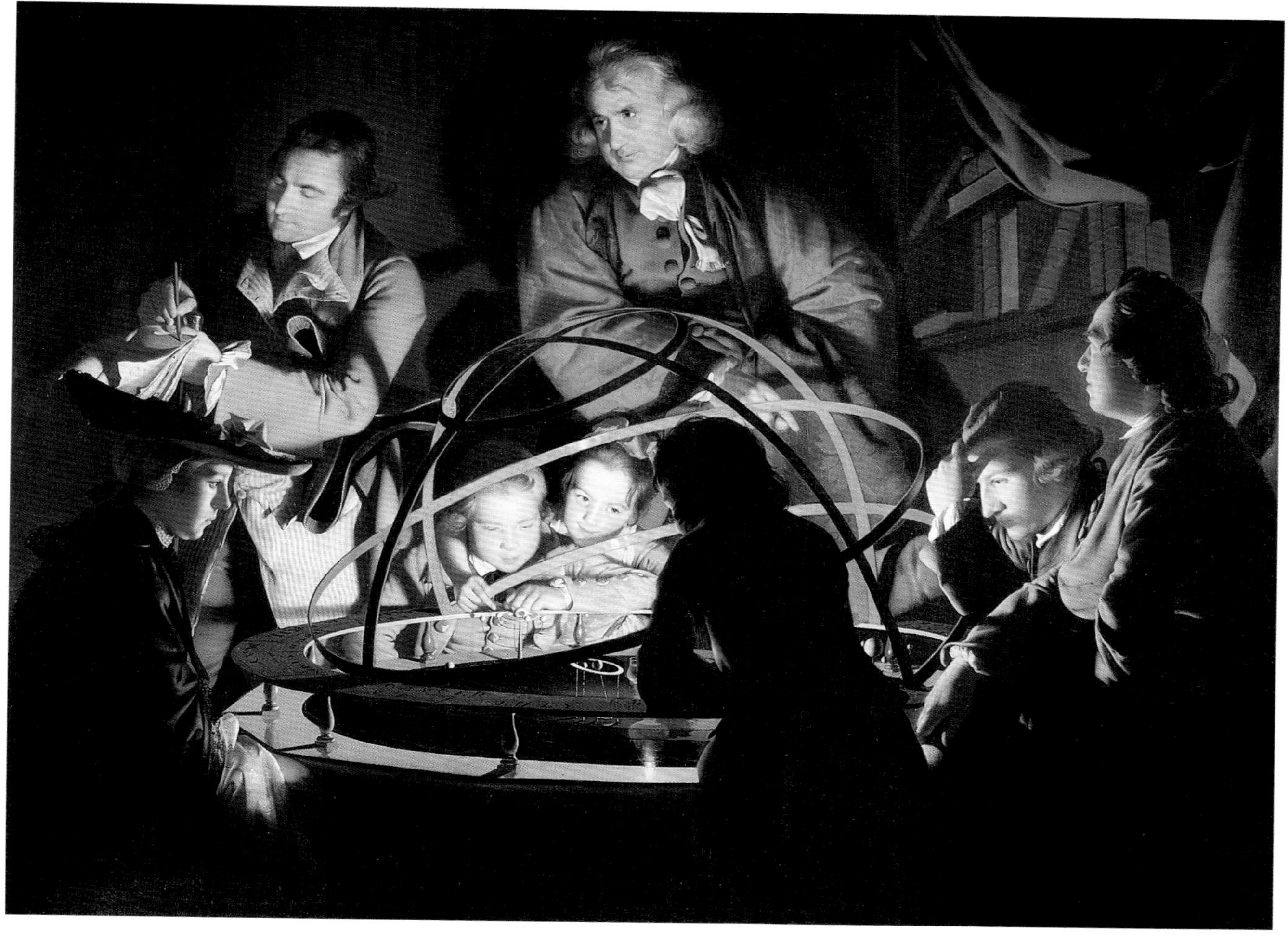

Fig. 7 Charles-Nicolas Cochin (1715–1790), *Expériences d'électricité* (? electrotherapy), ? 1760s. Engraving, 6.1 × 10.9 cm.

Whether Wright attended them is not known; the lectures were fairly elementary, and he had enough scientific friends among members of the Lunar Society[31] to have become familiar with 'apparatus' such as the orrery and the air pump and their workings. Far more novel in the 1760s were demonstrations with electricity, such as Charles-Nicolas Cochin depicts in *Expériences d'électricité* (fig. 7). But Wright's purpose in painting *The Air Pump* was not to depict a novel experiment, but to celebrate a new appetite for learning. If he attended Ferguson's lectures, he is likely to have been as interested in the reactions of the audience as in the content of the lectures.

The air pump was the focal point of any lecture on pneumatics. The lecturer often began by taking a pair of Magdeburg hemispheres – in Wright's *Air Pump*, these are the two small linked objects lying on the table near the glass phial of murky liquid – and demonstrating that if the air between them is completely pumped out they become inseparable. Experiments with liquids might follow. But the culminating point was always a demonstration of the potentially lethal effects of depriving living creatures of air. It was possible to demonstrate this in either of two ways: by simulation, placing in the glass receiver a bladder or 'lungs-glass' which could be seen to inflate with air or collapse without it, thereby feigning death; or by placing within the receiver a living creature which would sustain life (increasingly painfully) so long as some air was left in the receiver for it to breathe; the lecturer then enjoyed the god-like power of either expelling air completely and thus killing the creature, or quickly admitting air and thus reviving it. Lecturers being what they are, most chose the more sensational demonstration on a living creature. Schupbach quotes a dialogue from Benjamin Martin's *The Young Gentleman and Lady's Philosophy*, 1755;[32] alas, extracts only can be given here. The young gentleman, dignified by the name of Cleonicus, is bent on demonstrating the air pump to his young and tender-hearted sister Euphrosyne.

> *Euphrosyne*. See here comes *John*, with a lovely, young Rabbit. I hope that tender Creature is not to be sacrificed for my Sake. –
>
> *Cleonicus*. You are like all the Rest of your Sex. – You think it Cruelty to attempt the Life of a large Animal, but are quite regardless of the Destruction of those which expire under your Feet in every walk of Pleasure you take. – ... But to mitigate your Concern, I shall only show, in this Experiment, that the poor Creature does really depend upon the Air for Life; and after that, I shall put it into your Hands, as well as you see it now. – Here, *John*, put the Rabbit under the Glass. – And now, my good Euphrosyne, have a good Heart, and look on; for turning away your Face will boot the Animal nothing. – See, upon exhausting [the receiver], how uneasy it appears. – As the air is more rarefied, the Animal is rendered more thoughtful of its unlucky Situation, and seeks in vain to extricate himself. – He leaps and jumps about. – A Vertigo seizes his brain. – He falls, and is just upon expiring. – But I turn the Ventpiece, and let in the Air by Degrees.- You see him begin to heave, and pant. – At length he rouzes up, opens his Eyes, and wildly stares about him. – I take off the receiver, and shall now deliver it as recovered from the Dead.
>
> *Euphrosyne*. Poor innocent creature! ... Thou shalt always be my darling Rabbit, as by thee, I have been obliged to learn how necessary the Air is for animal Life, and Respiration.

Unlike Cleonicus, Ferguson believed that to experiment with a living creature in the air pump container 'is too shocking to every spectator who has the least degree of humanity'.[33] He preferred to simulate death by using the bladder or lungs-glass, and almost certainly would have done so when lecturing on pneumatics in Derby. Ferguson no doubt gave a thoroughly sound lecture; but his use of a bladder to simulate a life at risk could hardly have inspired the high pictorial drama of Wright's picture.

Wright's choice of a 'living creature' as the subject of his *Experiment on a Bird in the Air Pump* is likely to have been at least partly inspired by the following lines in *The Wanderer*, a long poem by Richard Savage:

> So in some Engine, that denies a Vent,
> If unrespiring is some Creature pent,
> It sickens, droops, and pants, and gasps for Breath,
> Sad o'er the Sight swim shad'wy Mists of Death;
> If then kind Air pours pow'rful in again,
> New Heats, new Pulses quicken ev'ry Vein,
> From the clear'd, lifted, life-rekindled Eye,
> Dispers'd, the dark and dampy Vapours fly.

Richard Savage (d.1743),[34] Dr Johnson's early friend, had himself been reprieved from sentence of death; tried for murdering a stranger in a tavern, he was convicted and taken to the condemned cells at Newgate, but received a royal pardon. *The Wanderer* was first published in 1729, the year following his reprieve.[35] At some point he must, surely, have witnessed an experiment on 'some Creature' in an air pump, whose survival of the ordeal inspired his image of 'life-rekindled'. Wright had a taste for literature, encouraged by his friend and patron, the poet William Hayley; he took several of his subjects from near-contemporary verse,[36] as well as from Shakespeare and Milton.

In Wright's first rough sketch for a picture of *The Air Pump* (fig. 8),[37] the apparatus itself is at the side of the picture; the lecturer is a patient, unassertive figure and the bird he has placed in the receiver is a fairly inconspicuous common or garden songbird – a lark or a thrush – such as was normally used in this experiment. His big picture is altogether more dramatic. On the table, we see the rim of a brass candlestick. The candle it holds is the only source of light in this picture; but it is concealed from us by a large rounded glass, within which (as Schupbach noted) there appears to be a carious

Fig. 8 *First idea for An Experiment on a Bird in the Air Pump*, painted on the verso of Wright's *Self Portrait* of *c.*1767–8. Oil on canvas, 62.2 × 76.2 cm. Private collection.

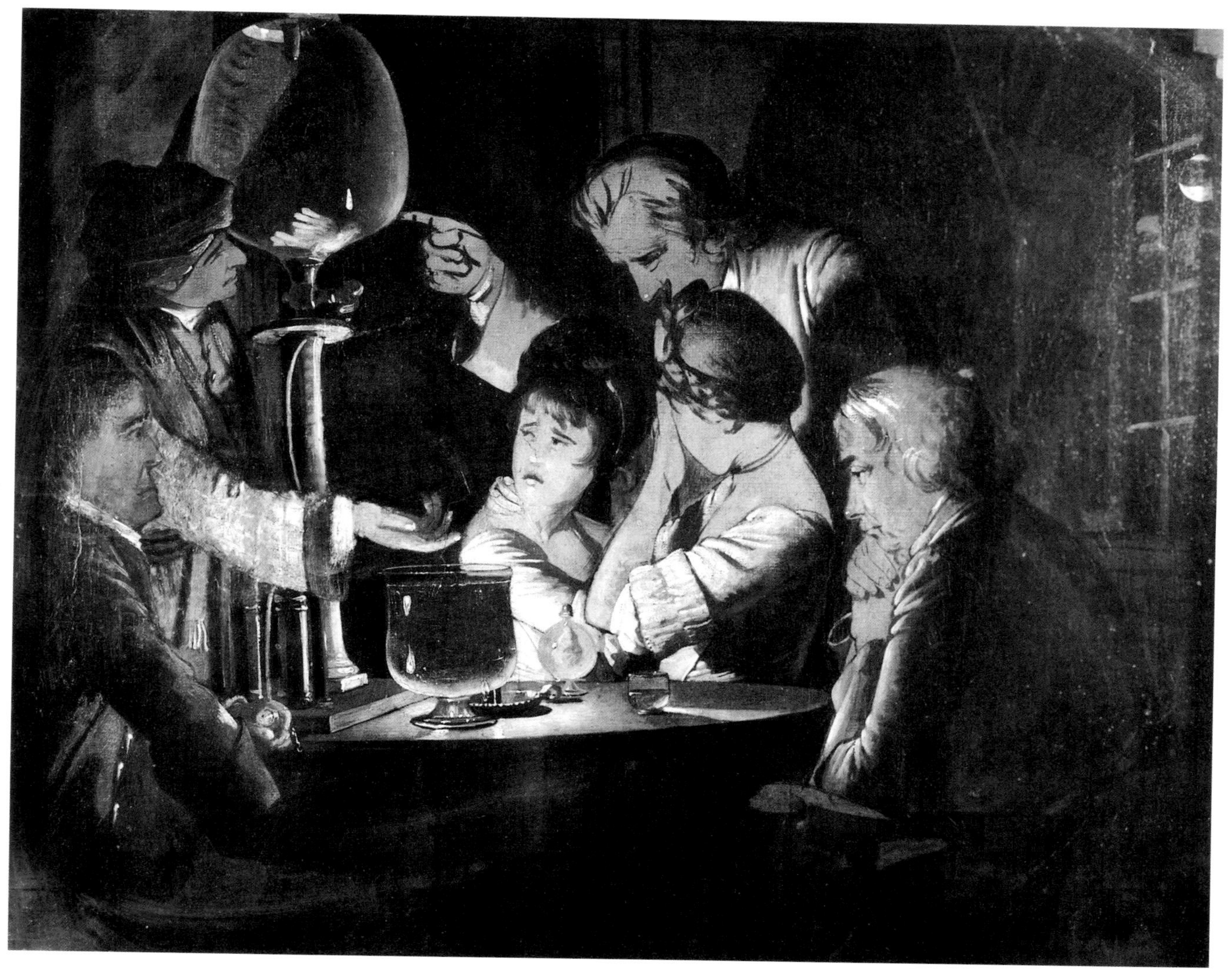

human skull.[38] As Schupbach observes, 'Skull and candle are traditional companions in iconography, the candle demonstrating the consuming passage of time, the skull its effect'; as emblems of mortality, they remind us that death is inevitable, and imply that the bird will die if deprived of air.[39] If this is what Wright intended, he has strangely underplayed the role of the skull, perhaps because he does not wish to distract attention from his central image. Instead of the usual hollow-eyed, nose-destroyed, starkly recognisable skull of traditional vanitas paintings, he shows only part of a carious (diseased) skull, seen from behind, and lacking the mandible or lower jaw.[40] His chief reason for placing it in the glass beaker may have been to add to the concealment of the candle behind it. It remained unrecognised as a skull for two centuries before Schupbach identified it.

The experiment Wright depicts is evidently taking place in a private house. Probably the man next to the lecturer, pointing upwards, is the host: but who is who hardly matters compared with the fact that the audience is made up of both sexes and of people of widely differing ages. A long tradition identifies the couple on the left as Thomas Coltman and Mary Barlow, both then living in Derby and both friends of the artist; they were to marry in 1769, and sit to Wright for the double portrait *Mr and Mrs Coltman* (NG 6496, pp. 344–9). Flaubert saw them as lovers. He saw the *Air Pump* when he was in London in 1865–6, noting in his journal: 'Wright: Expérience de la machine pneumatique. Effet de nuit. Deux amoureux dans un coin, charmants. Le vieux (à longs cheveux) qui montre l'oiseau sous le verre. Petite fille qui pleure. Charmant de naïveté et de profondeur.' The spectators range in age from the two little girls on the right – the elder a pure 'Euphrosyne', whose (?) father may well be saying to her 'Have a good Heart, and look on; for turning away your Face will boot the Animal nothing'. The oldest is the man seated on the right, not watching the experiment but seemingly sunk in thought. This figure is closely derived, as Michael Wynne has shown,[41] from a pastel drawing by Frye of *An Old Man leaning on a Staff*, of about 1760; but Wright has lowered the man's head, so that his gaze seems to centre on the candle and the skull, as if brooding on their implications.

The most detached spectator is the man partly turned away from us, holding a stop-watch with which to time the convulsions of the 'subject'. The only person present who watches the experiment with genuine curiosity is the boy next to him, leaning forwards, and, as Kate Atkinson recently observed, 'craning his neck to see better, utterly absorbed by his observation' (see fig. 3).[42]

Within the glass receiver, Wright depicts a white cockatoo, a rare bird in the Midlands in the 1760s, and one whose life would never in reality have been risked in an experiment such as this:[43] but Wright had already painted a white cockatoo in his portrait of *Mr and Mrs William Chase*,[44] and knew that its white plumage was just what he needed to show to dramatic advantage in the shadows of this room. As for the lecturer, Wright has transformed him into a *magus* with a sense of theatre, and placed him so that candlelight heightens the effect of every furrow of his brow and every curl of his silver locks. Busch 1986 sees precedents in an early Netherlandish type of painting of the Holy Trinity – where God the Father points upwards towards the dove of the Holy Spirit, while Christ extends a hand towards the people – in Wright's central group of the lecturer, the bird and the man pointing upwards.[45]

The lecturer's magnetic expression illustrates only the most obvious of the effects which Wright achieved in this, the most ambitious of all his 'candlelights'. Illumined faces seen in close-up, angled necks such as Mary Barlow's in her softly dark, sinuously stranded jet necklace, profiles such as the young boy's half-hidden in shadow, these are only part of those effects. Just as interesting to Wright is what happens to colours as they recede from light. The lecturer's showy robe – flashier than any other demonstrator wears in his scenes – can be seen immediately above the light to be of light red damask, woven with arabesques; as the eye travels upwards, further from the light, the stuff darkens to magenta. This observation of changes in colour as light recedes continues throughout the picture. One other example may be given: the young 'Euphrosyne' who averts her eyes from the experiment wears, like her sister, a dress of palest lilac. In the light of the candle, these dresses are pale indeed; but as the elder girl turns away from the experiment, her dress deepens from lilac to purple, and finally to black. This, perhaps, is what the *Gazetteer* meant when praising the effects of light 'diffused throughout his great picture'.

Wright depicts the moment when much of the air has already been pumped out of the glass container, by means of the handle attached to the barrels encasing pistons. The bird gasps, and sinks to the bottom of the cage; but it is not yet lifeless. The lecturer's left hand is poised on the stop-cock at the top of the receiver; if he turns it in time, the bird will revive; if not, it will die. The lecturer seems to stare out at us as if he had god-like power of determining life or death; but he will almost certainly have conducted this experiment before, may wish to be invited again (for a fee), knows that actual death distresses a family group like this, and is probably counting under his breath each second of risk he can take before reviving the bird.

Wright's painting leaves us uncertain of the outcome. A boy by the window holds the cords of a birdcage, waiting for his cue: is he to lower the cage to receive the revived bird, or haul it out of sight because the bird is dead? We cannot be certain: but it should be noted that when Valentine Green engraved his mezzotint of the subject, he indicated – with a few strokes of the graver, and presumably with Wright's sanction – a just perceptible return of air into the receiver.

Much of the power of Wright's painting was retained in the mezzotint engraved by Valentine Green. As Tim Clayton 1990 notes, this was based on Green's own faithful drawing, presumably made soon after the painting's completion. The mezzotint was exhibited at the Society of Artists in 1769

Fig. 9 *An Experiment on a Bird in the Air Pump*, detail

(271); the plate was promptly purchased by John Boydell, who published it for sale at fifteen shillings. Good impressions were in demand, both in Britain and on the Continent. Increasingly weak impressions continued to be printed throughout the nineteenth century.[46]

In the Paris Salon of 1771, Charles-Amédée-Philippe van Loo (1719–95) exhibited *Une Expérience physique d'un oiseau privé d'air à la machine pneumatique*,[47] but this has little in common with Wright's picture; the figures are dressed in the style of the previous century, suggesting that this was in effect a history painting, depicting the air pump while it was still a recent invention, and the vaguely aristocratic characters register distinct *ennui*: Diderot commented 'Expérience où aucun des spectateurs n'est à ce qu'il fait.'[48] A decade later, probably in the early 1780s, Amédée van Loo returned to the subject, but this time very differently. He painted his own family gathered together to watch an experiment with the air pump (fig. 10),[49] with himself in the role of lecturer, Mme van Loo rather nervously clutching a pet dog (but she need not be so apprehensive, for there seems already to be some small creature in the receiver), a boy cranking the apparatus and various members of the family looking on, mostly rather urbanely. It seems likely that Amédée van Loo had seen the mezzotint after Wright's *Experiment on a Bird in the Air Pump*, and that he adapted Wright's idea of integrating the subject into a domestic setting.

Wright's own image of the bird imprisoned in the glass receiver may in a sense have haunted his thoughts. After the gravely beautiful *An Academy by Lamplight*, exhibited the following year,[50] he painted no more 'candlelights', instead painting a series of 'night pieces', 1771–3, foreshadowed by the glimpse of a full moon riding above clouds in *The Air Pump*. But at the same time, he was preoccupied with subjects of captives and prisoners. He showed *A Captive King* (now lost) at the Society of Artists in 1773.[51] Then he painted *The Captive, from Sterne's Sentimental Journey*, completing one version in Rome in 1774 and another which was exhibited at the Royal Academy in 1778;[52] he also painted several small prison scenes. These pictures were largely inspired by Sterne's 'picture' of a man confined in a dungeon; but it may be recalled that the key passage in Sterne describes Yorick having lost his passport in Paris, joking to himself about being 'clapp'd up into the Bastile'. Then he walks into the street, where he hears 'a voice which I took to be of a child, which complained "it could not get out" '. He saw it was 'a starling hung in a little cage – "I can't get out – I can't get out", said the starling'. Thereafter Yorick could think of nothing but 'the miseries of confinement'.

Fig. 10 Charles-Amédée-Philippe van Loo (1719–1795), *Self Portrait as Philosopher, performing an Experiment with the Air Pump before his Wife and Family*, c.1780. Oil on canvas. Archangel'skoe Museum.

NOTES

1. See Wright's Account Book (coll. Derby Art Gallery): the picture is twice listed, under 'Candlelight pictures', p. 35, as 'The Air Pump – 210' and again, under the same heading but now paid for, as 'The Air Pump Pd 200'; elsewhere in the Account Book is a note that Dr Bates paid for it in instalments. Dr Benjamin Bates, physician, of Little Missenden, Bucks, and friend of Dr Erasmus Darwin, had already bought Wright's *Three Persons viewing the Gladiator* in 1765, for £40 (he also bought Wright's 'Galen', a picture about which nothing is now known: see Nicolson 1968, p. 236). Bates was also the patron of John Hamilton Mortimer and Thomas Jones, see John Sunderland, 'John Hamilton Mortimer: His Life and Works', *Walpole Society 1986*, vol. LII, 1988, under cat. no. 85: *The Progress of Vice*, four paintings of 1774 painted for Dr Bates, of which two survive; and ed. A.P. Oppé, 'Memoirs of Thomas Jones', *Walpole Society 1946–48*, XXXII, 1951, pp. 33–5, 38.

2. Quoted by Robinson 1958, p. 214.

3. Coll. NGA, Washington (880), with a companion picture, *Soap Bubbles* (881).

4. See in particular Benedict Nicolson, 'Artificial Light in Painting in the 17th Century', text of a lecture given in the 1970s, published in ed. L. Vertova, *Caravaggism in Europe*, Turin 1979, vol. I, pp. 25–8. See also Wright 1995, *passim*, including 75 ills. in colour.

5. Nicolson 1968, pp. 39–40; and see p. 47: 'When we come to discuss Wright's genre scenes, it will be to Honthorst and Terbrugghen to whom we shall most often refer.'

6. The Caravaggio *Supper at Emmaus* was engraved by Pierre Fatoure in 1629. The Honthorst (NG 3679) was engraved by Pietro Fontana (1762–1837), i.e. too late to have influenced Wright's candlelights. No engraving of the Schalken (NG 999) is recorded in MacLaren/Brown 1991.

7. See Andrew W. Moore, *Dutch and Flemish Painting in Norfolk*, exh. cat., Norfolk Museums Service 1988, p. 8, noting particularly two versions of Schalken's *Boy blowing on a Firebrand* ('The Boy blowing the Coal') in English collections by the mid-eighteenth century: (1) recorded at Althorp, in 1746 (Kenneth Garlick, 'A Catalogue of Pictures at Althorp', *Walpole Society 1974–1976*, XLV, 1976, p. 76, cat. no. 585); now coll. NGS; (ii) in the collection of Henry Bell at King's Lynn. Moore also notes (p. 26) three small candlelights by Schalken in the collection of the dealer and collector Matthew Boulter of Yarmouth by 1778.

8. Wright 1995, p. 133, under no. 68.

9. Nicolson 1968, p. 48. For his discussion of Frye as an influence on Wright, see pp. 42–4, 46, 48–9.

10. See Michael Wynne, 'Thomas Frye (1710–1762)', *Burlington Magazine*, CXIV, 1972, pp. 79–84, figs. 13–31.

11. See *A Girl reading a Letter by Candlelight, with a Young Man peering over her Shoulder*, *c.*1760–2, coll. Col. R.S. Nelthorpe; Nicolson 1968, cat. no. 207, plate 45; Egerton 1990, cat. no. 14, repr. in colour. See also *A Girl reading a Letter, with an Old Man reading over her Shoulder*, ? exh. SA 1767 or 1768; Nicolson 1968, cat. no. 205, plate 77; Egerton 1990, cat. no. 15, repr. in colour.

12. See Mary Bennett, 'Boy with a Candle', *Burlington Magazine*, CXIX, 1977, p. 857. Another picture by Romney of a boy (probably also his brother James) with a candle was formerly with Sidney Sabin.

13. Exh. SA 1764 (73). Walpole's catalogue annotation is quoted by Graves 1907, p. 175. There are many versions, including one in the Tate Gallery (N 05471), whose collection also includes *A Lady's Maid soaping Linen* and *A Laundry Maid Ironing*.

14. For Foldsone, see Waterhouse 1981, p. 128.

15. Coll. National Trust (Upton House); exh. SA 1783 (203). See Laing 1995, p. 70, repr. p. 71 in colour.

16. Ozias Humphry, MS 'Particulars of the Life of Mr Stubbs', coll. Liverpool City Libraries.

17. Exh. SA 1765 (163). Private collection; Nicolson 1968, cat. no. 188, plate 52; Egerton 1990, cat. no. 22, repr. in colour.

18. Nicolson 1968, p. 50. Private collection; Nicolson 1968, cat. no. 206, plate 76; Egerton 1990, cat. no. 16, repr. in colour.

19. Coll. Iveagh Bequest, Kenwood House, London; Nicolson 1968, cat. no. 212, plate 75; Egerton 1990, cat. no. 17, repr. in colour. This subject is derived from an engraving by Charles-Nicolas Cochin of 1740.

20. Coll. Derby Art Gallery; Nicolson 1968, cat. no. 190, plate 54, with details figs. 37–8; Egerton 1990, cat. no. 18, repr. in colour; and see David Fraser in Egerton 1990, pp. 16–17.

21. Quoted by Francis Maddison, 'An Eighteenth Century Orrery by Thomas Heath and some earlier orreries', *Connoisseur*, CXLI, 1958, pp. 163–4.

22. Published in *Philosophical Transactions of the Royal Society, Abridged*, vol. II, 1672–83, London 1809, pp. 239–40.

23. See Schupbach 1987, p. 341.

24. Schupbach 1987, p. 341.

25. See *William Constable as Patron 1721–1791*, exh. cat., Ferens Art Gallery, Kingston-upon-Hull 1970; both the air pump supplied by Cole and his receipt for William Constable's payment were exhibited (cat. nos. 128–9).

26. Among these, Schupbach 1987 lists John Theophilus Desaguliers (1683–1744), Benjamin Worster (*fl.* 1719–30), Benjamin Martin (1704/5–76) and Adam Walker (?1731–1821), as well as James Ferguson (1710–76).

27. See E. Henderson, *Life of James Ferguson, F.R.S.*, Edinburgh, London and Glasgow 1867, p. 133. See also John R. Millburn, *Wheelwright of the Heavens: The Life and Work of James Ferguson, F.R.S.*, London 1988.

28. Ferguson, *Tracts and Tables*, first published 1767, with lists of apparatus to be used in the lectures, in Henderson 1867, pp. 343–8.

29. This is the syllabus as published in 1769; see Henderson 1867, p. 355.

30. Henderson 1867, p. 268. Henderson records that in the Midlands Ferguson gave 'his usual course of lectures on Astronomy, Mechanics, Hydraulcs. &c.'; but almost certainly it would have included the customary lecture on pneumatics (including the air pump). Ferguson repeated his course of lectures in Derby in 1771.

31. For the Lunar Society, established in Birmingham around 1764–5, see Robert F. Scholfield, *The Lunar Society of Birmingham*, Oxford 1963; a short account is given by Fraser (in Egerton 1990), p. 15. Its members were Midlands scientists, manufacturers, doctors, etc. Wright was not himself a member of the Lunar Society; his closest contacts with that Society were through his friend and near neighbour in Derby, John Whitehurst FRS (1713–88), maker of clocks, barometers and other instruments, and Dr Erasmus Darwin, who moved from Lichfield to Derby in 1783. For Wright's portraits of Darwin and Whitehurst, see Egerton 1990, cat. nos. 144–5, 147.

32. Quoted by Schupbach 1987, pp. 342–3, from Martin 1755, vol. I, pp. 398–9.

33. James Ferguson, *Lectures on Select Subjects*, London 1760, p. 200; quoted by Nicolson 1968, p. 114.

34. For Richard Savage, see Richard Holmes, *Dr Johnson and Mr Savage*, London 1993, *passim*. The quotation is taken from ed. Clarence Tracy, *The Poetical Works of Richard Savage*, Cambridge 1962, p. 128.

35. See ed. Tracy 1962, pp. 94–5. *The Wanderer* was begun in 1726–7. In December 1727 Savage was tried for murder, and condemned to death; he was pardoned in January 1728, and completed the greater part of *The Wanderer* later that year.

36. For instance, *Edwin, from Dr Beattie's Minstrel* (Nicolson 1968, cat. no. 235); *The Dead Soldier* (Nicolson 1968, cat. nos 238–40), taken from John Langhorne's *The Country Justice* (and various scenes from Sterne).

37. Private collection. Painted *c.*1767 on the reverse of a *Self Portrait*, 62.2 × 76.2 cm, turned sideways. Nicolson 1968, cat. no. 193, plate 59.

38. Schupbach 1987, p. 346.

39. Schupbach 1987, p. 346.

40. In correspondence with the compiler 1988–90, Schupbach observes that the skull is lacking part of the jaw.

41. See Michael Wynne, 'A Pastel by Thomas Frye', *British Museum Yearbook II: Collectors and Collections*, London 1977, pp. 242–4, fig. 204; also repr. Egerton 1990, p. 61, fig. 10. The drawing appears to have belonged to the Tate family of Liverpool, perhaps to Thomas Moss Tate, Wright's pupil; thus it was probably easily accessible to Wright.

42. Kate Atkinson, 'Author's Picture Choice', in *NG News*, June 1997 [pp. 1–2].

43. Schupbach 1987, p. 347.

44. Private collection, New York; *c.*1762–3, Egerton 1990, cat. no. 13, repr. in colour.

45. Busch 1986, pp. 26–49.

46. See Clayton 1990, p. 235.

47. Repr. *Diderot: Salons*, ed. Jean Seznec, Oxford 1967, vol. IV, fig. 81, as 'ancienne collection Youssoupoff' (USSR). The compiler is indebted to her colleague Humphrey Wine for drawing this picture to her attention.

48. *Diderot: Salons*, p. 175.

49. The painting is reproduced here from a reproduction in Charles Oulmont, 'Amédée van Loo', *Gazette des Beaux-Arts*, 1912, 2 parts, Pt ii, p. 149.

50. Coll. Yale Center for British Art; exh. SA 1769 (197), Nicolson 1968, cat. no. 189, plate 60; Egerton 1990, cat. no. 23, repr. in colour.

51. Exh. SA 1773 (370). Walpole thought the figure 'bad and inexpressive', and noted that he had 'a lanthorn hanging over him'. Nicolson 1968 (cat. no. 214, as untraced) thinks this captive was probably the crusader Guy de Luignan.

52. *The Captive*, 1774, is coll. Vancouver Art Gallery; Egerton 1990, cat. no. 53, repr. in colour. *The Captive*, exh. RA 1778 (360), is coll. Derby Art Gallery (Nicolson 1968, cat. no. 217, plate 162).

NG 6496

Mr and Mrs Thomas Coltman

? exhibited 1771
Oil on canvas, 127 × 101.6 cm (50 × 40 in.)
Inscribed verso (by a later hand, after 1826) *Thomas Coltman and his first wife Mary* and, below his name, *Nat. 1747 Ob. 1826*, below her name *nee Barlow Ob. 1786 aet. 39* and below both names *Wright of Derby pinx^{t}*

Provenance

Painted for Thomas Coltman (in Wright's Account Book as *M^{r} & Mrs Coltman a Conversation £63.0.0.*: the note *R^{d} – x – 100* between the title and the price suggests that Coltman's payment of £100 was made up of £63 for this picture and the balance for others, perhaps for Coltman's two 'Candle-light' pictures, as suggested below); thence by family descent through Coltman's younger brother George until sold Christie's 23 November 1984 (94), bt Agnew's for the National Gallery, with contributions from the National Heritage Memorial Fund and the Pilgrim Trust.

Exhibited

Probably SA 1771 (203, 'A small conversation'); London, Henry Graves & Co. Ltd., *Loan Exhibition of Works by Joseph Wright ARA of Derby*, 1910 (18); Derby, Corporation Art Gallery, *Wright of Derby ... Bicentenary Exhibition*, 1934 (6); RA, *British Portraits*, 1956–7 (306); British Council tour 1957–8 (18); Tate Gallery and Liverpool, Walker Art Gallery, *Joseph Wright of Derby*, 1958 (9); Kenwood House, Iveagh Bequest, *The Conversation Piece in Georgian England*, 1965 (48); Paris 1972 (339); NG, *Mr & Mrs Coltman*, 1986 (4); British Museum, National Heritage Memorial Fund, *Treasures for the Nation*, 1988–9(33); London, Tate Gallery, Paris, Grand Palais and New York, Metropolitan Museum of Art, *Wright of Derby*, 1990 (29).

Literature

Nicolson 1968, I, pp. 33, 36–8, 107, II, plate 91; David Fraser, 'Joseph Wright's Portraits of Mr and Mrs Coltman and Colonel Heathcote', in ed. Mark Wrey, *Christie's: Review of the Season 1985*, Oxford 1985, pp. 48–50; Allan Braham, *Wright of Derby: Mr & Mrs Coltman*, NG exh. booklet, 1986, *passim*; Ribeiro 1995, p. 35, colour plate p. 3.4; Martin Wyld and David Thomas, 'Wright of Derby's "*Mr and Mrs Coltman*": An Unlined English Painting', in *NG Technical Bulletin*, 10, 1986, pp. 28–31, figs. 1–5.

Copy

Oil on canvas, 50 × 40 in., by Barrington Bramley, made for the previous owner of the original picture after its acquisition by the National Gallery, and placed in the original frame.

Technical Notes

Unlined and in very good condition. Cleaned soon after acquisition in 1984 when the treatment and research described in Volume 10 of the *NG Technical Bulletin* were carried out.

Cleaning showed that there had been a colour change in the sky: a strip of paint along the top edge which had been protected by the rebate was bluer than the remainder. Microscopical examination of samples identified the pigments of the sky as lead white, vermilion, smalt and charcoal. The smalt in the exposed area had degraded and partially lost its colour, leaving the vermilion in the sky more prominent than it had been originally, while beneath the rebate the smalt was relatively undiscoloured.

The X-ray shows minor alterations in the position of the house at the right edge, in Thomas Coltman's left arm, and in the horse's ears. However, cracks in the top layer of paint suggested that foliage had once covered much of the sky on the right, and that a broad tree trunk had originally been placed to the left of the horse's legs.

These larger changes are not detectable by X-ray or infra-red photography.

The sitters are Thomas Coltman and his wife Mary, portrayed probably a year or so after their marriage in October 1769. Wright entered the portrait in his Account Book as *M^{r} & Mrs Coltman a Conversation*, on an undated page, among other portraits painted around 1770–1;[1] and it may well be the picture he exhibited at the Society of Artists in 1771 (203) as 'A small conversation'.

Thomas Coltman was a friend of Wright's, though thirteen years younger than the artist. Born in 1747, he was the second son of John Coltman of Hagnaby Priory,[2] near East Kirkby, Lincolnshire, an estate with a modest house and 1200 acres purchased thirty years earlier by his grandfather, Henry Coltman of St Margaret's, Westminster. Thomas Coltman did not expect to succeed to the estate, and seems to have been content to spend the years around 1767–74 in Derby; there he was one of Wright's tenants, renting one of three houses in the Close which Wright and his brother had inherited from their father, who had been Town Clerk of Derby.[3] When Coltman's elder brother died unexpectedly in 1768 and Thomas Coltman succeeded to the Hagnaby estate, he promptly mortgaged it for £2000, and continued for several years to live in Derby.

Presumably this accession of funds enabled him to marry Mary Barlow in 1769. She, born like her husband in 1747, came from the small town of Astbury in Cheshire (not far from that county's border with Derbyshire, and some forty miles from Derby itself). Thomas Coltman and Mary Barlow were married by licence at Astbury parish church on 2 October 1769. The marriage licence records that Mary Barlow was the daughter of John Barlow, tanner,[4] who was evidently sufficiently prosperous to settle some property on his daughter when she married. How she met Thomas Coltman is not recorded, but she may have been living in Derby for a year or more before their marriage. In Wright's great painting *An Experiment on a Bird in the Air Pump*, exhibited in 1768 (NG 725; pp. 332–43), Mary Barlow and Thomas Coltman are

Fig. 1 Detail from *An Experiment on a Bird in the Air Pump*: Thomas Coltman and Mary Barlow portrayed among the spectators

Fig. 2 *Mr and Mrs Coltman*, detail

almost certainly the models for the young couple on the left (fig. 1),[5] with eyes only for each other – 'Deux amoureux dans un coin, charmants', Flaubert called them, when he saw the picture in 1865–6. As noted earlier, Wright's friend James Handon observed that Wright often used 'relations or friends' as models in his subject-pictures. Thomas Coltman owned two of Wright's smaller 'candlelight' pictures of the later 1760s, *A Girl reading a Letter, with an Old Man reading over her Shoulder* and its companion, the wonderfully ferocious *Two Boys fighting over a Bladder*.[6] Wright entered these in his Account Book as 'A Girl with a Letter & its companion Boy [? pair] for my friend Coltman': the entry (undated, but probably made about 1767–8) was later crossed through, either because the pictures were given to Coltman or (perhaps more likely) because their price was added to the £63 for the double portrait to make up the sum of £100 which Coltman paid (as noted under Provenance).

The informality of Wright's portrayal of the Coltmans itself suggests that the painter and his sitters were on easy and affectionate terms. Both poses are relaxed, and seemingly natural, though the relationship between the two figures must have been very carefully worked out. They are posed as if about to set out on a morning ride. Mrs Coltman, mounted side-saddle, wears a rose-red riding-habit, a waistcoat trimmed with braid and a small hat decorated with a little bunch of ostrich feathers. Her grey hack is a reliable-looking animal, probably one she rode every day, but adorned for the purpose of this portrait or her whim with a browband of old rose to match her riding-habit. Thomas Coltman's pose is charged with masculinity and physical energy. He wears a lightweight summer frock-coat over a blue waistcoat trimmed (as Ribeiro 1995 notes) with silver twist *à la hussar*; its every twist and turn is painted with Wright's habitual delight in the play of light on intricate surfaces, and thanks to the painting's superlative unlined condition, none of the impasto has been flattened. Coltman's leather riding-breeches fit sufficiently closely for us to observe the outline of a coin in (presumably) an inner pocket; its presence may refer to some private wager or joke between Wright and Coltman, or perhaps just to the fact that Coltman liked to ride in close-fitting breeches. The silver spurs from Thomas Coltman's topboots, the grey horse's bit and the riding crops which appear in the picture survive, and were displayed in the National Gallery's 1986 exhibition *Mr & Mrs Coltman* (8, figs. 13 and 14).

A groom leads Thomas Coltman's bay horse forward, presumably from stables behind the pedimented, two-storey house whose front Wright depicts, obliquely, in the background. The house has been identified as Gate Burton Hall, near Gainsborough, Lincolnshire,[7] which Coltman leased from William Hutton after his marriage (while continuing to rent a house in Derby from Wright). Thomas Buxton,[8] who stayed with the Coltmans at Gate Burton in the spring of 1776 ('my amiable friend Mrs Coultman very well who was glad to see me in Lincolnshire, he so so'), described the house as 'an exceeding good one ... very beautiful situated on an eminence 5 miles SE of Gainsborough w^{h} commands a very extensive view into Nottinghamshire to ye S to ye SE Lincoln Minster is very plaine to be seen tho 15 miles off'. This, perhaps, explains the gesture which Thomas Coltman makes as he waits for his horse: gazing forward, pointing towards a view which his wife must have seen countless times and doesn't bother to look at again, he may be indicating for our benefit the direction of Lincoln Cathedral.[9] A similar gesture later occurs in Wright's portrait group *Revd D'Ewes Coke, his wife Hannah and Daniel Parker Coke*,[10] although in that picture it is evidently a loyal bid to point out picturesque views for Mrs Coke's portfolio of sketches.

The freshness of the landscape background in this double portrait signals a new development in Wright's work. Almost suddenly, from about 1771, he stops contriving backgrounds in his studio and starts painting landscape backgrounds studied from nature and lit by daylight. Noting that Wright's backgrounds had previously been 'dropped like stage scenery' behind earlier sitters, Nicolson observes of the Coltman picture that 'Here for the first time landscape comes into its own', and notes that the picture is in fact contemporary with Wright's first pure landscape, the intently observed *Rocks with Waterfall*.[11] Wright's visit to Italy in 1774–5 was to heighten his perception of landscape. Meanwhile, the massive trees in the background of such portraits as *'Captain' Robert Shore Milnes* and *Colonel Charles Heathcote* (both exhibited in 1772), though more harshly coloured, also testify to Wright's growing interest in landscape. The pictorial value of natural elements in the landscape which the Coltmans inhabit has been finely judged; the tall slanting tree trunk adds solidity without dominating the group, the autumnal foliage behind it acts as a foil to the charming profile of Mrs Coltman in her delicately feathered hat, while trees recede on the left to give the hint of a park. Overhead the sky is windswept, unreliable, the shifting clouds offering the artist the chance to vary the fall of light throughout his picture. Thin sunlight falls on the red-brick of the house and edges the lower clouds, but stormier clouds are gathering and may yet prevent the morning ride. Again suddenly, Wright has begun to paint credible English weather as well as landscape.

Not everybody in the early 1770s liked Wright's new style. To exhibition-goers accustomed to Wright's 'candlelights' and 'night pieces', his daylight portrayal of sitters such as the Coltmans, Milnes and Heathcote must have seemed strange. In his catalogue of the Society of Artists' exhibition of 1771, against the title of Wright's 'A small conversation' Horace Walpole noted 'highly finished, but glaring'.[12] Although the Coltman picture is (so far) not positively identifiable as that 'small conversation', Walpole's adjective 'glaring' for one of Wright's 1771 exhibits must indicate his dislike of some aspect of Wright's work. Over the next few years, Walpole added the same or a similarly disapproving adjective against each of Wright's exhibits which featured a landscape: 'Trees too hard & too green', he noted in 1772 (against *Portrait of an Officer*: Milnes or Heathcote); 'Hard', he noted against *An Earth-Stopper on the Banks of the Derwent* (1773), and 'Very fine, tho' hard' against *The Old Man and Death* (1774). By contrast, Walpole thought each of the blacksmiths' shops and iron forges exhibited during the same years were 'good', or 'very good'. Artists' critics are rarely tolerant of transitional stages.

Fig. 3 Sir Joshua Reynolds, *The Duke and Duchess of Hamilton* (detail), 1779, reproduced from a photograph of *c.*1905. (Oil on canvas, reputedly 'very large'; formerly collection The Earl of Iveagh, but destroyed by fire.)

Two suggestions for sources Wright may have used for Coltman's pose should be noted here. Nicolson 1968 (p. 37) suggests that Wright may have looked at the figure of John Milbanke in Stubbs's *The Milbanke and Melbourne Families* (NG 6429: see p. 249), perhaps exhibited a year earlier. Braham (1986, fig. 15) suggests a very different influence, from the classical statues of the so-called 'Horse-Tamers' in the Piazza del Quirinale, Rome (which Wright had not yet seen, but would have known through engravings). Both suggestions remain possibilities. A different possibility – perhaps a probability – is that Reynolds was sufficiently impressed by the Coltmans' poses to adapt them some eight years later for his own double portrait of *The Duke and Duchess of Hamilton* (fig. 3).[13]

Coltman's friendship with Wright continued at least until Wright's departure for Italy in the autumn of 1773. Presumably at some stage between painting this double portrait and leaving for Italy, Wright made a pair of charcoal portrait studies of Thomas Coltman and his wife; her portrait is signed and dated J. WRIGHT / 177..., but the final digit of the date is not legible.[14] Nicolson's dating of 1772–3 suggests that these were drawn after the portrait was painted.

Coltman helped to finance Wright's visit to Italy, as Wright related to his brother in a letter of 23 October 1773, on his way to take ship: 'My good friend Coltman has behaved wonderfully generous and genteel to me he wrote to Mr Commersley the Banker to give me a Letter of Credit for £500. I refused taking any, but he insisted upon my taking one for three hundred.'[15] Wright wrote to Coltman from Italy (but the letters appear not to have survived), and sent cordial messages to him when writing to his brother and sister.[16] 'Give my compts to my good friend Coltman (to whom I wrote 7 or 8 weeks ago)', Wright wrote to his sister from Rome, 4 May 1775, asking her to tell Coltman that he might return home via Bordeaux and see 'some of his friends there' (possibly the Coltman family had business interests in France).[17] Thomas Coltman owned the best of all Wright's self portraits, the *Self Portrait at the Age of about Forty*,[18] in a *persona* which owes something to Rembrandt, something to Wright's own exotic *Miravan*;[19] perhaps painted about 1772–3, not long before Wright set out for Italy, this revealing self portrait (which remains with descendants of Coltman's family) may have been given rather than sold to Coltman as a gesture of thanks for financial support when most needed.

The Coltmans' marriage ended with Mary's death on 23 September 1786,[20] at the age of 39. There were no children. In 1789 Thomas Coltman remarried, this time choosing a wealthy widow and heiress, Mary Burton. The marriage settlement stated that the mortgage on Hagnaby would be redeemed; it was duly reconveyed in 1791, and Coltman purchased additional properties.[21] Now fully accepted by the Lincolnshire landed gentry, Coltman became a JP and was 'many years chairman of the Quarter Sessions for the South Division of Lindsey' (the only fact recorded about him in the *Gentleman's Magazine*'s obituary notice[22]); in 1791 he served under the Duke of Ancaster as Deputy Lieutenant of Lincolnshire, and in 1800 he was appointed one of the two commissioners for collecting land tax in Lindsey.[23] Glimpses of the life he lived in Lincolnshire are offered in a series of twenty-two letters written by Coltman during 1791–7 to Sir Joseph Banks.[24] He sends Banks news of disputes over hunting rights, cures for sheep with rot and 'remarks on the management of Nut-trees'; he also sends Banks (3 November 1796) a flannel waistcoat as a precaution against gout. Repeatedly, as the war with France rolls on, he stresses the increasing urgency of recruiting supplementary militia. Local riots in November 1796 kept him so busy as a magistrate that he had to abandon fox-hunting 'until the country is tranquil again'.[25] In the 1790s Coltman kept or was responsible for a pack of hounds at Sausthorpe, near Hagnaby. In a letter of 1797 to Banks, he wrote: 'I propose to go out with the Hounds in the morning wch I can do more easily than write a letter. No uncommon thing with a Sportsman.'[26] Coltman died at Hagnaby on 11 November 1826. There were no children by either marriage, and the estate passed to his younger brother George Coltman MD. With it passed Thomas Coltman's links with Wright: the *Self Portrait* of an artist who had, surely, gained much from his friendship with his younger and more extrovert friend, the two candlelight pictures and this matchless portrait of a happy marriage.

NOTES

1. Other portraits entered on the same page of the MS Account Book (to which the compiler has added plate numbers in Nicolson 1968) include 'Mrs Pool and Child £63' [88]; 'Mr Day a half length £42' [80]; 'Capt Heathcote small full length £31' [115]; 'Capt. Milnes ditto £31' [114], and various copies.

2. One mile west-south-west of East Kirkby; about ten miles north of Boston. A plan of 1768 showing Thomas Coltman's estates in Hagnaby, East Kirkby, Bolingbroke, Keal and Stickford is in Lincolnshire Archives Office, which holds ten boxes of Coltman title deeds and legal papers on deposit, summarised in *Lincolnshire Archives Committee: Archivists' Report 19*, 1967–8, pp. 9–11. This *Report* notes that before the Reformation, Hagnaby was a small house of Premonstratensian canons, given by the founder of Revesby Abbey; on the dissolution of the monasteries, the estates of Revesby were given to Charles Brandon, Duke of Suffolk. Hagnaby later changed hands several times before being purchased in 1716 by Henry Coltman, apparently an official of the Exchequer, for £5500. The *Report* also notes (p. 9) that 'The 19th century assumption of the name "Hagnaby Priory" for the main residence seems to be a romantic innovation.'

3. Farington noted on 28 October 1796 that Wright inherited 'abt. £100 a year' from his father (*Diary*, vol. III, p.684). This income was chiefly derived from his half-share (with his brother) of 'the 3 Closes on the Burton Road the property of myself & Bro.' (MS Account Book p. 40), which were let to tenants. While Wright was abroad (October 1773–September 1775), his brother Richard Wright kept accounts for him, making entries (under the heading *Brother's Accounts*, p. 48) in the Account Book which Wright himself chiefly used for entries relating to pictures. Here (p. 48) Richard Wright entered Thomas Coltman's payment on 20 July 1774 of £21. 10. 0. for 'one years Rent for the Close in St Werbs parish', a payment repeated the following year; but early in 1774 Coltman sub-let the Derby house, presumably because he had moved with his wife to Gate Burton Hall. Wright (then in Rome, answering a letter from his brother on 12 February 1774) was not pleased to learn that Coltman had sub-let his lease of the Close ('quitting the Close' before 'he has brought it into as good condition as he found it'). No record of when Coltman's tenancy began appears to have survived.

4. The compiler is grateful to the Cheshire Record Office for a copy of the marriage licence bond dated 1 October 1769. This states that Thomas Coltman of the parish of St Wirburgh in the county town of Derby, gentleman, and John Barlow of the parish of Astbury in the county of Chester, tanner, are bound in the sum of £100. In the affidavit Thomas Coltman is described as a bachelor aged 21 years and upwards, and Mary Barlow 'of the parish of Astbury in the county and diocese of Chester' as a spinster aged 21 years and upwards.

Little else is known of John Barlow, Mary's father, or of his business as a tanner; his social status was perhaps roughly equivalent to that of George Stubbs's father, a currier. As part of his daughter's marriage settlement, he made over some property to her: a deed dated 28 September 1769 ('Parties: John Barlow of Midgebrook parish of Somerford Booths, Chester and Mary his daughter...') settles on her a 'messuage and land in Midgebrook and messuage and land in Marton', Somerford Booths, Midgebrook and Marton all being close to Astbury (Lincolnshire Archives Office, Coltman Papers, 1/8/13–15, listed by National Register of Archives, no. 13771, Coltman of Hagnaby Priory). The Cheshire County Archivist notes that an administration of the effects of John Barlow of Somerford, tanner, 1783 is recorded, but is no longer extant.

5. See Fraser 1985, p. 50.

6. Nicolson 1968, cat. nos. 205, 206; plates 77, 76; Egerton 1990, nos. 15, 16, repr. in colour. Perhaps exhibited at the SA, either 1767 (189, 190, 'A small candle-light' and Ditto, its companion) or 1768 (194, 'Two candle-lights'). Coltman may have purchased them after he came into funds in 1768.

7. The identification was made by Edward Saunders and Maxwell Craven, in correspondence. Their suggestion that the house may have been designed by Wright's friend Joseph Pickford (noted in Egerton 1990, p. 73) was later abandoned. For Gate Burton Hall, see N. Pevsner and J. Harris, *The Buildings of England: Lincolnshire*, Harmondsworth 1964, p. 246. William Hutton rebuilt Gate Burton Hall between 1774 and 1780. It is not clear how long the Coltmans remained at Gate Burton Hall. They may have moved to Hagnaby in or about 1780, or when Hutton's rebuilding was complete.

8. Extracts from the diary of Thomas Buxton, of Bradbourne, Derbyshire (Derby Public Library, ref. 9233), have been kindly communicated by Edward Saunders.

9. Braham 1986, p. 8, suggests that Coltman 'points towards the source of light on the distance, as though meditating on the weather and the course the ride should take'.

10. Nicolson 1968, cat. no. 40, plate 225; Egerton 1990, cat. no. 142, repr. in colour.

11. Nicolson 1968, cat. no. 328, plate 112; Egerton 1990, cat. no. 107, repr. in colour p. 177.

12. Walpole, *Notes ... on Exhibitions*, p. 82.

13. Waterhouse 1941, p. 71, as 1779 (not exh.); Graves and Cronin, pp. 419–20, repr. vol. IV, facing p. 1504.

14. Nicolson 1968, cat. nos 42, 43, plates 119, 118.

15. Joseph Wright to Richard Wright, MS.2, Derby Public Library.

16. For references to Wright's correspondence with Coltman see Wright to his brother Richard Wright, from Rome 12 February 1774, and to his sister, from Rome 22 May 1774.

17. Derby Public Library. Wright's letter adds 'Perhaps he [Coltman] will write to some of his friends there [at Bordeaux] to know what encouragements I might meet with there for a couple of months.' Coltman's elder brother died at Marseilles in 1768.

18. Nicolson 1968, cat. no. 167, p. 229; frontispieces, vol. I and vol. II (detail). Egerton 1990, cat. no. 94, repr. in colour p. 157. As noted above under NG 725, the *Self Portrait* is painted on the reverse of a canvas used earlier to sketch a preliminary idea for the *Experiment on a Bird in the Air Pump*, see p. 339, fig. 8.

19. Nicolson 1968, cat. no. 222, plate 107; Egerton 1990, cat. no. 42, repr. in colour p. 93.

20. *Gentleman's Magazine*, 1786, p. 908, under 23 September: 'Mrs. Coltman, wife of Thomas C. esq.; of Hagneby, co. Linc.'

21. *Lincolnshire Archives Committee: Archivists' Report 19*, 1967–8, p. 11, where some account of Mary Burton's financial standing is also given.

22. Ibid.

23. Lindsey, roughly in the north of Lincolnshire (and including Lincoln itself), is one of the three administrative parts of Lincolnshire, the other two being Kesteven and Holland.

24. Ed. Warren R. Dawson, *The Banks Letters: A Calendar of the MS. Correspondence of Sir Joseph Banks...*, London 1958, pp. 224–6.

25. Ibid., letter of 28 November 1796.

26. Letter of 10 November [?1796], Lincolnshire Archives Office.

Johan Zoffany

1733–1810

Born near Frankfurt 13 March 1733, the son of Anton Franz Zauffaly, cabinet maker; trained in Regensburg under Martin Speer and in Rome in 1750 under the fashionable portraitist Masucci. After a sojourn in Rome and a period of service for the Elector of Trier, came to England in 1760.

Garrick was his first major patron. Zoffany's paintings of Garrick on the stage and of Mr and Mrs Garrick at Hampton (see Webster 1976, nos 10–13), all of 1762, made his reputation. Zoffany's German background appealed to George III and Queen Charlotte, for whom he painted a number of family portraits, introducing – notably in *Queen Charlotte with her two Eldest Sons* (Millar 1969, no. 1199, plates 26–8) – a refreshing note of informality into royal portraiture. Exhibited at the Society of Artists 1762–9, and at the Royal Academy 1770–1800, where he showed in 1772 a now famous group portrait of *The Academicians of the Royal Academy*, presumably commissioned by George III, who himself nominated Zoffany as a member of the Royal Academy; but the RAs resented such royal interference, and Zoffany (who was to be elected to the Academies of Florence, Bologna and Cortona) remained a 'Nominated Member' of the RA only. Papers of denization granted 1772.

In Florence 1772–8, with a commission from Queen Charlotte to paint *The Tribuna of the Uffizi*, a *tour de force* depicting dilettanti admiring a gallery crowded with works of art and antiquities, designed to give the royal couple an idea of the Grand Tour they could not themselves make. Returned to find the market for conversation pieces overtaken by others. Worked in India for six years 1783–9, chiefly in Calcutta and Lucknow, on commissions from Warren Hastings and various nabobs; his picture of *Colonel Mordaunt's Cock Match* (1784–6) is in the Tate Gallery. Returned to England, but did not exhibit after 1800. Died 11 November 1810.

References

Mary Webster, *Johan Zoffany*, exh. cat., National Portrait Gallery 1976; Millar 1969, cat. nos. 1195–1211, plates 24–42.

NG 4931

Mrs Oswald

*c.*1763–4

Oil on canvas, 226.5 × 158.8 cm (89¼ × 62½ in.)

Provenance

Presumably commissioned by Richard Oswald (d.1784), the sitter's husband, for Auchincruive, his Ayrshire house; after the sitter's death in 1788, passed with Auchincruive and its contents to his nephew and heir, George Oswald, and thence by descent to Richard Alexander Oswald of Auchincruive (d.1921), by whose executors sold Sotheby's 14 June 1922 (106), bt Leggatt Brothers for Lord Lee of Fareham, from whom purchased by the National Gallery 1938.

Exhibited

Glasgow Institute, 1914 (430); RA 1934 (271; *Memorial Catalogue*, 1934, plate LXX); NPG, *Johan Zoffany*, 1977 (28, repr.).

Literature

Lady Victoria Manners and Dr G.C. Williamson, *John Zoffany RA*, London 1920, pp. 159, 224–5, repr. following p. 158; Tancred Borenius, *A Catalogue of Pictures, Etc ... collected by Viscount and Viscountess Lee of Fareham...*, Oxford 1923, p. 53, repr. p. 54; Davies 1946, pp. 183–4; Davies 1959, pp. 111–12; Mary Webster, *Johan Zoffany*, exh. cat., NPG 1977, no. 28, p. 37, repr. p. 36.

Technical Notes

In very good condition, with no significant loss or damage. Though the picture is lined, the impasto has not been flattened.

Manners and Williamson report a tradition that a portrait of Richard Oswald 'exists behind a cloud' in the picture.[1] X-ray photographs of the upper part of the canvas taken in 1993 reveal nothing behind the cloud; they do however show what was possibly a large male head (? sculpted, as part of an urn) in the top right area, subsequently painted over with foliage. Too large to have formed part of the composition of *Mrs Oswald*, this may have been part of an earlier work which was abandoned; before being painted over, it might have given rise to the 'legend'. The large slanting tree trunk behind Mrs Oswald may also have been painted over earlier work.

The sitter is Mary Oswald, portrayed perhaps at the age of about fifty.[2] Born probably in Kingston, Jamaica, she was the only child of Alexander Ramsay, a Glasgow-born merchant who settled in that island with a group of fellow-Scots, acquiring plantations and considerable wealth there and in the southern American colonies. On her father's death in 1738, Mary Ramsay was the sole heir of his substantial estate; since she also inherited the Jamaican estates of her mother's brother James Ferguson (in 1740) and was to inherit those of another uncle, Andrew Ramsay (d. 1755), she was a highly marriageable proposition.[3] By November 1750 Mary Ramsay was contracted in marriage to Richard Oswald, a Scottish entrepreneur with an exceptionally keen nose for trade. The marriage settlement, dated 16 November 1750,[4] placed all her assets ('Land Tenements Hereditaments ... Goods, Chattels, Real or personal, Negroes ... or effects Whatsoever & wheresoever belonging to her ... either in the Island of Jamaica or in Great Britain') in the hands of three trustees, at least one of whom was in Richard Oswald's employ. The marriage, though childless, appears (from the meagre evidence that survives) to have been reasonably happy. Since information relating directly to Mrs Oswald is slight, her later life can be glimpsed or guessed at only through her husband's activities – and from the manner in which Zoffany portrays her.

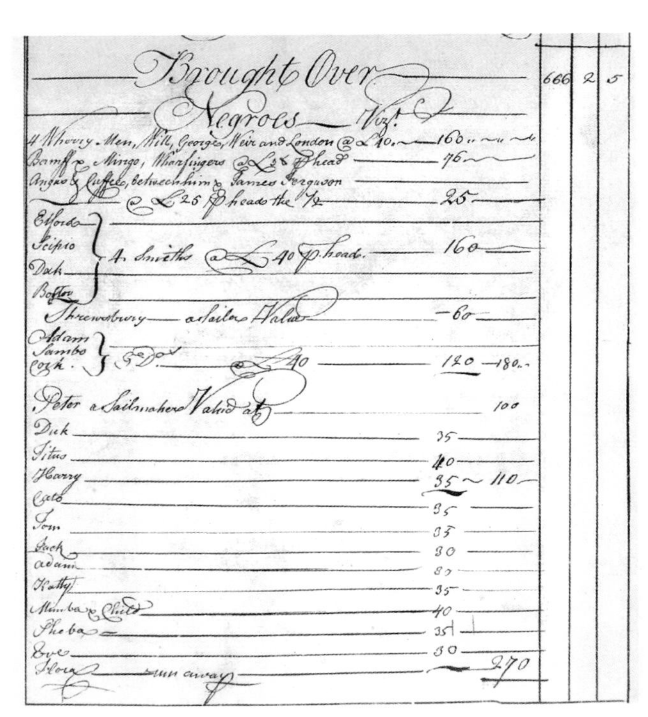

Brought Over — 666 2 5
Negroes — Viz:
4 Whorry Men, Will, George, Weir and London @ £40 — 160
Bamff & Mingo, Wharfingers @ £38 ℘ head — 76
Angus & Cuffee, between him & James Ferguson @ £25 ℘ head the ½ — 25
Elford, Scipio, Dick, Boston } 4 Smiths @ £40 ℘ head — 160
Shrewsbury — a Sailor Valued — 60
Adam, Sambo, Cork } Ditto @ £40 — 120 — 180
Peter a Sailmaker Valued at — 100
Dick — 35
Titus — 40
Harry — 35 — 110
Cato — 35
Tom — 35
Jack — 30
Adam — 30
Katty — 35
Mimba & Child — 40
Sheba — 35
Eve — 30
Flora — run away — 270

Fig. 1 *Extract from an inventory of goods and chattels inherited by Mary Oswald from her father in 1738*. Jamaica, Spanish Town, The Jamaica Archives and Records Department.

Richard Oswald (*c.* 1705–84),[5] merchant, shipowner, slave trader and (finally) negotiator of the peace treaty which concluded the War of American Independence, was the younger son of a Caithness minister. His elder brother James went into the church, becoming Moderator of the General Assembly of the Church of Scotland; Richard Oswald went into trade, and flourished. When he married Mary Ramsay in 1750, he already had large trading interests in South Carolina and the West Indies. This trade was chiefly in sugar and in slaves. One quotation from his correspondence with the South Carolina merchant Henry Laurens[6] must suffice here not only as evidence of Oswald's active participation in the slave trade, but also of the profits it could yield: Laurens reports to Oswald from Charlestown, 15 September 1756, '...we have Sold to this day 69 of your Slaves the Total Amount £12,750 Currency ... the Sale was more brisk than was Expected at the rate of £220 to £240 for the fine men.'[7] An extract from the inventory of 'goods and chattels' inherited by Mrs Oswald from her father is reproduced here as fig. 1. Her upbringing in Jamaica must have accustomed her to take the slave trade and slavery itself for granted as the basis of the Ramsay and Oswald fortunes.[8]

Richard Oswald's flair for business was further demonstrated during the Seven Years War (1756–63) and the War of American Independence (1775–83); in both wars he operated as an army supplies contractor, astutely combining reasonably efficient service with profiteering. He became known in government circles as 'holding very liberal views on economic and commercial questions, being a disciple of Adam Smith'.[9] As the war with America dragged on, Oswald's first-hand knowledge of American affairs was increasingly drawn on by government ministers. When (late in 1782) it became clear, in George III's phrase, that 'Independence was to be the dreadful price offered to America'[10] for peace, Oswald was deputed to negotiate a treaty with Benjamin Franklin[11] in Paris. George III, after reading Oswald's reports, commended him as a 'man of sense'.[12] Franklin himself described Oswald as 'an old man [who] seems now to have no desire but that of being useful and doing good'. Franklin and Oswald are said to have exchanged portraits of each other.[13] By 1782 Oswald was aged 77, still shrewd, but partly deaf and walking with a stick; to the Americans he seemed to epitomise England's spent force.[14]

The 'man of sense' had become, some twenty years earlier, a man of property in his native Scotland. By the late 1750s or early 1760s, Oswald had acquired the estate of Auchincruive, three miles from Ayr; by 1764 he completed the building of a new 'Mansion house' (a two-storey seven-bay central block set between two wings) to designs at least partly made by Robert Adam for the previous owner. Oswald commissioned further designs from Adam for ceilings for the hall, dining-room and drawing-room (1766),[15] and for what was to be Auchincruive's most distinctive feature (and Mrs Oswald's only 'folly'), a battlemented tower incorporating a circular 'tea room' (1778). But the Oswalds appear chiefly to have lived in London, in Great George Street, Westminster; and the cockpit of their business affairs continued to be a counting-house in Philpot Lane off Fenchurch Street, in the City of London.

Zoffany's portrait of Mrs Oswald was presumably commissioned for Auchincruive soon after Oswald acquired the estate. One of the largest of all Zoffany's paintings,[16] it must have been destined from the start for an appropriately lofty room, and is likely to have hung under one of Robert Adam's ceilings. Oswald was a collector of paintings; the anonymous author of *A Tour in 1787, from London to the Western Highlands of Scotland* noted after a visit to Auchincruive that 'Mr. Oswald, who was possessed of a considerable taste for painting, has decorated the rooms, which are handsome and commodious, with the works of several good masters', but regretted that no catalogue was available.[17] Richard Oswald had died in 1784. Mrs Oswald's will of 1788[18] requested that the pictures that were 'hung up' in Auchincruive should remain there, 'as a Specimen of my husband's good Taste in that Art as well as in all others in which he had an Opportunity to shew it'. Her portrait by Zoffany remained at Auchincruive until 1922.

Mrs Oswald's costume and hair-style are consistent with a date of about 1764 for Zoffany's portrait. Stella Mary Newton notes that Mrs Oswald's hair is dressed in the fashion of the first half of the 1760s, with 'a roll of hair above the forehead which made the hair and face, when seen together from the front, look heart-shaped'.[19] Her wired and be-ribboned cap echoes the same fashion in headdress. The lustrous blue taffeta dress with its ruches, bows and wide lace sleeve ruffles is in the same fashion as that worn by various sitters to Ramsay and Reynolds in the first half of the 1760s; it is close in style, for instance, to that worn by the Countess of Mount Edgcumbe in 1762, when sitting to Reynolds for her portrait.[20] Webster 1976 notes that 'the seam in the finely painted blue drapery [clearly visible to the left of the sitter's lap] is a characteristically literal touch' by Zoffany. The lace 'modesty piece' which Mrs Oswald has elected to wear above its neckline may be to protect the fashionable pallor of her skin from the sun (no one would guess that this pale lady grew up in Jamaica) or to conceal the onset of wrinkles (or both). Mrs Oswald is portrayed carrying a flat straw hat over her arm, a currently fashionable mode which Pierre-Jean Groseley described to readers abroad as giving 'à celles qui le portent cet air fripon [roguish]', and contributing to their features 'une vivacité qui n'y est point naturellement'.[21] It fails to do the trick for Mrs Oswald. The girlish straw hat is inappropriate both to her age and to the rest of her attire, and probably came out of the artist's property box rather than her own hat-box; it appears to be identical to that carried by Mrs Garrick, in *David Garrick and his Wife by his Temple to Shakespeare at Hampton* of 1762 (see fig. 2).[22] Apart from actresses, Zoffany painted comparatively few portraits of women on their own, and those whom he did paint frequently look glum,[23] seeming to need to gain animation from group portraits, preferably with children.

Mrs Oswald was almost certainly painted in Zoffany's Covent Garden studio. Mrs Oswald may have been surprised on seeing the finished picture to find that she was sitting on a very large rock with the bole of a large slanting tree trunk beside her. Such background trees recur in Zoffany's portraits, though they are not usually as large as this; as suggested under Technical Notes, this large tree may have been painted over earlier, discarded work. On the left there is a glimpse of a landscape which the artist perhaps hoped would be acceptable as 'Scottish'. Though Zoffany had many Scottish patrons,[24] he is not known to have visited Scotland. Winding water is presumably intended to represent the River Ayr, which meanders 'amidst rocks and shady groves' through the grounds of Auchincruive and is 'the greatest ornament to the place'.[25]

Zoffany evidently detected little zest for life in Mrs Oswald. The pose and the setting seem to expose her solitude; a child or two clambering about the tree (as in such Scottish groups as *John, 3rd Duke of Atholl and his Family* or *The Three Sons of John, 3rd Earl of Bute*[26]) might have lent animation; but the Oswalds were childless. Perhaps some lack of social skills is revealed; perhaps merely a reluctance to sit.

A few surviving letters of the 1760s from Mary Oswald to her husband,[27] almost all of them beginning 'My dearest life...', suggest that though childless, the marriage was not unhappy. She had accompanied her husband to the Netherlands and Germany during the Seven Years War; while he was attached to the Duke of Brunswick's army headquarters as supplies contractor, she almost comes to life, looking forward to his occasional visits ('but I know too well the Importance of Business'), almost glad of the chance to be useful by sending him such comforts as 'two pound Tea in

Fig. 2 Detail from *David Garrick and his Wife by his Temple to Shakespeare at Hampton*, 1762 (oil on canvas, 102.2 × 134.6 cm). New Haven, Yale Center for British Art, Paul Mellon Collection.

paper have no Cannesters nor can't get' or one pound [sic] of English mustard; but her letters suggest that she was neither physically nor spiritually robust. Easily fatigued, she had constant resort to 'Heartshorn Jelly', sulphur powders, 'a Spoonful of my Draught' and 'a little rest upon the bed'.[28]

Little is known of her until, after her death, a bizarre conjunction of events conferred an immortality upon her for which she could hardly have wished. Richard Oswald had died in 1784, at Auchincruive, where he was buried. Mrs Oswald died on 6 December 1788 in their London house,[29] having requested that she too should be buried at Auchincruive. Accordingly, in the dead of winter, her body was taken by coach on the long journey north to Ayrshire.

Her funeral cortège had nearly reached its destination when, on a bitter January night, a blizzard forced it to seek shelter at an inn in Sanquhar, Ayrshire. Inside the inn, sharing 'a smoking bowl' with the landlord, was Robert Burns.[30] He had been riding home when the storm forced him to shelter in the inn, where he had hoped to spend the night: instead, 'in wheels the funeral pageantry of the late great M:rs Oswald, and poor I, am forced to brave all the horrors of the tempestuous night'. Burns rode home in fury, and that same night wrote the following savage verses:

Ode, Sacred to the Memory of M:rs Oswald, of Auchencruive

Dweller in yon dungeon dark,
Hangman of creation! mark
Who in widow-weeds appears
Laden with unhonoured years,
Noosing with care a bursting purse,
Baited with many a deadly curse!

Strophe

View the weathered beldam's face
Can thy keen inspection trace
Aught of humanity's sweet melting grace?
Note that eye, 'tis rheum o'erflows,
Pity's flood there never rose.
See those hands, ne'er stretched to save
Hands that took – but never gave,
Keeper of Mammon's iron chest,
Lo! there she goes – unpitied and unblest!
She goes, but not to realms of everlasting rest!

Antistrophe

Plunderer of armies, lift thine eyes,
(A while forbear, ye torturing fiends)
Seest thou whose step unwilling hither bends?
No fallen angel, hurled from upper skies;
'Tis thy trusty quondam mate,
Doomed to share thy fiery fate,
She, tardy, hell-ward plies.

The *Ode* was published in the *Morning Star* on 7 May 1789, with an accompanying letter in which Burns states that he did not know Mrs Oswald personally, 'but I spent my early years in her neighbourhood, and among her servants and tenants I know that she was detested with the most heart-felt cordiality'.[31] Burns, Ayrshire-born and bred, was evidently sufficiently familiar with local stories about the making of the Oswald fortune to be able to direct well-informed abuse at them: Richard Oswald, to whose ghost the 'Antistrophe' is addressed, is for instance described as 'Plunderer of armies', suggesting that as an army supplies contractor he was no ordinary profiteer. There appears to be more underlying the *Ode* than pique at being turned out into a snowstorm, though there is now insufficient evidence to know how much of Burns's hatred of the Oswalds was due to their 'bursting purse'. Had Burns ever seen Zoffany's *Mrs Oswald* when he exhorted us to 'View the weathered beldam's face', questioning:

Can thy keen inspection trace
Aught of humanity's sweet melting grace?

NOTES

1. Letter from Richard Alexander Oswald to the Librarian, Boston Public Library, *c.*1898, quoted in Charles Coleman Sellers, *Benjamin Franklin in Portraiture*, New Haven and London 1962, p. 417. A variant of this tradition is given in Manners and Williamson 1920, p. 224.

2. Mary Oswald's date and place of birth have not been traced. The sitter is mistakenly identified by Manners and Williamson (p. 159) as the wife of James Townsend Oswald of Dunnikier, who (as Davies 1959 notes) was not only of the wrong generation (dying in 1842) but also of the wrong Oswald family. The portrait called 'Mrs Oswald of Auchincruive', by or attributed to Raeburn, sold Christie's 23 April 1887 (26), untraced, is too late to be of this sitter.

3. For information about properties Mary Ramsay inherited from her father the compiler is indebted to Michele Creed-Nelson, Jamaica Archives, Spanish Town, Jamaica, (Inventories 1B/11/3/19, f.80, 26 April 1738; 1B/11/4/1 f.181, 25 March 1742); from James Ferguson (1B/Il/18/6, f. 93, 10 April 1740; 1B/11/3/32 f.178, 11 September 1742) and from Andrew Ramsay (1B/11/18/13 f.187, 9 January 1755; 1B/11/3/35, 30 April 1755).

4. The settlement between 'Richard Oswald of London merchant and Mary Ramsay of London spinster only Child and Heir of Alexr Ramsay late of the Island of Jamaica Mercht. deceased' is dated '16 November in 24th year of George II' and states that the marriage is shortly to be solemnised. Copy in Scottish Record Office, Edinburgh, Register of Deeds, RD4/240 f.1054.

5. Much of the information about Richard Oswald's early career is taken from his notice in *DNB*.

6. See ed. P.M. Hamer, G.C. Rogers and P.J. Wehage, *The Papers of Henry Laurens*, II, Columbia, South Carolina 1970, pp. 169, 184–5, 205, 233, 246, 270, etc.; see also Oswald MSS, Dk.1.30 f.98, Edinburgh University Library. Henry Laurens (1724–92), South Carolina planter and merchant, was active in the American Revolution, and served as President of the Continental Congress; on his way to Holland he was captured by the British and imprisoned for a year in the Tower of London, being released on bail from Richard Oswald.

7. Ed. Hamer, Rogers and Wehage 1970, p. 317.

8. Jamaica Archives 1B/11/3/19 (cited in note 3).

9. Lord Edmond Fitzmaurice, *Life of William, Earl of Shelburne, afterwards First Marquess of Lansdowne*, 1876, III, p. 176. Oswald's negotiations as peace commissioner in Paris are outlined pp. 175–302. Fitzmaurice states (p. 176) that Oswald owed his introduction to Lord Shelburne (Home Secretary, 1782) to Adam Smith.

10. George III to Lord Shelburne, 25 May 1782, quoted in Fitzmaurice 1876, p. 195.

11. The draft agreement which Oswald and Franklin signed in Paris in November 1782 was ratified by the Treaty of Versailles the following year.

12. Fitzmaurice 1876, p. 193.

13. A portrait of Benjamin Franklin owned by Richard Oswald was in the group of works from Auchincruive sold at Sotheby's (with Zoffany's portrait of Mrs Oswald), 14 June 1922 (lot 72); it is now in the Benjamin Franklin Collection, Yale University Library. It appears to be one of many copies by Joseph Wright after a pastel by J.S. Duplessis dated 1778, now New York Public Library (see Monroe H. Fabian, *Joseph Wright, American Artist 1756–1793*, exh. cat., NPG, Washington 1985, p. 281, repr. p. 96, no. 33). If Richard Oswald gave Benjamin Franklin a portrait of himself, it is now untraced. The compiler is grateful to James Holloway, Scottish National Portrait Gallery, for the information that there is a portrait of Richard Oswald, 1747, by the Scottish portraitist William Denune, in the collection of a descendant in Portugal ; no later portrait of him has been traced.

14. Letter to Lord Shelburne, quoted by Fitzmaurice 1876, p. 193.

15. Two drawings by Robert Adam for Auchincruive are in Sir John Soane's Museum, London; see Walter L. Spiers, *Catalogue of the Drawings and Designs of Robert and James Adam in Sir John Soane's Museum*, Cambridge 1977, p. 2. See also Alistair Rowan, 'Robert Adam's Last Castles', *Country Life*, 22 August 1974, p. 495, in which the Tea House is repr. p. 495.

16. Apart from the very large group portrait *Pietro Leopoldo, Grand Duke of Tuscany, with his family*, completed 1776 (325 × 398 cm, Kunsthistorisches Museum, Vienna; repr. Webster 1976, fig. 1), only a few of Zoffany's portraits are on as large a scale as *Mrs Oswald*: these include *Charlotte, Princess Royal, and Prince William*, ? painted early in 1770, presumably for George III or Queen Charlotte (132.4 × 200 cm; coll. Her Majesty The Queen; Webster 1976, no. 62), and the pendant portraits of *General Norman MacLeod of MacLeod* and *Sarah, second wife of Norman MacLeod*, 1787 (each 244 × 160 cm; by descent; Webster 1976, nos. 106, 107, both repr.).

17. [? Stebbing Shaw], *A Tour in 1787 from London to the Western Highlands of Scotland... with minute Descriptions of the principal Seats, Castles, Ruins, &c...*, London 1788. The compiler is most grateful to James Holloway for tracing this. Many of the pictures in the sale of 'The Property of the late R.A. Oswald, Esq.', Christie's, 14 June 1922 (lots 64–105, including NG 4931, lot 106), were probably collected by Richard Oswald.

18. PRO, Prob 11/1173.

19. Typescript notes on Mrs Oswald's costume, hair-style etc., with a list of comparative examples, compiled for Martin Davies *c.*1959, in NG catalogue dossier. The compiler is grateful to Professor Aileen Ribeiro for discussing these with her.

20. 127 × 101 cm, coll. Earl of Mount Edgcumbe; repr. Waterhouse 1941, plate 79.

21. Groseley, in *Londres*, Lausanne 1770, ii, p. 24; quoted by Stella Mary Newton, typescript notes on NG 4931, NG Archives.

22. Coll. Yale Center for British Art.

23. For example, 'Miss Matilda Clevland', 1777, private collection, USA; Webster 1976, cat. no. 83, repr.

24. Including the 3rd Duke of Atholl and his family, the sons and daughters of the Earl of Bute, Sir Lawrence Dundas and his grandson, General Norman MacLeod of MacLeod and his wife (painted in India), and Andrew Drummond.

25. [Stebbing Shaw] 1788 (cited in note 17), p. 117.

26. Both in private collections; both repr. Webster 1976, pp. 38, 30.

27. Letters from Mrs Oswald to her husband in Germany etc., 1761–3, in letter books coll. Major R.A. Oswald, on deposit, Scottish Record Office, GD 223/52–3. There is a large group of letters from various correspondents to Richard Oswald, 1764–84, Edinburgh University Library, DK.1.30.ff.1–186.

28. Quotations are from MS letters from Mrs Oswald to Richard Oswald 1761–3, GD 223/52, ff. 115–16, 215, 270, etc.

29. *Gentleman's Magazine*, LVlll, 1788, p. 1129, under *Deaths*, 6 December 1788, 'In Great George-Street, Westm., Mrs. Oswald, relict of Rich. O. esq. of Auchencruive, commissioner for the last general peace'.

30. From 1784 to 1788 Burns farmed with his brother at Mossgiel in Ayrshire.

31. The Ode is printed in ed. James Kinsley, *The Poems and Songs of Robert Burns*, Oxford, 1968, III, p. 446, no. 243 (for *Commentary*, see pp. 1292–3); the full text of the letter 'To the Editor of the Morning Star, London' enclosing the Ode is printed in J. De Lancey Ferguson, *The Letters of Robert Burns*, ed. G. Ross Roy, 2nd edn, Oxford 1985, I, pp. 408–9, no. 339.

Part II

Sir Thomas Lawrence RA

1769–1830

For biographical notes, see p. 194.

NG 6370

John Julius Angerstein, aged about 55

*c.*1790
Oil on canvas, 75.8 × 62.5 cm (29⅞ × 24⅝ in.)

Provenance
By descent from the sitter to his great-great-granddaughter Miss May Rowley, by whom bequeathed to the National Gallery 1965.

Exhibited
New Haven, Yale Center for British Art, Fort Worth, Texas, Kimbell Museum of Fine Arts, Richmond, Virginia Museum of Fine Arts, *Sir Thomas Lawrence: Portraits of an Age, 1790–1830*, 1993 (3).

Literature
Garlick 1989, cat. no. 29(c), p. 137.

Technical Notes
In good condition. Cleaned on acquisition in 1965. The X-radiograph shows that originally this or another sitter's body was painted face on to the viewer, with the jacket open and more of a stock showing. The head has also been reworked, and the outline of the hair reduced. The impasto of the painted-out right shoulder, collar and hair shows through the final version.

Paint samples show that the picture is painted on a white ground. A cross-section from the background, lower left edge, shows a complex reworked paint structure. Five paint layers are present here over the ground: mixed mid-brown; thick dark brown; thin mid-dull green; light orange-brown; cream. No intermediate varnish layers were detected by ultra-violet microscopy.

The sitter's coat comprises a layer of grey with a blue-green 'glaze' of Prussian blue on top. The final glaze layer has the appearance of a tinted varnish, but it seems not to be soluble in acetone or alcohol, and does not fluoresce in ultra-violet light under the microscope.

The crimson curtain to the right is simply painted in a combination of red lake, vermilion and ivory black, and was present, though in a different form, in the original composition.

Angerstein, some thirty-five years older than his portraitist, became his friend and patron soon after Lawrence's arrival in London in 1787. The two men, seemingly oddly matched in age and experience, remained firm friends until Angerstein's death. Lawrence was to portray Angerstein, his family and his circle of close friends many times, both in oils and in portrait drawings.[1] Lawrence was quite incapable of managing money and was repeatedly in debt (Farington reported in 1801 that his 'circumstances are now so notoriously bad as to be a common talk... – said to be 30 actions against him & it must end in bankruptcy'[2]). Angerstein undertook to act as his banker, and cleared some of his debts. His commissions to Lawrence for portraits of his family and friends only partly made up for loans to Lawrence amounting, in 1807, to between four and five thousand pounds, for which no interest or repayment was ever claimed. A long letter from Lawrence to Angerstein, written in 1819 from Rome, where he was engaged on one of his most brilliant portraits, that of *Pope Pius VII*,[3] refers to himself as 'your painter of so many years, and grown exceedingly old and grey in your service'.[4]

This is the earliest of four known portraits by Lawrence of Angerstein, and was probably painted around 1790, when the sitter was aged about fifty-five and the painter was about twenty. A few years later, Lawrence exhibited a life-size double portrait of *John Julius Angerstein with his second wife, Eliza* (fig. 1) at the Royal Academy in 1792;[5] it is now in the Louvre. A head and shoulders portrait probably made around the same time is now in a private collection.[6] Lawrence's last portrait of Angerstein (NG 129, pp. 366–9) depicts him at the age of about eighty-five.

This portrait of about 1790 appears to have been painted impromptu, on a canvas previously used for an unfinished (perhaps unsuccessful) portrait of a different man who faced the artist more squarely.[7] As the Technical Notes observe, evidence of the earlier head and dress now show through. As repainted, this may be the portrait mentioned by a reviewer in *The Public Advertiser*, 30 April 1790, presumably after a visit to Lawrence's studio: after praising 'Mr LAWRENCE's unrivalled portrait of Mr LOCKE', painted at a single sitting (the portrait Angerstein had commissioned of his friend and fellow-collector William Lock of Norbury, no. 19 in the Royal Academy exhibition that year),[8] the reviewer added more chattily that 'Mr ANGERSTEIN's portrait was done at the same time, and in the same manner, Mr LOCKE saying to Mr A. – "If you know when you are well, you will not wish Mr LAWRENCE to do any more".' If painted at the same time as *William Lock*, this portrait of Angerstein must also have been painted at much the same time as *Queen Charlotte* (NG 4257, see pp. 194–9), in every way a more taxing subject, which

Fig. 1 *John Julius Angerstein with his second wife, Eliza*, c.1791. Oil on canvas, 100 × 62 cm. Paris, Musée du Louvre.

was shown as no. 100 in the Royal Academy exhibition of 1790. The plainness of Angerstein's attire seems to have been habitual; Farington, his friend and regular visitor, noted in 1804 that 'His dress was a blue Coat, striped printed Waistcoat, – drab cloth breeches, & mixed coloured woollen stockings, – buckles in his Shoes, very plain, but respectable.'[9]

John Julius Angerstein was born in St Petersburg in or about 1735,[10] and is believed to have come to London in 1750 at the invitation of Andrew Poulett Thomson, of the firm of Thomson and Peters which traded with Russia. Rumours that Andrew Poulett Thomson was in fact Angerstein's father circulated in Farington's day,[11] and have persisted – along with wilder surmises that Angerstein's mother was the Empress Catherine the Great or, if not her, the Empress Anne of Russia – ever since.[12] There seems no reason to doubt the evidence of the pedigree duly recorded in 1827 by his son John Angerstein MP, when applying to the College of Arms for a Grant of quarterly Arms. This pedigree states that John Julius Angerstein was born in St Petersburg in 1735 and shows that he was the son of George Angerstein MD, who was born in the Duchy of Coburg in Germany and died in St Petersburg.[13] No name is shown for his mother. By the age of 21 Angerstein had become an underwriter of marine insurance at Lloyd's, then a loose and possibly corrupt association of merchants and brokers which took its name from Lloyd's Coffee House in Lombard Street. In 1769 Angerstein led a breakaway group to re-establish the business on sound commercial lines, first in premises in Pope's Head Alley and, from 1773, in the Royal Exchange. In effect, Angerstein established the modern Lloyd's, of which he was chairman from 1790 to 1796;[14] he was to be active in business for fifty-five years.

Angerstein's interest in pictures may originally have been stimulated by William Lock of Norbury Park,[15] amateur artist and collector, who became a close friend: Angerstein's son William married Lock's daughter Amelia. Many of Angerstein's earlier purchases were of British pictures. The earliest portrait of Angerstein is by Reynolds, who portrayed him in 1765, half-length, in Van Dyck collar and black slashed doublet.[16] In 1771 he bought (but not directly from the artist) Reynolds's *Garrick between Tragedy and Comedy*.[17] By the 1790s he was chiefly drawn to paintings by old masters, but the work of British artists continued to appeal to him. At Christie's in 1792,[18] he bought Hogarth's self portrait *The Painter and his Pug* (NG 112, later transferred to the Tate Gallery). Five years later he purchased the six paintings of Hogarth's *Marriage A-la-Mode* (NG 113–18, pp. 146–81) privately from the bankrupt and discredited heir of the kindly John Lane who had purchased them from Hogarth fifty years earlier.[19] In 1799 he bought three monumental canvases by the Swiss-born artist Henry Fuseli RA, Professor of Painting in the Royal Academy, who was to be a lifelong friend. Angerstein's Fuselis were three dramatic subjects from Milton's *Paradise Lost*: a particularly electrifying representation of *Satan starting from the Touch of Ithuriel's Spear* ('as when a spark lights on a nitrous powder'),[20] *The Birth of Eve* and *The Deluge*. They hung on the staircase at 100 Pall Mall, where William Hazlitt remembered seeing 'some of Mr Fuseli's stupendous figures from his Milton Gallery';[21] but they were silently ignored in negotiations for the purchase of Angerstein's collection for the National Gallery. Angerstein's last acquisition of a work by a British artist was in 1811, when he commissioned Wilkie to paint *The Village Holiday*.[22]

Angerstein was most active as a picture-buyer in the 1790s and early 1800s, the era in which the effects of the French Revolution 'shook the foundations of the property of states, as well as of individuals ... [and] brought an immense number of works of art into the market' (from a well-known passage in Dr Waagen).[23] Dr Waagen listed Angerstein's name after those of the Duke of Bridgewater, the Marquess of Stafford and Lord Kinnaird as among the first to seize the opportunities to collect works of art newly on the market. To discuss all his acquisitions is impossible here; the various National Gallery Schools catalogues give full details of their provenance as well as of the paintings themselves. Here only a few examples are given. In the Orléans sale in 1798, Angerstein bought (among other things)[24] the Sebastiano del Piombo of *The Raising of Lazarus*, which in popular opinion came to be thought of as his most 'important' picture, partly because it was very large and partly because after it entered the National Gallery with his collection, it was given the number NG 1. But he also kept an eye on opportunities presented by the usual incidence of death and misfortune at home. In the sale of the late Sir Joshua Reynolds's collection in 1795, he bought Van Dyck's *Portrait of George Gage with Two Attendants* (NG 49); in the same sale, less wisely, he bought a Claude which Reynolds had reputedly 'painted on ... and spoilt' (weeded out, with some other early purchases, five years later[25]) as well two pictures attributed to 'Parmigianino' and 'Rubens', evidently also sold.

Angerstein also bought from dealers who imported pictures, in this way acquiring two of his most famous paintings, Claude's *Landscape with the Marriage of Isaac and Rebekah* ('*The Mill*') (NG 12) and its pendant *Seaport with the Embarkation of the Queen of Sheba* (NG 14, fig. 2); painted for the Duc de Bouillon in 1648 (and thus known as the Bouillon Claudes), they had been secreted in France during the French Revolution and were imported into England in 1803 for the dealer Erard, who sold them immediately to Angerstein – at an 'enormous' price, according to the rival dealer Buchanan, in whom the Claudes inspired a rare moment of near-aesthetic appreciation: 'the sun coming sparkling over the Sea, and the waves highly finished with yellow white and green tints – Landscape – Buildings etc. ... such pictures fall to the lot of few.'[26] Forty years later, when J. M.W. Turner made a specific bequest to the National Gallery of his *Dido building Carthage* (NG 498) and *Sun rising through Vapour* (NG 479), it was on the condition that they should hang next to these two Claudes (as they still do). Angerstein may have bought the first of his five paintings by Claude, *Seaport with the Embarkation of Saint Ursula*, in or soon after 1791.[27] He bought two newly imported paintings by Claude in 1805, the *Landscape with Cephalus and Procris reunited by Diana* (NG 2) and *A Seaport* (NG 5). One of these *Seaports* was to move the young Turner to tears (see below), and to emulation.

By about 1805, Angerstein had become well known as the owner of a small but very choice collection,[28] to which he occasionally added, but with no wish to accumulate a large number of pictures. It was (and still is) often assumed that he had 'advisers', and that the most important of these were Benjamin West, Reynolds's successor as President of the Royal Academy and some fifteen years older than Angerstein, and the much younger Thomas Lawrence, RA from 1794

Fig. 2 Claude Gellée (called Claude Lorrain: ?1604/5–1682), *Seaport with the Embarkation of the Queen of Sheba*, 1648; purchased by Angerstein 1803. Oil on canvas, 148.6 × 193.7 cm. London, National Gallery.

and West's successor as PRA in 1820. Certainly Buchanan believed both West and Lawrence had considerable influence over Angerstein; he drafted and finally actually sent a letter to West[29] offering him five per cent of the price of any pictures he could persuade Angerstein to buy, explaining to one of his agents that 'I did not tip Lawrence any hint of percentage as I understand he fights shy on that score'.[30]

Whether Lawrence, West or any one else influenced the growth of Angerstein's collection can only be guessed at. Little correspondence and no documentation relating to Angerstein's purchase of pictures appear to have survived. Lawrence's eye and enthusiasm are likely to have been more stimulating than any advice West might have offered; but Angerstein by no means followed all Lawrence's recommendations. What consultation there may have been is likely to have been on the spot, in front of prospective purchases, or over dinner at Angerstein's hospitable table.[31] Largely, Angerstein seems to have backed his own judgement. He was, after all, a professional risk-taker, accustomed to making decisions on the basis of such information as might be available, but with no guarantee of golden results.

To Buchanan, probably the most ignorant as well as the most opportunistic of dealers in London at the time, Angerstein was an exasperatingly independent collector. Buchanan believed that Angerstein ought to have snapped up his offer of Rubens's *Landscape with Het Steen* (NG 66)[32] and his subsequent offer of Rubens's *Minerva protects Pax from Mars* (NG 46),[33] and would have done better to have bought his own 'great Gaspard' than to spend his money on two more Claudes from a rival dealer.[34] But any attempts to make Angerstein do what he did not choose to do were useless. Politely, he parried all Buchanan's thrusts by intimating that 'except in small pictures he is no longer a purchaser' or that 'he is full now'.[35] Farington reports that when Benjamin West offered to sell him two of his own paintings (stating that '"*crowned Heads & principal Nobility* only had any of his works"'), 'Mr A.'s family friends said He must either accept the offer or break with him, but A. in a manly manner declined the offer, but soon after invited Him to dinner.'[36] It seems evident throughout that nobody, not even Lawrence, could persuade Angerstein to act against his better judgement.

In the case of Rembrandt's painting *The Woman taken in Adultery* (now NG 45), entries in Farington's *Diary* help to fill out an episode which is as much to do with risk-taking as with Rembrandt. When the painting appeared at Christie's in June 1807, artists and connoisseurs hastened to see it. Opinions were conflicting. Fuseli thought it was 'very fine' on the whole, but that the figure of our Saviour was 'difficient in expression' and 'painted from Rembrant's Taylor'.[37] Richard Payne Knight considered that it was 'a damaged picture ... the head of our Saviour has been rubbed almost to extinction of the parts, & that the *glazing* has been taken off the picture' (but Samuel Rogers said sharply that 'Knight knew nothing of pictures, & was becoming an Old Woman').[38] Richard Cosway was reputedly among the 'persons who had pretended to doubt *its originality*'.[39] But Lawrence, Farington and Thomas Hearne had no such doubts. After they had studied the picture together at Christie's 'after breakfast' on Saturday 13 June (some four or five hours before the sale was to begin) and agreed that it was the finest by Rembrandt ever seen in England, Lawrence 'took a Chaise & set off to Mr Angerstein at Woodlands to induce him to bid largely for the picture'.[40] He came back with a bid of 4000 guineas from Angerstein for the Rembrandt, but reached the saleroom too late to make it. Christie's informed him that the picture had been bought in at 5000 guineas, and that if its owner (the dealer P.J. Lafontaine) did not get that sum, he would offer it to the Louvre or keep it 'as a Corner Stone' to demonstrate his expertise (pure bluff: no dealer could afford to 'waste' such an asset).[41]

Angerstein's own opinion of the Rembrandt is not recorded, but he admired it enough to act decisively – and swiftly. On the morning of Sunday 14 June he picked up Lawrence, called on Lafontaine and offered him a price which the dealer accepted, but 'desired Him not to mention'. Lawrence later told Farington that he thought it was '4000 pounds or guineas': if guineas, then Angerstein paid exactly what he had decided to bid at Christie's, ignoring all bluffs. 'At noon the picture was carried to Mr Angerstein's.'[42] Angerstein called on Fuseli the day after he had bought the Rembrandt, '& smiling said He (Lawrence) will ruin me'.[43]

Angerstein did not follow Lawrence's advice – exhortation might be a better word – to buy two paintings by Correggio which he saw in Vienna in 1818.[44] These were *Mercury instructing Cupid before Venus* (NG 10, sometimes called '*The School of Love*') and *Ecce Homo* (NG 15). Both were to enter the National Gallery's collection,[45] but were never in Angerstein's, though Lawrence considered that they would have 'crowned your collection'. Lawrence's admiration for them was passionate; when he returned to England in 1820 he also returned to the attack over the Correggios. Eventually Angerstein made a low offer, which was refused, as Lawrence knew it would be. Perhaps because Angerstein did not have the chance to see the pictures for himself (and he had made mistakes over Correggio in the past),[46] perhaps because by 1820 he was well over eighty years old, he could not make the response Lawrence looked for.

By 1800 Angerstein's collection was well-known, and regularly visited (upon application in advance for a ticket) by artists as well as by rival collectors. In November 1802 Buchanan called it 'the most select of any Collection in any single room in London',[47] listing eighteen works in the 'Great Room' (counting *Marriage A-la-Mode* as one), but noting for his own future reference that 'he has no picture of Guido, Domenichino, Parmigiano, Albano or N. Poussin, L. da Vinci or A. del Sarto, and has one Raffaelle which is a portrait' (the last, dismissive reference is to Raphael's portrait of *Pope Julius II*, NG 27).[48] Angerstein had no wish for a large collection, and certainly no wish (as Buchanan supposed) to splash out in a way which would get his name 'in the papers' and 'astonish the Natives'.[49] By 1804, Benjamin West was reported by Buchanan as saying 'that Angerstein's collection though it consists of only 25 pictures is nevertheless the First and most celebrated Collection in Great Britain'. *The Picture of London* for 1807 concurred: Mr Angerstein's collection in

Fig. 3 Charles Joseph Hullmandel (1789–1850), *The Louvre, or the National Gallery of France* and *N° 100, Pall Mall, or the National Gallery of England.* Lithograph, *c.*1830, on one plate, 30.5 × 21.6 cm, with a caption including the quotation *'Look here upon this picture and on this, / The counterfeit presentment of two brothers!'*. London, National Gallery Archives.

Pall Mall is 'far from being the most numerous, but is perhaps the most select of any in London'.[50]

Visitors were welcome, by permission. Turner's friend George Jones RA relates that 'When Turner was very young he went to see Angerstein's pictures. Angerstein came into the room while the young painter was looking at the Sea Port by Claude [fig. 2], and spoke to him. Turner was awkward, agitated, and burst into tears. Mr. Angerstein inquired the cause and pressed for an answer, when Turner said passionately, "Because I shall never be able to paint anything like that picture".'[51] As Andrew Wilton notes, the incident acquires poignancy through the fact that in 1799, when Turner (not yet even an ARA) exhibited a watercolour of *Caernarvon Castle*,[52] his first attempt to paint a seaport in the manner of Claude, Angerstein bought it for 40 guineas. Farington commented in astonishment that 'the price was fixed by Mr. A. & was much greater than Turner wd. have asked'.[53] Benjamin Robert Haydon visited the collection on 9 May 1821, and 'studied deeply'.[54] Angerstein was a willing lender to Old Master exhibitions at the British Institution, of which (in 1805) he was a founding Governor.

To Lawrence, though no judge of financial acumen, 'In all speculation of business there seems a solidity of thought and view of the future in Mr. Angerstein that justify his success in life.'[55] Angerstein became very well off, building himself a 'charming little villa' at Blackheath, 'faced with durable stucco' and named Woodlands,[56] content to entertain his chosen circle of friends there with no wish to cultivate high society, acquiring Weeting Hall, a country house with forty acres on the Norfolk-Suffolk border in 1808;[57] but he was never immensely rich, like his fellow-collectors William Beckford, for instance, or the Marquess of Stafford (later Duke of Sutherland). Farington noted in 1803 that 'his fortune is not esteemed to be of the first rate, perhaps not more, if so much as £100,000, but his expences will be borne by his income *from business* which must be very considerable'.[58] He lived quietly, and without ostentation.

Angerstein's later years are briefly discussed under Lawrence's later portrait of him, NG 129 (pp. 366–9). He died in 1823. He had envisaged that the collection in his Pall Mall house[59] would be sold; his executors[60] began to prepare for sale, first publishing a handsome illustrated catalogue of the collection.[61] The idea of buying Angerstein's pictures for the nation was first mooted in the House of Commons in July 1823, by George Agar-Ellis (later 1st Baron Dover, and a founding Trustee of the National Gallery), who later recorded in his diary that 'the House cheered, & seemed on the whole favourably disposed towards my proposition'.[62] The first formal move towards negotiating the purchase of the collection at 100 Pall Mall for the nation, with the intention of using it as the foundation of a National Gallery,[63] was made in a letter from the Prime Minister, Lord Liverpool, to Angerstein's son John Angerstein MP on 19 September 1823; but behind the scenes there had been correspondence between Sir Charles Long (see pp. 376–87) and Angerstein's executors, and consultations with Lawrence over the importance of the collection. Negotiations were finally concluded on 19 December 1823, when Angerstein's executors accepted the government's offer to purchase 38 of Angerstein's pictures then at 100 Pall Mall, at a valuation (£57,000) provided at the government's request by William Seguier[64] (see pp. 388–98).

In the following March, the government took up the remainder of the lease of Angerstein's relatively small house at 100 Pall Mall for the purpose of 'the Preservation and Public Exhibition of the Collection of Pictures which belonged to the late J.J. Angerstein'. Thus the National Gallery came into being, in a hardly palatial house in Pall Mall (fig. 3). Benjamin Robert Haydon, who had previously had to obtain permission to see Angerstein's collection, remarked in May 1824 that 'It was delightful to walk in to the Gallery just as you felt inclined without trouble or inconvenience'; he declared the government's purchase and public display of the collection to be 'the greatest step since the Elgin Marbles'.[65]

Angerstein's collection nearly went up in smoke in the small hours of 31 January 1809. Lawrence reported that day that Angerstein had had 'a very narrow escape from losing his House and fine Collection by Fire. A house in that little Court in the back of his premises took fire at half past five this morning and in a short time caught the back part of his House but by great exertions of the Firemen and with the loss of part of a Wall and part of the Ceiling of the first floor Drawing Room was prevented from extending further. One Picture in the Removal was damaged but only one.'[66]

Had the fire spread to all Angerstein's pictures, the creation of the National Gallery might well have had to wait – possibly for many years – for some other cue to call it into being.

NOTES

A selection of pictures purchased from Angerstein was displayed in Room 1 of the National Gallery in 1996–7, under the title National Gallery Collectors: John Julius Angerstein *(no catalogue, but a hand-list). For a discussion of Angerstein's collection, see Thomas Tuohy's review of this display,* Apollo, *CXLV, 1997, p. 57.*

1. Discussed and illustrated by Kenneth Garlick, 'Lawrence's Portraits of the Locks, the Angersteins and the Bouchere tts', *Burlington Magazine*, CX, 1968, pp. 669–74; and see entries under these surnames in Garlick 1989.

2. Farington, *Diary*, 18 March 1801, vol. I, pp. 1524–5.

3. Coll. Her Majesty The Queen; Millar 1969, cat. no 909, plate 204.

4. Lawrence to Angerstein, Rome, Palazzo Quirinale, 23 May 1819, published in D.E. Williams, *Life and Correspondence of Sir Thomas Lawrence, Kt.*, London 1831, vol. II, p. 172 (mistakenly dating the letter 1818, and misreading 'Mr... Angerstein' for 'Mrs...').

5. 254 × 157.5 cm (100 × 62 in.); RA 1792 (25) as 'A gentleman and his lady'; Garlick 1989; cat. no. 29(a), pp. 136–7. When exhibited at the NPG, *Sir Thomas Lawrence*, 1980 (7), Michael Levey noted in the catalogue (p. 29) that 'the distant glimpse right of the sea and a sailing ship seem to hint at Angerstein's mercantile interests'.

6. 76.2 × 63.5 cm (30 × 25 in.); Garlick 1989, cat. no. 29(b), as *c.*1791.

7. In correspondence with Michael Levey in 1973, Kenneth Garlick suggested that the features of the man in the underlying portrait bear some resemblance to those of the 2nd Viscount Barrington, whose finished portrait Lawrence exhibited at the RA in 1792 (Garlick 1989, cat. no. 66, repr.), and that Lawrence might have begun a commissioned replica which the Barringtons did not take, and which was then painted over.

8. Coll. Museum of Fine Arts, Boston; Garlick 1989, cat. no. 499, p. 226, repr.

9. Farington, *Diary*, 26 February 1804, vol. VI, p. 2254.

10. There is some uncertainty about the year of Angerstein's birth, though the month would appear to be January. On 28 March 1812 Farington noted that 'Mr Angerstein told us that He was 76 years old in Janry. last, & that He began business 56 years ago. He was born in 1735' (*Diary*, vol. XI, p. 4099). The memorial tablet to Angerstein in the Parish Church of St Alphege, Greenwich, states that he 'died 23rd Jany. 1823 aged 91 years...', which would suggest that he was born in 1732.

11. Farington, *Diary*, 8 November 1796: 'Minet told me that Mr. Angerstein is a natural son of Mr Thomson a Russia merchant', and 19 August 1796: 'Mr Angerstein, is the natural Son of a Mr Thomson a Russian merchant (the firm Thomson and Peters), who had also other natural Children...' (vol. II, pp. 400, 645; for further illegitimate children credited to Mr Thomson, see the entry for 22 August 1796, p. 761).

12. In *John Julius Angerstein and Woodlands*, exh. cat., Woodlands Art Gallery, London 1974, Cyril Fry notes (p. 1) a continuing legend that John Julius was the illegitimate son of Andrew Poulett Thomson and Catherine the Great, but prefers to believe, on the evidence of family notes 'written at the turn of the twentieth century' and recently 'discovered in an Angerstein deed box', that 'Angerstein's mother was the Empress Anne of Russia, and that Angerstein was the natural son of Anne and Andrew Poulett Thomson, the Russia merchant.'

13. The compiler is most grateful to Thomas Woodcock, Somerset Herald, for tracing the pedigree which John Angerstein, son of John Julius Angerstein, recorded and signed 9 June 1827, in the presence of Charles Young, York Herald and F. Townsend, Rouge Dragon, at the College of Arms (ref. 12D14/41). The omission of a mother's name is not uncommon. The document said by Commander E.A. Angerstein-Burton (see Garlick 1989, p. 136) to show that John Julius Angerstein's parents were married in Archangel, and said to have been registered with the College of Heralds, has not been found. Both *DNB* and the *Annual Register* give his year of birth as 1735, though his tombstone (Greenwich parish church) states that he was 91 when he died in January 1823.

14. See Charles Wright and C. Ernest Fayle, *A History of Lloyd's*, London 1928, pp. 114ff. They note (p. 198) that as an underwriter, Angerstein's name was so highly valued that 'when his name appeared on a policy, it was a sufficient recommendation for the rest to follow ... and policies sanctioned by his subscription received the honourable nickname of "Julians".' They also list the names of various firms in which he traded as a broker.

15. William Lock or Locke (1732–1810), of Norbury Park, Surrey, was an amateur artist as well as a collector of works of art.

16. 91.5 × 75.1 cm; Cormack 1970, p. 110 ('Mr Angustin. [£] 52.10.'). Graves and Cronin, I, p. 24. Now coll. Saint Louis Art Museum, Missouri. Reynolds also painted Angerstein's first wife and infant daughter in 1773; Graves and Cronin, I, p. 25.

17. Private collection; see ed. Penny 1986, cat. no. 42, pp. 205–7, plate 115, in colour.

18. Christie's 10 March 1792, an extra lot, appearing only in Christie's own annotated copy of the sale catalogue.

19. The compiler is grateful to her colleague Humphrey Wine for the information that the Angerstein papers in the Guildhall Library include an assignment dated 24 February 1797 of the six *Marriage A-la-Mode* paintings to J.J. Angerstein on Mr Angerstein's purchase thereof and receipt for the purchase money (F/ANG/066-1). The six paintings had been offered by James Fenton Cawthorne at Christie's 10 March 1792 (72), bt in at 910 guineas; subsequently he mortgaged them. For further details of John Lane and his nephew J.F. Cawthorne, see *Marriage A-la-Mode*, pp. 146–81. Angerstein retained his interest in Hogarth, remarking to Farington during the British Institution's exhibition of 1814 on his liking for Hogarth's works.

20. Now coll. Kunsthalle, Hamburg. Exh. RA 1780 (179) with a quotation from Milton's *Paradise Lost* (including the line quoted here). 13ft 10in. × 11ft 6in. Repr. in John Young's catalogue of the Angerstein collection (cited in note 61), cat. no. 40, and Gert Schiff, *Johann Heinrich Füssli*, Zurich 1973, cat. no. 898.

21. William Hazlitt, *Criticisms on Art ... now first collected. Edited by his Son*, London 1843, p. 18.

22. In Angerstein's day, known as 'The Inn Door'. Acquired for the NG in 1824 among the 38 pictures purchased by the government; transferred in 1919 to the the Tate Gallery, where it is now N 00122.

23. More fully quoted in the entry on NG 124, pp. 399–405.

24. At the Orléans sale he also bought two studies as by Correggio (NG 7 and 37), now deemed to be 'after Correggio', Ludovico Carracci's *Susannah and the Elders* (NG 28) and Valentin's *Four Ages of Man*, which did not enter the NG's collection.

25. The compiler is indebted to Humphrey Wine for the information that the sale conducted by Peter Coxe, Burrell & Foster, 25–26 March 1800 ('...the Property of Angerstein and Gerard Levinge van Heythhusen...') included, among pictures known to have belonged to Angerstein, the Claude which he had bought in Reynolds's sale, now in the Timkin Art Gallery, San

Diego, California, as well as landscapes by or attributed to H.W. Schweickhardt, I. or F. de Moucheron, H. van Swaneveldt and 'Barrat', presumably the elder George Barrett.

26. Ed. Hugh Brigstocke, *William Buchanan and the 19th Century Art Trade: 100 Letters to his Agents in London and Italy*, published privately for the Paul Mellon Centre for Studies in British Art, London 1982, Letter 40, Buchanan to Irvine, 20 March 1804, p. 206.

27. See Michael Kitson, 'Turner and Claude', *Turner Studies*, 2, no. 2, 1983, p. 5 and n. 27.

28. Details of the 38 pictures which were purchased from his collection for the NG in 1823 can be found in the NG Catalogues of the various schools.

29. Ed. Brigstocke 1982; draft enclosed in letter to Stewart, 31 January 1804, p. 131; letter sent to West by 27 February 1804, p. 151.

30. Ed. Brigstocke 1982, Buchanan to Stewart, 31 January 1804, p. 131; 23 December 1804, p. 362.

31. Farington often recounts dinner at Angerstein's, course by course.

32. Bought by Lady Beaumont for her husband, and given by Sir George Beaumont to the NG in 1826.

33. Brigstocke 1982, p. 11, notes that Buchanan offered Angerstein both pictures, but Angerstein declined them on the grounds of shortage of space. *Landscape with a View of Het Steen* (NG 66) was purchased by Lady Beaumont for her husband, and entered the NG with his gift in 1826. *Minerva protects Pax from Mars* was bought by the Marquess of Stafford, later Duke of Sutherland, who presented it to the NG in 1828.

34. Ed. Brigstocke 1982: Buchanan to Irvine, 26 March 1805, p. 388. Buchanan's reaction to the news that Angerstein 'paid 4000 guineas the other day for two Claudes' (NG 2 and 5) was that he would have done better to buy 'my great Gaspar', the *Landscape with the Union of Dido and Æneas* by Gaspard Dughet (figures by Carlo Maratta), on which Buchanan set enormous store, and which he finally succeeded in selling to Revd Holwell Carr (it is now NG 95).

35. Ed. Brigstocke 1982: Buchanan to Irvine, 23 July 1803, p. 89; 7 February 1805, p. 375.

36. Farington, *Diary*, 6 September 1804, vol. VI, p. 2405. According to Farington, the two paintings West offered were 'Apollo & Phaeton' and 'Cicero's Villa'; these are identified in Helmut von Erffa and Allen Staley, *The Paintings of Benjamin West*, New Haven and London 1986, as cat. nos. 148 and (probably) 23.

37. Farington, *Diary*, 9 July 1807, vol. VIII, pp. 3084–5.

38. Farington, *Diary*, 7 July 1807, vol. VIII, p. 3081.

39. Farington, *Diary*, 13 June 1807, vol. VIII, p. 3066.

40. Farington, *Diary*, 13 June 1807, vol. VIII, p. 3067.

41. Farington, who attended the sale throughout, noted that the saleroom was crowded with 'Amateurs and many picture dealers'. The Rembrandt was the last lot. 'It was knocked down for 5000 guineas; but it soon appeared to have been bought in.' That 'soon' in 'it soon appeared to have been bought in' may mean that it soon became evident that bidding after a certain point was merely against the reserve price (evidently 5000 guineas). There was probably a buzz of gossip from the 'many dealers' present, from which it may have emerged that genuine bidding did not reach (or did not pass) the level of 4000 guineas which Angerstein had given Lawrence, but which he arrived too late to make; if so, this would have been useful intelligence to convey to Angerstein.

When Farington and Lawrence together talked to James Christie (the auctioneer) immediately after the sale, he told them that 'the picture was bought in, and would not be sold for less than 5000 guineas. If that sum should not be obtained it would be taken abroad & offered to the French Museum, or kept by the Proprietors as a Corner Stone to support the credit of their future sales' (*Diary*, 13 June 1807, vol. VIII, p. 3067).

42. Farington, *Diary*, 14 June 1807, vol. VIII, p. 3068.

43. Farington, *Diary*, 9 July 1807, vol. VIII, p. 3084.

44. Lawrence to Angerstein, from Rome, 23 May 1818, published in D.E. Williams, *Life and Correspondence of Sir Thomas Lawrence*, London 1841, II, p. 172.

45. Both purchased from the 3rd Marquess of Londonderry in 1834.

46. Three pictures originally attributed to Correggio in his collection (two *Groups of Heads*, NG 7 and 37, and *The Agony in the Garden*, NG 76) were doubted in his own day, even Buchanan noting that Angerstein's collection was 'beautiful ... barring the Correggios' (ed. Brigstocke 1982, cited in note 26, p. 51); they were subsequently catalogued as 'after Correggio'.

47. Ed. Brigstocke 1982, Buchanan to Irvine, 19 November 1802, pp. 51–2.

48. The portrait by Raphael is identified as of 'Pope Julius 2d' in a further letter from Buchanan to Stewart, 8 June 1804, ed. Brigstocke 1982, p. 327.

49. Ed. Brigstocke 1982, Buchanan to Stewart, 23 December 1803, p. 111. The context here is that Buchanan hopes to sell a 'Parmigiano' to Angerstein: 'although that Gentleman may have hitherto fought shy, yet as it is a long time since his name made a fuss in the papers so he may probably begin the new year with something to astonish the Natives...'.

50. 8th edn, printed for Richard Phillips, Blackfriars, London.

51. George Jones, 'Recollections of J.M.W. Turner', published in Gage 1980, p. 4. Gage suggests (p. 4 n. 1) that the Claude was probably *Seaport with the Embarkation of the Queen of Sheba* (NG 14), which Angerstein acquired in 1803 (when Turner was 23); alternatively, it may have been the *Seaport with the Embarkation of Saint Ursula* (NG 30), acquired some time after 1791 (when Turner was about 16).

52. Andrew Wilton, *Turner in his Time*, London 1987, pp. 40–1, repr. p. 41.

53. Farington, *Diary*, 27 May 1799, vol. IV, p. 1229.

54. Haydon, *Diary*, 9 May 1821, vol. II, p. 330.

55. Lawrence to Farington, letter of 7 December 1819, Lawrence Papers, RA Library, LAW 2/31.

56. By George Gibson, completed in 1774. Briefly described in N. Pevsner, *The Buildings of England: London, except the Cities of London and Westminster*, Harmondsworth 1952, p. 157. An engraving of *Woodland House, in Kent. The Seat of John Julius Angerstein, Esq., by J.Walker*, 1786, published in the *Copperplate Magazine*, ii, 1794, is repr. in Woodlands Art Gallery exh. cat., 1974 (cited in note 12), following p. 74. The house is now occupied by the Woodlands Art Gallery.

57. Demolished in 1942.

58. *Diary*, 19 June 1803, vol. VI, p. 2059.

59. The pictures hanging at Woodlands, including Reynolds's *Garrick between Tragedy and Comedy* and Valentin's *Four Ages of Man*, were left to his son John, and were thus not (at this stage) eligible for purchase.

60. Angerstein's will (Public Record Office, PRO 11/1666; dated 16 January 1823, proved 28 February 1823) appointed two executors, Sir George Martin, Admiral of the Blue, and Andrew Henry Thomson (the son of the Andrew Poulett Thomson who had first encouraged Angerstein to move from St Petersburg to London). To these two, Angerstein bequeathed 'all the pictures and prints which shall be in or about my house in Pall Mall ... at the time of my decease ... upon the trust that they ... do and shall exhibit sell and dispose of the same either together or in parcels', the proceeds to be added to his estate.

61. John Young, *A catalogue of the celebrated collection of pictures of the late John Julius Angerstein...*, London 1823.

62. Quoted by Martin 1974, p. 27.

63. Negotiations for its purchase are thoroughly documented and have been recounted elsewhere; see particularly Whitley 1930, pp. 65–71 and Martin 1974, pp. 24–8.

64. A.H. Thomson's letter to Sir Charles Long of 19 December 1823 accepting the government's offer of £57,000 is reprinted by Whitley 1930, p. 70.

65. Haydon, *Diary*, May 1824, vol. II, pp. 486, 496.

66. Lawrence to Farington, 31 January 1809; Lawrence Papers, RA Library, LAW 1/206. Lawrence does not say which picture was damaged. The house at 100 Pall Mall was not structurally sound. When excavations for the nearby Reform Club shook its foundations in 1834, the pictures had to be removed to 105 Pall Mall. The dangers of fire remained William Seguier's abiding concern (see p. 393).

NG 129

John Julius Angerstein, aged over 80

1824, replica of a portrait of 1816
Oil on canvas, 91.5 × 71 cm (36 × 28 in.)

Provenance

Commissioned by George IV, paid for in April 1824 and delivered to Windsor Castle in 1828; with the throne, inherited in 1830 by George IV's younger brother William IV, by whom presented to the National Gallery 1836.

Exhibited

BI 1833 (33 in Lawrence section); British Council tour, Hamburg and Scandinavia 1949–50 (67); British Council tour, Moscow and Leningrad 1960 (49); London, National Gallery, *National Gallery Collectors: John Julius Angerstein*, 1996–7 (no cat.).

Literature

Farington, *Diary*, XIV, p. 4767; D.E. Williams, *The Life and Correspondence of Sir Thomas Lawrence*, 1831, II, pp. 168, 172; ed. A. Aspinall, *The Letters of King George IV*, Cambridge 1938, III, pp. 485, 488–91; Davies 1959, pp. 72–4; Millar 1969, p. 60; Garlick 1989, p. 137, under cat. no. 29(d), as replica.

Versions

The prime version, 90.2 × 71.1 cm, painted for the sitter in 1815–16, was inherited by his elder son John, remaining with descendants until sold in 1896; since *c*.1952, in the collection of Lloyd's of London (Garlick 1989, cat. no. 29(d); repr. Garlick 1954, plate 73). Garlick notes that several other versions are recorded, and considers (judging from a photograph) that the version now in the Metropolitan Museum of Art, New York, 'has some claim to be at least in part from Lawrence's hand'[1] (90.4 × 71.1 cm, Acc. no. 65.181.9, repr. Katharine Baetjer, *European Paintings in the Metropolitan Museum of Art*, 1980, II, p. 273). A small version, probably a copy, head and shoulders, 24 × 19¾ in., formerly Boston Museum of Fine Arts (Acc. 99.304), was sold as 'Circle of Sir Thomas Lawrence', Christie's New York 10 October 1992 (182, repr.), and is now in a private collection. Various other copies reported.

Engraved

in stipple by Edward Scriven, 'from the picture in the National Gallery', published as a plate to Jerdan's *National Portrait Gallery*, 1830. An earlier engraving from the original picture, in stipple by W.T. Fry, published by T. Boys 1822, sets the portrait within an ornamental border of emblems of commerce (fig. 1).

Technical Notes

Cleaned in 1959. In good condition except for some cracking and wrinkling of the darks in the sitter's costume.

This is a replica, painted wholly by Lawrence himself, of the portrait for which John Julius Angerstein is known to have sat in January 1816. The invaluable Farington noted in his *Diary*, 24 January 1816: 'Mr. Angerstein aged 84 sat to Him [Lawrence] yesterday';[2] there were probably other sittings. The original portrait was exhibited at the Royal Academy in 1816 (12). Lawrence considered it among his best works. When the Prince Regent sent him abroad in 1818 to portray Allied dignitaries assembled in Aix-la-Chapelle and Vienna,[3] and then on to Rome to paint Pope Pius VII,[4] Lawrence took a dozen or so portraits with him as proof of his art. Angerstein's portrait was one of them. Writing home to Angerstein on 23 May 1819,[5] he declared that among the male portraits (which included those of Alexander I, Emperor of Russia, Field-Marshal Blücher, Antonio Canova and Prince Metternich[6]), 'yours ... is the favourite'.

One can see why. The expression, at once shrewd and kindly, has something of Hogarth's *Captain Coram*[7] in it. Though not a philanthropist on Coram's scale, Angerstein was 'much respected for his good heart & intentions'.[8] He not only meant well: he was also an effective fund-raiser for certain chosen causes. From 1789, he was a governor of the Veterinary College, whose primary aim was to ensure the welfare of animals by providing thorough training in veterinary science. In the 1790s meetings were often held in Angerstein's Pall Mall house.[9] Lord Heathfield, whom Reynolds had portrayed in 1787 (NG 111, p. 229), was a fellow-Governor, a fact which no doubt contributed (with Lawrence's admiration for the portrait) to Angerstein's purchase of it when it was offered for sale in 1809. As Chairman of Lloyd's during the years of the great naval battles of the Napoleonic Wars, he organised five of its Subscription Funds[10] – entitled *The Glorious First of June* (1794); *St Vincent* (1797); *The Nile* (1798); *Copenhagen* (1801); and *Nelson's attack on Boulogne* (1801) – to assist seamen's widows and orphans (and to present engraved plate to their commanders). Donations came from large organisations such as the Bank of England and the City Livery Companies as well as private individuals. Expressing thanks for help given by the Fund to the wounded after the Battle of St Vincent, 1797, Lord Nelson wrote to Angerstein: 'You, sir in particular at the head of it stamps your character as one of the very best men of the age we live in.'[11] In another letter to Angerstein, written from aboard the *St. George*, 15 June 1801, Nelson writes 'We are all obliged by your humane attention to us Seamen'.[12] Angerstein, not short of pictures for his walls, chose to hang 'Prints of our Naval Heroes' in his dressing-room.[13]

Angerstein was particularly involved with a society established in 1803 to end the employment of children as 'Climbing Boys', or chimney-sweeps,[14] perhaps through friendship with its Treasurer, the Revd William Tooke (1744–1820), who had been chaplain of the English church at St Petersburg and who published *A History of Russia* in 1800. On behalf of the society Angerstein wrote in 1807 to the Prince of Wales. The Prince responded with ten guineas,[15] but no doubt continued to be unaware that among the little girls employed for chimney-sweeping 'there are two of the name

Fig. 1 William Thomas Fry after Sir Thomas Lawrence: *John Julius Angerstein*. Stipple engraving with borders of emblems of commerce, 11 × 7.5 cm. Published 1 January 1822. National Portrait Gallery Archives.

of Morgan at Windsor, daughters of the chimney-sweeper who is employed to sweep the chimneys of the Castle.'[16]

In old age Angerstein remained clear-headed and hospitable. At the age of 76, he was reported as saying that he 'had now quitted business after having been engaged in it 55 years, a long time said He, I ought to have done my business in a shorter time';[17] but three years later he told Lawrence 'that "He should die in harness", – meaning that he should act in business to the last'.[18] He remained well-informed about Russian affairs, and was delighted when Lawrence sent him (in 1818) his 'first drawing' for the portrait of Alexander I, Emperor of Russia,[19] whom Angerstein had met when the Tsar was in London in 1814, and whom he greatly admired.

Angerstein had never been grand in manner. Farington notes that he is 'considered defficient in Education, & very embarrassed on all occasions when He is required to express himself';[20] but such 'embarrassment' did not prevent Angerstein from exercising a judgement which was invariably shrewd and generally kindly. Commenting in 1814 on the rapid growth of London, he particularly noted 'the increase of the number of Musick shops and Fishmongers stalls'.[21] Twice widowed, and wanting 'domestic society', he proposed (at the age of 86 or 87) marriage to 'an old Scotch countess', but got out of it when he found that she wanted a separate establishment (or 'separate bed', as Farington interpreted it).[22] As the fur-lined gown in which Lawrence portrays him suggests, he felt the cold keenly, kept stoves burning at Woodlands, and fretted when Lawrence wrote to say that he was going to Rome in January 1819: 'Going to see the large out-door buildings must be starving work – you must get furs for that purpose – if not flannel.'[23]

Angerstein died on 23 January 1823. A death-mask[24] was taken, by anon; had Farington (who died in 1819) been there, he would have recorded who took it, on what day and for what purpose. Angerstein would have approved of the fact that a death-mask was made, having urged Nollekens to take a cast from the face of William Pitt after his death in 1806.[25]

Negotiations to purchase his collection as the nucleus of a National Gallery have been outlined in the previous entry; here our concern is only with Lawrence's last portrait of him. The original portrait painted in 1816[26] (see Versions, above) was inherited by his son John Angerstein MP. During an audience with Lawrence on 5 December 1824, nearly a year after Angerstein's death, George IV expressed his wish to have a replica of it. Over the years, he had had some personal contact with Angerstein,[27] whom he evidently liked and respected; he may also have drawn on his advice over his personal finances. Lawrence therefore wrote to Angerstein's son John: 'I ... have it in command from His Majesty to request of you, as personally from himself, that you will lend me the portrait of dear Mr Angerstein, that I may make an exact copy of it.'[28] The finished replica was included in a list of pictures painted for George IV which Lawrence submitted six months later, on 4 May 1824 ('Kitcat portrait of the late Mr. Angerstein ... £210'),[29] and was promptly paid for.[30]

The portrait itself was not delivered to Windsor until 1828. It was to be framed by George Morant & Sons, New Bond Street, London, Lawrence's regular framers. On 8 November 1828,[31] while the frame for the King's replica was being finished, Lawrence wrote once more to John Angerstein, asking to borrow his original portrait back again for a few days, since he was 'desirous of retouching the copy, after the long interval that has elapsed since it was painted'. On 22 November 1828 George Morant sent in a bill to the Keeper of the Privy Purse for various frames, including ' a richly ornamented frame' for the portrait of Angerstein, price £12 18. 0.[32] The portrait remains in Morant's frame, which fulfils Lawrence's requirement that 'A good frame should be sufficiently broad and rich, but the ornament of the richness composed throughout of small parts, and usually it should be unburnished.'[33] Five days later, Lawrence reported that he had despatched the portrait to the King at Windsor, 'as perfect a copy as I could possibly make it'.[34]

NOTES

1. Davies 1959, p. 73, notes several versions, but in fact his notes 10 and 11 both relate to the picture now in the Metropolitan Museum (as Garlick's provenance for it makes clear).

2. Farington, *Diary*, 24 January 1816, vol. XIV, p. 4767. Farington's statement that Angerstein was 84 in January 1816 lends support to the possibility that Angerstein was born in 1732 (as his memorial tablet also suggests) rather than in 1735, as is usually stated. Angerstein's date of birth has never been established (see NG 6370, p. 364, n. 10).

3. For this group of portraits see Millar 1969, cat. nos. 891–2, 897, 900, 905, 907, 911–12, 915.

4. Millar 1969, cat. no. 909, plate 204. Lawrence's portrait of Cardinal Consalvi, also painted in Rome for the Prince Regent, is Millar 1969, cat. no. 893, plate 203.

5. Williams 1831, p. 168.

6. For these portraits see Garlick 1989, cat. nos. 17, 115, 162 and 558.

7. Coll. Thomas Coram Foundation for Children, London; repr. *Hogarth the Painter*, exh. cat., Tate Gallery 1997, p. 32.

8. Farington, *Diary*, 19 June 1803, vol. VI, p. 2059.

9. See L.P. Pugh, *From Farriery to Veterinary Medicine*, Cambridge 1962, pp. 48, 54, 96. NG 129 is repr. facing p. 47.

10. See *John Julius Angerstein and Woodlands*, exh. cat.,Woodlands Art Gallery, London 1974, pp. 13–14, for an informative note on the Subscription Funds, drawn on here. Explaining the Lloyd's tradition of such charitable funds, it notes: 'It was of course in the interest of those engaged in marine insurance that the seas should be safe for merchant shipping, but the charitable activities that were carried out by Lloyd's were by no means obligatory. Lloyd's had collected subscriptions for relief funds throughout the eighteenth century, and in 1793 they received subscriptions for "The United Society for the Relief of Widows and Children of Seamen, Soldiers and Marines and Militiamen". The subscriptions proved insufficient and after the battle of "The Glorious First of June" in 1794 Lloyd's began the first of a series of Subscription Funds that followed the great naval engagements... The funds were unofficial in that they were begun by the subscribers at Lloyd's who were acting as private individuals, but because of this they became identified with Lloyd's. Large organisations like the Corporation of London, the Bank of England and the City Companies subscribed, as well as individuals of small means.'

After the short Peace of Amiens and the renewal of war in 1802, the Subscription Funds were replaced by the Patriotic Fund which continued throughout the war; this was begun at Lloyd's, but became a national undertaking. Lloyd's opened a book for subscribers; in 1810 Angerstein was Chairman of its Committee of Treasury.

11. Letter from Lord Nelson to J.J. Angerstein, 9 March 1801, quoted in Woodlands Art Gallery exh. cat., 1974, cat no. 11, p. 14; see also cat. nos 12–14.

12. Published in N.H. Nicolas, *Dispatches and Letters of Vice-Admiral Lord Nelson*, vol. V, London 1845, p. 2.

13. Angerstein to Lawrence, Woodlands, 21 January 1819; Lawrence Papers, RA Library, LAW 3/6.

14. See [William Tooke], *Copy of the Report presented to the House of Commons by the Committee appointed to examine the several Petitions, which have been presented to the House, against the Employment of Boys in sweeping of Chimneys*, London 1817, reprinted in *The Pamphleteer*, vol. X, 1817, pp. 483–91. For the more general campaign, see Henry Mayhew, *Life and Labour of the London Poor*, vol. II, London 1851, pp. 392–3.

15. Robert Gray to J.J. Angerstein, Duchy of Cornwall offices, 30 December 1807, reporting His Royal Highness's willingness to donate ten guineas; published in A. Aspinall, *Correspondence of George Prince of Wales 1770–1812*, vol. VI, Cambridge 1969, no. 2449, p. 240. An endorsement recording that William Tooke Esq. is 'Treasurer to the Society' identifies Angerstein's connection with him.

16. Mayhew 1851, p. 393.

17. Farington, *Diary*, 22 September 1811, vol. XI, p. 3999.

18. Farington, *Diary*, 3 September 1816, vol. XIV, p. 4896.

19. Lawrence Papers, RA Library, LAW/2/335. The oil is coll. Her Majesty The Queen; Millar 1969, cat. no. 883, plate 194; begun in London in 1814 and finished at Aix-la-Chapelle in 1818. Millar notes that the Tsar gave Lawrence seven sittings, 'including two for a drawing with which the sitter was much satisfied'. Lawrence also gave Angerstein a portrait study of the Emperor of Austria: see LAW/3/6.

20. Farington, *Diary*, 19 June 1803, vol. VI, p. 2059.

21. Farington, *Diary*, 26 May 1814, vol. XIII, p. 4525.

22. Farington, *Diary*, 9 September 1819, vol. XV, p. 5405.

23. Letter from Angerstein to Lawrence, 21 January 1819: Lawrence Papers, LAW 3/6.

24. Coll. Farrer & Co., and preserved at Lloyd's; lent to the *National Gallery Collectors: John Julius Angerstein* display at the NG, 1996–7 (no cat.).

25. Farington, *Diary*, 30 March 1806, vol. VII, p. 2705. See Walker 1985, p. 393.

26. Garlick 1989, cat. no. 29(d), p. 137.

27. Angerstein evidently presented at least one (unidentified) work of art to the Prince of Wales, in 1816, when the Prince's equerry wrote to say that 'it has long excited His Royal Highness's admiration both for likeness & exquisite painting', and conveyed thanks 'for this fresh mark of Mr Angerstein's attention'; letter to Angerstein from Colonel Bloomfield, 17 August 1816; Lawrence Papers, LAW 2/157.

28. Lawrence was in close touch with William Angerstein over the sale of John Julius Angerstein's collection to the nation (see previous entry, pp. 358–65).

29. For a complete list of pictures painted by Lawrence for George IV, and tables of payments for them, see Aspinall 1938, nos. 1592–3, pp. 488–91. The list of pictures includes the 'Waterloo Collection' of 17 portraits.

30. Aspinall 1938, p. 485.

31. Williams 1831, p. 265.

32. Windsor MS. 26558, kindly communicated to the NG in 1957 by Oliver Millar.

33. See Paul Mitchell and Lynn Roberts, *A History of European Picture Frames*, London 1996, p. 68.

34. Williams 1831, p. 266.

John Hoppner RA

1758–1810

Portrait-painter; born 4 April 1758 in London, of German parents. His father had come to England as one of George II's physicians; both his parents probably held places in the household of George III. Mrs Papendiek (for whom see under Lawrence, *Queen Charlotte*, NG 4257) always renders the artist's surname as 'Höppner'. Farington[1] notes that the young Hoppner was recommended as 'a lad of genius' to George III, who placed him with John Chamberlaine, Keeper of the royal drawings and medals; he was also trained as a chorister in the Chapel Royal. Entered the Royal Academy schools 1775, where he was a contemporary of Gainsborough Dupont, and also of the American artist Joseph Wright, whose sister Phoebe he married in 1781. Exhibited at the RA from 1780 to 1809, showing chiefly portraits, with some 'fancy' pictures (such as the *Sleeping Venus* admired by Sir George Beaumont in 1792) and *A Gale of Wind*, a rare landscape exhibited 1794 (Tate Gallery).

In 1784 Hoppner established a studio and gallery in Charles Street, St James's Square, easily accessible to fashionable sitters, where he lived and worked for the rest of his life. By 1785 he enjoyed royal patronage, later (1793) becoming Principal Portrait Painter to the Prince of Wales. He was influenced by Reynolds; but Waterhouse (1981, p. 181) notes that he 'looked at Romney as well as at Reynolds'. The style Hoppner evolved has frequent grace, but more stolidity than that of Reynolds or Romney. From the early 1790s Hoppner was aware that his chief rival was the rapidly rising Lawrence; he must also have realised that he could never equal Lawrence's brilliance.

Hoppner had a sarcastic manner which alienated many fellow artists; recurring illness did not improve it ('Bad health, sad looks & ill temper', Farington reported of him in April 1806[2]). He died on 23 January 1810.

Reference

John H. Wilson, 'The Life and Art of John Hoppner', PhD dissertation, Courtauld Institute, 1992.

NG 6333

Sir George Beaumont

1803, exhibited 1809
Oil on canvas, 76.5 × 63.8 cm (30¼ × 25⅛ in.)

Provenance

Commissioned by the sitter; presented by him in 1810 to his friend the 1st Earl of Mulgrave in return for Mulgrave's portrait by William Beechey; by descent from Henry Phipps, 1st Earl of Mulgrave and 1st Viscount Normanby (d.1831), through his son, 2nd Earl of Mulgrave, cr. 1st Marquess of Normanby, to his great-grandson, 3rd Marquess of Normanby, by whom sold to Agnew's, January 1903;[3] bt from Agnew's November 1903 by Charles Sedelmeyer, Sedelmeyer Gallery, Paris (in his stock exh., *100 Paintings by Old Masters*, 9th Series, 1905 (81, repr.)), purchased by Sir Edward Albert Sassoon (d.1912); his son Rt. Hon. Sir Philip Sassoon (d.1939); the latter's sister Sybil, Marchioness of Cholmondeley, by whom sold to Frank Partridge and Sons 1950; Leggatt Brothers, from whom purchased in 1950 by Claude Dickason Rotch, by whom bequeathed to the National Gallery 1962.

Exhibited

RA 1809 (54); Leicester Museums and Art Gallery, *Paintings and Drawings by Sir George Beaumont*, 1938 (unnumbered, repr. as frontispiece); RA 1951–2 (410); Leicester Museums and Art Gallery, *Sir George Beaumont and his Circle*, 1953 (7, repr. as frontispiece); Manchester, Whitworth Art Gallery, *The Arrogant Connoisseur: Richard Payne Knight* (catalogue ed. Michael Clarke and Nicholas Penny), 1982 (179); London, National Gallery, *Noble and Patriotic: The Beaumont Gift*, 1988 (unnumbered, repr. p. 6).

Literature

Farington, *Diary*, vols. V–X, *passim*; *NG Report June 1962–December 1964*, 1965, pp. 43–4; Walker 1985, pp. 30–1; Felicity Owen and David Blayney Brown, *Collector of Genius: A Life of Sir George Beaumont*, London 1988, *passim*; Owen and Brown exh. cat. 1988, *passim*; John H. Wilson, 'The Life and Art of John Hoppner', PhD dissertation, Courtauld Institute, 1992, pp. 102, 232, 255, 258.

Engraved

(1) in mezzotint by William Say, published 26 December 1808; repr. Walker 1985, plate 64; (2) in stipple by J.S. Agar, from John Wright's copy after Hoppner (see below), lettered 'From an original Picture by J. HOPPNER Esq. R.A. in the Possession of the Right Honble Lord Mulgrave...', published 16 January 1812 by Cadell and Davies in *British Gallery of Contemporary Portraits*.

Copy
by John Wright, watercolour on paper, 7¼ × 6 in., coll. NPG 3157, repr. Walker 1985, p. 30, plate 65.

Technical Notes
Unlined; in very good condition.

Sir George Howland Beaumont, 7th Bt (1753–1827), connoisseur, collector, amateur artist and the National Gallery's first great benefactor, is here portrayed at the age of 50. He had already sat to Reynolds, in 1787 (fig. 1),[4] and to Lawrence, in 1793 (for the first of two portraits).[5] Beaumont had repeatedly expressed a low opinion of Hoppner as a portraitist, and was presumably persuaded to sit to him by his lifelong friend Lord Mulgrave, also a collector and patron of the arts, whom Hoppner had painted in or about 1800.[6] Beaumont's only known sittings to Hoppner are briefly noted by Farington, 27 March 1803: 'Sir George has sat twice to Hoppner.'[7]

Both before and after sitting to Hoppner, Beaumont repeatedly criticised his work – as he criticised the work of most contemporary artists. His judgements were coloured by his undying admiration for Reynolds, whose friend he had been and whose memory he revered. The 'Cenotaph' which Beaumont erected to the memory of Reynolds in the grounds of his home at Coleorton was to be depicted by Constable in a painting of 1836 (NG 1272, pp. 58–63). Hoppner, working in Reynolds's wake, was particularly vulnerable to Beaumont's criticism, especially as many of Hoppner's portraits were of Beaumont's friends. Beaumont was to praise Hoppner's *Sleeping Nymph* (exh. RA 1806) as 'the best coloured picture that has been painted since Sir Joshua's death';[8] but in portraiture Beaumont continued to maintain that Hoppner lacked 'the delicate precission of Sir Joshua'.[9] In April 1806, Beaumont went further, declaring that he 'did not think Hoppner has any original *talent*. He is all imitative. In the time of Hudson, had he then lived He wd. have been his imitator. He is now in Portrait an Imitator of Sir Joshua Reynolds, – & in Landscape of Gainsborough... Hoppner He said, is more remarkable for *peculiarity* than for *originality*, or any great power, considering Him upon the whole.'[10] On 31 May 1806, Beaumont conceded that Hoppner 'is the best colourist since Sir Joshua Reynolds, but has too much of red in his flesh, – and wants the *neutralizing* of Sir Joshua'.[11]

The portrait shows Beaumont dressed in black, with a glimpse of white waistcoat showing above a white stock, against a plain crimson background. His gaze is averted from his portraitist. Wilson 1992 observes (p. 232) that Beaumont's portrait is typical of Hoppner's unflamboyant but psychologically acute portraiture of eminent male sitters in this decade; in particular he compares it with Hoppner's portrait of *William Wyndham Grenville, 1st Baron Grenville*, Prime Minister 1806–7 (coll. NPG, dated by Wilson to *c.*1803[12]). In these and other portraits painted at much the same time, Wilson notes Hoppner's flair for making the most of a range of colour restricted to 'the red of the backdrop curtain, the black of the sitter's coat, the white of the stock, the grey of the powdered hair, and the rouge tones of the skin'. What may have been either a preliminary oil sketch or a studio replica of Beaumont's portrait was included in Hoppner's studio sale in 1823 in a large group of 'Portraits and Sketches',[13] but is now untraced.

In June 1808 Hoppner asked Beaumont to give his permission for the portrait to be engraved. Before agreeing, Beaumont canvassed opinions as to whether the portrait was in fact a good likeness. Lord St Asaph thought it 'admirably like, & *Children* remarked the likeness'; Lord Mulgrave 'did not think so'.[14] Where portraits of himself were concerned, Beaumont's usually confident judgement faltered, and he relied on his friend Lord Mulgrave's opinion. Mulgrave's first reaction to Hoppner's portrait of Beaumont was that it was not a good likeness; he 'did not like the picture', and therefore urged Beaumont to sit to Lawrence again. Beaumont had 'two or three sittings' to Lawrence in 1808 and 1810, but when Mulgrave changed his mind in favour of the Hoppner, Beaumont cancelled further sittings to Lawrence, leaving that portrait 'in an unfinished state'.[15] Since Mulgrave had decided to think well of the Hoppner, it was engraved in mezzotint by William Say, and published on 26 December 1808.

Hoppner exhibited Beaumont's portrait at the Royal Academy in 1809, six years after it was painted, and in the last year of his life. Recurring illness meant that he had completed little recent work, and for the 1809 exhibition, he mostly called in earlier portraits. His portrait of Beaumont appears to have attracted no critical notice. Of the six portraits Hoppner showed in the exhibition, those of two other collectors, the *Earl of Essex* (53) and *Earl Spencer* (113), are similarly low-keyed. His most popular exhibit in 1809 was that of *Earl St Vincent* (170), victor of the battle of Cape St Vincent 1797, from which he took his title: commissioned by George IV, it shows the aging Admiral on the quarter-deck of the *Victory*, his flagship in that battle.[16]

In a gesture of friendship, Mulgrave and Beaumont exchanged portraits of each other. In May 1810, Beaumont presented Mulgrave with his portrait by Hoppner.[17] Presumably at about the same time, Mulgrave gave Beaumont the portrait which William Beechey had painted of him in 1807 and exhibited at the Royal Academy in 1808 (57). Hoppner's portrait of Beaumont remained at Mulgrave Castle from 1810 until it was sold by Mulgrave's great-grandson in 1903, entering the National Gallery in 1962. Beechey's portrait of Mulgrave, which J.P. Neale saw in 1818 in Beaumont's house, Coleorton, Leicestershire,[18] passed on Beaumont's death to his cousin and heir, eventually entering the National Portrait Gallery in 1984.[19] Beaumont and Mulgrave were portrayed together in 1820, with Mulgrave's two sons, by John Jackson, whom Lord Mulgrave first 'took up' (see p. 388), and whom both he and Beaumont supported.[20] For other portraits of Beaumont, see Walker 1985, pp. 30–1.

Fig. 1 Sir Joshua Reynolds, *Sir George Beaumont*, 1787. Oil on canvas, 76 × 63 cm. Pittsburgh, The Collection at Clayton.

George Howland Beaumont, only surviving son of Sir George Beaumont, 6th Bt, and his wife Rachel Howland, succeeded his father as 7th Bt at the age of eight. He also succeeded to considerable (but not vast) wealth, chiefly derived from coal mines and properties in Leicestershire, centring on Coleorton Hall. Beaumont was educated at Eton and Oxford (New College). He was at Eton while Alexander Cozens (1717–86) was drawing master; when Cozens demonstrated his various 'systems' and 'circumstances' of landscape, Beaumont is said to have been 'the only disciple who could make anything of the matter'.[21] Beaumont's drawings show an initial debt to Cozens, some debt to John Baptist Malchair (1729–1812), whose drawing school in Oxford he attended, and various debts to Richard Wilson, Joseph Farington, Thomas Girtin and Thomas Hearne;[22] his own work quickly reached and remained at a certain level of accomplishment, but hardly took on individual character.[23] Between 1779 and 1825 he exhibited 36 works (mostly drawings, but with a few oils) at the Royal Academy, as an Honorary Exhibitor, the customary designation for an amateur.

Beaumont married Margaret Willes in 1778. She too sat to Reynolds in about 1780, for a rather sketchy portrait.[24] She is said to have been 'a good creature – sensible, though oddish'. She evidently had money of her own, and was able to make her husband a present of Rubens's *Autumn Landscape with a View of Het Steen* when the dealer William Buchanan offered it for 1500 guineas in 1803. In 1790 Beaumont was elected MP for Bere Alston, a rotten borough near Plymouth; a supporter of Pitt, he held the seat for six years.

Beaumont's involvement with artists and art institutions chiefly concerns us here (for his friendships with Wordsworth, Coleridge and Southey, see Owen and Brown 1988, particularly chapters VIII and IX). From 1802 Beaumont was a member of the so-called Committee of Taste chaired by Charles Long to commission monuments for the nation (see p. 379). He enjoyed the friendship of Benjamin West PRA. But the most active part he played in public affairs was as a principal founder of the British Institution in 1805, and one of its most active governors thereafter. Beaumont evidently felt empowered by this role to draw attention to what he perceived as the shortcomings of contemporary artists. His outspoken opinions provoked the antagonism of many of them. Robert Smirke, whose bitterly satirical *Catalogues Raisonnés of the British Institution*, 1815–16, are quoted elsewhere in this catalogue (p. 382), gave the following pen-portrait of Beaumont as 'FIGGITY. – A man of some taste, and a tolerable Painter; but uncertain, capricious, and cowardly as a Hyena... This year he will admire a Yellow Picture, next year a brown one;[25] however, it is but just to acknowledge, that for 24 summer moons, he has been constant in his dislike to green leaves and blue skies...'[26]

Beaumont regularly called on Joseph Farington RA, whose *Diaries* record (occasionally with just perceptible weariness) Beaumont's diatribes. Beaumont's splenetic comments on the 'vicious practices of Turner and his followers'[27] prompted the mild Farington to fear that he would 'do Turner harm', but that was unlikely. Ruskin, writing in 1851, classed Beaumont among 'the feeble conventionalists of the period'.[28] Beaumont's enthusiasms were notoriously fitful. When he 'took up' Wilkie, Northcote commented 'So then ... He is to have a ride in the Flying Coach this year'.[29] For further repartee, see Whiting 1973.[30]

To John Constable, whom he first met in 1795 in Suffolk (Beaumont's mother lived at Dedham), Beaumont was kind and encouraging, though not to the point of buying any of his work. Constable spent over a month at Coleorton in 1823, with some quasi-tutorial duties (every morning 'we ... go to the painting room, and Sir George manfully like a real artist sets to work on anything he may fix on – and me by his side'[31]). 'Sir George is never angry, or pettish, or peevish':[32] it is an odd observation to make, unless such restraint is unexpected. Beaumont could be amiable and was frequently generous to those in need.[33] Above all, he had Claudes even in the breakfast-room. Although devoted to his family, Constable could hardly bring himself to leave a house so full of 'real Claudes, and Wilsons & Poussins &c.'[34]

Beaumont built up a relatively small but well-chosen collection of paintings, chiefly by Italian, French and Dutch masters. The formation of his collection is discussed and each of the sixteen paintings in his gift (including Richard Wilson's *Death of Niobe*, destroyed in the Second World War, 1944) is illustrated in Owen and Brown's catalogue of the 1988 National Gallery exhibition *Noble and Patriotic: The Beaumont Gift*.

The Beaumonts were childless. Approaching the age of sixty, Beaumont became increasingly concerned about the safety and care of his collection after his death. As Reynolds had done, he advocated a 'national gallery' for pictures; he told Farington as early as 1812 that if such an institution were to exist, he would be happy to leave his collection to it.[35] In the absence of a National Gallery, the British Museum served as the nation's 'general repository'. Long, himself a Trustee of the British Museum, advised Beaumont to leave his collection to the Trustees of the British Museum, on condition that a 'suitable home' should be created for his pictures and that he himself should also become a Museum Trustee. Accordingly, in 1822, by then nearly seventy, Beaumont added a codicil to his will bequeathing his collection to the British Museum.[36] But he continued to advocate the creation of a separate National Gallery. In 1823, the question of whether the government should or should not buy the late John Julius Angerstein's magnificent collection was discussed: if they bought it, it would form the nucleus of a national gallery, but sooner or later they would have to build a gallery for it. When the government hesitated, Beaumont issued what was in effect a masterly challenge, in a letter of eight lines, dated 17 July 1823 and addressed to the Trustees of the British Museum.[37] In it he expressed his readiness to give sixteen listed paintings to the nation 'whenever the Gallery about to be erected is ready to receive them'. Thus he converted his promised bequest into an offer to give his paintings to the nation in his lifetime. His challenge to the government was famously paraphrased as '*Buy* Angerstein's collection and I will give you mine.'[38] His offer effectively nudged the government into action; they bought Angerstein's pictures,[39] but deferred the creation of a special building by buying the rest of the lease of Angerstein's house in Pall Mall, which opened to the public as the 'National Gallery' on 10 May 1824.

The safety of his pictures mattered more to Beaumont than the point he had earlier insisted on, the creation of a special building for a national gallery. Confident that a 'safe asylum' had been provided in Pall Mall, Beaumont sent for his ever-reliable 'Mr Segar' (William Seguier, restorer and first Keeper of the National Gallery: see pp. 388–98) to escort the sixteen pictures in his gift to Pall Mall; by April 1826, they hung there with Angerstein's. Beaumont's gift included Rubens's *Autumn Landscape with a View of Het Steen* (NG 66), three landscapes by Claude, including *Hagar and the Angel* (NG 61), Canaletto's *The Stonemason's Yard* (NG 127) and *The Return of the Ark* by Sébastien Bourdon (NG 64), which Reynolds had bequeathed to Beaumont.[40] He sought (and received) permission to 'borrow back' for his lifetime his favourite picture, the Claude *Hagar and the Angel*. In the last year of his life, Beaumont rejoiced that his pictures were 'under the guardianship of a body that never dies'.[41] He died on 7 February 1827.

NOTES

1. *Diary*, 2 January 1795, vol. II, p. 286.

2. *Diary*, 27 April 1806, vol. VII, p. 2737.

3. The fact that the picture was in a small stock exhibition at Colnaghi's in May 1902 (14, catalogue untitled) suggests that he had hoped but failed to sell it through Colnaghi's the previous year.

4. Coll. Helen Clay Frick Foundation, with Reynolds's portrait of Lady Beaumont *c.*1780.

5. Beaumont sat to Lawrence in 1793, for a portrait exh. RA 1793 (15), and again in April 1808 and May 1810, for the same portrait, which was 'left in an unfinished state'. Garlick 1989 (p. 147) believes that the portrait exh. 1793 is untraced, and that the portrait now in the Louvre is the unfinished, later one. Owen and Brown 1988 (p. 93) consider that the portrait in the Louvre 'could be either the 1793 picture or its successor'.

6. This portrait is still at Mulgrave Castle; Walker 1985, p. 351, with the mezzotint by Charles Turner repr. plate 843.

7. Farington, *Diary*, vol. V, p. 2000: 27 March 1803: 'Sir George has sat twice to Hoppner'. Clarke and Penny 1982 (p. 178) state that Beaumont is recorded as sitting to Hoppner in 1806; but this is based on a misreading of Farington, *Diary*, vol. VII, p. 2774: 31 May 1806 [sic]: 'Sir George Beaumont & Mr Bowles and His Son called... – They said they were both sitting to Hoppner.'

8. Farington, *Diary*, 13 April 1806, vol. VII, p. 2718.

9. Farington, *Diary*, 3 May 1803, vol. VI, p. 2023.

10. Farington, *Diary*, 26 April 1806, vol. VII, p. 2735.

11. Farington, *Diary*, 31 May 1806, vol. VII, p. 2774.

12. Walker 1985, pp. 226–77 (there dated *c.*1800), colour plate XIII, fig. 518.

13. Christie's 31 May 1823 (1 of 4 in lot 27: 'Sir G. Beaumont, Mr Percy Windham, Mr Bradyll and Dr Langford'); lot 27 was one of 30 lots, each including four or more works, in a group headed 'Portraits and Sketches'. Possibly the work sold in 1823 was the portrait of Beaumont in Sir David Wilkie's sale, Christie's 30 April 1842 (674). Both Davies 1965, p. 44, and Walker 1985, p. 31, state that Hoppner executed 'several replicas' of Beaumont's portrait; this compiler has been able to trace only the work (? or two works) mentioned above.

14. Farington, *Diary*, 17 June 1808, vol. IX, p. 3298.

15. Farington, *Diary*, 7 May 1810, vol. X, pp. 3648–9. When Beaumont asked Farington whether he thought any payment was due to Lawrence, Farington, whose patience with Beaumont occasionally wore thin, firmly declared that 'Half price' ought to be paid in recompense. Only one portrait by Lawrence of Beaumont is now known, in the collection of the Louvre (Garlick 1989, cat. no. 79, repr.; Owen and Brown 1988, plate 42, with a detail as frontispiece). Garlick believes this to be the unfinished portrait of 1808–10.

16. Coll. Her Majesty The Queen; Millar 1969, p. 55, no. 851 (replica NMM, GH42). For Hoppner's *Earl of Essex*, painted in 1806, see Walker 1985, p. 177. [2nd] *Earl Spencer*, painted 1808, is at Althorp (Garlick 1976, no. 285).

17. Farington, *Diary*, 7 May 1810, vol. X, p. 3648. Farington mentions that Beaumont has presented the Hoppner to Mulgrave. See also under Engraved: Agar's engraving, published 16 January 1812, states that the original picture is in the possession of Lord Mulgrave.

18. J.P. Neale, *Views of the Seats of Noblemen and Gentlemen...*, I, 1818 [p. 72: pagination erratic]: at Coleorton, Leicestershire: 'a well painted portrait by Beechey, of the Earl of Mulgrave'.

19. Sold Christie's 17 February 1984 (119, 'Portrait of a gentleman'), bt Leggatt for NPG. See *NPG Report 1984–5*, p. 15 (accession no. 5716).

20. Repr. Margaret Greaves, *Regency Patron: Sir George Beaumont*, London 1966, facing p. 23. W.J. Ward's engraving of it is repr. Walker 1985, plate 1598, and by Owen and Brown 1988, p. 193.

21. Henry Angelo, *The Reminiscences of Henry Angelo*, 1828, vol. I, p. 215. For Beaumont's Eton sketchbook, his early copies after Cozens and drawings by him which show a debt to Cozens, see Kim Sloan, *Alexander and John Robert Cozens*, New Haven and London 1986, pp. 44–50, 60, 150–5, 160–2.

22. See Ian Fleming-Williams, 'Two Patrons and an Historian', in Martin Hardie, *Water-Colour Painting in Britain*, vol. III, London 1968, Appendix III, pp. 268–77, figs. 282, 283.

23. Examples of his work repr. in Owen and Brown 1988 (no list of ills.), plates 3, 4, 14–21, 36–7, 44, 49, 53, 56, 59, 63–4, 85–8. Recent exhibitions: *Watercolours and Drawings by Sir George Beaumont*, Bradford City Art Gallery (and tour), 1969; *Sir George Beaumont*, Manning Galleries, London (and tour), 1969. Allan Cunningham devoted a chapter to Beaumont in his *Lives of Eminent British Painters*, VI, 1833, pp. 134–54.

24. Owen and Brown 1988, p. 38, plate 13; sold Sotheby's 8 November 1995 (49, repr.); present location untraced.

25. This is a reference to one of Beaumont's best-known pronunciamentos.

26. [Robert Smirke RA], *Catalogue Raisonné of the British Institution*, London 1816, Part II, p. v. The last sentence refers obliquely to a popular story related by C.R. Leslie, *Memoirs of the Life of John Constable*, 1845, ed. Jonathan Mayne, London 1951, p. 114: 'Sir George recommended the colour of an old Cremorna fiddle for the prevailing tone of everything, and this Constable answered by laying an old fiddle on the green lawn before the house.'

27. Farington, *Diary*, 3 June 1806, vol. VII, p. 2777. Beaumont classed Augustus Wall Callcott among 'Turner's followers', and condemned his work.

28. *Pre-Raphaelitism*, 1851 (*Works*, vol. XII, p. 372).

29. Farington, *Diary*, 21 April 1806, vol. VII, p. 2729.

30. Frederick A. Whiting, 'Art and Acrimony', *Apollo*, XCVIII, 1973, pp. 43–6. For a full discussion of Beaumont's attitude to contemporary art, see Owen and Brown 1988, particularly chap. X: 'Patronage'.

31. Constable to his wife, from Coleorton, 27 October 1823; *JCC*, vol. II, p. 291.

32. Constable to his wife, from Coleorton, 9 November 1823, *JCC*, vol. II, p. 297.

33. Fleming-Williams 1968 (cited in note 20) lists many whom he helped.

34. Constable to his wife, 21 October 1823; *JCC*, vol. II, p. 290.

35. Farington, *Diary*, 16 October 1812, vol. XII, p. 4218.

36. Owen and Brown 1988, p. 210.

37. Beaumont's letter is P 39710 in British Museum, Papers and Letters, vol. V.

38. Quoted in Owen and Brown exh. cat. 1988, p. 16 n. 5, from *The Builder*, 4 May 1867, pp. 307–8.

39. This account of complex negotiations is much condensed. For fuller accounts, see Martin 1974, pp. 280–7; Owen and Brown 1988, particularly pp. 210–16, and Owen and Brown exh. cat. 1988.

40. From Beaumont's 'List of pictures to be placed in the British Museum', MS Pierpont Morgan Library (photocopy NG Archives). Owen and Brown 1988, p. 215, note two changes in Beaumont's original list.

41. Owen and Brown 1988, p. 213.

Sir Francis Chantrey RA

1781–1841

Born in 1781 in the village of Norton near Sheffield, son of a small tenant farmer and carpenter. Apprenticed in 1797 to a woodcarver in Sheffield but left him in 1802; worked as a portraitist, and moved to London. Was later reported as saying 'that he had never worked for any other sculptor and had never had an hour's instruction from any sculptor in his life'. Received some commissions from 1805, and in 1808 exhibited a *Head of Satan* at the Royal Academy. Marriage to a cousin with a large dowry enabled him in about 1810 to establish a studio in London. Made his name with the plaster model of a bust of the radical politician Horne Tooke, exh. RA 1811, and in the same year won the competition to execute a statue of George III for the City of London, his first large-scale sculpture in marble. Commissions for busts, statues and monuments abundant thereafter. His best-known works include *Scott*, *Wordsworth* and *James Watt*. In Paris 1814; in Rome 1819, where he visited the studios of Thorwaldsen and Canova. Exh. RA 1804–41; ARA 1815; elected RA 1818. Knighted 1832.

After visiting Chantrey's studio in 1821, the poet Tom Moore commented 'never saw such a set of thinking heads'. Chantrey's work is lively and penetrating, but retains an air of informality and of independence from classicism. For an assessment of his style and aesthetic, see Potts 1980 (cited below), pp. 10–11. Friend and admirer of J.M.W. Turner. Left his fortune of £150,000, after his wife's death, to the RA to found the Chantrey Bequest. Died 25 November 1841. A *Self Portrait* of about 1810 is coll. Tate Gallery (N 01591, oil on canvas); a portrait by Thomas Phillips, 1818, is coll. NPG (86).

References

Rupert Gunnis, *Dictionary of British Sculptors 1660–1851*, London [1951], pp. 91–6, including list of works; Alex Potts, *Sir Francis Chantrey*, exh. cat., NPG, London, and Mappin Art Gallery, Sheffield 1981; Alison Yarrington, Ilene D. Lieberman, Alex Potts and Malcolm Baker, 'An Edition of the Ledger of Sir Francis Chantrey, R.A., at the Royal Academy, 1809–1841', *Walpole Society 1991–92*, LVI, 1994.

NG 2786

Charles Long, 1st Baron Farnborough

replica, 1834, of the bust sculpted in 1820
Marble, approximately 76.5 cm (30 1/8 in.) from top of head to bottom of socle, and 37 cm (14 1/2 in.) across top of chest.
Incised with chisel *LORD FARNBOROUGH – / F. CHANTREY SC 1836* on the back.

Provenance

Commissioned by anon. in 1833, but not paid for until 1842, when Colonel Samuel Long, one of the sitter's nephews and heirs, paid Chantrey's executors for it; passed to his cousin, the sitter's great-nephew Admiral Samuel Long RN (d.1893), by whose widow it was presented to the National Gallery 1911.

Literature

Davies 1946, p. 21; Davies 1959, p. 8; R. Lane Poole, *Catalogue of Portraits in ... Oxford*, 1912, vol. I, p. 211, no. 5611; Walker 1985, p. 180 (the original marble bust, NPG 421, repr. plate 420, with two preliminary drawings, NPG 316-a, repr. plate 420); Nicholas Penny, *Catalogue of European Sculpture in the Ashmolean Museum*, Oxford 1992, vol. III, Appendix I, 'Plaster Casts from the studio of Sir Francis Chantrey', Part II: 'Bust Portraits', no. 707 (the plaster cast, repr. p. 233); I. Lieberman, A. Potts, A. Yarrington, 'The Ledger [of Sir Francis Chantrey, RA, 1809–41] and Commentaries', *Walpole Society 1991–92*, LVI, 1994, pp. 118–19, no. 258a; Katharine Eustace, *Canova Ideal Heads*, exh. cat. Ashmolean Museum, Oxford 1997, pp. 91–4.

Technical Notes

Condition good; slight damage at extremity of each shoulder.

Dated 1836, this is a replica of the marble bust commissioned in 1819 by the sitter's father-in-law Sir Abraham Hume, who paid Chantrey £126 for it on 6 January;[1] that bust, dated 1820 and exhibited that year at the Royal Academy (1046), is now in the National Portrait Gallery (NPG 2090), with two preliminary studies for it (fig. 1) made, according to Chantrey's custom, with the aid of a *camera lucida*.[2] The next stage was the making of a plaster model; this is in the collection of Chantrey's models presented by his widow to the Ashmolean Museum, and is reproduced by Penny 1992.

From the existing plaster model, this replica was ordered thirteen years later: but who ordered it, and why, remains a mystery. Charles Long had by then been given a peerage, as Lord Farnborough. Under 'Lord Farnborough's Bust (2^{d})',

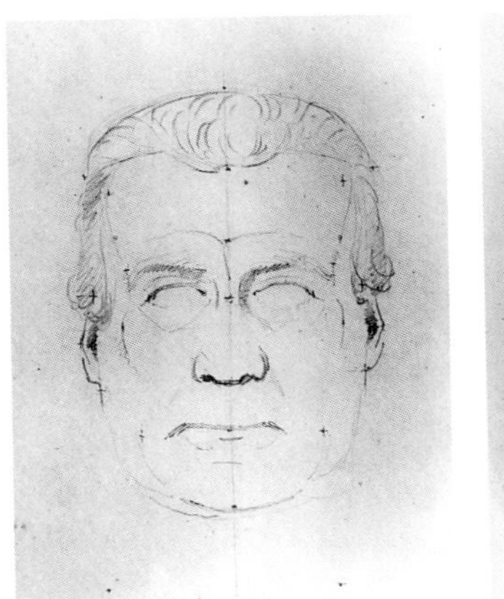

Fig. 1 *Preliminary studies by Chantrey for his bust of Sir Charles Long*, 1819. Pencil on paper, inscribed with sitter's name; facing, with vertical central guide line and guide marks, 42.9 × 27.1 cm; profile, 42.8 × 29.9 cm. London, National Portrait Gallery.

Chantrey recorded the order in 1833 for 'a duplicate bust' and its execution in June 1834, for a price of £105; but he left the name of whoever ordered it blank.[3] It was not paid for until 1842, by which time both Chantrey and Farnborough were dead; then Colonel Long, one of Farnborough's nephews and heirs, paid Chantrey's executors for it. When the original bust was sculpted, Lord Farnborough was 60. When the replica was ordered in 1833, he was 73, and had virtually retired from public life. Possibly a committee from one of the many institutions he had served had conceived but failed to carry out a notion of placing his bust in its corridors. It is barely conceivable that the sitter himself, a punctilious man and a former pillar of the Treasury, would have ordered a replica five years before his death and then defaulted on payment.

The best-known image of Charles Long – as he will chiefly be referred to here, regardless of his elevation to the peerage as Lord Farnborough at the age of 66 – is of the fairly colourless but evidently capable Treasury official portrayed in Hoppner's three-quarter-length of about 1806 (fig. 2).[4] Within the Treasury, he reached the post of Paymaster-General; outside it, he became involved in many of the art institutions of his day. A Trustee of the British Museum, the National Gallery and (*in absentia*) the Hunterian Museum,[5] a founding Governor of the British Institution (and its Vice-President from 1820), a Governor of Greenwich Hospital and – not least – friend and unofficial adviser on matters of art to the Prince of Wales (later George IV), Long seemed by the mid-1820s to have assumed the role of 'arbiter of England'[6] where the arts were concerned. Yet to many he seemed imperfectly qualified for that role. Conscientious, hard-working and determinedly interested in art, he was essentially a man of conventional taste; some considered him a cold fish. Benjamin Robert Haydon, who failed to get Long's support for government sponsorship for history paintings, believed that Long 'has the art, as it were, of icing every thing'.[7]

Born in Surrey in 1760, the fourth son of Beeston Long, a West Indies merchant,[8] Long was educated at Greenwich School, then went up in 1779 to Cambridge.[9] At about this time he formed enduring friendships with two utterly different men. One was the brilliant William Pitt, who was to become Prime Minister before he was 25. The other was the unworldly artist, writer and radical George Cumberland (1754–1848),[10] who achieved little attention in his lifetime, is unnoticed even in the recent *Missing Persons* addition (1993) to the *Dictionary of National Biography*, but is well-known for his forty years' friendship with William Blake. These two friendships reflect two different strands in Long's life. His friendship with Pitt determined his public career; but it was to Cumberland, with whom he corresponded over forty years, that Long declared (in 1821) that he was indebted 'in early life' for that love of art which has been 'my great delight through Life'.[11] Long married an artist – the watercolourist Amelia Hume, who had been Girtin's favourite pupil and whose work Farington considered 'far superior to any that I have seen made by an Amateur artist'.[12] Long formed a collection of pictures, modest in size compared with those of his father-in-law Sir Abraham Hume[13] or the Duke of Bridgewater (Hume's brother-in-law), and orthodox in taste. From this he bequeathed fifteen pictures to the National Gallery.

Long's political career is recounted by R.K. Thorne in *The House of Commons 1790–1820*;[14] it is merely outlined here. He entered Parliament in 1789; he was to sit in the House of Commons until 1826,[15] when he was given a peerage by royal favour. During Pitt's lifetime, Long supported him steadfastly but unobtrusively. Pitt's niece recalled that 'Mr Long used to slide in and slide out, and slide here and slide there – nobody knew where he went or when he came – so quiet'.[16] The offices he held were all in the Treasury, which he entered as junior Secretary 1791, and in which he rose to be Paymaster-General to the Army, 1817. In Karl Anton Hickel's vast group portrait *The House of Commons 1793–4*,[17] Long sits on the front bench behind Pitt, but few of the 'phyzzes' are more than rudimentary likenesses.[18] A more reliable portrait of Long was to be included in Sir George Hayter's *The Trial of Queen Caroline*, 1820–3.[19] Long declined Spencer Perceval's offers of high office (as Chancellor of the Exchequer and as Secretary at War), declaring that he 'never felt either disposed or fit for a cabinet office, and it would be to degrade the office to take it on any other terms'.[20] Long was no orator, and spoke in the House as little as possible. It was not he but Henry Bankes MP,[21] a British Museum Trustee, who was the chief spokesman for the arts in the House of Commons.

In an age of venal politicians, Charles Long appears to have attracted no accusations except those of behaving loftily yet lacking *panache*. Not even Gillray, who frequently lampooned the Treasury, could find much matter for satire in Long, beyond giving him the attributes of an ink-bottle and a *long* quill.[22] Curiously enough, Hoppner resorts to the same attributes in his portrait of Long (fig. 2), a late work probably painted at about the same time as his equally leaden portrait of Pitt, and exhibited at the Royal Academy in 1807.[23] Pitt died in 1806.[24] Long's legendary suavity was put to the test in May 1807, when Lawrence showed him his posthumous portrait of Pitt, and at once sensed that 'Long did not approve the likeness'; but Long said little except that 'the Coat was the best black' he had ever seen painted.[25] Lawrence later repainted it crimson.

Long's involvement in spending public money on the arts began in 1796, when as a Treasury official he became concerned by the fact that there was little or no financial control over commissioning monuments at public expense to commemorate naval and military heroes (and some civilians) in St Paul's Cathedral or Westminster Abbey. This business had been left to the Royal Academy, with escalating costs (and charges of favouritism). After Long had raised the subject in the House of Commons, a Committee for National Monuments was appointed by the Treasury in 1802, under Long's chairmanship.[26] Popularly known as the 'Committee of Taste', its members included (at various times) Henry Bankes MP, Charles Towneley, William Locke, junior, Sir George Beaumont (see pp. 370–5), Richard Payne Knight and Benjamin West (from 1817, as PRA).[27] An entry in Farington's *Diary* during 1802 gives an idea of how the Committee worked: 'Flaxman was the first called in. They gave him Lord Howe's monument, 6,000 guineas ... Banks was the next called. He is to have the Monument to Cptn. Westcott – 4,000 guineas... Westmacott was the third called in. They gave him Genl. Abercrombies 6,000 guineas...'[28] Each sculptor on accepting a commission had to sign a formal contract with Long, acting on behalf of the Treasury; payment was in three instalments, as work progressed.[29] Committee meetings were sometimes argumentative; Beaumont was often capricious in judgement, and Knight notoriously perverse in argument. In the chair, Long behaved with perfect detachment: 'Mr Long seemed to sit, as Chairman, only to see how the ayes & noes counted.'[30] In fact he was developing a taste for neoclassical sculpture; he particularly admired the work of Richard Westmacott the younger, of whom it was to be said that 'if he never reached the highest point of grandeur and beauty, he was always chaste, dignified and impressive'.[31] Westmacott secured eight of the 36 commissions from the Committee of Taste, including that for the Waterloo Memorial in Hyde Park, which also came within its remit, and for which Westmacott sculpted the statue of *Achilles*.[32] Westmacott became a friend of Long (and of Canova, as more fully noted below); Long's own collection was to include Westmacott's *Flora*.[33] But of the monuments erected under the control of his Committee of Taste, Whiting 1965 remarks not unfairly that 'few, in fact, rise above banality'.[34] Haydon wrote in 1812 of 'Masses of marble scarcely shaped into intelligible boots, spurs, epaulets, sashes, hats, & belts huddled on to cover ignorance and to hide defects... Year after year and day after day monuments & money are voted in ceaseless round without discrimination, without thought.'[35]

Fig. 2 John Hoppner, *Charles Long, later Lord Farnborough*, exhibited 1807. Oil on canvas, 127 × 101 cm. London, Tate Gallery.

Haydon passionately hoped for similar public expenditure on large history paintings to decorate public places. A long tirade in his *Diary* during December 1812 rehearses what he might say to the politicians if he got the chance: 'You lavish thousands upon thousands on sculpture without effect. You refuse all assistance, all public support, to painting. You load your churches, your halls, and your public buildings with masses of unwieldy stone, and allow not one side or one inch of your room for pictures, Is this fair? is it just? is it liberal?'[36] Determined to put the case for history paintings in public places, he drew up a petition to the House of Commons, and in February 1826 obtained an interview with Long in the hope of persuading him to present it. By then Haydon had known Long for some years, and knew that while he was remarkably efficacious in causes of which he approved (Long perhaps helped to secure the Prince of Wales's permission for two of the Raphael Cartoons to be exhibited at the British Institution in 1818/19, where Haydon and his enrapt students studied them), he was resistant to new ideas which would cost money to implement. Haydon records that although Long 'behaved very candidly' and was willing to present the petition if Haydon insisted, he seemed to have 'a rooted aversion' to Haydon's proposals, saying that from his experience any money voted by the House of Commons for art would be subject to strict supervision.[37] Finally he 'put on his glasses & looked over some papers'. Haydon is not always a reliable reporter, and was too passionate (and too self-interested) to be a good advocate; and Long was not a man of vision. He knew that while heroic monuments were considered to be easily comprehensible (they were, after all, a form of portraiture) and good for public morality, history paintings were an elevated art form considered proper to academies rather than to public places. Haydon bowed, took his leave, and later – deciding that Long 'cares not for Historical Painting ... his ambition is to be thought a man of Taste' – persuaded Lord Brougham instead to present his petition to the House of Commons where, predictably, it met with little response. Long

Fig. 3 Antonio Canova (1757–1822), *Ideal Head*, 1816. Presented by the sculptor to Sir Charles Long. Marble, height 56.3 cm. Fort Worth, Texas, Kimbell Art Museum.

had told Haydon that 'there was nothing less known than Art'[38] in the House of Commons. Pride in his own comparative singularity among politicians appears to have given Long a certain lofty manner in connoisseurship. But Haydon thought he was 'a Pretender in Art'.[39] Having observed Long uncertainly contemplating a statue of *Milo* at the sculptor John Graham Lough's private view in 1827, he later wrote: 'Never shall I forget Lord Farnborough's tone as, leaning his hand on the grand leg, he faintly ejaculated "It is *unquestionably* a *great* work".'[40]

Long was appointed a Trustee of the British Museum in 1812, serving until his death. As a Treasury official, he had played an effective part in helping to bring the protracted negotiations for the purchase of the Elgin Marbles to a conclusion; it was on the basis of the valuation he secured in 1811 that negotiations began slowly to proceed, gathering momentum at last during February 1816, when a Select Committee of the House of Commons called various artists – among them Benjamin West PRA, Lawrence, Flaxman, Chantrey, Westmacott and Haydon – to testify to the artistic merits of 'the Earl of Elgin's Collection of Sculptured Marbles'.[41] Canova, in London in the previous November, had already given his opinion that the marbles were 'memorable and stupendous'.[42] Agreement was finally reached. In the Commons debate of 7 June 1816 which secured a vote of £35,000 for their purchase, Long spoke only briefly and towards the end of the debate, conceding 'the unfitness of the time for any acts of lavish expenditure' (Cruikshank three days later was to publish a satire entitled *The Elgin Marbles! or John Bull buying Stones at the time his numerous Family want Bread!!*) but stressing that 'the present was an occasion, which could not again present itself, of acquiring for the country these exquisite specimens of art'.[43]

Long entertained Canova during his visit to England in November 1815. Farington reports that Canova 'visited Mr. Long at Bromley Hill, who took Him a ride & shewed Him London from the heights abt. *Sydenham*. Canova was in raptures at the prospect.' But Farington, always a sound trade-unionist where his fellow-artists were concerned, seems relieved to note that 'It is not intended to consult or employ him upon any of the proposed British Government Monuments'.[44] After his return to Rome, Canova despatched four 'ideal' heads ('buste ideali') to the four Englishmen whom he felt had contributed most to the success of his visit to England. These four were the Duke of Wellington, Lord Castlereagh, William Richard Hamilton and Charles Long. The busts, each inscribed by the sculptor for the recipient, arrived during 1818. Long's 'Ideal Head'(seen in profile, fig. 3) is inscribed CAROLO. LONGIO/ V.C.L./ ANTONIUS.CANOVA/ LIBENS.F. ('To Charles Long, an illustrious man, Antonio Canova freely made this bust').[45]

During 1823–4 Long played a crucial part in events which led to the foundation of the National Gallery, with pictures purchased from the late John Julius Angerstein's collection as its nucleus;[46] but the result may not have been quite what he most hoped for. In his capacity as a Treasury official, Long negotiated the purchase with Angerstein's executors, and assisted the Prime Minister Lord Liverpool in getting votes for funds and for the National Gallery establishment through Parliament. Meanwhile, in his capacity as a Trustee of the British Museum, he gave tactical advice to his old friend Sir George Beaumont, who approached Long in November 1822 because he intended to bequeath many of his paintings to the British Museum, but was concerned that there was nowhere in the Museum suitable for their display. Long, by then in the confidence of George IV, would have known that the King was about to present his father's magnificent library to the British Museum, a gift formally recorded in a Treasury minute of 16 January 1823;[47] and he also knew that having accepted the King's Library, the Museum would have to have a new building to accommodate it. A Select Committee suggested that the new building should include 'a fit receptacle' for any pictures that might be donated (presumably with Beaumont's promised bequest in mind). At Long's suggestion, Beaumont insisted on becoming a Trustee of the British Museum, so that he could help to urge the building of a gallery in the Museum suitable for pictures. Beaumont was made a Trustee in May 1823; and both he and Long were appointed to a sub-committee 'to consider a proper building for the Reception of the Royal Library and a Picture Gallery over it',[48] to be designed by Robert Smirke. Long and Beaumont both served on a sub-committee to supervise the Department of Paintings, Prints & Drawings. But the British Museum's plans for a gallery for paintings were overtaken by the offer to the nation of the Angerstein collection. When the government hesitated over its purchase, Beaumont issued his famous challenge, '*Buy* Angerstein's pictures and I will *give* you mine!' The purchase of the Angerstein collection was announced in Parliament on 23 February 1824, followed in March (or a few weeks later) by the establishment of the National Gallery. But both Beaumont and Long continued to be concerned that the National Gallery, temporarily accommodated in Angerstein's old house, had no permanent home of its own. When Beaumont finally gave his pictures in March 1826,[49] they went to hang with Angerstein's pictures in Pall Mall; but ownership was vested in the Trustees of the British Museum, who for some years kept a beady eye on the emergent National Gallery.

Probably Long would have preferred the British Museum to be the single repository of all the national collections, including paintings.[50] Of all the causes he served, the British Museum was the one to which he remained the most devoted. He had first acquired respect for the institution through Cumberland (a print scholar, among other things). In 1824 he welcomed the news of Payne Knight's bequest, 'said to be worth £60,000'.[51] In retirement from public office in the 1830s, Long told Cumberland that the British Museum had become 'a principal object of his care and attention... I have been a Trustee 20 years. When I began there were upon average 25 Readers a day – there are now 250.'[52] He added that he had presented the Museum with Bartolozzi's engravings after Guercino, and that 'we have nearly completed a collection of mezzotints after Reynolds – a little disgraceful we didn't have them before'.

When the National Gallery was established in 1824, Long was one of a committee of six British Museum Trustees appointed for its 'Superintendence'; the others were three Cabinet ministers (Lord Liverpool, Prime Minister; F.J. Robinson, Chancellor of the Exchequer, later Earl of Ripon; and the Earl of Aberdeen), the National Gallery's so far solitary benefactor Sir George Beaumont and Sir Thomas Lawrence PRA. Not until their meeting of 7 February 1828 were they designated as Trustees of the National Gallery; from that date, the National Gallery's life as a body independent of the British Museum effectively began. None of the Cabinet ministers regularly attended Trustees' meetings. Long attended almost all of them (until a year before his death), and took the chair. While Long declared in the House of Commons that 'none but first-rate works should have a place in the national collection',[53] it does not appear that the Trustees followed anything but an *ad hoc* policy for the acquisition of pictures. Purchases were recommended to the Treasury as and when opportunities presented themselves. Only one picture had been purchased (Correggio's *Madonna of the Basket*, NG 23, in 1825) when, in March 1826, the Chancellor of the Exchequer asked the House of Commons for a grant of £9000 for the simultaneous purchase of three paintings for the National Gallery: *Bacchus and Ariadne*, by Titian (NG 35), *Bacchanalian Revel before a Term of Pan*, by Poussin (NG 62) and *Christ appearing to Saint Peter on the Appian Way (Domine, Quo Vadis?)*, by Annibale Carracci (NG 9). The sum was voted without debate;[54] but the subject was taken up by 'Alfred' in a letter to *The Times* of 23 March 1826.[55] 'Alfred' did not question the merits of the three pictures; instead he attacked the men – and particularly Long – who decided on purchases for the National Gallery. 'Sir Charles Long ... is himself the chief director, aided by Sequier [sic] the picture-cleaner... Lord Aberdeen, Sir George Beaumont and Sir Thomas Lawrence are mere ciphers. That Sir C. Long should assume to be arbiter of England is not surprising, given the flattering unction he receives... Lord Aberdeen ... is submissive to the superior cunning of Sir Charles Long. Sir George Beaumont talks too much to think upon the subject...'

This letter evidently stung Long into contriving an opportunity to discuss the National Gallery, its committee and its purchases in the House of Commons the following month.[56] In an unusually lengthy speech, Long averred that 'he knew of no other way in which purchases for the National Gallery could be so satisfactorily effected as by the recommendation of a committee of competent persons'; he was confident that the House would find 'every security they could desire' in the names of the committee, and he made a point of praising Sir George Beaumont, who 'at the very time he was advising this purchase ... was presenting his own collection [hear, hear!]'. It was hardly a debate; Long's speech was followed by three short ones (Mr Bankes, Mr Colborne and Mr Hume) approving both the procedure for purchase followed at the National Gallery and the selection of the paintings recently purchased.

Long had spoken in the House of unwelcome aspects of his own role at the National Gallery, continually receiving letters offering collections and sometimes single pictures for sale; he felt he could no longer undertake 'the very thankless office of passing judgment on pictures in the possession of private individuals'. In fact it was William Seguier who undertook almost all this 'thankless' work (see his evidence to the Select Committees of 1836 and 1841, pp. 392–5). A good working relationship between Long and Seguier had developed through the British Institution, of which Long was a founder-Governor in 1805 and Vice-President from 1820 until his death,[57] while Seguier was its Superintendent; it continued at the National Gallery. But although 'Alfred' in 1826 referred to Long and Seguier as 'the inseparables', they were unequal in every way. Long enjoyed a position of increasing eminence; but Seguier's knowledge of pictures was greater than Long's. Long told Cumberland that 'My friends frequently ask me if I know of any good pictures for Sale';[58] in these cases, he is likely often to have conferred with Seguier.

Long's friendship with the Prince of Wales, later George IV, added to his eminence. Previously, he was reputedly respected by George III, with whom he may have had some contact through the British Museum and the British Institution; but as noted in the *Carlton House* exhibition catalogue 1991,[59] 'George IV relied on friends to alert him to suitable works of art for purchase and, on occasion, to advise him on their display.' Long had joined this select group by May 1814, when he played some kind of intermediary role in the Prince Regent's purchase of 86 pictures (almost all by

Dutch seventeenth-century artists) from Sir Thomas Baring.[60] Long also helped to secure the return to the Royal Collection of Van Dyck's celebrated *Portrait of Charles I in Three Positions*;[61] despatched by the sitter to Bernini in Rome to assist in the making of a marble bust, it had remained in the Palazzo Bernini until 1802, when it was purchased by the dealer William Buchanan and brought back to England, passing through several hands[62] until it ended up with J.M.W. Turner's friend, the artist William Frederick Wells. Long enlisted Farington's help in offering Wells 500 guineas for it on the Prince's behalf;[63] it finally entered the Royal Collection in 1822 for 1000 guineas.

Crowned in 1820, George IV continued to use Long as a channel of communication with artists. It was through Long, in 1821, that he conveyed his command that Lawrence should go to Rome to paint the Pope (and through Long that Lawrence hoped he would be recompensed for time lost to portrait commissions at home, as well as for travel expenses).[64] More indirectly (and presumably because he was not personally acquainted with J.M.W. Turner), Long conveyed through Farington the King's dissatisfaction with the only work any member of the Royal family commissioned from Turner, the large *Battle of Trafalgar*, which did not enter the Royal Collection but was presented instead to Greenwich;[65] and it is likely to have been Long, a Governor of Greenwich Hospital (and responsible, with J.W. Croker, for hanging pictures in its Painted Hall), who suggested that solution. Long also gave advice when asked on the decoration and display of pictures in the various palaces. William Seguier's appointment as Conservator to the Royal Collection in 1820 is likely to have been made on Long's recommendation.

By January 1819, Farington reports that in matters respecting Art '"the Prince Regent saw through Mr. Long's spectacles"'.[66] The accolade came – literally – on 20 May 1820, when Long was created a Knight of the Order of the Bath. Farington relates (again at third hand) that His Majesty told Long that he was to create a certain number of Knights of the Bath, including 'two Civil Knights ... Sir Charles Bagot to be one of them; "the other, I have reserved for a friend – it is yourself".'[67] A peerage followed (8 July 1826), and the King's Memorandum of August 1827 refers to 'The King's most excellent & valued friend Ld Farnb^gh^'.[68] According to a *List of Portraits painted by Sir Thomas Lawrence by the King's Command...*,[69] Long was one of three friends for whom the Prince of Wales ordered replicas (? studio copies) of his portrait, at £315 each; since the Duke of Devonshire (on the same list) received a copy of the full-length 'official' portrait in Garter robes now in Dublin (and recalled going with William IV to a room in Kensington Palace which was full of replicas, copies and variants of this portrait),[70] that was probably what Long got too, but his copy is untraced.

George IV (both before and after his accession in 1820) had often publicly expressed the desire to promote British art; he was successively Vice-President, President and Patron of the British Institution, and lent regularly and generously to its winter exhibitions. Long's influence there as Vice-President from 1820 was not needed to encourage him in this, but may have contributed to the fact that the exhibitions of 1826 (164 pictures) and 1827 (185 pictures) were entirely composed of paintings from George IV's collection.[71] Long's connection with the British Institution will be discussed only briefly here. One of its founding-Governors in 1805, he was one of the most effective in its later management. His most innovative proposal – at a time when reverence for Reynolds still dominated attitudes towards British art – was for the first retrospective exhibition of works by Hogarth, Gainsborough and Wilson, which he organised in 1814.[72] In the satirical *Catalogue Raisonné* of the British Institution published anonymously by Robert Smirke in 1816, Long is thinly disguised as *Jang*, who 'has acquired the reputation of a profound Critic, and a man of exquisite taste; nobody knows how';[73] but he is less savagely attacked than most of the Governors. 'We entertain some opinion of ... his general good sense, and we do not in matters of taste degrade him to the level of the Marquis of Stafford; but we cannot certainly consent to see him enthroned, as Arbiter.' This was to be a recurring reservation about Long. His undoubted efficiency, combined with the disinclination of many other gentlemen to undertake any real work, largely accounted for the conspicuous and not undeserved parts he played in the history of the National Gallery, the British Institution and the Royal Collection. 'Mr. Long will effect it' – a phrase from Farington's *Diary* – was the key to his success.

The British Institution had originally been founded as an exhibition space for the work of living British artists; but while their work continued to be shown each summer, the introduction of winter exhibitions of old masters lent from its supporters' collections proved more satisfying to most of its Governors. But the 'living British artists' hoped for more material advantages than the chance to study old masters. The Directors had provided them with a market-place; the artists tended to think they should also push sales and procure patrons. Letters to Cumberland during 1813–14 recount Long's considerable efforts to help 'your friend Bird' (the Bristol artist Edward Bird 1772–1819); but it is not certain that Long would have made such efforts if George IV had not already bought a picture by Bird and shown him some favour.[74] Long confided to Cumberland (? in 1831) the difficulties of 'being supposed to possess much more power to assist artists than really belongs to me, and when I have felt myself quite unable to do what has been desired, it has often been imputed to want of inclination – not, as really was the case, to want of means, and I have not escaped a good deal of abuse in consequence, for I need not say that an unsuccessful artist is not the most placable man alive.'[75]

'What British artist has ever tasted the sweets of a shilling of Lord Farnborough's?', Haydon asked in 1827.[76] It seems that despite his long association with the British Institution, Long bought only one work by a contemporary British artist: James Burton's *Old Houses at Gravesend*, exhibited at the British Institution in 1825 (28), which passed to his nephew; but he also owned a *Landscape with figures* by Sir George Beaumont, perhaps the picture Beaumont gave him as a wedding-present.[77]

As Lord Farnborough (his title from 1826), Charles Long bequeathed fifteen paintings to the National Gallery, of which ten were Dutch or Flemish; other works in his collection passed to his three nephews.[78] Before going into Parliament, he had spent two years abroad (from late 1786 to mid-1788), partly in Rome, in the company of Cumberland, the gem engraver Nathaniel Marchant and the artist Charles Grignion, partly travelling in Italy, Germany, France and Switzerland,[79] qualifying himself (successfully) for election to the Society of Dilettanti in 1792.[80] At this stage his collecting activities were mainly directed towards the purchase of bronzes, vases and gems;[81] but he bought some paintings, and related to Cumberland after his return that 'Sr Joshua Reynolds fell in love with a little bit of Julio Romano which I gave a few sequins for at Bologna & which I have exchanged with him for a fancy of his own that I like extremely'.[82] Possibly what Long got in exchange was the spontaneous version of *The Age of Innocence* (1788) which passed to his nephew and is now in Plymouth.[83] He owned two other works by Reynolds, a replica of *The Infant Samuel* (NG 162, later transferred to the Tate Gallery),[84] and *Cupid and Psyche*, bought in Reynolds's sale in 1796 but later sold at Christie's, where Samuel Rogers bought it.[85]

Long particularly admired Gainsborough's landscapes. At the Schomberg House sale in 1789 he bought three chalk drawings, reporting to Cumberland the next day (from 'the Committee Room of the Westminster Election', and not without pride): 'I was fool enough yesterday to give thirty Guineas for three little Sketches in chalk...'[86] He bought the well-known upright (oil) *Coastal Scene* (with sailing-boats and cows on the bank)[87] at the Delmé sale in 1790 (eventually bequeathing it to a nephew); and in Mrs Gainsborough's third sale in 1797 he bought *The Watering Place*, writing to George Cumberland with an excitement he never allowed himself in the Treasury: 'I have enrichd my collection of pictures by the best Landskip of Gainsborough I ever saw.'[88] He was to present this to the National Gallery in 1827; it is now NG 109 (see p. 109). In the Orléans sale the following year, he bought one of his few Italian pictures, Pier Francesco Mola's small and tender *Rest on the Flight into Egypt* (now NG 160);[89] he also owned a less respectable *Leda and the Swan* by 'Mola' (now NG 151.1, 'style of Mola'),[90] damaged by a member of the public in 1844 (see p. 395). His Canaletto of *Venice: The Upper Reaches of the Grand Canal with S. Simeone Piccolo* (NG 163) may have been purchased in Venice, from the same dealer from whom he bought some Canaletto drawings.[91]

By June 1810 Long had acquired Rubens's *Sunset Landscape with a Shepherd and his Flock* (fig. 4, NG 157),[92] later reporting to Cumberland that 'West is in raptures with my Rubens'. At some point before 1819, he acquired a *Pastoral Landscape: Sunrise* by Claude which had formerly belonged to Reynolds; this too passed to his nephew rather than to the National Gallery, and is now in the Metropolitan Museum of Art.[93] His most applauded purchase was of Gaspard Dughet's wide *Landscape in the Roman Campagna* (now NG 161) from the Colonna Palace, which he bought for 650 guineas in William Young Ottley's sale in 1811. 'Mr. Christie on knocking down this picture, exclaimed "I give it as Alexander did

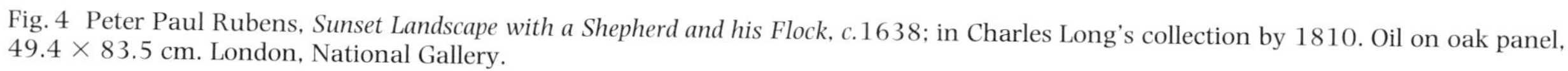

Fig. 4 Peter Paul Rubens, *Sunset Landscape with a Shepherd and his Flock*, *c.*1638; in Charles Long's collection by 1810. Oil on oak panel, 49.4 × 83.5 cm. London, National Gallery.

extensive collection of prints and smaller collection of paintings) must have come through forty years in the art trade.

The two men chiefly responsible for steering Seguier into official roles were Sir George Beaumont (see pp. 370–5) and Charles Long, Lord Farnborough (see pp. 376–87), each of whom had employed him in the care of their collections. Both were founding Governors of the British Institution, established in 1805 at 52 Pall Mall to encourage 'rising British artists' by holding exhibitions of their works for sale;[29] and they were largely responsible for appointing Seguier, then aged 33, and previously privately employed by both of them, as its Superintendent. The direction of the British Institution was in the hands of those noblemen and gentlemen who had founded it. Below them was a Keeper, a role successively allotted, in Seguier's day, to eminent engravers[30] – painters, to their chagrin, were excluded from the management – and below the Keeper was Seguier, the Superintendent (he is frequently described as the Keeper, but he was not).[31]

Seguier's duties as Superintendent chiefly consisted of organising and hanging the exhibitions (on scarlet-papered walls), and arranging copying days for students.[32] From 1815, the Directors decided to hold summer exhibitions of Old Masters, largely from their own collections; but the implication that British artists 'needed teaching' caused much resentment, and the first two exhibitions were savagely lampooned by Robert Smirke (anonymously) in his *Catalogues Raisonnés of the British Institution* for 1815 and 1816. It was chiefly Seguier (who knew most of the artists) who had to cope with their disgruntlement, often vociferous. Most of them hoped (and many needed) to sell their work; but as the exhibitions increased in size (over 300 works were shown in 1820, and over 500 in 1830), the complaints of those who believed their work was not hung to advantage increased, and jealousies developed. When two works by R.P. Bonington (d.1828) were included in an Old Masters exhibition of 1832, Constable accused Seguier of 'carrying on a Humbugg'.[33] Without aspiring to be judge and arbiter, Seguier found himself regarded as both. To the artists, the factotum began to seem a man of real power. After Seguier had made 'a friendly visit' to his studio in 1833, Constable ironically wrote of receiving a call from 'a much greater man than the King – the Duke of Bedford – Lord Westminster – Lord Egremont or the President of the Royal Academy –"MR SEGUIER"'.[34]

The second of Seguier's posts was allotted to him in 1820, when he stepped (in a sense) into the shoes of Benjamin West PRA. West had been Surveyor of the King's Pictures since 1791; he died in March 1820, shortly after the Prince Regent succeeded (at last) as King George IV. Charles Long, a close friend of the new King, was chiefly responsible for the appointment of Seguier in West's place.[35] Seguier had worked on some of the royal pictures from about 1818 (when he repaired Rubens's *Farm at Laeken*, the panels 'having Slightly opened where they are joined ... at the Top'[36]). Now he was appointed Surveyor, Cleaner and Repairer of the King's Pictures, though without the same status as Benjamin West. Money is again a pointer: West had received £1000 per annum,[37] whereas Seguier in 1841 stated that his annual salary as 'Keeper of His Majesty's pictures' was £142 16. 0.[38] He held this post until his death.

Seguier's duties were to survey the collections of pictures in the various royal palaces, to give advice when asked and to repair and clean pictures when this was agreed to be necessary. When he began, the number of pictures in the Royal Collection was unknown; he set to work, cataloguing the pictures at Carlton House, Kensington, Buckingham Palace, St James's, Kew and Hampton Court. Seguier's 'catalogues' were hardly more than lists of titles and attributions; but for the first time, they provided a reasonably complete inventory of the royal pictures, with the exception of those at Windsor.[39] In Kensington Palace Seguier reputedly found 'hoards of Pictures never noticed – of 650 he has taken account of, only 360 are in any catalogue'.[40] The lesser pictures were sent to Hampton Court, where Seguier did his best to rehang them, with results that did not please everybody.[41] Many criticised Seguier's lack of attention to the history of the royal (and later the National Gallery) pictures. The antiquarian Edward Balme remarked that 'He knows nothing of History and merely considers them as works of art'.[42] The remark, intended to be rebarbative, in fact almost sums up Seguier's own view of his curatorial responsibilities: for him pictures were first and foremost 'works of art', and he left iconography to others.

Because Seguier was a professional picture-cleaner and dealer, it was (and still is) often assumed that he 'cleaned' pictures indiscriminately; but all the evidence is otherwise. Seguier believed that pictures in reasonably good condition should be left alone: as his obituarist in *The Times* was to remark, 'Where little was required, little was done; but that judiciously.'[43] Evidence of his restraint as conservator of the royal pictures can be found in Oliver Millar's meticulously detailed catalogue of *Later Georgian Pictures in the Royal Collection* (Millar's catalogue numbers are used below). In 1820 he 'cleaned and repaired' Zoffany's *The Academicians of the Royal Academy* (1210) and *The Tribuna of the Uffizi* (1211); since both were 'sent to Seguier', he presumably worked on them in his own studio. A third Zoffany (the double portrait *George, Prince of Wales and Prince Frederick*, 1203) was sent to him in 1826 to be relined, repaired and given a new stretcher.[44] George IV requested Seguier to undertake minor work on some of the many portraits he had commissioned from Lawrence.[45] For cleaning and varnishing *Pope Pius VII* (909), painted in Rome in 1819 but still in Lawrence's studio at his death in 1830, Seguier charged four guineas, which appears to have been his standard price for such work: at a time when posting a letter over any distance from 10 to 120 miles cost 10d., such charges were modest. In the case of two or three of Lawrence's swiftly painted portraits of dignitaries (destined for the Waterloo Room), he was required in addition to do some 'finishing': to 'the hand and dress' in *Charles Philip, Prince Schwarzenberg* (912), for example, or 'The background and Accompaniments' to *Francis I, Emperor of Austria* (897), and in these cases he charged ten guineas. But when the question of cleaning Reynolds's *Cymon and Iphigenia* (1030) was discussed, Seguier quite simply 'refused to clean it and persuaded the King that in attempting to remove [the dirt] we should destroy some of the beautiful glazings'.[46] Occasionally Seguier acted for the King in the saleroom, securing Claude's *Rape of Europa* from Lord Gwydir's sale (for instance);[47] equally occasionally (for he used other agents and dealers), George IV bought a picture from Seguier, including one of his last acquisitions, De Hooch's *Courtyard in Delft*, bought in May 1829.[48]

Haydon was to allege that 'His King does nothing without Mr. Seguier's advice.'[49] The published correspondence of George IV does not include a single letter to or from Seguier.[50] George IV was (and as Prince Regent had long been) keenly interested in his pictures and in the decoration of his palaces, as were many of his circle. If the King asked Seguier's advice, it is likely to have been over practical matters, and can only have been in occasional discussion; but the King is more likely to have relied for advice on Lord Farnborough, who had helped to develop his taste for Dutch and Flemish pictures and his liking for the work of David Wilkie. Seguier remained Conservator of the Royal Collection under William IV (who took little interest in his collections), and into the reign of Queen Victoria (who preferred portraits of her relations to old masters).

When the National Gallery was established in 1824 (see pp. 380–1), William Seguier was appointed as its first Keeper. His principal duties were defined in his letter of appointment by the Lords of the Treasury, 31 March 1824:[51]

> To have the charge of the Collection and to attend particularly to the preservation of the Pictures:–
>
> To Superintend the arrangements for admission, when the same shall have been determined upon:–
>
> To be present occasionally in the Gallery, and to value and negociate (if called upon) the purchase of any Picture that may in future be added to the Collection.

The National Gallery opened to the public six weeks after his appointment, on 10 May 1824. Its entire collection then consisted of the 38 paintings purchased from Angerstein's collection after Seguier's valuation (see p. 363); and it was housed until 1838 in Angerstein's private house, 104 Pall Mall, in rooms described by Dr Waagen as dirty in appearance, ill-lit and with no security against fire.[52] Sir George Beaumont had – famously – promised in 1823 to give sixteen paintings from his own collection if the government created the nucleus of a National Gallery by purchasing Angerstein's collection, and when suitable accommodation was provided for them.[53] Beaumont, appointed a founding Trustee of the National Gallery, watched and waited until March 1826, by which time it had become clear that no more 'suitable accommodation' was likely in his own lifetime. Then he sent for Seguier[54] to collect his pictures from Leicestershire and transport them to Pall Mall. Announcing his proposed gift in 1823, he recounted that over the years he had 'the mortification of observing the number of pictures which are annually destroyed by injudicious and unnecessary cleaning'. Beaumont's knowledge that 'Segar' would be their Keeper is likely to have contributed to his decision finally to allow his pictures to go to the 'asylum' (Beaumont's own word) of the National Gallery. By April 1826 most of them were hanging with Angerstein's pictures and with three purchases: Correggio's *Madonna of the Basket* (NG 23), Poussin's *Bacchanalian Revel before a Term of Pan* (NG 62) and Titian's *Bacchus and Ariadne* (NG 35). With the arrival of Holwell Carr's bequest of 35 pictures in 1831(see p.439),the National Gallery collection had outgrown Angerstein's house and the Treasury commissioned William Wilkins to design the new building in Trafalgar Square. In 1838 the National Gallery moved into its west wing, and the Royal Academy into the east wing.

The best account of Seguier's role as Keeper of the National Gallery is contained in his own evidence to two Select Committees, the *Report from the Select Committee on Arts and their Connexion with Manufactures*, 1836, and the *Report from the Select Committee on National Monuments and Works of Art*, 1841.[55] They interviewed Seguier, Thwaites (Assistant Keeper) and J. Wildsmith, senior warder (as well as numerous officials from other institutions including the British Museum, the Royal Academy and the Institute of British Architects). Extracts from Seguier's evidence to both committees are given below, mostly verbatim, offering a first-hand report not so very different in style from those which Henry Mayhew was collecting at much the same time from crossing-sweepers, baked-potato men and rat-catchers.[56]

Asked to state his duties at the National Gallery, Seguier replied: 'My duties are to have the superintendance of the gallery, to be called upon, upon any occasion, to give my opinion as to the value of any purchases that may be made, to take charge of the collection and to attend there occasionally to admit students.'[57] He was responsible to Trustees appointed by the Treasury. Most of those Trustees were 'chosen probably from the offices they held', but there were 'others' (non-political appointments), such as Samuel Rogers, and 'many of them are very competent judges'. By 1841 the Trustees met '10 or 12' times a year, and meetings were minuted; 'eight or ten' usually attended; three formed a quorum.[58] 'I am always present at all their meetings; and when I am called upon to give an opinion, I am bound to give it.'[59] He was not invariably consulted about proposed purchases,[60] but was usually asked to give or check valuations. He made written reports on the state of the Gallery twice a year; he reported verbally on pictures on offer which he was requested to inspect.[61] He tabled a statement of the entire staff of the National Gallery in 1841: W. Seguier, Keeper, £200 per annum; G. Thwaites, Assistant Keeper and Secretary, £150 per annum; J. Wildsmith, J. Weeks, J. Kinnear and W.H. Binley, warders (two guineas each per week); H. Newman, Porter and Messenger (£80 per annum); a Police Officer 'in attendance' (he stood at the doors to 'keep the peace', £1 4. 0. per week);[62] M. Callaghan, stoker (18 shillings per week); Martha Herst, housemaid ('to attend the fires and clean the apartments', £50 per annum) and Elizabeth Steele, assistant

Fig. 1 Henry Gritten (1818–1873), *View of the National Gallery and Royal Academy*, exhibited 1838 (the Royal Academy then occupied the East Wing). Oil on canvas, 52 × 87.5 cm. Photo National Gallery Archives.

housemaid (£20 16. 0. per annum).[63] Seguier kept establishment accounts and submitted them half-yearly to the Treasury.[64] Asked what other offices he himself held, Seguier replied that he was 'keeper of the King's pictures', and also had 'the superintendance of the British Institution, but that is a thing that occupies me a very small part of the year'.[65]

Asked, in 1836, 'Do you not think this nation ought to have a gallery equal to the Louvre?', Seguier replied – 'I do, indeed.'[66] Asked whether he was consulted over the design of the Trafalgar Square gallery, he said that he was not consulted.[67] Asked if any part of it was fire-proof, he replied 'I would not allow a picture to be moved into it till it was certified under the hand of the surveyor of Woods and Forests, that it was fire-proof.' With that certificate, insurance was no longer considered necessary.[68] Questioned about the condition of the pictures in the National Gallery, he answered 'Some few, some very few, need cleaning'; mostly 'they are in excellent condition', despite the smoke of London and the dust created by 'the great number of persons that come'. 'Occasionally we wipe the dust off', and three or four times a year the frames are dusted: 'the same man has done it for years.'[69] No National Gallery pictures were cleaned during Seguier's Keepership;[70] most of them had come, after all, from a few well-kept collections. Asked about displaying the pictures ('Could you not have one room for Flemish, another for Italian, and another for English pictures?'), he agreed that arrangement according to schools was desirable, but pointed out that the National Gallery's collection, so far dominated by Italian pictures, was not yet sufficiently comprehensive for this: 'one room would not hold the Italian, and would more than hold the Flemish.'[71] As for the British collection, it was small and he hoped for its increase.[72] And how many visitors in fact come to the National Gallery? 'We have had upwards of 10,000 in one day.'[73]

The suggestion that Seguier was 'regarded as at least nearly a *primus inter pares* by the Trustees'[74] is not borne out by his own evidence. He acted 'when he was called upon'; and he was chiefly 'called upon' to inspect and value paintings which the Trustees considered buying, sometimes without consulting him. Most of the Trustees were active collectors with their own opinions about desirable acquisitions. Occasionally they asked for outside opinions, particularly when nervous of attributions: before purchasing Lord Londonderry's two Correggios, *Venus with Mercury and Cupid* ('The School of Love', NG 10) and *Ecce Homo* (NG 15), written opinions were requested from Sir David Wilkie RA, William Hilton RA, William Young Ottley, Keeper of Prints at the British Museum, and the dealer Samuel Woodburn, among others.[75] Throughout his evidence, Seguier comes over as 'a sensible man who knew a lot about pictures', which is Oliver Millar's verdict on him as Keeper of the Royal Collection.[76] He was not of the intellectual calibre of Waagen or Eastlake, nor did he pretend to be. He made no attempt to inflate his own role nor parade his knowledge, but that knowledge was greater than his critics gave him credit for. A current clamour that Claude's *The Mill* (NG 12) was 'a copy' prompted

Fig. 2 Richard Doyle (1824–1883), *Visitors to the National Gallery study a newly acquired Murillo*. Pen and ink illustration (9 × 15 cm) in Doyle's MS Journal of 1840. London, British Museum.

questions from the 1836 Committee to which Seguier's answers (here run on) were accurate and concise: 'According to my opinion it is an original. A picture similar in subject is in the Doria palace. The picture in the National Gallery is recorded in the "Liber Veritatis"; it was painted for the Duke de Bouillon and was never out of that family till the French revolution. It does not follow that because there are two, that one is a copy by another hand.'[77] Critics complained that Seguier did not produce a *catalogue raisonné* of the National Gallery pictures, and he agreed that this was desirable;[78] but he knew that he was not the best person to undertake it, and he also knew that what the majority of the public wanted was a hand-list which cost sixpence (in 1836; one shilling in 1841). It might be added that compiling a *catalogue raisonné* was not one of the tasks the Trustees expected of him, and that the volume of work he did undertake for them would have defeated most scholars. Seguier served the emergent National Gallery ably for its first twenty years primarily because he belonged (to borrow a phrase from the Chairman of the 1836 Committee) to the class of 'practical persons'.[79]

The Trustees recognised that Seguier had other commitments. The day-to-day running of the National Gallery largely devolved upon the Assistant Keeper or Secretary.[80] To this post, Major George Saunders Thwaites was appointed. He happened to be William Seguier's first cousin; but while nepotism might have seemed wholly responsible for this unlikely appointment, Thwaites proved admirably suited to this post, continuing to serve as Secretary to general satisfaction until 1854, when he was superannuated at the age of 75.[81] In the course of time his name moved up the *Army List* until he reached the rank of Lieut.-General in 1854; but mostly he was known at the National Gallery as Colonel Thwaites, his rank 1830–46.

Colonel Thwaites is one of the unsung heroes of the National Gallery.[82] When appointed in 1824, he had over twenty years' active service behind him. He had fought in the desert in the campaign of 1801 in Egypt, and later under Wellington in the Peninsula (where he is said to have acquired a knowledge of Spanish pictures); he was present at the storming of Badajoz, and was twice wounded in the battles of Salamanca, Vittoria and the Pyrenees.[83] He was responsible for the day-to-day running of the Gallery, taking Board minutes (brief) and answering correspondence (voluminous). Between 1828 and 1847,[84] over 650 letters offering to give or more often to sell pictures were received. If the works sounded interesting, Seguier went to see them; but many letters were so clearly 'frivolous or absurd' that the Trustees empowered Thwaites to send polite stock replies.[85] After the move to Trafalgar Square, Colonel Thwaites lived 'above the shop', enjoying the distinction in London *Directories* of being the only resident of the National Gallery. The crowds which increasingly surged in on Open Days (Monday to Thursday 10–5 in the winter, 10–6 in the summer; Fridays reserved for students and copyists) did not in the least disconcert him; and his kindly personality permeated the Gallery. The Police Officer (originally from Bow Street Police Station) became one of the family; posted at the doors to admit visitors and to help with 'sticks and umbrellas', he kept the crowds good-humoured, especially on Bank Holidays, when they tended to 'come and go without paying very much attention to the pictures',[86] using the Gallery as a promenade. The 1841 Committee took pride in noting that there were sometimes 10,000 visitors in one day, 'a gratifying success for free admission'.[87]

Some idea of the crowded conditions in Trafalgar Square is offered by an illustration to Richard Doyle's *Journal* of 1840 (fig. 2). Here the Murillo of *The Infant Saint John with the Lamb* (NG 176) chiefly draws the crowd – a new acquisition and, as the newspapers reported, bought for 'a record-breaking price'.[88] Answering questions put by the Select Committee of 1841, Seguier and Thwaites both stated that the conduct of visitors, including 'women and children of all classes' and 'soldiers and their wives', was entirely orderly: 'There has not been a single accident since the opening of the gallery.'[89] This record remained unbroken until 1844, when 'a working-man on crutches' poked one of them through the mildly lewd *Leda and the Swan* bequeathed by Lord Farnborough, an incident indexed as *Outrage* in the Board Minutes.[90] The Select Committees had shown some concern that some of the pictures in the National Gallery were indecent. One of the first questions put to Seguier in 1841 concerned Poussin's *Sleeping Nymph surprised by Satyrs* (NG 91, from Holwell Carr's bequest). When asked whether there had ever been objections from 'individuals to taking their families to see that picture', Seguier (having already described it as 'a very fine work of art') replied with masterly simplicity: 'No. It was bequeathed to the National Gallery by a clergyman.'[91]

Seguier's own form of scholarship lay in building up (at home, 79 Sloane Street) an extensive collection of prints of all schools; many of these were of great rarity.[92] He owned a smaller collection of paintings,[93] chiefly of the Dutch and English schools, and on a modest scale compared with those of his affluent clients. The English pictures included four works by Bonington (the finest being *Calais Jetty*, now in the Yale Center for British Art[94]), whom Seguier had befriended and whose genius he had quickly recognised; it also included *The Abbott*, an illustration to Sir Walter Scott, painted by Wilkie for Seguier, and several works by his brother John Seguier. For George Watson Taylor (in his prime), Seguier had built up an entire Hogarth Room, containing such pictures as *The Graham Children* (NG 4756), *The Shrimp Girl* (NG 1162) and one of the versions of *The Beggars' Opera*; at Watson Taylor's sale in 1832 Seguier retrieved *The Savoyard Girl*,[95] the least important Hogarth in the sale, for his own collection.

Seguier remained on friendly terms with many artists. His long friendship with David Wilkie and John Jackson went back at least to 1808, when Wilkie records that he accompanied Jackson, Constable and Seguier to the Haymarket Theatre (on 2 August, when they would have seen the celebrated low comedian John Liston in Charles Dibdin's *The Waterman*).[96] Seguier was for a decade or so a friend whose judgement Haydon respected (in his diary for 19 June 1811, for instance, Haydon notes 'Seguier called, on whose judgment Wilkie and I so much rely...'[97]); but as Seguier's fortunes rose and his own declined, he came to regard Seguier as 'the most complicated mixture of good nature & spite, knowledge & ignorance, malice & simplicity, candour & intrigue, selfishness & generosity, pride & condescension, that his Friendship is a pang, and his enmity a fiendish dislike.' Prefaced with a pencil sketch inscribed 'William Seguier Esq., the Traitor!', Haydon's 'denunciation' of Seguier occupies several pages of his diary during June 1830 when, for the third time, he was in King's Bench prison for debt.[98] He seems under some compulsion to hate his former friend: 'Seguier I never liked. There was always a nasty sarcasm, a tattling scandal, an undervaluing sneer, against every body, even his most intimate Friends', though Haydon could not get those friends to agree with him: 'I spoke freely to Wilkie what I thought, but he with his usual caution, defended him. Jackson said nothing...'[99] Even Wilkie, for long Haydon's friend, had become the subject of his abuse ('I must own I get more & more estranged from Wilkie every day; his nasty detestable heartlessness, his mean sacrifice of his feelings to his interest, render him a very disgusting man...'[100]). This is not the place to rehearse the adversities and the mental torments which too often make Haydon an unsound witness. By 1830 he was in the grip of the paranoia which eventually drove him to suicide.[101] Eric George suggests that the 'denunciations' in Haydon's private diaries were 'in part at least – a safety-valve, a letting off steam, or an exercise in invective'.[102] Since Haydon in full rant makes lively reading, few have been able to resist quoting at length from his outbursts against Seguier; but these need to be measured against his even more venomous attacks on Fuseli, Northcote, Sir Martin Archer Shee PRA and others who had achieved the success which eluded him.

Haydon's most credible image of Seguier (coming from his artist's eye rather than from spleen) is of seeing him 'going down Bond St with a swing & roll of his body peculiar to him'.[103] Given his enormous load of work, it is not surprising that Seguier seems to have been in perpetual motion. The *Athenaeum*'s overweeningly patronising obituarist[104] was to allege that he spoke 'the vernacular *patois*, with all its characteristic redundancy and deficiency and vicarious interchange of letters' (by this he appears to mean that Seguier had a Cockney accent, dropped his aitches and could not pronounce 'v'). Haydon too mocks his accent ('I have heard him say in the first Society that "There is nothin*k w*ulgar in Ludo*w*ico Caracci"!'), but says that this was readily overlooked by 'refined people', who 'seek him for what they want, & he can inform them, and here is the whole secret of his influence'.[105] Seguier's manner of speech is probably more fairly caught by Constable, who records that on a visit to his studio in January 1833, Seguier 'was much delighted' with what he saw, and 'bestowed much extempore praise, such as – Did you do this! really – who made that drawing – you, really, very good indeed!!!'[106]

Jackson's portrait shows Seguier at the age of 58. The artist, an old friend of the sitter, died before finishing this work, so whether Seguier is portrayed holding official papers or a sheaf of prints must remain uncertain. A marble bust by Edward Hodges Baily RA (untraced) was lithographed by Miss Turner: but Seguier looks ill at ease in a toga.[107] A portrait by Henry William Pickersgill survives, in poor condition.[108] In Pieter Wonder's *Patrons and Lovers of Art*, of about 1826 (p. 403, fig. 2), Seguier is portrayed on the extreme right,[109] characteristically performing some service: he holds Roubiliac's bust of Newton, as if considering where best to place it.

William Seguier died on 5 November 1843. *The Times* obituarist lamented the passing of 'a gentle man'.[110] It paid tribute (as did the *Gentleman's Magazine*[111]) to his integrity, common-sense and kindliness, as well as to his knowledge of pictures. The *Athenaeum's* obituarist [George Darley],[112] while conceding the qualities mentioned in *The Times*, wondered 'how anyone who possessed no intellectual endowments or acquirements ... should have obtained the sovereign chair of connoisseurship', and hoped that when his successor was appointed, 'let him be a gentleman'.

In fact three men were needed thereafter to occupy the posts Seguier had held: John Seguier was appointed Superintendent of the British Institution, Thomas Uwins RA Surveyor of the Royal Collection and Charles Lock Eastlake RA Keeper of the National Gallery. Although Eastlake's qualifications were of a higher order than Seguier's, the post continued to carry the same title and salary until 1855, when Eastlake was reappointed as Director.[113]

NOTES

1. Seguier's portrait was not in the sale of virtually Watson Taylor's entire collection, enforced by his bankruptcy and conducted by George Robins at Erlestoke, 9–31 July 1832.

2. His letter offering the picture is in the NG Archives.

3. His account of William Seguier, edited and 'modified' by Lionel Cust, was published in *Proceedings of the Huguenot Society of London*, vol. VIII, 1906, pp. 157ff.

4. Alastair Laing in ed. Christine Sitwell and Sarah Staniforth, *Studies in the History of Painting Restoration*, forthcoming 1998.

5. *Report of the Select Committee on National Monuments and Works of Art*, 1841, Appendix 4, Seguier's report to Treasury on expenses of staff at the National Gallery notes that his own salary as Keeper was £200 per annum. In Appendix 6, requested to state any outside salaries received, he stated that he received £142 16. 0. as Keeper of His Majesty's Pictures. There appears to be no record of his salary as Superintendent of the British Institution, but it is unlikely to have been as much as either of the other two figures.

6. Previously he has invariably been said to have been born in 1771. For a record of his birth, see Register of Baptisms, St Martin-in-the-Fields, 1763–1775, MS, Westminster Archives, p. 215, under the year 1772: '[baptised] 6 December William Seguier [son] of David & Elizabeth [born] 9 November [1772]'.

7. Haydon, *Diary*, vol. III, p. 453.

8. [Francis Grose, enlarged], *Dictionary of the Vulgar Tongue*, 1811: 'TO COBBLE: to mend, or patch; likewise to do a thing in a bungling manner.'

9. F.P. Seguier MS, f.44.

10. 'Mr Seago Printseller of St Giles' is described in 'Portraits of Characters who were constant attendants at the Hatchards auctions' (MS, coll. BM, see note 11) as chiefly dealing in 'prints relating to the Statistical History of Great Britain ... maps, plans, roads, bridges canals machines implements of husbandry arts, manufactures, sport and war'. Ian Maxted, *The London Book Trades 1775–1800, A Preliminary Check-List of Members*, London 1977, p. 200, identifies him as 'Seago, John, printseller, High Street St Giles 1777–1809'.

11. Coll. BM, Department of Prints and Drawings (1892–4–11–116 (4)). A small pen and ink profile sketch of this 'Seago' follows the written 'sketch'. The compiler is grateful to Sheila O'Connell for bringing this MS to her attention. In the anonymous stipple engraving of 22 heads on one plate known as 'Printsellers in London, 1784', their names added in MS (BM, *Catalogue of Engraved British Portraits*, vol. V, 1922, p. 82), David Seguier and his brother John are presumably *Seguar* and *Seago*.

12. See J.T. Smith, *Nollekens and His Times*, 2 vols, London 1828, vol. I, p. 266.

13. F.P. Seguier MS. Redgrave 1874, p. 385, also states that he painted London views, giving as examples *Covent Garden Theatre when on fire*, *The church of St Paul, Covent Garden, on fire* and *A View of Seven Dials*; these are not mentioned by F.P. Seguier, who notes only small landscapes and various sketches by William of members of his family, some in watercolour, some in chalk, some in pencil, and may rather be by John Seguier. Laing (1996, n. 14) notes that a *Frost Scene* by William Seguier formerly in the Fitzwilliam Museum was de-accessioned and sold at Phillips, 7 October 1952 (43), now untraced. Seguier's sale, Christie's 4 May 1844, included one example of his own work, Lot 38, 'A woody Scene with trees, near a pool of water; admirably painted in the manner of Ruysdael'.

14. F.P. Seguier MS. Possibly the 'Peter Seager' noticed by Gunnis 1951, p. 346.

15. Twelve 'views', mostly in and around London, including two views of 'the residence of G[eorge].W[atson].Taylor, Esq., in Cavendish Square' (1820: 147, 741). A small signed view of *Excavating the Regent's Canal, with a View of Marylebone Chapel*, in the collection of the Yale Center for British Art, was exhibited there in *Presences of Nature*, 1982, no. V.10.

16. Haydon, *Diary*, vol. III, p. 453.

17. David Seguier was a friend of Nollekens's father. Haydon notes that Seguier's sons William and John both inherited his 'sarcastic humour'.

18. Notably in the obituary notice of Seguier published in the *Athenaeum*, 18 November 1843, p. 1028 (written by George Darley). There was some attempt by the Select Committee of 1836 (see pp. 392–4) to stress that he had 'never been in Italy', nor visited Munich; 'I know the galleries in Flanders, Holland and France', he replied, and 'I have seen most of the Italian pictures in this country.' (answer to Question 1491). Laing 1996 notes that Seguier had accompanied Sir Abraham Hume to Holland in 1829 (presumably to buy pictures).

19. See Owen and Brown 1988, p. 215; Farington, *Diary*, *passim*; Constable to Lucas, 16 December 1835 and 11 November 1836, *JCC*, vol. IV, pp. 427, 430; David Pike Watts to Constable, 14 June 1811, *JCC*, vol. IV, p. 29.

20. Evidence relating to the place of William Seguier's business is taken from *London Directories*: Pigot's, 1809–11; Kent's, Robson's, 1820; Pigot's, 1828; Robson's, 1834; and Robson's, 1838, the first place in which 'Seguier & Co.' are listed at 3 Russell Court (among *Picture Dealers* and *Picture Cleaners*).

21. Several hundred transactions by 'Seguier' (probably by then mostly by William and his younger brother John, rather than by their father David) are recorded in the *Getty Provenance Index 1800–1815*. William Seguier's saleroom commissions from Sir Robert Peel are indicated in MacLaren/Brown 1991; most of the entries indexed under 'Seguier' on p. 539 relate to pictures bought for Sir Robert Peel, later entering the National Gallery with the Peel Collection in 1871.

22. According to an entry in Haydon's *Diary*, June 1830, William Seguier by 1805 had 'the whole & sole care of Mr Hope's collection'; vol. III, p. 453.

23. Sale by George Robins, at Erlestoke Mansion, Wilts, 9 July 1832 'and Twenty succeeding Days'. For an account of Watson Taylor and his fluctuating fortunes, see *House of Commons 1790–1820*, V, 1986.

24. For a full account, see C.M. Kauffmann, *Catalogue of Paintings in the Wellington Museum*, London 1982, pp. 5–6; for Seguier's work (and that of his brother John) for the Duke, see Kauffmann, Introduction, pp. 5–15 and Simon Jervis, 'Picture frames and picture hanging in Apsley House', in Kauffmann 1982, pp. 17–20.

25. F.P. Seguier, MS.

26. 165 pictures (a list rather than a catalogue), reprinted in Kauffmann 1982, pp. 157–60, from the 1901 Apsley House catalogue.

27. Noted by Laing 1996, with acknowledgments to Jane Munro.

28. See *Holden's Triennial Directory* for 1809–11; Robson's *London Directory*, 1826, 1834, 1838.

29. For an account of the founding of the British Institution, see Smith 1860, and Whitley 1928, pp. 106–11.

30. The British Institution's first Keeper was Valentine Green; on his death in 1813 he was succeeded by John Young, from whom William Barnard took over in 1825.

31. Smith 1860, p. 193, states that Seguier 'held the important appointment of Superintendent at the British Institution, the duties of which he carried out for many years, to the entire satisfaction of the Directors and Governors'. Seguier's obituarist in the *Gentleman's Magazine*, January 1844, p. 97, refers to him as the Keeper, and this error has frequently been repeated, e.g. in Gregory Martin, 'The Founding of the National Gallery in London', Part 7, *Connoisseur*, October 1974, p. 108.

32. A view of the interior of the British Institution with copyists at work, by Thomas Rowlandson and Augustus Pugin, was published in Rudolph Ackermann's *The Microcosm of London*, 1808–10; reprinted in F. St Aubyn, *Ackermann's Illustrated London*, Ware, Hertfordshire 1985, p. 117.

33. Constable to C.R. Leslie, 6 July 1832; *JCC*, vol. III, p. 73.

34. Constable to C.R. Leslie, 11 January 1833; *JCC*, vol. III, p. 88. Constable, who often repeated his jokes, uses a similar phrase of Seguier ('a far greater man than the king nowadays') to David Lucas, (? November) 1836; *JCC*, vol. IV, p. 430.

35. Some pictures from the Royal Collection had been sent to him before his appointment, e.g. Wheatley's portrait *Lord Spencer Hamilton* (Millar 1969, cat. no. 1173) was 'sent to Seguier' in 1818 to be relined, repaired and given a new stretcher.

36. Oliver Millar, *The Queen's Pictures*, London 1977, p. 231 n.14; 1996 (17, plate 33); on p. 117 it is noted that the painting was transferred on to a new oak panel in 1940.

37. Until 1810, when West's stipend was suspended because his political loyalties were suspect.

38. 1841 *Report*, p. 179, Appendix 6, under *Salaries independent of the National Gallery*.

39. See Millar 1977, p. li.

40. Millar 1977, p. 128, and see cat. no. 39; Laing 1996, p. 15.

41. *Gentleman's Magazine*, 1843, p. 97: 'to him the public are indebted for the admirable arrangement of the pictures at Hampton-Court Palace'; but contrast Mrs Jameson: 'The only idea seems to have been to hang them up out of the way as quickly as possible' (*A Handbook to the Public Galleries of Art In and Near London*, London 1854, II, p. 284).

42. Edward Balme to Thomas Kerrich, quoted by Millar 1977, p. 148.

43. 1836 *Report*: Seguier's answer to Question 1542.

44. Seguier also cleaned a very large Qadal of *George III at a Review* (Millar 1969, cat. no. 995).

45. See Millar 1969, cat. nos. 878, 883, 885–93, 897, 900, 903–4, 907, 909–10, 912, 915, 917–18, 921.

46. Millar 1969, p. 106. Millar (1977, p. 148) concludes that Seguier was 'a sensible man' to whom (perhaps with the cleaner George Simpson) 'must be given no little credit for the quality and state of preservation of George IV's pictures'.

47. Gwydir sale, 8–9 May 1829; in this sale *The Market Cart* (NG 80) was lot 87.

48. Millar 1977, pp. 156–8.

49. *Diary*, vol. III, p. 455.

50. Ed. A.A. Aspinall, *The Letters of King George IV 1812–1830*, 3 vols., Cambridge 1938.

51. Seguier's original letter of appointment is in the NG Archives. When asked by the Select Committee of 1836 what his duties were (Question 1440), he quoted directly from it.

52. Waagen 1838, p. 185.

53. See Owen and Brown 1988, pp. 212–17.

54. Owen and Brown 1988, p. 215.

55. Both *Reports* were published, with full 'Minutes of Evidence', by the government printer.

56. *London Labour and the London Poor*, 3 vols., London 1851 (first published in parts in the *Morning Chronicle* during the 1840s).

57. 1836 *Report*: answer to Question 1440; and see 1841 *Report*: answer to Question 2476.

58. 1836 *Report*: answers to Questions 1443–6. Of the six Trustees appointed on the Gallery's foundation in 1824, four were politicians: the Earl of Liverpool (Prime Minister), the Earl of Aberdeen (the Scottish representative peer, later Foreign Secretary), F.J. Robinson (Chancellor of the Exchequer; created Viscount Goderich and later Earl of Ripon) and Charles Long (later Lord Farnborough); the two others were Sir George Beaumont, the Gallery's first benefactor, and Sir Thomas Lawrence, as PRA. By 1841 there were 16 Trustees.

59. 1841 *Report*: answer to Question 2478.

60. 1841 *Report*: answer to Question 2481.

61. 1841 *Report*: answer to Questions 2478–81.

62. 1841 *Report*: Thwaites's answer to Question 2594.

63. 1841 *Report*, Appendix 4.

64. 1836 *Report*: answers to Questions 1478–81.

65. 1836 *Report*: answers to Questions 1467–81.

66. 1841 *Report*: answer to Question 1621.

67. 1836 *Report*: answer to Question 1665.

68. 1841 *Report*: answers to Questions 2532–5.

69. 1836 *Report*: answers to Questions 1538–42; 1841 *Report*: answers to Questions 2510–15.

70. *Report of the Select Committee on the National Gallery*, London 1853: p. viii: 'During the Keepership of Mr William Seguier there is no record of any picture having been cleaned.' Nevertheless, some 'connoisseurs' tended to blame Seguier for any imperfections they detected in the Gallery's pictures; thus William Beckford, contemplating a Murillo (of the two Murillos in the collection in Beckford's lifetime (1759–1844), probably *The Two Trinities* (NG 13), purchased in 1837, rather than *The Infant Saint John with the Lamb* (NG 176), purchased in 1840), observed: 'It is fine, but the execrable Seguier has scrubbed away its bloom and virginity. Skinners of pictures, these cleaners, scraping and scrubbing, and making spots over the finest works like bluebottle flies' ([Cyrus Redding], *Memoirs of William Beckford*, London 1859, vol. II, p. 293).

71. 1836 *Report*: answers to Questions 1594–1602; 1841 *Report*: answers to Questions 2520–2.

72. Hogarth's six *Marriage A-la-Mode* scenes, his *Self Portrait with a Pug*, Reynolds's *Lord Heathfield* and Wilkie's *The Village Holiday* (these are NG 113–18; NG 112, transferred to the Tate Gallery in 1951; NG 111; and NG 122, transferred to the Tate Gallery in 1919).

73. 1841 *Report*: answer to Question 2652.

74. Martin 1974 (cited in note 31), p. 108.

75. Their replies are printed in the 1841 *Report*, Appendix 13.

76. Millar 1977, p. 148.

77. 1836 *Report*: answers to Questions 1496–1501.

78. The 1836 Committee discussed this: see their *Report*, Questions and answers 1567–76. The 1841 Committee appears to have been more concerned that the public should be able to buy a cheap catalogue, at one shilling.

79. See Question 1523.

80. 1841 *Report*: Question 2617 ff.

81. NG Board Minutes, 1 May 1854.

82. He appears to have been ignored in previous accounts of the Gallery's history. There are scattered references to his last ten years in the Gallery in David Robertson's meticulously researched *Sir Charles Eastlake and the Victorian Art World*, Princeton 1978. For an obituary notice, see *Gentleman's Magazine*, 1867, p. 259; see also Boase, vol. III.

83. *Army Lists*: 2nd Lieut. 12 September 1795; Lieut. 23 December 1795; Captain 1803; Major 1814; [on half-pay from 1817]; Lieut.-Colonel 1830; Colonel 1846; Major-General 1852; Lieut.-General 1851. Thwaites received the Sultan's Gold Medal of the Order of the Crescent and the Silver War Medal with five clasps, for Egypt, Badajoz, Salamanca, Vittoria and the Pyrenees.

84. The span of the first volume of NG Board Minutes.

85. NG Board Minutes, vol. I, p. 111.

86. 1841 *Report*: Question 2584. Asked by the Committee whether the public showed much interest in the pictures (Question 2584), Colonel Thwaites replied: 'I do not think the mass of the people who attend, particularly on holidays, take any particular interest in them; they come and go without paying very much attention to the pictures.'

87. Seguier, in answer to Question 2562 of the Select Committee of 1841 (*Report*, p. iv).

88. With a companion picture, *The Good Shepherd*, *Saint John* had come up for sale at Christie's in May 1840. The NG Trustees empowered Seguier to bid up to 2500 guineas for each of them, but the Gallery was outbid on both. *Saint John* was bought by Lord Ashburton, but learning that the NG was the underbidder, he generously ceded it to the Gallery.

89. Questions 2537–8.

90. *Leda and the Swan* was then thought to be by Mola (it is now 'style of Mola'); the man later appeared before a Magistrates' Court, where he was fined £5 and, in default of payment, sentenced to two months' imprisonment with hard labour (NG Board Minutes, 23 January, 5 and 19 February 1844, pp. 219, 228–9, 238).

91. 1841 *Report*: answers to Questions 2487–9.

92. His print collection was dispersed in a five-day sale, Christie's, 29 April 1844 and four following days, catalogued as *The Very Celebrated Collection of Painters' Etchings and Engravings of William Seguier, Esq., deceased, Late Conservator of the Royal and National Collections*, and lengthily reported in the *Gentleman's Magazine*, 1844, pp. 631–2; it included, beside rare Rembrandt and Claude states, the only known set of proof etchings of Naiwincx. Prices fetched totalled £2800 18. 0. See letter of 26 February 1847 from W. Smith to William Carpenter, Keeper of Prints and Drawings, British Museum, in ed. Antony Griffiths, *Landmarks in Print Collecting*, London 1996, p. 300.

93. See *Catalogue of The Choice Cabinet of Pictures, chiefly of the Dutch and English Schools, of William Seguier, Esq., Deceased; Late Conservator of the Royal and National Galleries*, sold Christie's 4 May 1844. The total fetched by 105 lots was £1895 1. 0. The top price was fetched by Ruysdael's *View of a Canal at Amsterdam* (lot 99), bought by Lord Normanton for £95 11. 0.

94. Seguier sale 4 May 1844 (58, sold for 14 guineas). See Patrick Noon, *Richard Parkes Bonington*, exh. cat., Petit Palais, Paris and Yale Center for British Art, 1991 (no. 25, repr. p. 111).

95. Watson Taylor sale 1832, 14th day (lot 53); Seguier sale 1844 (101); now in the collection of the Huntington Art Gallery, San Marino, California.

96. Allan Cunningham, *Life of Sir David Wilkie*, vol. 1, 1843, p. 186. [John Genest], *Some Account of the London Stage*, Bath 1842, vol. VIII, p. 109: Haymarket 1808: '2 August. Waterman. Robin = Liston'. For Liston see *DNB*.

97. Haydon, *Diary*, vol. I, p. 120.

98. Haydon, *Diary*, vol. III, pp. 453–61. Haydon's MS Diaries are in the collection of W.B. Pope, their editor; the sketch of Seguier is not known to have been reproduced.

99. *Diary*, vol. III, p. 454.

100. *Diary*, vol II, p. 213.

101. See Eric George, *The Life and Death of Benjamin Robert Haydon*, Oxford 1967, *passim*; see also John Jolliffe, *Neglected Genius, The Diaries of Benjamin Haydon*, London 1976, pp. vi–xii.

102. George 1967, p. 358.

103. *Diary*, June 1830, vol. III, p. 459.

104. George Darley; see note 112.

105. *Diary*, vol. III, pp. 455, 456.

106. Constable to Leslie, 11 January 1833; *JCC*, vol. III, p. 88.

107. Reproduced by Holmes and Collins-Baker 1924, p. 3.

108. Whitley 1930, p. 221, noting the *Morning Chronicle*'s review of the RA exhibition of 1831, mentions a work showing Seguier's 'fat unintellectual face': presumably this refers to P.C. Wonder's group portrait, repr. p. 402.

109. His presence there may have been an afterthought; he does not appear in the preliminary study for the group on the right (Lord Farnborough, Sir Abraham Hume and Sir David Wilkie): coll. NPG (793).

110. 15 November 1843, p. 3.

111. 1844, pp. 97–8.

112. No. 838, 18 November 1843, p. 1028; the writer is identified as George Darley in Claude Colleer Abbott, *Life and Letters of George Darley, Poet and Critic*; London 1928, where this notice is reprinted, pp. 165–7. Darley, a self-appointed watchdog for 'Art' with a gift for violent diatribe, was one of the art critics of the *Athenaeum* from 1834 until his death in 1846. His career is outlined in Margaret Drabble, *Oxford Companion to English Literature*, Oxford 1985, p. 242.

113. Eastlake was Keeper 1843–7, when he resigned, to be succeeded by Thomas Uwins. Eastlake was a Trustee of the National Gallery 1850–5, when he was appointed Director. See Robertson 1978, chapters V, VII, VIII.

NG 124

Reverend William Holwell Carr

*c.*1827–8

Oil on canvas, 75.6 × 62.9 cm (29¾ × 24¾ in.)

Provenance

Commissioned by the sitter *c.*1827–8 to hang with the collection of pictures he was to leave to the National Gallery; bequeathed with the rest of his collection 1831.

Literature

Davies 1946, p. 124; H.C. Morgan, 'Life and Works of John Jackson RA', 1956, unpublished thesis, Brotherton Collection, Leeds University Library, p. 263; Davies 1959, pp. 70–1.

Engraved

(1) in stipple by B. Holl, published in *The National Gallery*, 1840 (no pagination); (2) lithograph, anon., vignette.

Technical Notes

The paint is severely affected by wrinkling and by drying cracks. The appearance is not enhanced by a very discoloured varnish which is ingrained in the surface of the paint, giving a spotty appearance. By 1878 the work was noted by the artist's son to be in 'a desperately dilapidated state. Some of the shadows – the lakes – bitumen &c., are completely gone and the work, if not attended to, likely to perish altogether' (letter from M.P. Jackson to the Director of the National Gallery, 25 July 1878, see below, p. 404).

The sitter, who bequeathed thirty-five paintings to the National Gallery six years after its foundation, was one of the founders of the British Institution, an Honorary Exhibitor at the Royal Academy (where between 1804 and 1821 he showed twelve landscapes, all now untraced)[1] and a Fellow of the Royal Society (1806). He was also, and almost incidentally, a clergyman; but his energies were chiefly devoted to collecting pictures.

Born in 1758 as William Holwell (he was to take the additional surname Carr in 1798), he was the son of Edward Holwell, an Exeter apothecary. He went up to Oxford (Exeter College) in 1776, remaining there as a Fellow of Exeter College until 1793,[2] but is said to have 'employed much of his Time in Painting'.[3] In 1781, at the age of 23, he was 'allowed to travel' and went to Italy, where he studied art and began to buy pictures. As the son of a provincial apothecary, he is unlikely to have been able to make the Grand Tour on the same scale as the 'flock of travelling boys' in Zoffany's *Tribuna of the Uffizi* (completed in 1779);[4] but he began to collect pictures, presumably financing his early purchases through picture-dealing. Lewis Vaslet's pastel portrait of Carr, drawn at Oxford in 1790, shows him wearing a modish stock and striped waistcoat under his academic gown. There is an unmistakably determined glint in his eye. A note on the back reads 'A strong likeness'.[5]

An opportunity to acquire virtually effortless income presented itself in 1791, when the rich benefice of Menheniot in Cornwall fell vacant. The living was in the gift of the Dean and Chapter of Exeter College; only Fellows of Exeter College were eligible. Hastily, Holwell acquired a degree in Divinity.[6] On 17 November 1791 the Dean of Exeter College presented him with the living of Menheniot, worth £1134 per annum.[7] He never resided there, but drew the revenues for life, employing a curate at £100 per annum to undertake his duties, in due course defending his absenteeism on the grounds that the climate was 'very inimical to my health'.[8] Such abuses were rife in the Church of England:[9] Holwell Carr might almost have been Trollope's model for 'The College Fellow who has Taken Orders'.[10]

In 1797 Holwell's fortunes further improved with his marriage to Lady Charlotte Hay, eldest daughter of the 15th Earl of Erroll and his wife Isabella Carr, and heiress to large Carr estates in Northumberland. She was 35, and may have had her own reasons for marrying a man who had no property in the sense to which she was accustomed, no blue blood and no relatives of note except an uncle (Revd William Holwell) who had compiled *The Beauties of Homer*[11] and an aunt (Zephaniah Holwell) who had achieved fame by surviving the Black Hole of Calcutta. The Northumberland estates devolved upon Lady Charlotte the following year; in order to claim them, both she and her husband took the additional name of Carr, and from that point he is known as Holwell Carr (or simply Carr). His wife died in 1801, after giving birth to their only child, a son who died at the age of five; on his death the Carr estates reverted to his mother's family.

The extent to which four years of marriage to Lady Charlotte Hay had increased Holwell Carr's purchasing power can only be guessed at. Certainly it appears that he acquired his most important pictures after his marriage, and thereafter devoted his energies single-mindedly to refining his collection. Dr Waagen, Director of the Berlin Art Gallery, methodically listing the most distinguished collections in England since 1792 'in the order in which those collections became of some importance', placed Holwell Carr a long way behind in the race whose front runners included the Duke of Bridgewater, the Marquess of Stafford, Lord Kinnaird, John Julius Angerstein, Samuel Rogers and Lord Radstock. English collectors and dealers of the period had unparalleled opportunities, as Dr Waagen sonorously recounted:

> For, when the storm of the French Revolution burst over the different countries of Europe, and shook the foundations of the property of states, as well as of individuals, the general distress, and the insecurity of property, brought an immense amount of works of art into the market, which had for centuries adorned the altars of churches as inviolably sacred, or ornamented the palaces of the great, as memorials of ancient wealth and splendour. Of these works of art, England has found means to obtain the most and the best.
> For scarcely was a country overrun by the French,

when Englishmen skilled in the arts were at hand with their guineas.[12]

Holwell Carr's studies had made him 'skilled in the arts'; from the late 1790s, he evidently had the 'guineas'. Dr Waagen's roll-call of the bereft 'palaces of the great' included the Aldobrandini, Barberini, Colonna, Corsini, Falconieri, Giustiniani, Chigi and Lancelotti. Holwell Carr was to collect pictures from each of these palazzos in his house at 29 Devonshire Place and although he bought most of them in the London salerooms, he was to extol their noble provenance to the end of his days.

From about 1805, Holwell Carr became well known (and was sometimes taunted) as a 'gentleman-dealer': but he was hardly unique in that (George III reputedly said that every gentleman who went to Italy 'came back a *picture-dealer*'[13]). He haunted the salerooms and the dealers' showrooms, weeding out inferior works, buying and selling in his own name in the saleroom,[14] but evidently also unloading the no longer desirable 'property of a gentleman' anonymously. For a while (according to Farington) he was 'connected ... in purchasing and disposing of pictures' (i.e. dealing) with a retired Admiral of the Fleet, William Waldegrave, 1st Baron Radstock.[15] There are occasional hints that Holwell Carr (himself an amateur artist, as noted at the start of this entry) touched up or restored paintings. William Seguier, asked by Sir George Beaumont in 1807 for his opinion of a Richard Wilson then on the market, 'looked at it & thought the edges of some of the trees were painted by *Carr*';[16] and 'patcher' was one of the insults selected for Carr in the broadside against directors of the British Institution in 1816 (see below).

For just over a year from March 1805, Holwell Carr owned a one-sixth share[17] in William Buchanan's highly speculative trade in importing old masters from Italy. Arthur Champernowne, a rival *marchand-amateur*, had a half-share.[18] Holwell Carr now enjoyed the right to select pictures for himself as soon as they arrived from Buchanan's agents in Italy, and on special terms; during 1805 Buchanan ceded to him, for instance, Barocci's *Madonna and Child* ('*Madonna del Gatto*', NG 29) and Rubens's oil sketch of *Saint Bavo about to receive the Monastic Habit at Ghent* (NG 57). In the same year, Carr's sharp practice over Andrea del Sarto's *Madonna and Child with Saints Elizabeth and John the Baptist* (NG 17) caused something of a scandal, still recounted a decade later, when Farington records it.[19] Having reserved the Sarto for himself at a special price of 300 guineas agreed with Buchanan, but not yet paid, Carr offered it to Admiral Radstock for 500 guineas as a picture from his own private collection. This 'trick of Carr, who had not paid a farthing of the money He was engaged to give caused a breach between Radstock & Carr.'[20] Whether Buchanan knew of Carr's attempt to cut him out of the profits is not known. Carr certainly got the better of Buchanan over Gaspar Dughet's *Landscape with the Union of Dido and Æneas*, newly imported from the Falconieri Palace. Buchanan believed that 'grand Landscapes' were 'all the rage' with English collectors,[21] and when the Dughet (a very dark picture) reached London in February 1805, he instantly pronounced it (in his favourite phrase) to be the artist's *chef d'œuvre*, thereafter referring to it as 'the Great Gaspar'. He offered it to William Beckford for 2000 guineas; Beckford declined it, as did other clients. Carr wanted it, but was astute enough to play a waiting game. The price gradually came down; within the year, it had dropped to 1200 guineas. Then Carr acted; he offered £1100, and secured 'the Great Gaspar' for himself (it is now NG 95).[22] Carr's relationship with Buchanan soon soured. Holwell Carr had a genuine eye for a good picture; Buchanan, the son of a Glasgow hat manufacturer and himself almost wholly ignorant about art, merely had a nose for trade. Increasingly uneasy over Buchanan's more speculative purchases, and dismayed at the risks repeatedly taken in shipping works of art from wartime Europe (when one long-delayed crate of pictures finally arrived, 'several fell to pieces in taking them out of the case ... the others are one mass of mould, damp, and ruin'[23]), Holwell Carr first remonstrated, then finally withdrew his stake in the business – to the relief of Buchanan, who pronounced Carr 'a perfect Grumbler' and 'a damned bore'.[24]

Holwell Carr had meanwhile acquired more solid status by becoming one of the founding subscribers, with such distinguished collectors as Sir George Beaumont, Lord Northwick, John Julius Angerstein and Sir Abraham Hume, to the British Institution, established in 1805 at 52 Pall Mall.[25] Its stated purpose was 'to encourage and reward the talents of the artists of the United Kingdom, and to open an exhibition for the sale of their productions'. He was not interested in British art; his only recorded remark about a British artist, prompted by seeing Turner's *Dido building Carthage* (NG 498, pp. 272–81) was that 'Turner did not comprehend His Art',[26] and his collection included no works of the British School apart from the mediocre portrait by Jackson which alone qualifies Holwell Carr for inclusion in this catalogue.

He was better pleased when, from 1815, the British Institution also began regularly to present exhibitions of Old Masters; he lent generously to such exhibitions and in 1820 doubled his subscription. The Preface to the catalogue of the first of these (to which Carr lent his Rubens of *Saint Bavo*, NG 57, and two so-called 'Rembrandts') injudiciously hoped 'that such productions may excite in the British Artist the ardour of emulation. They offer them to him not that he may copy, but that he may study them.'[27] The 'British Artist' instantly scented condescension, and reacted with hostility. Lawrence, 'his face boiling with rage', grated out between his teeth, 'I suppose they think we want teaching.'[28] The anonymous author [Robert Smirke RA] of the bitterly sarcastic sham 'Catalogues' of the exhibitions of 1815 and 1816 was more outspoken, ridiculing the pretensions of the directors of the British Institution. As Farington noted, these contained 'very serious animadversions ... particularly on Mr. Payne Knight, – Sir George Beaumont, – and the Revd Holwell Carr'.[29] Carr was pithily described as 'Priest patcher and picture dealer; more ignorant and impudent than all the rest tied in a bunch. He with these qualifications has wriggled himself into a dependent acquaintanceship with the other members of the Society, who despise him while they use him.'[30] Constable

Fig. 1 Pieter Christoffel Wonder (1780–1852), *George Watson Taylor (kneeling), William Holwell Carr, Sir John Murray and (behind him) the artist*: a study *c.*1826 for one of the four groups in *An Interior of a Picture Gallery with Portraits* (fig. 2). Oil on canvas, 54.9 × 48.3 cm. London, National Portrait Gallery.

confided to his friend Fisher in 1824 that he had little inclination to exhibit his work at the British Institution: 'Consider who are our judges–Carr, the Magnus–Sir Cs. Long–Priapus Knight – none of them have any affection for new art.'[31]

Over the next decade Holwell Carr added to his collection such works as Titian's *Holy Family and a Shepherd* (NG 4), Claude's *Landscape with David at the Cave of Adullam* (NG 6) and Domenichino's *Vision of Saint Jerome* (NG 85) and, in the following decade, Tintoretto's *Saint George and the Dragon* (NG 16), Guercino's *The Dead Christ mourned by Two Angels* (NG 22) and Garofalo's *Saint Augustine with the Holy Family* (NG 81). Of the 35 paintings he was to bequeath to the National Gallery, the great majority (26) were by Italian masters of the late fifteenth to mid-seventeenth centuries; six were by French artists influenced by Italy – Poussin, Claude and Gaspar Dughet. His only Flemish painting was the Rubens oil sketch of *Saint Bavo about to receive the Monastic Habit at Ghent* (NG 57), noted above. His only Dutch pictures were two called Rembrandt. One of these (*Landscape with Tobias and the Angel*, NG 72) is now given to Jan Lievens. The other is the incomparably beautiful *Woman bathing in a Stream* (NG 54). Purchased for £165 at Lord Gwydir's sale in 1829, when Holwell Carr was 71, it is the last purchase he made, and in many ways the most courageous he ever made.

The 'crown of Holwell Carr's collection' was generally agreed to be his 'Leonardo', *Christ among the Doctors* (NG 18); it was to be the only picture mentioned by name in his obituary notices.[32] Its provenance alone was music in Carr's ears, for it had belonged to Olimpia Aldobrandini-Pamphilj, later passing into the Borghese collection. Carr bought it from Lord Northwick in 1824, for an undisclosed sum, reckoned to be £3000. That figure, coupled with the power of Leonardo's name (and that name was written three times on the back of the picture) suspended critical judgement, at least in England; and when Revd Thomas Dale reproduced it, with pious verses, in his evangelical magazine *The Iris* in 1830,[33] the 'Leonardo' was elevated to seemingly unassailable status. But there were scholars abroad who maintained that the 'Leonardo' was in fact by his Milanese emulator Bernardino Luini.[34] Fortunately for Carr's *amour propre*, he died eight years before 1838, when Dr Waagen's *Art and Artists in England* was published, for he would not have relished the passage in which Dr Waagen wondered how anyone could fail to recognise the hand of Luini in *Christ among the Doctors* ('However beautiful the features of Christ are, much as they bear in general the well-known school type of Lionardo, and though the expression of a tender melancholy is very attractive, yet they have not the deep seriousness, the great meaning, which Lionardo gave to his countenances').[35] The attribution to Luini was accepted by the National Gallery soon after it received the bequest.

Gradually, by virtue of the works he had acquired, Holwell Carr was admitted to the company of the great and the good of the art world. The accolade, in a sense, came with his inclusion in the large painting by Pieter Christoffel Wonder known as *Patrons and Lovers of Art, or The Imaginary Picture Gallery*, perhaps completed in 1826 (fig. 2).[36] In the study for the group on the left (fig. 1), the tallest man (with top hat and stick) is not our hero, but Sir John Murray Bt who commissioned the picture, with the shy artist behind him. Holwell Carr is the dumpy figure in dark coat, drab breeches and gaiters; this notably inelegant dress suggests that his passion for art no longer extended to the niceties of fashion. On the left George Watson Taylor (a rival collector) is portrayed kneeling in front of Titian's *Bacchus and Ariadne* (NG 35), then a recent and justly celebrated acquisition by the National Gallery, bought in March 1826. Paintings from various collections are mingled in this 'Imaginary Gallery', with some deference to pictures collected by those who are portrayed in it. Holwell Carr's Garofalo of *Saint Augustine with the Holy Family and Saint Catherine of Alexandria* is partly visible in this study (and fully visible in the finished picture), behind the Titian. A Parmigianino *Madonna and Child* then belonging to George Watson Taylor hangs beside it.[37] In the finished picture, Holwell Carr's 'Leonardo' hangs on the right side of the central wall, in a prime if improbable position below Rubens's *Chapeau de Paille*, later purchased by the National Gallery with the Peel collection (NG 852). In the finished picture, William Seguier (see NG 6022, pp. 388–98) stands near the 'Leonardo'. Other eminent collectors portrayed include Charles Long, Lord Farnborough (see under

NG 2786, pp. 376–87), Lord Aberdeen, George Agar-Ellis, 1st Baron Dover (one of the prime movers in Parliament for the purchase of the Angerstein collection for the National Gallery), Sir Robert Peel and the 3rd Earl of Egremont, Turner's patron (NPG, no. 795). Carr's inclusion in such company is a recognition of his contemporary reputation as one of the foremost collectors and connoisseurs in England; but whereas Lord Aberdeen and Lord Farnborough were Founding Trustees of the National Gallery and Lord Dover and Sir Robert Peel became Trustees in 1827, Carr's association with the art trade precluded such honours.

Holwell Carr could be disputatious, assertive and graceless. From an episode reported by Farington, it is clear that he was not generally liked. In May 1814, 'in the presence of Lord Ashburnham, Lord Mulgrave, the Marquiss of Stafford & others', he attacked Thomas Lawrence RA, who helped to form Angerstein's collection, on the subject of 'the picture by Corregio at Mr. Angerstein's' (presumably *The Agony in the Garden*, purchased by Angerstein on the advice of Benjamin West and Thomas Lawrence, and now NG 76): 'Holwell Carr with His arms akimbo went up to Lawrence & sd. "Mr. Lawrence, the picture at Mr. Angerstein's which is called a Corregio, I say, is a Copy", to which Lawrence replied "Mr. Carr, that picture is well known to Mr. West and to myself, and to several other Artists, & we and they think [it] a true & a fine picture by Corregio, & would hold in contempt Mr. Carr's opinion in opposition to their opinion".' Farington learnt this story from Arthur Champernowne, who knew Carr well and who 'told it in a triumphant way as a proper check upon the presumption of Carr'. Champernowne added that 'Sir George Beaumont was going abt everywhere & telling it to everybody.'[38] There are other glimpses of Carr publicly trumpeting his opinions. Farington notes his 'unhandsome conduct' in telling Mr Christie that the Titian *Actæon* in the late Benjamin West's sale 'was not by Titian'.[39] Holwell Carr pronounced Lord Lansdowne's 'beautiful little Claude' to be 'a good Pater',[40] and a Gaspard Dughet in Cardinal Fesch's collection to be 'not original'.[41] Carr was sometimes right but as often wrong, as shown by many re-attributions of paintings in his bequest (see list on p. 439).

Carr barely figures otherwise in contemporary memoirs. He appears to have led a mostly solitary life, his gregariousness limited to the Roxburghe Club[42] and the Athenaeum,[43] of each of which he was a founder-member. Obsessed with provenances, and possessing the dreadful gift of total recall for past prices of works of art, he appears to have had no small talk. When Thomas Moore was admiring Parmigianino's great altarpiece of *The Madonna and Child with Saints*

Fig. 2 Pieter Christoffel Wonder (1780–1852), *Interior of a Picture Gallery with Portraits* (also known as 'Patrons and Lovers of Art or The Imaginary Picture Gallery'), exhibited 1831. Oil on canvas, 160.7 × 208.4 cm. Private collection.

John the Baptist and Jerome (now NG 33) in George Watson Taylor's sale in June 1823, Holwell Carr came up to him and 'traced the price ... from £120 to £7000' (Moore noted in his diary 'Connoisseurship in paintings is to me a "sealed fountain"; there seems to be no standard of merit in it but the price'[44]). Carr lived in Devonshire Place, at the top of Wimpole Street, where 'an old manservant' looked after him. There his collection was hung 'in two drawing rooms'. Occasionally he showed it to eminent visitors. Prince Pückler-Musgau records such a visit in May 1828:

> I went with Prince E – yesterday to see the small private collection of a clergyman (Mr. Carr), which consists of not above thirty pictures, has cost him twenty thousand pounds, and is quite worth it. There are as many master-pieces as pictures... Here is a Garoffolo, of such unearthly transparency and brightness, of so holy and deep a poetry, that you think you behold a picture of Eden, not of this earth; and a large Claude, also of the highest order of beauty... In an adjoining room were some beautiful landscapes by Domenichino and Annibal Caracci... In a third room you reach the crown of the whole collection, a picture by Leonardo da Vinci ... of a beauty, truth and perfection, which leaves nothing to desire...[45]

Jackson's portrait was commissioned by Holwell Carr to be placed with the pictures he intended to bequeath to the nation. It is likely to have been painted not long before 28 August 1828, when Carr signed his will, a very short document bequeathing 'the whole of my collection of Ancient Pictures which are now in my two Drawing Rooms' to the nation – specifically 'to the Trustees of the British Museum for the benefit of the public'[46] and 'my own Portrait to be placed with them'. Since the National Gallery had no building of its own, Holwell Carr followed Beaumont's precedent in leaving his collection to the Trustees of the British Museum. Carr died in Devonshire Place on 24 December 1830. Six months later, his pictures were delivered to William Seguier, Keeper of the National Gallery. Somehow, Seguier managed to find room to hang them in the Gallery's temporary and increasingly overcrowded home in Angerstein's Pall Mall house.

As Jackson portrays him, Carr's appearance is consistent with a date of about 1827–8, when he would have been nearly seventy, and a few years older than in Wonder's study of him (fig. 1). Jackson may have been selected as his portraitist because he was a protégé of Lord Mulgrave, whom Carr evidently knew.[47] Forty years after the portrait was painted, Mulgrave Phipps Jackson (the artist's son, named after his first patron) noted that it was already 'in a desperately dilapidated state'.[48] He believed this was due to its having been placed where it was 'exposed to the sun's rays'; but the work appears to have been hastily and rather carelessly executed. Carr may not have been prepared to pay as much as Sir John Soane, who paid Jackson 100 guineas in 1828 for a pair of portraits in oil;[49] and Jackson, a devout Methodist (he contributed many portraits of venerated Methodist ministers to the *Wesleyan Methodist Magazine*), may have found this sitter unsympathetic. Jackson has evidently tried to make Holwell Carr look benign; equally evidently, it has been uphill work. Unlike most of Jackson's portraits, it was not exhibited. Thomas Moore remarked that 'some one said ... that it looked as if in the act of saying "The original is in the Borghese Gallery."'[50]

Holwell Carr described himself in his will as 'Vicar of Menheniot in the County of Cornwall', which indeed he was, nominally, from 1791 until his death. He had been an absentee throughout, yet a forgiving tablet in Menheniot parish church (rather high up in the nave) commemorates him as 'an accomplished Scholar, a Proficient in painting – he proved his taste and judgment by forming a select collection of pictures of the highest class in Art...'[51] In financing that 'select collection', Holwell Carr owed much to his Menheniot benefice. Over a period of forty years, he must – after paying his curate £100 a year – have cleared at least the £20,000 which his collection (according to Prince Pückler-Musgau) evidently cost him. He bequeathed his 'select collection' to the nation; to the poor of Menheniot he left £500. There is matter here for a sermon, possibly on the parable of the talents, though Holwell Carr would not have been the most suitable person to deliver it.

NOTES

1. Carr is briefly noticed in Redgrave 1878, p. 71, but no description of his work is given there.

2. His academic and clerical careers are outlined in Revd Charles William Boase, *Register of the Rectors and Fellows of Exeter College, Oxford*, Oxford 1879, pp. 111–12.

3. Farington, *Diary*, 3 April 1814, vol. XIII, p. 4480: Farington called on Samuel Lysons, the antiquary (1763–1819), and his brother Daniel. 'They spoke of the Revd Holwell Carr. S. Lysons knew Him when He was at Exeter College, Oxford, 30 years ago, and at that time He employed much of his Time in Painting. They sd. He was born in Devonshire, and was nephew to *Zephania Holwell*, one of the Survivors, of those who were inclosed in the Black Hole of Calcutta in the year 1759.– Holwell Carr obtained the valuable living of Hengenmoit [Menheniot] in Cornwall, worth more than £2000 per year. It is in the sole gift of the Dean of Exeter, must be given to a *Member of Exeter College*. He married a Sister of the late Lord Errol, and took the name of Carr in addition to that of Holwell. By Her (who died some years ago) He had one Child, a son, who also died at a young age. Had He lived He would have inherited a very large estate through His Mother from His Grandfather.'

4. The phrase is Walpole's, in a letter to Sir Horace Mann, 31 October 1779, *Walpole Correspondence*, vol. XXIV, p. 520. Zoffany's *Tribuna* is in the collection of Her Majesty The Queen, Millar 1969, cat. no. 1211, pp. 154–5.

5. 7¾ × 6 in., oval; coll. Exeter College; R.L. Poole, *Catalogue of Portraits in the Possession of the University, Colleges, City and County of Oxford*, vol. II, Oxford 1925, p. 74 (Exeter College no. 34). A photograph kindly supplied by the College is in the NG Archives.

6. The compiler's inference of opportunism merely echoes that of *DNB*, which records that Carr was 'said to have taken orders with the object of accepting this preferment'.

7. Farington, in a garbled account of Holwell Carr, 3 April 1814 (see note 3), reported that the Menheniot living was 'worth more than £2000 per annum'. Anon., *A Complete*

Parochial History of the County of Cornwall, III, n.d., p. 311, gives the annual value of the living in 1840 as £1134 (this probably included the value of the vicarage, in which the curate lived). By comparison, the Revd Robert Stephen Hawker's living of Morwenstow was worth £365 per annum in 1834.

8. See Carr's reply to 'queries' addressed to incumbents in the diocese of Exeter in 1821, in ed. Michael Cook, *The Diocese of Exeter in 1821, I, Cornwall*, Devon and Cornwall Record Society, New Series, vol. 3, Torquay 1958, p. 54.

9. Absenteeism is analysed in C.K.F. Brown, *A History of the English Clergy 1800–1900*, London 1953, pp. 32–9. The compiler is indebted to Enid Nixon for this reference.

10. Anthony Trollope, *Clergymen of the Church of England*, 1866, ed. Ruth ap'Roberts, London 1974, pp. 78–91.

11. Revd William Holwell (1726–98), noticed in *DNB*, was Vicar of Thornbury, Gloucestershire, and compiler of classical anthologies such as *Beauties of Homer*, 1775. Carr's obituary in the *Gentleman's Magazine*, 1831, p. 370, is in error in stating that Carr was the son (rather than the nephew and namesake) of Revd William Holwell.

12. Waagen 1838, I, p. 50. For a particularly lively modern account of these opportunities and the men who made much of them, see Haskell 1976, pp. 25–7.

13. Haskell 1976, p. 26 n. 9, quoting from *Annals of the Fine Arts for 1817*, p. 203. Haskell notes that besides Holwell Carr, other English 'gentlemen-dealers' of the period included Arthur Champernowne, Sir Simon Clarke, George Hibbert, Sir Gregory Page Turner – 'and there were many more'.

14. Thanks to the *Getty Provenance Index* (published to date: vols I–III, 1801–15), light work is made of tracing such transactions; e.g. for Holwell Carr's sales of pictures, see Dyck 1806/03/17; Monti 1806/13/27; Titian 1810/03/23; Grimaldi 1814/06/04; Mazzolino 1812/04/11; Veronese 1813/06/02.

15. Farington, *Diary*, 24 November 1816, vol. XIV, p. 4929.

16. Ibid., 28 April 1807, vol. VIII, p. 3033.

17. William Buchanan, *Memoirs of Painting, with a Chronological History of the Importation of Pictures by the Great Masters into England since the French Revolution*, 2 vols, London 1824, vol. II, p. 163; Hugh Brigstocke, *William Buchanan and the 19th-Century Art Trade*, privately published by The Paul Mellon Centre for Studies in British Art, London 1982, pp. 17 and 464; Letters 86, 88, 90, 91, 95-8.

18. Buchanan ed. Brigstocke 1982, p. 369.

19. Farington, *Diary*, 24 November 1816, vol. XIV, pp. 4928–9. This 'anecdote', recounted to Farington by Thomas Phillips RA, 'who had frequently heard Tresham relate [it]', was presumably revived in the wake of criticism of Carr in [Smirke's] *Catalogues Raisonnés* of 1815 and 1816.

20. Farington, *Diary*, 24 November 1816, vol. XIV, p. 4929.

21. Buchanan ed. Brigstocke 1982, pp. 89, 91.

22. For the tale of 'the Great Gaspar', see Brigstocke 1982, pp. 91, 98, 110–11, 126, 144, 152, 158, 172–3, 315, 360, 366, 374, 377, 382, 386, and finally p. 428: 'Carr took the Grand Gaspar of the Falconieri at £1100.'

23. Buchanan to Irvine, 26 July 1805, Buchanan ed. Brigstocke 1982, p. 423.

24. Buchanan ed. Brigstocke 1982, pp. 424, 431.

25. He was one of the fifteen men present at the first meeting of subscribers, 4 June 1805; Smith 1860, p. 2. Subscribers of 100 guineas got four tickets to evening receptions; subscribers of 50 guineas got two tickets. Holwell Carr subscribed 50 guineas until 1820, thereafter subscribing 100 guineas.

26. Farington, *Diary*, 4 June 1815, vol. XIII p. 4637.

27. Preface to the catalogue of the exhibition *Rubens, Rembrandt, Vandyke and other artists of the Flemish and Dutch Schools*, BI, 1815, p. 9.

28. B.R. Haydon, *Autobiography*, ed. Tom Taylor, 2 vols, London 1926, I, p. 205, under 29 April 1815.

29. Farington, *Diary*, 10 June 1815, vol. XIII, p. 4643.

30. *A Catalogue Raisonné of the Pictures now Exhibiting in Pall Mall*, 1816. Carr lent two paintings by Claude to this exhibition. Under 'David Encamped...' (65: now NG 6, as *Landscape with David at the Cave of Adullam*), the writer noted: 'We are sorry to be under the necessity of observing, that of all the Pictures constituting the stock in trade of the above named Gentleman – Apothecary – Parson – Picture-Dealer, this is one of the best... Of two Pictures, by this master, in the possession of Mr H. C—r, he has chosen to send the least objectionable to the Gallery.' Presumably Carr sent his 'other Claude' (unidentified) to the saleroom.

31. Constable to Fisher, 7 January 1824; *JCC*, vol. VI, p. 149.

32. For example the *Gentleman's Magazine*, 1831, p. 370, where it is stated that Carr bought the Leonardo from Lord Northwick for £2600; Boase 1879 (cited in note 2), p. 112.

33. Vol. I, London 1830, facing p. 126. The compiler is indebted to Lorne Campbell for this reference.

34. See Davies 1961, p. 318 n. 5.

35. 1838, I, p. 187.

36. Four oil studies for the picture are in the NPG (nos. 792–5). They are fully catalogued and reproduced, with the whole picture and Wonder's key drawing of it (in the collection of the Rijksprentkabinet, Amsterdam) in Walker 1985, nos. 792–5, pp. 615–18, plate 1591, with the works identified below plate 1597.

37. Nollekens's bust of Wellington, from the Angerstein collection, presides over this group in the study (but was replaced in the final picture by Rysbrack's bust of Locke). For a full identification of the works in this, the other three studies and the finished picture (with the present locations of the works), see Walker 1985.

38. Farington, *Diary*, 16 May 1814, vol. XIII, pp. 4515–16. If the Correggio disputed by Carr was indeed *The Agony in the Garden*, then later scholarship, which has pronounced it to be a copy after the picture in Apsley House, has proved Carr right. But Carr failed to perceive that an *Ecce Homo* in his own collection (as by Ludovico Carracci, NG 96) is in fact a copy of a Correggio (NG 15).

39. Farington, *Diary*, 19 June 1820, vol. XVI, p. 5523.

40. Ed. Lord John Russell, *Memoirs, Journals and Correspondence of Thomas Moore*, vol. VI, 1854, p. 56.

41. Ibid., vol. III, p. 57.

42. Founded 1812. Carr complied with the rule that every member shall present a book by presenting, in 1817, Luigi da Porto, *Istoria novellamente ritrovato di due nobili Amanti*, 1542, a version of the story which influenced Shakespeare's *Romeo and Juliet*.

43. The Athenaeum was founded in 1824 by Sir Walter Scott and Thomas Moore 'for the association of individuals known for their scientific and literary attainments, artists of eminence in any class of the fine arts, and noblemen and gentlemen distinguished as liberal patrons of science, literature or the arts'.

44. Russell 1854 (cited in note 40), vol. IV, p. 79.

45. 'By a German Prince', *Tour in Germany, Holland and England in the years 1826, 1827 & 1828*, 4 vols., London 1832, vol. IV, pp. 308–10. The compiler is indebted to Nicholas Penny for this reference.

46. Carr's decision to bequeath his collection to the NG appears to have been taken at least ten years earlier, and to have been discussed with Sir George Beaumont. Like Beaumont, Holwell Carr was concerned over the lack of space in the NG's rooms in Pall Mall; his will therefore bequeathed his collection in trust to the Trustees of the British Museum, 'to be placed in the same building with the late Mr Angerstein's and Sir George Beaumont'. After the National Gallery's new building in Trafalgar Square was completed in 1838, Holwell Carr's collection was duly transferred there.

47. The works Carr showed as an Honorary Exhibitor at the RA included, in 1813, two views of, or in, the grounds of Mulgrave Castle (183, 302).

48. Letter to the Director of the National Gallery, 25 July 1878, NG Archives.

49. Honour 1957 (see Biography, p. 92).

50. Thomas Moore to Lord Lansdowne, 29 June 1829, Russell 1854, vol. VI, London 1854, p. 57.

51. Quoted by Geffrey Wills, 'A Collector to be Thankful For: W.H. Carr (1758–1830)', *Country Life*, 136, I, 24 September 1964, pp. 788–9.

John Linnell
1792–1882

Born 16 June 1792 in Bloomsbury, London, son of James Linnell, carver, gilder and frame-maker. In 1804–5, studied under John Varley, and began sketching from nature; entered Royal Academy Schools November 1805. Prolific exhibitor at RA 1807–81 and BI 1808–59; subjects chiefly portraits up to the 1840s, then landscapes; also painted in watercolour, and made etchings and mezzotints. Was ahead of his time in his love of early Northern European art, frequently visiting the Aders collection and communicating his enthusiasm to William Blake (whose friend and positive supporter he became from 1818) and to Samuel Palmer, who married Linnell's daughter in 1837. A *Self Portrait* of about 1860 is in the National Portrait Gallery (1811).

References

Katherine Crouan, *John Linnell*, exh. cat., Fitzwilliam Museum, Cambridge, and Yale Center for British Art, 1982; David Linnell, *Blake, Palmer, Linnell & Co.*, Lewes, East Sussex 1994.

NG 4142

Samuel Rogers

1846, replica of portrait begun 1833
Oil on panel, 44 × 36.5 cm (17⅜ × 14½ in.)

Provenance

Retained by the artist; Linnell Trustees sale, Christie's 15 March 1918 (42), bt Martin £10 10s.; anon., sold Christie's 31 July 1925 (142), bt Greenstreet; J. Leger & Son, from whom purchased by the National Gallery (Mackerell Fund) 1926.

Exhibited

Huddersfield, Public Library and Art Gallery, *Two Hundred Years of British Painting*, 1946 (96); Leicester Museums and Art Gallery, *Sir George Beaumont and his Circle*, 1953 (11); V&A, *Byron*, 1974 (E1, plate 16).

Literature

The artist's MS record book inscribed 'Outlines and Account of Portraits' (private collection), under 1834; the artist's MS Journal (now untraced), transcript by A.H. Palmer (private collection); A.T. Storey, *Life of John Linnell*, 1892, II, pp. 15, 249; Davies 1946, p. 76; Davies 1959, p. 76; Walker 1985, listed p. 422 within Rogers's iconography, pp. 419–22.

Technical Notes

In good condition. The support is a single-member mahogany panel, with the grain vertical; the white ground is chalk.

This is a replica of a portrait which Samuel Rogers did not commission and never owned, but for which he agreed to give Linnell several sittings in 1833–4.[1] An 'outline' or rough sketch of the original portrait (fig. 1) is included in Linnell's 'Outlines and Account of Portraits', on a page dated 1834 (the finished original is dated 1835). Linnell's annotations to this, coupled with entries in his MS Journal, indicate that he painted both the original portrait and the replica in the hope that Samuel Rogers's reputation would be sufficient to attract an engraver for his portrait. This hope did not materialise.

In September 1846, Linnell agreed to sell the original portrait to his new patron John Gibbons; but, as he noted in his 'Outlines and Account' book, he 'reserved Copyright to JL', and also reserved the right to paint a replica. On 7 November 1846 he began work on the replica, meanwhile

Fig. 1 Antonio del Pollaiuolo (*c.*1432–1498), *Apollo and Daphne*, ? 1478–80. Oil on wood, 29.5 × 20 cm. Purchased by Wynn Ellis, *c.*1850. London, National Gallery. The image might stand for a collector 'saving a work of art for the nation', though that thought is not uppermost in Apollo's mind.

Wynn Ellis had attached one condition to the acceptance of his bequest: that the Trustees of the National Gallery should devote one gallery 'in the National Gallery and not elsewhere' to the display of the pictures selected from his bequest. For at least ten years after his death Gallery XI (later renumbered Gallery 41) was accordingly reserved for the display of the Wynn Ellis Gift (from 1877 to 1886).

Pollaiuolo's *Apollo and Daphne* (fig. 1: NG 928) and three notable Canalettos (NG 937, 938 and 942) were among the sixteen Italian pictures selected. Dutch pictures dominated their choice. Outstanding among these are Jacob van Ruisdael, *A Landscape with a Ruined Castle and a Church* (NG 990), Aelbert Cuyp, *A Milkmaid and Cattle near Dordrecht* (*The Large Dort*) (NG 961) and Jan van de Cappelle, *A River Scene with a Large Ferry* (NG 967). Two fine Netherlandish works selected were Dieric Bouts, *Portrait of a Man* (NG 943), and Marinus van Reymerswaele, *Two Tax Gatherers* (NG 944). A haunting Claude, *Landscape with Æneas at Delos* (NG 1018), was one of three French works chosen (the others being two small paintings by Greuze). Wynn Ellis had also bought excellent examples of works by British artists; but these came into the category of 'modern pictures', and were not offered to the National Gallery. They were dispersed at Christie's in a sale on 6 May 1876 which included *The Top of Cader Idris* by Richard Wilson,[20] and five other works by him; six paintings by J.M.W. Turner, including *The Temple of Jupiter Panhellenius Restored*,[21] and Gainsborough's *Duchess of Devonshire* (noted above) and two of his landscapes.

According to the *Warehousemen and Drapers' Trade Journal*,[22] Ellis was 'a man of strong will and determined character – unostentatious, cautious, moderate, and simple and inexpensive in his habits, and a strict disciplinarian in business', with an 'intense dislike to betting, horse-racing and gambling'. On such evidence, Ellis appears to have been an exemplar of the philosophy of Samuel Smiles: a self-made man who made his pile and was not greatly concerned with the fate of those whom he had left behind in the race. He was well-known in his lifetime for maintaining that 'work and wages' were more beneficial than 'eelymosynary aid'. Legacies in his will reveal a softer heart. A long list of carefully selected bequests throws light on this childless man's choice of good causes, as well as providing reassuring evidence that not all collectors are monomaniacs. Wynn Ellis's largest single bequest was £50,000 to the Trustees of the Simeon Fund, founded by the Revd Charles Simeon of the Church Missionary Society for the purpose of procuring church patronage for evangelical views.[23] The man well-known in his lifetime for the slogan 'work and wages' was revealed after death to have had much compassion for waifs and strays. Over forty different hospitals, orphanages, asylums and benevolent societies received substantial bequests, including the Hospital for Sick Children, the Deaf and Dumb Asylum in the Old Kent Road, the Industrial Home for Crippled Boys (in Wright's Lane, Kensington), the Asylum for Idiots, Earlswood, and the Home for Little Boys, address not given. There were bequests to the Field-Lane Ragged School, Saffron Hill, the Seaside Convalescent Hospital and the Shipwrecked Mariners Society; nor did he forget the Metropolitan Drinking Fountains Association.

In 1814 Ellis had married Mary Maria Smith, a Lincoln girl. They had no children. When she died in 1872, Ellis commissioned Charles Barry junior to design a mausoleum in the churchyard of All Saints, Whitstable, where she was buried. After his death on 20 November 1875, he too was buried there.

The bust entered the National Gallery as by 'Seguier', a name sufficiently associated with the early history of the National Gallery (see pp. 388–98, NG 6022) to explain an evident mistake on the part of the donor, the sitter's nephew. Although Davies (1946, 1959) declined positively to attribute it, there can be little doubt that this is the bust of Wynn Ellis exhibited by R.W. Sievier at the Royal Academy in 1843. Comparison with other examples of Sievier's work, such as the bust of Lawrence in the Soane Museum (noted above) or the bust of the bibliophile Sir William Bolland in Trinity College, Cambridge, shows many stylistic similarities: the bust of Bolland is particularly close in its Chantrey-esque purity of line, in the adoption of august toga-like drapery and in the rather dry modelling of facial hair.

This was the second of two busts of Wynn Ellis which Sievier modelled; the sitter rejected the first,[24] but was evidently sufficiently pleased with the second to allow it to be exhibited at the Royal Academy in 1843 (1438), opposite Sievier's bust of *Mrs Ellis* (1517, now untraced). These were almost the last sculptures Sievier exhibited before moving away from sculpture towards india-rubber.

Companion busts of Wynn Ellis and his wife by Sir Joseph Edgar Boehm, presented to the National Gallery by S.W. Graystone in 1906, were later transferred to the Tate Gallery (N02243–4).

NOTES

1. Coll. Sir John Soane's Museum; repr. A.T. Bolton, *Life of Sir John Soane RA*, 1927, p. 492, plate 43.

2. Royal Society, MS Certificates of Election, vol. IX f.44, quoted by kind permission of the Council of the Royal Society (see also Misc. Corr. V–VI).

3. Rupert Gunnis, *Dictionary of British Sculptors 1660–1851*, London [1951], p. 352. See Gunnis pp. 351–3 for Sievier's sculptures (not all signed); see also selection of photographs in Courtauld Institute of Art, Conway Library.

4. *Warehousemen and Drapers' Trade Journal*, 27 November 1875, p. 618, notes that Ellis's mergers 'culminated in the large establishment of John Howell and Co. Limited'.

5. Gaskell 1990, [p. 5], emphasises this point.

6. Waagen 1838, II, p. 403; Waagen 1854, II, pp. 293–8.

7. Ellis's collection was not static. Two large [anonymous] weeding-out sales at Christie's in 1858 and 1864 in particular improved it. It is not clear to what extent Ellis bought on advice. Michael Levey notes that 'Pearce' acted on many occasions as buyer for Wynn Ellis (1971, p. 27 n. 8).

8. See MacLaren/Brown 1991, pp. 387–90, for its earlier provenance and for versions of the composition.

9. See MacLaren/Brown 1991, pp. 49, 257.

10. Sold anonymously at Christie's, see Gaskell 1990, p. [5].

11. *Athenaeum*, 4 December 1875, pp. 756–7.

12. See John Newman, *The Buildings of England: North-East and East Kent*, Harmondsworth 1969, p. 477. The house, built for Charles Pearson of Whitstable, was inherited by his great-niece, Wynn Ellis's wife. Now known as Whitstable Castle, in Pearson's and the Ellises' day it was called Tankerton Tower.

13. See Graves, *Loan Exhibitions, 1813–1912*, vol. III, Index.

14. Board Minutes, vol. V, p. 69.

15. Wynn Ellis's bequest was announced to the Trustees in the form of a letter from his lawyers, read to the Board at their meeting on 4 December 1875. Besides the Director and Secretary, there were only two Trustees present, William Russell Esq. (in the chair) and Viscount Hardinge. At a Board Meeting on 10 April 1876 (attended by the same people plus one other Trustee, Sir Walter James), the Trustees announced their selection of 94 works (as listed on pp. 440–1). See Board Minutes, vol. V, pp. 69–70, 76.

16. Henry Layard (see pp. 426–30), the Trustee with the greatest knowledge and flair, was abroad.

17. Not yet knighted; knighted 1884.

18. See Lorne Campbell, *The National Gallery: The Early Netherlandish School* (forthcoming).

19. Lot 63; for its sale, theft (by 'Adam Worth') and recovery, see Geoffrey Agnew, *Agnew's 1817–1967*, London 1967, pp. 77–86.

20. Lot 128, as 19 × 28 in.; ? the picture presented by Sir Edward Marsh to the National Gallery on VE Day 1945, later transferred to the Tate Gallery (N 05596), or a version of it.

21. B & J 1984, cat. no. 133; the others are cat. nos 36, 40, 116–17, 141.

22. Cited in note 1.

23. *Encyclopædia Britannica*, London 1911, vol. 25, p. 122.

24. See Henry Churchill's letter to the Director of the National Gallery, 15 June 1878 (NG Archives), offering to present the bust of his uncle to the National Gallery.

Sir William Boxall RA

1800–1879

Portraitist; Director of the National Gallery, 1866–74. Born in or near Oxford 29 June 1800, son of Thomas Boxall, Clerk to the Collector of Excise. Educated at Abingdon Grammar School; entered the Royal Academy Schools 26 March 1819, having already (as 'Master W. Boxall') exhibited a 'Portrait of a lady' at the RA in 1818. Between 1823 and 1866, exhibited over 80 works at the RA and 11 at the BI; ARA in 1851; RA in 1864. Travelled frequently in Italy, studying and making notes on galleries and collections. A friend of Sir Charles and Lady Eastlake from about 1850, he may have been Eastlake's nominee as his successor as Director of the National Gallery. Appointed Director 8 February 1866 and held the post until retirement through ill-health in 1874; knighted 24 March 1871. Died 6 December 1879.

NG 6482

Self Portrait at the Age of about Nineteen

*c.*1819

Oil on canvas, 53 × 41.6 cm (20¼ × 16⅜ in.)

Provenance

Given by the artist to his sister Anne (d.1846), who m. Revd Charles Boxall Longland; by descent to the artist's great-nephew Austin Charles Longland QC, by whose widow sold Christie's 15 June 1973 (3), bt Murdock, by whom resold Christie's 9 November 1973 (229); bt Christopher Wood, by whom presented to the National Gallery 1983.

Literature

Boxall Papers, NG Archives, *passim*; Michael Liversidge, 'John Ruskin and William Boxall: Unpublished Correspondence', *Apollo*, LXXXV, 1967, pp. 39–44; Michael Levey, 'A Little-known Director: Sir William Boxall', *Apollo*, CI, 1975, pp. 354–9.

Technical Notes

The picture had been lined and partly cleaned some time before it was given to the Gallery. The condition is fair. The darker paint of the hair is badly cracked and has been retouched, and the shadowed parts of the face are worn and retouched.

Painted at the age of about nineteen, or when Boxall was about to enter the Royal Academy schools, and given to his sister. This small work, in which the head is rather less than three-quarters the size of life, may be a study for the now untraced 'Oil portrait (bust) of Mr Boxall by himself – painted in 1818 or 1820 – framed (life size)', which was hanging (in the spare bedroom) in Boxall's house when he died.[1]

Boxall's ambition to be a painter of affecting scenes from literature (such as *Milton's Reconciliation with his Wife*, exhibited in 1829,[2] or *Lear and Cordelia*, exhibited in 1831) was frustrated by the need to earn a living. As he wrote to his sister in 1827, 'Portraiture seems the only sure means, at all events less precarious than any other, in the point of getting a good living and I think I had better dedicate myself as much as possible to it.'[3] Attempts to escape from portraiture proved abortive. In the 1830s he designed illustrations for annuals such as *The Keepsake*, *Heath's Book of Beauty* and *Portraits of Principal Female Characters in the Waverley Novels*, wistfully depicting nubile heroines in the popular manner aptly described by Andrew Wilton as '*Keepsake* cheesecake'.[4] The 'Portrait of a beautiful young Arabian girl who served as a model in London', still in Boxall's painting-room when he died,[5] may have been a relic of this brief period of 'prettiness', of which he later told John Gibbons he was 'heartily ashamed'.[6] Boxall's *Geraldine* (the glittering succubus in Coleridge's *Christabel*) was of slightly stronger stuff; exhibited at the Royal Academy in 1850 (287), it was presented by John Kenyon to the National Gallery in 1856 (later transferred to the Tate Gallery).[7] In the mid-1840s Boxall was elated by a commission to design murals for Wyatt's newly built 'Italian Romanesque' church at Wilton, and spent two years on designs for 'colossal figures', only to have his entire work rejected by the Bishop of Salisbury, who would sanction only 'arabesques' on church walls.[8]

Relentlessly, 'the drudgery of portraiture' overtook him. Most of his portraits are small half-lengths, serious, uningratiating, unrelieved by decorative detail and almost invariably gloomy. Sometimes called 'noble', they were rarely acclaimed as likenesses.[9] His sitters included the artists David Cox,[10] Anthony Vandyke Copley Fielding,[11] John Frederick Lewis,[12] Thomas Stothard,[13] the sculptor John Gibson (noted below) and his American pupil Harriet Hosmer,[14] the architect C.R. Cockerell[15] and the writers Allan Cunningham[16] and Walter Savage Landor.[17] Boxall's portrait of William Wordsworth was particularly dour; Wordsworth wrote 'I cannot get any of my Friends and Acquaintances to be pleased [with it] ... much too dark and gloomy.'[18] Boxall's gravitas was particularly popular with dignitaries and with far-flung clergymen, leading to commissions for *The Lord Bishop of Guiana* (1843), *Archdeacon W. Williams of New Zealand* (1852) and *The Lord Bishop of Mauritius* (1855). His most important commission was for a full-length *Portrait of the Prince Consort as Master of the Trinity House*.[19] Boxall's portrait of his friend John Gibson RA, exhibited at the Royal Academy as Boxall's Diploma work in 1864 (fig. 1), prompted comments from the *Art Journal* which, while not unkind, fairly catch Boxall's general portrait style: 'simply yet nobly rendered, abstemious of distracting accessories, and coloured in unobtrusive greys'.[20] Ruskin believed Boxall's fault to be an 'excess of delicacy and tenderness'.[21] The lapse of thirteen years between Boxall's election as ARA (in 1851) and as RA (in 1864) suggests that his fellow-artists did not rate his talents very high. 'Who *raves* about Boxall?' asked Frith's patron John Gibbons in 1843.[22]

Boxall was not gregarious. He belonged to the Anonymous Society, later called the Sterling Club,[23] but figures little in contemporary memoirs. But he appears to have been liked by his fellow-artists; his acquaintance ranged from Turner[24] to the young Whistler, whose portrait he exhibited in 1849.[25] In 1828, 1834–6 (for nearly two years) and on many later visits, he travelled widely in Italy, making detailed notes on pictures in galleries and private collections.[26] A chalk drawing of the 'Head of Christ' from Leonardo's *Last Supper* (to study that work intently was the 'chief object' of Boxall's journey to Milan in 1845) was engraved,[27] and helped to strengthen his reputation for having a sound knowledge of the techniques of the early masters. Ruskin, whom he met in Italy in 1845, and with whom he corresponded for about two years, ruthlessly picked Boxall's brain, especially when asked to review Eastlake's *Materials for the History of Oil Painting*, 1847.[28] Boxall's closest friends by the early 1850s were probably Sir Charles Eastlake RA, Director of the National Gallery 1855–65, and Lady Eastlake, whose portrait he painted in 1854[29] (Millais described it as 'very good, but not very like'), and who took Boxall under her wing. Boxall accompanied the Eastlakes on picture-hunting tours in Italy. Both the Eastlakes probably had Boxall in mind as Eastlake's successor.

Sir Charles Eastlake died in Italy on 24 December 1865. Within four days, various proposals for the directorship circulated. Queen Victoria suggested Mr Robinson, Superintendent of Art at the South Kensington Museum. The Prime Minister, Lord John Russell, wanted his Under-Secretary at the Foreign Office, Austen Henry Layard (see NG 5449, pp. 426–30), but Layard himself believed the post should go to an artist. Landseer's name was aired, but it was generally felt that he was by now too disordered by alcohol to undertake it. Gladstone (then at the Treasury), who may have discussed the matter with Eastlake before his death, proposed Boxall, and carried the day. On 9 February 1866 the Queen approved Boxall's appointment as Director. Ten days later he made his first appearance at a meeting of the National Gallery Trustees.

Boxall, who by 1866 had lost impetus as an artist, was revivified by his appointment to the National Gallery. He now 'ceased his labours as an artist',[30] exhibiting no further work. Instead, he threw himself into the task of travelling in search of purchases for the National Gallery. The fact that Lady Eastlake promptly lent him Eastlake's detailed Italian journals strengthens the probability that Boxall was the choice of both Eastlakes.[31] Lady Eastlake continued to keep a kind but beady eye on Boxall, pursuing him by correspondence throughout Italy ('I know all your ground so well that I follow in my mind's eye everywhere');[32] her approval that Boxall was *en poste* was signified by her readiness in 1867 to sell to the Gallery, at the prices Eastlake had paid for them, fifteen pictures from his private collection ('my dear one's pictures'), as well as his library.[33] Boxall's loyalty may sometimes have been strained by Lady Eastlake's habit of referring to the institution of which he was now Director as '*his* National Gallery';[34] nevertheless his painting *The Knight and the Lady* may have symbolised his devotion to Lady Eastlake, and he presented her with his oil sketch for it.[35]

As Michael Levey observes, 'Boxall has never properly emerged from the shadows cast both by his great predecessor and by his successor, Sir Fredric Burton';[36] but he was to prove an able and perhaps surprisingly forceful Director. In making purchases, Boxall enjoyed the same degree of independence of action as Eastlake had; as Wornum noted on 15 October 1867, 'Every recommendation for purchase is the personal act of the Director.'[37] Each year Boxall made a long Continental tour to look at possible acquisitions; but he was well aware that great works 'are as rare as diamonds of the

first water',[38] and that when they were offered, 'only millionaires or madness could buy them'.[39] To give an account of all the acquisitions he made is impossible here. Levey 1975 discusses most of his major purchases; here only a few for which Boxall's own comments survive are recounted.

Boxall's first visit to Italy as Director, early in 1866, began with an attempt to conclude Eastlake's negotiations for the purchase of two generally acclaimed works, Bellini's *Coronation of the Virgin*[40] and Signorelli's *Pan and the Gods*, but high prices prevented him from securing either. Though he realised that the Signorelli was in poor condition, and 'not in a sympathetic class for the English public',[41] the picture affected him powerfully, and continued to haunt his thoughts.[42] His first purchases were two pictures (NG 755 and 756) which Eastlake had attributed to Melozzo da Forli (they were later given to Joos van Wassenhove).[43] More sensationally, in July 1866 Boxall bought, for £7000, *Christ blessing the Children* (NG 757), which he and many others called 'the great Rembrandt' (also known, from its previous owners, as 'the Pommersfelden' or 'the Schönborn Rembrandt'). Three years later, this purchase prompted a debate in the House of Lords in which the attribution, the price paid and the Director's independence of action were all questioned.[44] The attack on the 'Rembrandt', led by Lord Winchilsea, was stoutly defended by Lord Overstone, Chairman of the National Gallery Trustees.[45] He defined the relationship between the Director and his Trustees,[46] emphasised that 'in the present case, the Director reported to the Trustees in the usual way, and they recorded no dissent, and so they participated in the responsibility' and proceeded to cite numerous opinions (including those of the late Sir Charles Eastlake, M. Thoré-Bürger, Dr Waagen, Keeper of the Berlin Gallery, Cavalier Giuseppe Mollini of the Brera Gallery, Milan, and M. Reiset of the Louvre) that the picture was a remarkably fine work by Rembrandt. Lord Winchilsea proceeded to table a motion which read: 'That henceforth it be an instruction to Mr Boxall, RA, to buy no picture in England without previously submitting it to the judgment of the Trustees of the National Gallery, or any picture in foreign parts which has not got an authentic pedigree from the date of its being painted by the master to whom it is ascribed to the day of purchase, unless by special permission in writing'; briefly discussed at the next session, the motion was then withdrawn.[47] The attribution of NG 757 to Rembrandt was retained until 1880, when it was catalogued as a School painting; it is now generally accepted as by Nicolaes Maes.[48]

Fig. 1 *John Gibson RA*, exhibited 1851 and deposited with the Royal Academy as William Boxall's Diploma work in 1864. Oil on canvas, 97.8 × 72.4 cm. London, Royal Academy.

At much the same time as he bought 'the great Rembrandt', Boxall bought, for £160, and as a 'speculation' of the kind Eastlake had himself often boldly made, a 'dreadfully dirty' tempera portrait of a woman in yellow – 'something that looks very like Piero della Francesca' – which he would be happy to keep for himself if it did not clean satisfactorily: but it did, entering the Gallery as NG 758, *Portrait of a Lady*, later attributed to Baldovinetti. In 1867 he purchased what became another much-loved Gallery picture, *Tobias and the Angel* (NG 781), now attributed to Verrocchio. In these and many subsequent purchases, Boxall demonstrated that he was less concerned with 'names' than with (in his recurring phrase) 'the work of an original mind'.

Boxall's purchase of Michelangelo's *Entombment* (NG 790) in 1868 demonstrates his sureness of judgement at its best. In a simply worded but effective memorandum of 26 July 1869 to the Gallery Trustees, he wrote: 'There is no history to guide us as to the authorship of this picture; we must therefore trust entirely to the internal evidence of the work itself.' He felt sure that the picture was by a sculptor, adding 'We feel the presence of a great mind throughout the whole of this work, notwithstanding its rugged and unfinished condition.'[49] Boxall also succeeded (in 1870) where Eastlake had failed (in 1845),[50] in persuading the Trustees to purchase Michelangelo's *Madonna and Child with Saint John and Angels* (the so-called 'Manchester Madonna', NG 809).

Boxall particularly exerted himself to buy thirteen panels (then in the collection of Prince Anatole Demidoff) from the polyptych painted by Crivelli as the altarpiece of S. Domenico, Ascoli Piceno, and later broken up; having strongly recommended their purchase to the Trustees in 1866, he had the satisfaction of concluding the purchase two years later, at a rather lower price.[51] In 1870 he bought the Cima altarpiece of *The Incredulity of Saint Thomas* (NG 816), though well aware that it was 'very much injured'. He himself cleaned it, with the aid of the restorer Henry Merritt, recording that they removed 'only a load of varnish, opaque patchy and disfiguring ... it

Fig. 2 Anna Lea Merritt (1844–1930), *Sir William Boxall RA with his dog Garibaldi*, c.1875. Oil on canvas, 119.4 × 90.2 cm. London, Royal Academy.

has been done by Merritt and myself, simply by the hand without a drop of spirit'.[52] Picture cleaning was usually left to the supervision of Ralph Wornum, Boxall's second-in-command; Boxall advocated minimum cleaning, adjuring Wornum to 'use no other process than the simple washing with pea meal and leather'.[53]

Boxall also had a good eye for Dutch pictures; he bought the first Pieter de Hooch to enter the National Gallery (*A Woman and her Maid in a Courtyard*, purchased in 1869, NG 794), and two years later purchased Hobbema's *The Avenue at Middelharnis* (NG 830). The purchase of Sir Robert Peel's collection of 77 pictures in 1871[54] greatly helped to increase the Gallery's representation of the Dutch School, as did the Wynn Ellis bequest (see under NG 2239, pp. 414–18) of mostly Dutch pictures in the year after Boxall's retirement.

Boxall took a keen interest in displaying and lighting pictures. With the departure of the Royal Academy to Burlington House in 1869, the eastern half of the Trafalgar Square building at last became free; after a public competition, the architect Edward Middleton Barry RA was commissioned to reconstruct the Gallery and to design a new wing comprising the present eastern dome and seven extra rooms. Scrappy but emphatic notes by Boxall,[55] probably made in connection with this, stress that 'The first condition of a picture gallery is that every work exhibited shall be perfectly seen ... the Building should be a Picture Gallery – not a cathedral nor a Theatre... The primary consideration is unobstructed light' (top-lighting, wherever possible).[56] He believed that very long galleries were 'tedious to the spectator'; one long gallery of, say, 50 feet, was desirable, but the others should be smaller, their height nearly equal to their width, with exits and entrances at their ends to give maximum hanging space. The foundations for the new wing were laid in 1872 during Boxall's directorship; it opened in 1877, three years after his retirement.

In 1871, in his seventieth year, and having served as Director for five years, Boxall wished to retire, but was persuaded to stay on. One of his last and most generally acclaimed purchases was Mantegna's *Introduction of the Cult of Cybele at Rome* (NG 902). He finally retired in 1874, on grounds of 'ill-health', a term which disguised the depression that had dogged him for most of his adult life.[57] Boxall had not married; his last years were forlorn. He was usually to be found 'sitting in an armchair with a soft rug over his knees and his dog Garibaldi squeezed into the chair beside him', as Anna Lea Merritt described and portrayed him in about 1875 (fig. 2);[58] under the sofa was 'a large quantity of paper for drawings', unused.[59] Boxall died on 6 December 1879.[60]

NOTES

BP/NG = *Boxall Papers, National Gallery Archives*

1. BP/NG 14/85: MS inventory of Boxall's house after his death, no. 1, in 'Friends Bed-Room'. In Boxall's bedroom (unnumbered in the inventory) were two framed and glazed 'Portraits (bust, small prop.) of Mr B.'s father and mother, in coloured crayons drawn by Mr B. in 1835 previously to his departure for Italy.' These are now untraced. They may or may not relate to two small oil portraits which were presented by H.W. Standen to the NG in 1964 as a self portrait of Boxall and a portrait of Boxall's wife (NG 6352/3, both repr. *CIC* 1995, p. 74; both NG Archive Collection). Since Boxall was unmarried, NG 6352 cannot be of his wife. Possibly this pair of portraits, which appear to date from about 1840, are of Boxall's parents. H.W. Standen believed that they were given by Boxall before 1853 to his great-grandfather, an Oxford picture dealer called James Wyatt.

2. The *Gentleman's Magazine* reviewer, 1829, p. 539, described this as 'A scene of the deepest feeling. How imploringly she requests forgiveness; and what a fine expression of sorrow for the past and hope for the future is displayed in the poet's countenance. His affection slept, but never died.'

3. Quoted by Liversidge 1967, p. 39, from privately held Boxall papers.

4. See Andrew Wilton, 'The "Keepsake" Convention: Jessica and Some Related Pictures', *Turner Studies*, 9, no. 2, 1989, p. 23. Engravings of some of Boxall's Beauties (*The Enchantress, Meditation, Louisa, Francesca*, etc.) are in the Witt Library, Courtauld Institute.

5. BP/NG 14/85: MS inventory, no. 57.

6. John Gibbons, letter of 1843 to W.P. Frith, fully quoted in W.P. Frith, *My Autobiography and Reminiscences*, 3 vols, London 1888, III, pp. 202–3.

7. Later transferred to the Tate Gallery (N 00601); in poor condition, and not displayed since records were kept.

8. See Lord Coleridge 1880 (cited in note 57), pp. 181–2.

9. Boxall's portrait of Walter Savage Landor appears to have been an exception: Charles Dickens described it as 'A singularly good likeness, the result of close and subtle observation' (*All the Year Round*, 24 July 1869, pp. 181–2).

10. NPG 1986; Ormond 1973, p. 119, plate 218.

11. NPG 601; Ormond 1973, pp. 173–4, plate 328.

12. NPG 1470; Ormond 1973, p. 270, plate 531.

13. Exh. RA 1829 (410), untraced.

14. Hanging in Boxall's house when he died (BP/NG MS inventory, between nos 24 and 25); in the same (Longland) sale as NG 6482 (Christie's 9 November 1973, as lot 5, repr., but lot nos 5 and 6 have been transposed. Repr. (but untraced) by Dolly Sherwood, *Harriet Hosmer, American Sculptor 1830–1908*, Columbia and London 1991, facing p. 150. According to Sherwood (p. 271), Hosmer 'flirted a deal' with Boxall, probably to disguise her preference for her own sex.

15. Coll. RIBA.

16. Untraced.

17. Exh. RA 1853 (159); coll. V&A; Parkinson 1990, pp. 7–8, repr. Before sitting, Landor wrote to John Forster: 'He [Boxall] is incomparably our best painter, I have seen pictures by him that would have done honour to Titian' (quoted in R.H. Super, *Walter Savage Landor*, New York 1954, p. 411). The *Art Journal* (1853, p. 141) described it as 'a small study, very simple in treatment, and we think unhealthy in complexion'. Repr. as frontispiece to John Forster, *Walter Savage Landor*, London 1879.

18. Letter to John Gardner, late 1832 or early 1833, published in Alan G. Hill, *The Letters of William and Dorothy Wordsworth*, V, part 2, Oxford 1979, p. 578. For the portrait, see Frances Blanshard, *Portraits of Wordsworth*, London 1959, pp. 70–1, 154–5 for (i) the preliminary oil sketch of early 1831, no. XVIII, plate 12a; (ii) the finished portrait, late 1831 or early 1832, no. XIX, plate 12b (descendant's collection).

19. Trinity House, London; repr. Levey 1975, p. 355; see also Ormond 1973, p. 13.

20. Exh. RA 1864 (54); repr. *Royal Academy: Paintings and Sculptures in the Diploma and Gibson Galleries*, London 1931, p. 16, no. 35; Liversidge 1967, p. 41, fig. 2. See *Art Journal*, 1864, p. 162. An earlier portrait by Boxall of Gibson was exh. RA 1851 (180).

21. Ruskin, *Academy Notes*, 1855, *Works*, vol. XIV, 1904, p. 8.

22. John Gibbons to Frith, see W.P. Frith 1888 (cited in note 6), p. 203.

23. See Robertson 1978, pp. 46–7; a dining-club founded by John Sterling, its members included Allan Cunningham, Carlyle, Tennyson and Monckton Milnes.

24. Tim Hilton notes that Boxall was a fellow-guest of Turner's at Ruskin's father's house in 1846 and 1848 (*John Ruskin, The Early Years*, London 1985, p. 101).

25. Exh. RA 1849 (48, as 'A portrait'); Hunterian Museum, Glasgow; see Robin Spencer, 'Whistler's early relations with Britain and the significance of industry and commerce for his art', *Burlington Magazine*, CXXXVI, 1994, p. 223, repr. fig. 16.

26. BP/NG includes many such notes; see for example BP/NG 14/119.

27. Boxall to his sister, from Milan, 14 September 1845: 'I have now finished the head of Leonardo da Vinci, the chief object of my journey. The picture is fast perishing, and the Head of Christ is much changed since I was here before, when I made the sketch from it. It has also suffered from retouching since that time so that the task has been extremely difficult – I have done as much as I can with it, but the original is now little more than a shadow and I fear a few years more will wear it quite away', quoted in Liversidge 1967, p. 39. Liversidge reproduces Boxall's preliminary drawing, p. 43, fig. 3; the finished drawing was engraved by F.C. Lewis and Francis Holl, published 1850.

28. Ruskin to Boxall, 11 July 1847: '...I should be truly grateful to you, if you have read Eastlake's book, if you would jot down for me at any leisure moment, any points of it which you think it would be well to bring more distinctly before the public, and to give me your own general notions about grounds and varnishes, roughly, and advise me of any passages or anecdotes bearing on the subject which you happen to know of in other books. I am in no hurry – a month hence will do quite well...' On 13 September 1847 Ruskin wrote thanking Boxall 'for your kind long letter – it is exactly what I want, and everyway useful. I hope you will not regret having written it when you find it encourages me "to ask for more"...' (he then does so, at length). Both passages quoted are from letters published in full in Liversidge 1967, p. 43.

29. The portrait is repr. Mary Lutyens, *Millais and the Ruskins*, London 1967, facing p. 210 (and in Robertson 1978, p. 119); Lutyens quotes Millais's comment on the portrait p. 197. Boxall's pencil study for it is in the Ashmolean Museum, Oxford. Liversidge 1967 suggests, p. 39, that it was the influence of Lady Eastlake, who had played a large part in urging Effie Ruskin to sue for annulment of her marriage in 1854, which led to the abrupt cessation that year of Boxall's correspondence with Ruskin.

30. *Art Journal*, 1880, p. 83.

31. Boxall to NG Trustees, 1 November 1866, BP/NG 5/165.

32. Lady Eastlake to Boxall, 9 September 1867, BP/NG 14/18.

33. See Robertson 1978, p. 236, and p. 276 for Lady Eastlake's list of the fifteen pictures to be offered to the NG, at the prices Eastlake had paid for them. In April 1876, on Boxall's recommendation, the Trustees purchased nine of the fifteen.

34. Lady Eastlake to Boxall, 2 August 1867: she can bear to part with 'My Dear One's pictures' knowing that they will be safe in '*his* National Gallery'. Original in University of North Carolina Library.

35. Lady Eastlake sale, Christie's 2 June 1894 (52, 'A Knight and Lady, seated by a monument: moonlight – a sketch 17½ × 23½ [in.]'; bt Prideaux). The finished picture remained with Boxall; inventory no. 59; both untraced. Boxall owned the *Portrait of a Man in Profile* by Boltraffio, which had first impressed Eastlake in Bergamo in 1855, and which Boxall bought for himself in Milan *c.*1864; it is listed in the MS inventory of his house (see note 1) after his death. The Boltraffio was in Lady Eastlake's sale in 1894 (60); but it is not clear how she acquired it. In Martin Davies, *National Gallery Catalogues: Earlier Italian Schools*, 1951, and later editions, it is stated that Boxall bequeathed his Boltraffio to Lady Eastlake; but his will (copy, BP/NG) included no bequests to Lady Eastlake. The picture entered the NG with the Mond Collection in 1924 as NG 3916.

36. Levey 1975, p. 354.

37. Wornum to Robert Boyle, BP/NG 14/125.

38. Boxall to Wornum, Milan, 2 November 1867, BP/NG 5/170.

39. Boxall to Professor Grüner, Dresden, 22 October 1867, BP/NG 14/125.

40. Pesaro, Ducal Palace.

41. See Boxall to Layard, Milan, 21 June 1866, BP/NG 14/125.

42. The Signorelli was bought for the Gemäldegalerie, Berlin. In 1945 it was destroyed by fire, with some 400 other pictures, while in store in an anti-aircraft bunker. Repr. Hennin Bock et al., *The Gemäldegalerie, Berlin*, London 1986, p. 30, fig. 5.

43. See BP/NG 14/6.

44. *Hansard*, vol. CXCVIII, 26 July 1869, pp. 654–66, followed by a brief debate on 3 August 1869, ibid., pp. 1140–2.

45. Ibid., pp. 654–9.

46. 'The Director ... was vested with plenary authority in the choice and purchase of pictures, and nothing could be done except on his judgment and with his full responsibility. But the Director was surrounded by a body of Trustees, to whom he was bound to report all his proceedings. If, in any case, they doubted, dissented or condemned, it was their duty to record their opinion, which opinion was necessarily laid before Parliament; but if they abstained from any such expression of opinion, they by their silence acquiesced and shared in the responsibility of his acts.' Ibid., p. 654.

47. Ibid., p. 1142.

48. See MacLaren/Brown 1991, pp. 242–5; Frances Suzman Jowell, 'Thoré-Bürger – a critical role in the art market', *Burlington Magazine*, CXXXIII, 1996, pp. 120–1. The NG's purchase of the picture was the subject of a debate in the House of Lords, 26 July 1869.

49. In the House of Lords debate of 26 July 1869, Lord Overstone quoted Boxall's comments on the *Entombment* as an instance of his sound judgement.

50. See Robertson 1978, p. 84.

51. The thirteen panels in the National Gallery's collection are NG 788.1–13. For a concise summary of the existing component parts of the Crivelli polyptych, see the *NG CIC* 1995, pp. 160–2; for a reconstruction, see p. 741, Appendix A.

52. Boxall to Wornum, 12 August 1870, BP/NG 14/113.

53. Boxall to Wornum, from Dresden, 21 September 1867, BP/NG 5/170.

54. Boxall's report to the Chancellor of the Exchequer on the desirability of purchasing the Peel Collection, 2 March 1871, is BP/NG 14/113.

55. BP/NG 14/105/120.

56. Boxall made a point of studying lighting systems in Berlin, Dresden and Vienna; see BP/NG 14/99/9. The introduction of gas-lighting threatened to end his good relationship with his Chairman, Lord Overstone, who wrote furiously: 'Why purchase other than specimens when they will all be burned by gas at night?' (Lord Overstone to Boxall, 9 March 1870, BP/NG 14/35/1869).

57. A passage in a long memoir of Boxall by his old friend Lord Coleridge (*The Fortnightly Review*, CLVIII, New Series, 1880, pp. 188–9) comes close to a diagnosis of clinical depression: 'No doubt he had faults of temper, no doubt to some men he was difficult and irritable. His health was never strong; he lived much alone; and those only who have experienced the terrible suffering of nervous weakness, and have risen superior to its depressing effects, are entitled to condemn a fellow-creature who has, it may be, allowed such suffering sometimes to overpower his self-control.'

58. Presented to the RA by Sir Edward Poynter in 1879. Anna Lea Merritt's descriptions of Boxall at this time are in 'Memories from 1844 to 1927', typescript, copy NPG Archives, pp. 174–5.

59. BP/NG 14/85: MS inventory.

60. Studio sale Christie's 8 June 1880.

John Warrington Wood

1839–1886

Sculptor of mythological and biblical subjects, and of portrait busts. Born 1839 at Warrington, Lancashire, son of the Deputy Borough Surveyor; trained there (as a stonemason) and eventually died there. To distinguish his name from that of the older sculptor John Wood (1801–70), he adopted Warrington as his middle name. Moved in 1861 to Rome, where he chiefly worked; sculpted medallion of Keats for the Protestant Cemetery, Rome, 1876; elected to Guild of St Luke, Rome, 1877. Exhibited at the Royal Academy 1868–74. Wood's statues of Raphael and Michelangelo stand at the entrance to the Walker Art Gallery, Liverpool. Some of his best work is in Warrington Art Gallery.

References

T. Wilmot, 'John Warrington Wood, Sculptor', *Magazine of Art*, 1891, pp. 136–40; Mary J. Taylor, 'Between Phidias and Bernini. The Life and Work of John Warrington Wood 1839–1886', unpublished dissertation for the Diploma in Art Gallery and Museum Studies, University of Manchester, 1984, p. 6 and *passim.*

NG 5449

Sir Austen Henry Layard

1881, remodelled from the bust of 1869

Marble, approximately 64 cm (25¼ in.) from top of head to bottom of plinth; 37 cm (14½ in.) across top of chest. Chiselled *AUSTEN HENRY LAYARD* across lower front and *J. Warrington Wood / Sculpt Roma 1881* across lower right edge.

Provenance

Commissioned by the sitter; his widow (d.1912), then passed to Arthur du Cane, his nephew by marriage, and from the latter to his nephew Vice-Admiral Arthur John Layard Murray, by whom presented to the National Gallery 1943.

Exhibited

(in its first state) RA 1870 (1101, as 'The Rt. Hon. Austen Henry Layard, Her Majesty's minister in Madrid; marble').

Literature

MS Journals of Lady Layard, the sitter's wife, BL Add. MSS. 46153 (vol. I), 46158 (vol. VI), 46159 (vol. VII).

Technical Notes

Condition fair; a small discoloured streak in the forehead; two small chips in the base.

Fig. 1 George Frederic Watts (1817–1904), *Austen Henry Layard as a Young Man*, *c.*1851. Black chalk on paper, 59.7 × 49.5 cm. London, National Portrait Gallery.

Austen Henry Layard[1] was born on 5 March 1817 in an hotel on the Left Bank in Paris. His parents were Henry Layard, an amateur of the arts but asthmatic, and Marianne Austen, a banker's daughter. In search of a kinder climate, they eventually settled in Florence, renting a floor of the Palazzo Rucellai from that by then impoverished family. Layard was largely brought up in Florence, and had fluent Italian. His first contact with art is said to have been hurling a shoe at Filippino Lippi's Rucellai altarpiece *The Virgin and Child with Saints Jerome and Dominic* (now NG 293), having aimed it at his brother.[2] Later his father took him to galleries in Florence. He was sent back to England and to a school in Richmond; then qualified as an attorney, but found the work so boring that he decided to ride across the Ottoman Empire and Persia to Ceylon, where he had relatives who might find him more congenial work. In Constantinople he was taken on temporarily as secretary to the ambassador, Stratford Canning. While there, he learned of the Frenchman Paul Botta's archaeological discoveries at Mosul. The prevailing spirit of international rivalry demanded that the British

AUSTEN HENRY LAYARD

should not allow themselves to be outpaced by the French in this or any other field. Layard picked up local rumours of 'palaces underground' at Nimrud and, with financial backing from Canning, determined to dig there, using local tribesmen as labourers. On the first day of his dig, Layard found himself uncovering the marble walls of the palace of Ashurnarsipal II, who reigned in Assyria from 883 to 859 BC. Over the next five years, his finds were astonishing.

Layard's excavations in Assyria made his name. At the peak of his fame, around 1850, he was still only in his early thirties. He entered Parliament, and held Cabinet office; he served as ambassador in Madrid and Constantinople; he became a Trustee of the National Gallery; and he built up a large collection of paintings, most of which he bequeathed to the National Gallery. While fairly full accounts have been offered above of comparatively neglected National Gallery benefactors, such as the Revd William Holwell Carr (pp. 399–405) and Sir Charles Long, Lord Farnborough (pp. 376–87), Henry Layard's career, his character and his collection are so well-documented that they are merely outlined here. References to authoritative studies of particular aspects of his career will be given during the course of this sketch. For a thoroughly informative biography which spans every aspect of his career and is also an excellent read, see Gordon Waterfield, *Layard of Nineveh*, London 1963.

Layard's greatest achievement was his discovery and excavation of the palaces of Assyrian kings at Nimrud and Nineveh, during the years 1845–51. He had no training as an archaeologist; but he is seen at his best planning (almost single-handedly) the digs, recording his discoveries and finally organising the transport of his massive finds, most of which (at Canning's stipulation) were destined for the British Museum. Each winged bull alone weighed over ten tons; every item had to be floated precariously on rafts down the Tigris to the Persian Gulf as the first stage of the long journey to the forecourt of the British Museum (fig. 2). When Prince Albert saw the newly arrived antiquities, he is reputed to have said 'These things are without price; no thousands could buy them, and they have cost the country nothing.'[3] Layard's finds form the greater part of the British Museum's collection of Assyrian antiquities,[4] his winged lions and bulls compelling attention, and his friezes and ivories equally repaying it. Layard's discovery of the 'great library' of cuneiform tablets in Sennacherib's palace at Nineveh provided the basis for the whole study of Assyriology. Layard's first book, *Nineveh and its Remains* (first published by John Murray, London 1849), made him famous overnight; 'No one speaks of any other book but *Nineveh*', Layard's uncle noted.[5] A second expedition to Mosul 1849–51 was followed by *Nineveh and Babylon*[6] (1853). Both books ran into many editions, and Layard became one of John Murray's best-selling authors. The sale of his books (*Nineveh and its Remains* alone gave him an income of £1500 a year[7]) helped to finance Layard's picture-buying. Subsequent publications include *Early Adventures*, published in 1887, and an *Autobiography*,[8] published in 1903, after his death. For Layard as archaeologist, see Waterfield 1963, Parts I–II; Julian Reade, *Assyrian Sculpture*, British Museum Publications, London 1983, *passim*; Ian Jenkins, *Archaeologists & Aesthetes in the Sculpture Galleries of the British Museum 1800–1939*, London 1992, pp. 155–8.

Layard's winged bulls had carried him to such a height of fame that it seemed that he was *capable de tout*. He was everywhere praised and fêted. Lord Ellesmere wrote of him: 'He is one of those men of whom England seems to have a monopoly, who go anywhere, surmount anything and achieve everything without assistance, patronage or fuss of any kind.'[9] In 1852 Layard was elected to Parliament.[10] In January 1853 the Prime Minister, Lord John Russell, invited him to be Under-Secretary for the Foreign Office. Layard, still only 35, lacked all experience but accepted the post. He sat increasingly noisily in the House of Commons until 1868–9. *Punch* personified him as one of his own winged bulls;[11] and Disraeli voiced a general opinion in considering that Layard was 'too passionate and prejudiced' to be effective in politics. Layard's 'passionate' character is caught in G.F. Watts's black chalk portrait drawing of him, made about 1851 (fig. 1). Layard held office as Under-Secretary of State for Foreign Affairs 1861–6, and as First Commissioner of Works and Buildings 1868–9; in the latter role, he was closely involved with the decoration of the Albert Memorial,[12] and with the redecoration of the Central Hall of the House of Commons.[13] Impetuous and far from diplomatic by nature (Labouchere's word for him was 'bumptious'[14]), he was appointed British Ambassador in Madrid 1869–77, and in Constantinople 1877–84, from whence he had to be recalled. See Waterfield 1963, Parts III–V; Sir Ashley Clarke, 'Layard and Diplomacy', pp. 93–100 in ed. F.M. Fales and B.J. Hickey, papers of the Layard *Symposium*, Venice 1987.

Layard began collecting paintings in 1855, with a purchase of three fragments from a fresco by Spinello (NG 1216.1–3). He frequently returned to Italy, eventually retiring to Ca' Capello in Venice. By far the largest part of his collection was of works by Italian artists. He was ahead of most of his contemporaries in admiring the work of the so-called 'primitives'. Most of his purchases were made between about 1865 and 1875; he backed his own judgement, and his fluency in Italian enabled him to negotiate directly with Italian families: thus, in one coup, he acquired Bramantino's *Adoration of the Kings* (NG 3073) and Tura's *Allegory* (NG 3070), among a large group of works purchased from the Costabili collection in Ferrara. Layard had a flexible mind and an ever-alert eye. He had once poured scorn on 'early Gothic daubs', but was stopped in his tracks by seeing in Vicenza a painting of *Christ Nailed to the Cross*: 'dreadful to look at, but for expression and power one of the most extraordinary bits of painting I ever saw'.[15] He had no idea who it was by, but determined to have it and, after three days' bargaining, secured it. It is now recognised as by Gerard David (NG 3067). Layard came to value the advice of Giovanni Morelli, with whom he regularly corresponded, and to whose *Italian Painters* (in the English translation, 1892) he contributed a long introduction. His own writings on art include essays on early fresco painters for the Arundel Society,[16] of which he was an active member, and various long articles in the *Quarterly Review*, notably a long review of the *Manchester Art Treasures* exhibition of 1857 and critical comments on the National Gallery in 1859 and 1886.[17] In 1887 he translated and updated F.T. Kugler's *Handbook of Painting*, first published in 1837.

Layard was a friend of both Sir Charles and Lady Eastlake.[18] After Eastlake's death in 1865, Lord John Russell PM wanted to appoint Layard as Director of the National Gallery while retaining his services as Under-Secretary for Foreign Affairs. Layard was willing to do both jobs simultaneously (forgoing a salary as Director), but the Trustees and Queen Victoria decided otherwise, making the sounder if less glamorous appointment of Boxall (see pp. 419–25). Instead, Layard was appointed a Trustee of the National Gallery, serving for nearly thirty years until his death in 1894.

In March 1869 Layard married Enid Guest, presenting her with a necklace, earrings and ring of Mesopotamian cylinder seals, made up by a Bond Street jeweller;[19] she wore the necklace to a dinner-party at Osborne House, where it was passed round to be admired by Queen Victoria and her guests, and set a new 'Assyrian style' fashion in jewellery. They had no children. Layard bequeathed the greater part of his collection after his wife's death to the National Gallery.

Layard died in London on 5 July 1894. When the news reached Windsor, Queen Victoria wrote to her daughter the Empress Dowager of Germany: 'I was sure you would be sorry for Sir Henry Layard. He was a great encourager of Art, but not a safe politician.' It is by no means an unjust summary.

Wood's bust was originally modelled in London in November 1869, during the fortnight before Layard's departure to take up the post of Ambassador to the Court of Madrid; Lady Layard recorded on 13 November 1869: 'Mr Warrington Wood finished & took away Henry's bust he had been doing this last week – despite the rush & packing it promises to be very like' (Journals, IV, f.30r). The bust modelled in 1869 was exhibited in marble at the Royal Academy the following year; but Wood himself was evidently not satisfied with it, and took the opportunity twelve years later to remodel it.

In 1881 Layard commissioned Wood to execute a bust of Lady Layard; and at the sculptor's request, Layard himself gave Wood several further sittings so that his own bust could be remodelled. This time the sittings were in Rome, in Wood's studio in the Villa Campana. The first of Layard's re-sittings was on 26 January 1881; Lady Layard noted 'Henry went with me to the Villa Campana to give Mr Wood a sitting for his portrait wch he wishes to alter' (Journals, VI, f.67). Layard sat to Wood six times in all between 26 January and 10 February 1881. The busts of both the Layards were delivered to them in London on 6 February 1882, Lady Layard recording that day 'Henry & my bust done by Mr Warrington Wood arrived from Rome' (Journals, VII, f.99). Wood's high-minded neo-classical manner is in marked contrast to the florid style of Boehm's bust of Layard.

Layard's Italian pictures will be more fully discussed by Nicholas Penny in his forthcoming National Gallery catalogue. Among the published papers of the Layard *Symposium*, ed. Fales and Hickey, Venice 1987, see particularly Jaynie Anderson, 'Layard and Morelli' (pp. 109–37), Madeline Lennon, 'Layard's Letters to Morelli' (pp. 139–47), Judy Rudoe, 'Lady Layard's Jewellery and the "Assyrian Style" in Nineteenth-Century Jewellery Design' (pp. 213–26) and Irene Favoretto, 'La Collezione Layard: Storia, Formazione e Vicende' (pp. 227–36).

Fig. 2 *'Reception of Nineveh Sculptures at the British Museum'*, published in *The Illustrated News*, 28 February 1852.

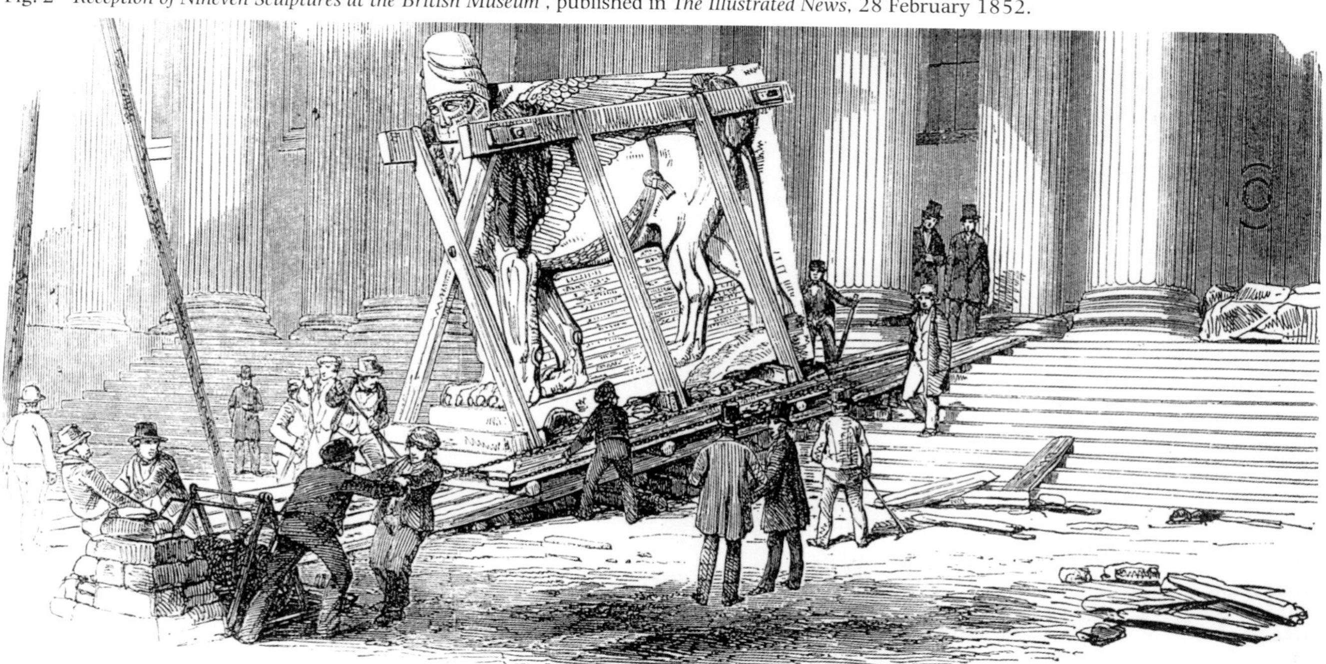

The Layard Bequest

For a note on Layard's bequest to the National Gallery (disputed by a nephew, reduced from 91 to 88 works as a result and not received until 1916), see Martin Davies, *National Gallery Catalogues: The Earlier Italian Schools* (1951), reprinted London 1986, p. 574, Appendix IV. See also the list on pp. 441–2.

Fig. 3 Ludwig Johann Passini (1832–1903), *Sir Austen Henry Layard in his Study at Ca' Capello, Venice*, 1891. Watercolour on paper, 60.3 × 45.1 cm. London, National Portrait Gallery.

NOTES

1. For most of his life he used his first Christian name, Henry, but later he preferred to be called Austen.

2. See Layard's 'Autobiography', ed. by the Hon. William A. Bruce and published as *Sir A. Henry Layard G.C.B., D.C.L., Autobiography and Letters...*, 2 vols, London 1903. Vol. I, p. 27 quotes Layard: 'Over the bed in which I slept was the fine altar-piece by Filippino Lippi, now in the National Gallery'; to which the editor adds the following note: 'The picture still bears the traces of a wound inflicted by the heel of Henry Layard's shoes, flung at his brother in a childish quarrel.' However, the Filippino Lippi altarpiece seems to have hung in the Rucellai Chapel of St Jerome in St Pancrazio, Florence, until it was sold by Cavaliere Giuseppe Rucellai to the National Gallery in 1857 (see Davies 1961, p. 286); and it shows no mark which might have been inflicted by Layard's shoe. Perhaps a copy of it hung in the Palazzo Rucellai.

3. Quoted by Waterfield 1963, p. 191.

4. Not all his finds entered the collection of the British Museum. He was allowed to keep some 'duplicates' for himself: thus two Assyrian bas-reliefs from the palace of Ashurnarsipal II were given to his benefactor and friend Sir John Guest, of Canford Manor, Dorset, later a school, where they were whitewashed. Rediscovered in 1993, they were sold at Christie's and are now in the Metropolitan Museum of Art.

5. Letter of 1849, quoted by Waterfield 1963, p. 191.

6. The full title is *Discoveries in the ruins of Nineveh and Babylon with travels in Armenia, Kurdistan and the Desert, Being the result of a Second Expedition undertaken for the Trustees of the British Museum.*

7. Waterfield 1963, p. 228.

8. Ed. W. Bruce; see note 2.

9. Lord Ellesmere to Charles Arbuthnot, 8 February 1849, see Waterfield 1963, p. 194.

10. As Liberal candidate for Aylesbury.

11. *Palmerston's Nightmare, Baiting the Nineveh Bull*, and *The Member for Nineveh digs out the British Bull*, three cartoons from *Punch*, 1855, are repr. Waterfield 1963, pp. 250, 267 and 268.

12. See A.H. Layard. 'Paper on Mosaic Decoration', read before the Royal Institute of British Architects, published in *The Builder*, 11 May 1862, p. 357.

13. See M.H. Port, *The Houses of Parliament*, London 1976, p. 180.

14. Henry Labouchere, in a long and abusive article in *Truth*, 14 October 1880, quoted by Waterfield 1963, p. 445.

15. Letter of 11 October 1860, published in ed. W. Bruce, *Autobiography* (see note 2), II, 1903, p. 228.

16. *Giovanni Santi and the Frescoes of Cagli*, 1859; *Domenico Ghirlandaio and his fresco of the death of St. Francis*, 1860; *The Brancacci Chapel and Masolino, Masaccio and Filippino Lippi*, *c.*1860; and see his article on Publications of the Arundel Society; Fresco-Painting, *Quarterly Review*, October 1858.

17. See *Quarterly Review*, 'The Manchester Art Treasures', July 1857; 'The National Gallery', April 1859; 'Architecture of all Countries', October 1859; 'German, Flemish and Dutch Art', April 1861; 'Italian Painters', July 1872; 'The National Gallery', October 1886; 'The National Portrait Gallery', April 1888.

18. See Robertson 1978, *passim*.

19. See Gordon Waterfield, 'Henry Layard: Nineteenth Century Aesthete', *Apollo*, March 1966, p. 166; necklace, earrings and ring repr. p. 167.

Appendix

The two paintings catalogued below do not properly belong to the British School but were included for convenience in Martin Davies's *British School Catalogue* of 1959. They will eventually be transferred to their appropriate Schools catalogues.

FILIPPINO LIPPI
NG 927 *An Angel Adoring*

LODEWIJCK VAN LUDICK
NG 1007 *A River between Rocky Cliffs, with a Waterfall on the left*

MARINUS VAN REYMERSWAELE
NG 944 *Two Tax Gatherers*

GABRIEL METSU
NG 970 *Two Men with a Sleeping Woman*

FOLLOWER OF DE MOMPER THE YOUNGER
NG 1017 *A Music Party before a Village*

AERT VAN DER NEER
NG 969 *A Frozen River by a Town at Evening*

FOLLOWER OF VAN OSTADE
NG 963 *An Inn by a Frozen River*

STYLE OF PATENIR
NG 945 *The Virgin and Child with a Cistercian (?) Nun*

CORNELIS VAN POELENBURGH
NG 955 *Women bathing in a Landscape*

ANTONIO DEL POLLAIUOLO
NG 928 *Apollo and Daphne*

AFTER RAPHAEL
NG 929 *The Madonna and Child*

STYLE OF ROSA
NG 811 *Tobias and the Angel*
NG 935 *A Coastal Scene*

ROSSO FIORENTINO
NG 932 *A Knight of Saint John*

PETER PAUL RUBENS
NG 948 *A Wagon fording a Stream*

JACOB VAN RUISDAEL
NG 986 *Two Watermills and an Open Sluice at Singraven*
NG 987 *A Torrent in a Mountainous Landscape*
NG 988 *A Road winding between Trees towards a Distant Cottage*
NG 989 *Three Watermills with Washerwomen*
NG 990 *A Landscape with a Ruined Castle and a Church*
NG 991 *A Landscape with a Ruined Building at the Foot of a Hill by a River*

IMITATOR OF RUISDAEL
NG 996 *A Castle on a Hill by a River*

CORNELIS VAN DER SCHALCKE
NG 974 *An Extensive River Landscape, with Two Sportsmen and their Greyhounds*

GODFRIED SCHALCKEN
NG 997 *An Old Woman scouring a Pot*
NG 998 *A Woman singing and a Man with a Cittern*
NG 999 *A Candlelight scene: A Man offering a Gold Chain and Coins to a Girl seated on a Bed*

JOHANNES SPRUYT
NG 1013 *Geese and Ducks*

ATTRIBUTED TO TENIERS THE YOUNGER
NG 949 *A Gipsy telling a Peasant his Fortune in a Hilly Landscape*

DAVID TENIERS THE YOUNGER
NG 950 *A View of a Village with Three Peasants talking in the Foreground*
NG 951 *Peasants playing Bowls outside a Village Inn*

AFTER TENIERS THE YOUNGER
NG 952 *A Country Festival near Antwerp*

IMITATOR OF TENIERS THE YOUNGER
NG 953 *Personification of Autumn(?)*

AFTER TITIAN
NG 933 *A Boy with a Bird*

ADRIAEN VAN DE VELDE
NG 982 *The Edge of a Wood, with a Sleeping Shepherd, Sheep and Goats*
NG 983 *A Bay Horse, a Cow, a Goat and Three Sheep near a Building*

WILLEM VAN DE VELDE
NG 978 *A Dutch Yacht surrounded by Many Small Vessels, saluting as Two Barges pull alongside*
NG 979 *A Dutch Ship, a Yacht and Smaller Vessels in a Breeze*
NG 980 *Boats pulling out to a Yacht in a Calm*
NG 981 *Three Ships in a Gale*

STUDIO OF WILLEM VAN DE VELDE
NG 977 *Small Dutch Vessels in a Breeze*

PIETER VERBEECK
NG 1009 *A White Horse standing by a Sleeping Man*

PAOLO VERONESE
NG 931 *Christ addressing a Kneeling Woman*

JACOB VAN WALSCAPPELLE
NG 1002 *Flowers in a Glass Vase*

JAN WIJNANTS
NG 971 *A Landscape with a High Dune and Peasants on a Road*
NG 972 *A Landscape with Two Dead Trees, and Two Sportsmen with Dogs on a Sandy Road*

PHILIPS WOUWERMANS
NG 973 *A Stream in the Dunes, with Two Bathers*
NG 975 *A Stag Hunt*

ATTRIBUTED TO WOUWERMANS
NG 976 *Cavalry attacking Infantry*

Sir Austen Henry Layard Gift, 1886

SPINELLO ARETINO
NG 1216.1–3 *Saint Michael and Other Angels/Decorative Border*

Bequest, 1916

JACOPO DE' BARBARI
NG 3088 *A Sparrowhawk*

ATTRIBUTED TO GENTILE BELLINI
NG 3099 *The Sultan Mehmet II*
NG 3100 *Doge Niccolò Marcello*

WORKSHOP OF GIOVANNI BELLINI
NG 3078 *The Virgin and Child*

STYLE OF BERGOGNONE
NG 3080 *Saint Paul*
NG 3081 *Saint Ambrose (?)*

FRANCESCO BISSOLO
NG 3083 *The Virgin and Child with Saints Michael and Veronica and Two Donors*

STYLE OF BONIFAZIO DI PITATI
NG 3109 *The Labours of the Months: January–June*
NG 3110 *The Labours of the Months: July–December*

AFTER BONIFAZIO DI PITATI
NG 3106 *Dives and Lazarus*

FRANCESCO BONSIGNORI
NG 3091 *The Virgin and Child with Four Saints*

PARIS BORDONE
NG 3122 *Christ baptising Saint John Martyr, Duke of Alexandria*

FOLLOWER OF BOTTICELLI
NG 3082 *The Virgin and Child*

BRAMANTINO
NG 3073 *The Adoration of the Kings*

GIOVANNI BUONCONSIGLIO
NG 3076 *Saint John the Baptist*

ANDREA BUSATI
NG 3084 *The Entombment*

VITTORE CARPACCIO
NG 3085 *Saint Ursula taking Leave of her Father (?)*

ATTRIBUTED TO CARPACCIO
NG 3098 *The Adoration of the Kings*

ROSALBA GIOVANNA CARRIERA
NG 3126 *Portrait of a Man*

AFTER CARRIERA
NG 3127 *Rosalba Carriera*

ATTRIBUTED TO CICOGNARA
NG 3069 *Mystic Figure of Christ*

AFTER CIMA
NG 3112 *The Virgin and Child with Saint Paul and Saint Francis*

ATTRIBUTED TO CIMA
NG 3113 *The Virgin and Child with Saint John the Evangelist (?) and Saint Nicholas*

LORENZO COSTA
NG 3103 *The Story of Moses (The Israelites gathering Manna)*
NG 3104 *The Story of Moses (The Dance of Miriam)*
NG 3105 *The Adoration of the Shepherds with Angels*

GERARD DAVID
NG 3067 *Christ Nailed to the Cross*

STYLE OF VAN DYCK
NG 3132 *Portrait of a Woman*

GAROFALO
NG 3102 *The Virgin and Child with Saints Dominic and Catherine of Siena*

ATTRIBUTED TO GAROFALO
NG 3118 *Saint Catherine of Alexandria*

GAUDENZIO FERRARI
NG 3068 *The Annunciation*

ATTRIBUTED TO GIROLAMO GENGA
NG 3119 *A Jesse-Tree*

GEROLAMO DA VICENZA
NG 3077 *The Dormition and Assumption of the Virgin*

GIAMPIETRINO
NG 3097 *Christ carrying his Cross*

FOLLOWER OF HUGO VAN DER GOES
NG 3066 *The Virgin and Child*

AFTER EL GRECO
NG 3131 *Saint Peter*

ITALIAN
NG 3117 *A Man and his Wife*
NG 3125 *The Holy Family*
NG 3130 *Portrait of an Old Man*

ITALIAN, FLORENTINE
NG 3120 *Head of a Male Saint*

ITALIAN, VENETIAN
NG 3086 *Augustus and the Sibyl*
NG 3108 *A Naval Battle*

JACOMETTO
NG 3121 *Portrait of a Man*

BERNARDINO LICINIO
NG 3075 *The Madonna and Child with Saint Joseph and a Female Martyr*

WORKSHOP OF LORENZETTI
NG 3071 *A Crowned Female Figure (Saint Elizabeth of Hungary?)*
NG 3072 *A Female Saint in Yellow*

ATTRIBUTED TO LORENZO MONACO
NG 3089 *Illuminated Letter B (Abraham and the Angels)*

WORKSHOP OF LUINI
NG 3090 *The Virgin and Child*

NICOLAES MAES
NG 2954 *Portrait of a Man in a Black Wig*

LODOVICO MAZZOLINO
NG 3114 *The Nativity*

AFTER VAN MIERIS THE ELDER
NG 2952 *An Old Fiddler*

ATTRIBUTED TO MONTAGNA
NG 1696 *The Virgin and Child*

BARTOLOMEO MONTAGNA
NG 3074 *Saint Zeno, Saint John the Baptist and a Female Martyr*

MORETTO DA BRESCIA
NG 3094 *The Madonna and Child with Saint Nicholas of Tolentino and Saint Anthony of Padua*
NG 3095 *Portrait of a Man at Prayer*
NG 3096 *Christ blessing Saint John the Baptist*

GIOVANNI BATTISTA MORONI
NG 3123 *Chastity*
NG 3124 *Leonardo Salvagno (?)*
NG 3128 *Portrait of a Man*
NG 3129 *Portrait of a Man*

NETHERLANDISH
NG 3116 *The Magdalen Weeping*

CASPAR NETSCHER
NG 2953 *Portrait of a Lady and a Girl*

ATTRIBUTED TO PALMA VECCHIO
NG 3079 *Saint George and a Female Saint*

WORKSHOP OF PATENIR
NG 3115 *Landscape with the Rest on the Flight into Egypt*

ANDREA PREVITALI
NG 3087 *Salvator Mundi*

ATTRIBUTED TO PREVITALI
NG 3111 *The Virgin and Child with Two Angels*

ATTRIBUTED TO RAFFAELLINO DEL GARBO
NG 3101 *Portrait of a Man*

ATTRIBUTED TO ROMANINO
NG 3093 *Pegasus and the Muses*

GIAN GIROLAMO SAVOLDO
NG 3092 *Saint Jerome*

LAMBERT SUSTRIS
NG 3107 *Solomon and the Queen of Sheba*

COSIMO TURA
NG 3070 *An Allegorical Figure*

and the following British pictures, transferred to the Tate Gallery 1921, and now bearing its inventory numbers:

BENJAMIN BLAKE
N 02946 *Still Life*

JAMES BURNET
N 02947 *View on the Thames*

JULIUS CAESAR IBBETSON
N 02948 *Sand Quarry at Alum Bay*

FREDERICK R. LEE
N 02949 *Lake in a Park*

PATRICK NASMYTH
N 02950 *Falls of the Tummell*
N 02951 *Landscape with a Ruin*

DAVID ROBERTS
N 02956 *A Cathedral Porch*

JAMES HARDING
N 02955 *Old Mills* (destroyed in the flood of 1928)

Technical Bibliography

COMPILED BY JO KIRBY

Eighteenth- and Nineteenth-century Literature on Painting Methods and Materials

A very large number of books partly or wholly concerned with the methods and materials of painting were published during the eighteenth and nineteenth centuries. They include dictionaries and compendiums of useful knowledge, books on branches of painting such as landscape or portraiture, and on individual techniques such as oil or watercolour painting. Many were written by authors who had some training in the arts or were professional painters; a few were written by colour makers. During the eighteenth century several series of handbooks were published by dealers in prints, who also often traded in artists' materials; this trend was developed in the following century by colour merchants, such as Rudolph Ackermann, George Blackman, George Rowney, and William Winsor and Henry C. Newton, who produced series of small manuals intended for students or the rapidly growing amateur market, similar to those published today. The techniques described are generally conventional, but in practice probably widely used.

Much of this literature is not original in its content. Many titles went through countless editions over many years, but frequently with little or no revision of the original text, which in some cases – John Smith's *The Art of Painting in Oyl* (2nd edn, London 1687) is an example – first appeared in the seventeenth century. Very frequently text was copied (usually unacknowledged) from well-known books, such as those by Thomas Bardwell or Robert Dossie. Thus it is necessary to bear in mind that the information presented, particularly in the anonymous or more pedestrian handbooks, may not be particularly up-to-date, even at the time of publication of the first edition. In some cases, however, extracts from texts of proven value were combined into a convenient, useful handbook; *A Practical Treatise on Painting in Oil Colours*, of 1795, is one example.

A selection of the most informative literature is given below. Out of date or derivative works have been omitted; literature on watercolour painting and other forms of painting not represented in the National Gallery collection have also been excluded. Some of the small nineteenth-century manuals written as aids for amateurs or students are instructive in their early editions, but very old-fashioned in editions reprinted late in the century. Those published by artists' colourmen often include a catalogue of artists' materials. A few books – Cawse and Ibbetson, for example – include printed or actual colour samples (sometimes sadly deteriorated). The authors of several of the later nineteenth-century books – Church, Muckley and Standage, for example – had educational connections with the Royal Academy of Arts or other institutions. More comprehensive bibliographies, together with discussions of the scope and content of this literature, will be found in the following books:

L. Carlyle, *The Artists' Assistant: Oil Painting Instruction Manuals and Handbooks in Britain, 1800–1900: With Reference to Selected Eighteenth-century Sources*, London (in press), forthcoming 1998.

R. D. Harley, *Artists' Pigments c.1600–1835: A Study in English Documentary Sources*, 2nd edn, London 1982.

The Artist's Repository and Drawing Magazine, 4 vols, London 1784–6; several later editions. The volume dedicated to materials later reprinted separately as *A Compendium of Colours*, cited below.

The Art of Landscape Painting in Oil Colours, 3rd edn, London 1850. Published by Winsor & Newton; includes catalogue. Many editions (the 11th (1856) is attributed to J. Edwards).

T. Bardwell, *The Practice of Painting and Perspective made easy, in which is contained the Art of Painting in Oil, with the Method of Colouring, etc.*, London 1756. Bardwell's book was one of the most influential and most plagiarised of the period: parts are found in the anonymous handbook, *The Art of Painting in Oil* (2nd edn London 1799, 12th edn, 1827), as well as in *A Compendium of Colours* and several of the other works cited below; see F. Schmid, 'The strange case of Thomas Bardwell', *Technical Studies in the Field of the Fine Arts*, IX, 1941, pp. 153–9. The examination of the materials he used in portraits dating from 1746–66 forms a particularly interesting comparative study: see M.K. Talley and K.M. Groen, 'Thomas Bardwell and his practice of painting: a comparative investigation between described and actual painting technique', *Studies in Conservation*, 20, 1975, pp. 44–108; R. White, 'An examination of Thomas Bardwell's portraits – the media', *Studies in Conservation*, 20, 1975, pp. 109–13.

J. Bouvier, *A Handbook for Oil Painting*, London 1885. Published by the London branch of the Paris colour merchants Lechertier, Barbe & Cie, including a list of French pigments supplied by the colourman G. Edouard.

P.-L. Bouvier, *The Manual of Oil Painting for Young Artists and Amateurs, condensed from the Works of Bouvier, with a Glossary of Terms of Art*, 2nd edn, London 1849 (Bogue's 'Manuals of utility' series). There was no complete English translation of Bouvier's influential book; this is abridged from Laughton Osborn's *Handbook of Young Artists and Amateurs in Oil Painting*, New York 1845 (and several later editions).

J. Bulkley, *A Treatise on Landscape Painting in Oil, in a series of Easy Examples*, London 1821. A small handbook published by the colour merchant George Blackman.

J. Cawse, *Introduction to the Art of Painting in Oil Colours ... with Plates explanatory of the different Pallets used in the Progress of Painting a Portrait or Landscape*, London 1822, 2nd edn 1829; rewritten as *The Art of Painting Portraits, Landscapes, Animals, Draperies, Satins &c in Oil Colours*, incorporating some text from Bardwell 1840. Published by the colourman Rudolph Ackermann.

A.H. Church, *The Chemistry of Paints and Painting*, London 1890, 2nd edn 1892, 3rd edn 1901. Church was Professor of Chemistry at the Royal Academy.

A. Clint, *A Guide to Oil Painting, Part II. Landscape from Nature*, London 1855. Published by George Rowney, with a catalogue of materials at the back. For Part I see Templeton, cited below.

J. Collier, *A Manual of Oil Painting*, London 1886, 2nd edn 1887.

A Compendium of Colours and other Materials used in the Arts dependent on Design, London, n.d. Vol. II of *The Artist's Repository*, 7th edn 1797.

R. Dossie, *The Handmaid to the Arts*, 2 vols, London 1758, 2nd edn 1764. Invaluable for its discussion of materials.

J. Elsum, *The Art of Painting after the Italian Manner*, London 1703. Late seventeenth century in its style, but some useful comments on the behaviour of pigments.

G. Field, *Chromatography: or, a Treatise on Colours and Pigments*, London 1835, 2nd edn 1841. Later editions produced by T.W. Salter, London 1869, and J. Scott Taylor, London 1885 (Winsor & Newton). An abridged version, *Rudiments of the Painter's Art*, London 1850, (reissued 1858) was published in the Weale's Rudimentary Series (several editions). One of the most influential books on materials. For Field, see J. Gage, *George Field and his Circle*, exh. cat., Fitzwilliam Museum, Cambridge 1989; for his manuscripts see R.D. Harley, 'Field's manuscripts: early nineteenth-century colour samples and fading tests', *Studies in Conservation*, 24, 1979, pp. 75–84.

T.H. Fielding, *On Painting in Oil and Water Colours for Landscape and Portraits*, London 1839. The 4th edn, *On the Theory and Practice of Painting in Oil and Water Colours*, 1846, is a substantial revision of this useful book, published by Ackermann. Several later editions.

G.H. Hurst, *Painters' Colours, Oils and Varnishes*, London 1892 (several later editions). The manufacture of painting materials in general at the end of the nineteenth century.

J.C. Ibbetson, *An Accidence or Gamut of Painting in Oil and Water Colours*, Part 1 [no more published], London 1803; 2nd edn, with a memoir of the author, 1828. Ibbetson claimed to be the inventor of 'Gumtion', a mastic-based painting medium.

W. Linton, *Ancient and Modern Colours, from the earliest Periods to the present Time*, London 1852. An account of early (Greek and Roman) pigments, followed by a discussion of the properties of pigments available in the mid-nineteenth century.

C. de Massoul, *A Treatise on the Art of Painting and the Composition of Colours*, London 1797. The author was a French colour maker.

J.-F.-L. Mérimée, *The Art of Painting in Oil, and in Fresco*, trans. with additional material by W.B. Sarsfield Taylor, London 1839 (originally published Paris 1830). French edition extremely influential.

W.J. Muckley, *A Handbook for Painters and Art Students on the Character and Use of Colours, also, Short Remarks on the Practice of Painting in Oil and Watercolours*, London 1880 (and later editions). Muckley also the author of several small manuals published by Winsor & Newton.

T. Page, *The Art of Painting in its Rudiments, Progress and Perfection; Delivered exactly as it is put in Practice, so that the Ingenious may easily understand its Nature, to perform it*, Norwich 1720. An interesting reflection of painting practice outside London.

A Practical Treatise on Painting in Oil Colours, London 1795. Includes material copied from Bardwell.

H.C. Standage, *The Artists' Manual of Pigments, Showing their Composition, Conditions of Permanency and Non-permanency*, London 1887, 3rd edn 1896. Lists the palettes of several later nineteenth-century Royal Academicians.

The Use and Abuse of Colours and Mediums in Oil Painting, 2nd edn, London 1892. Published by the colour merchants Reeves and Sons.

J. Scott Taylor, *Modes of Painting Described and Classified*, London 1890. The author was the Scientific Director of Winsor & Newton.

J.S. Templeton, *The Guide to Oil Painting*, 6th edn, London 1846. Author's preface dated 1845. Aimed at the amateur market and published by Rowney. Later editions entitled *A Guide to Oil Painting, Part I, Elementary*. Part II, on landscape painting, originally appeared under the name of A. Clint, cited above.

W. Williams, *An Essay on the Mechanic of Oil Colours*, Bath 1787. Includes incomplete recipes for varnishes and other products; the reader could obtain the missing information from the author.

SCIENTIFIC EXAMINATION OF MATERIALS

Artists' Pigments: A Handbook of their History and Characteristics: Vol. 1, edited by R.L. Feller, Washington and Cambridge 1986; Vol. 2, edited by A. Roy, Washington and Oxford 1993; Vol. 3, edited by E.W. FitzHugh, Washington and Oxford 1997. Other volumes in the series forthcoming.

J.S. Mills and R. White, *The Organic Chemistry of Museum Objects*, 2nd edn, London 1994. For the chemistry of oils, resins, waxes and other materials associated with the paint medium.

R. White, 'Brown and Black Organic Glazes, Pigments and Paints', *National Gallery Technical Bulletin*, 10, 1986, pp. 58–71.

Some materials widely used in eighteenth- and nineteenth-century paintings were adulterated, or were liable to show some alteration in their appearance over time, or have been responsible for some defect in the paint. These are discussed in the references above, and see also:

L. Carlyle and A. Southall, 'No Short Mechanic Road to Fame: The Implications of Certain Artists' Materials for the Durability of British Painting: 1770–1840', in R. Hamlyn, *Robert Vernon's Gift: British Art for the Nation 1847*, exh. cat., Tate Gallery, London 1993, pp. 21–6.

J. Kirby, 'Fading and Colour Change of Prussian Blue: Occurrences and Early Reports', *National Gallery Technical Bulletin*, 14, 1993, pp. 62–71.

D. Saunders and J. Kirby, 'Light-induced Colour Changes in Red and Yellow Lake Pigments', *National Gallery Technical Bulletin*, 15, 1994, pp. 79–97.

J.H. Townsend, L. Carlyle, N. Khandekar and S. Woodcock, 'Later nineteenth-century pigments: Evidence for additions and substitutions', *The Conservator*, 19, 1995, pp. 65–78.

TECHNICAL EXAMINATION OF WORKS BY INDIVIDUAL ARTISTS

Accounts of conservation and restoration treatments have been included only where there is some explanation of the artist's painting technique.

JOHN CONSTABLE

S. Cove, 'Constable's Oil Painting Materials and Techniques', in L. Parris and I. Fleming-Williams, *Constable*, exh. cat., Tate Gallery, London 1991, pp. 493–529.

THOMAS GAINSBOROUGH

D. Bomford, A. Roy and D. Saunders, 'Gainsborough's "Dr Ralph Schomberg"', *National Gallery Technical Bulletin*, 12, 1988, pp. 44–57.

H. Glanville, 'Gainsborough as Artist and Artisan' in *Paintings and their Context II: A Nest of Nightingales: Thomas Gainsborough, 'The Linley Sisters'*, exh. cat., Dulwich Picture Gallery, London 1988, pp. 15–29.

D.C. Goist, 'Technical Notes on Gainsborough's *Ralph Bell*', *North Carolina Museum of Art Bulletin*, XV, 1991, pp. 53–6. Observations made during conservation treatment; little scientific examination.

R. Jones, 'Gainsborough's Materials and Methods', in S. Foister, R. Jones and O. Meslay, *Young Gainsborough*, exh. cat., National Gallery, London 1997, pp. 19–26.

V. Pemberton-Pigott, 'The development of the portrait of Countess Howe', in *The Earl and Countess of Howe by Gainsborough: A Bicentenary Exhibition*, ed. A. French, exh. cat., Iveagh Bequest, Kenwood, London 1988, pp. 37–43.

WILLIAM HOGARTH

D. Bomford and A. Roy, 'Hogarth's "Marriage à la Mode"', *National Gallery Technical Bulletin*, 6, 1982, pp. 44–67.

THOMAS LAWRENCE

M. Levey, *A Royal Subject: Portraits of Queen Charlotte*, exh. cat., National Gallery, London 1977, pp. 16, 19. X-radiograph and infra-red photograph only.

JOSHUA REYNOLDS

B.A. Buckley, 'Sir Joshua Reynolds, *The Ladies Amabel and Mary Jemima Yorke*', *Bulletin of the Cleveland Museum of Art*, 73, 9, 1986, pp. 350–71.

M.K. Talley, '"All Good Pictures Crack": Sir Joshua Reynolds's practice and studio', in *Reynolds*, ed. N. Penny, exh. cat., Paris and London 1985/6, pp. 55–70.

GEORGE STUBBS

I. McClure and R. Featherstone, 'The Cleaning of Stubbs's "Hambletonian"', in J. Egerton, *George Stubbs 1724–1806*, exh. cat., Tate Gallery, London 1984, pp. 22–3.

J. Mills and R. White, 'The Mediums used by George Stubbs: Some Further Studies', *National Gallery Technical Bulletin*, 9, 1985, pp. 60–4.

R. Shepherd, 'Stubbs: A Conservator's View', in J. Egerton, *George Stubbs 1724–1806*, exh. cat., Tate Gallery, London 1984, pp. 20–1.

R. White, A. Roy, J. Mills and J. Plesters, 'Research Note. George Stubbs's "Lady and Gentleman in a Carriage": A Preliminary Note on the Technique', *National Gallery Technical Bulletin*, 4, 1980, p. 64.

R. Woudhuysen-Keller, 'George Stubbs, *Gimcrack with John Pratt up on Newmarket Heath*', *The Bulletin of the Hamilton Kerr Institute*, 1, 1988, pp. 126–7. Condition report and observations made during conservation treatment; no technical analysis.

JOSEPH MALLORD WILLIAM TURNER

N.W. Hanson, 'Some painting materials of J.M.W. Turner', *Studies in Conservation*, 1, 1954, pp. 1962–73.

J.H. Townsend, 'Picture Note 1 [on *Two Women with a Letter*]' and 'Picture Note 2 [on *Judith with the Head of Holofernes? ("The Procuress"?)*]', Turner Studies, 9,2, 1989, pp. 11–13, 34–5. (Both these paintings are in the Tate Gallery, London.)

'The Changing Appearance of Turner's Paintings', *Turner Studies*, 10, 2, 1990, pp. 12–24. On changes caused by the intrinsic properties and defects in the artist's materials and methods of painting.

Turner's Painting Techniques, exh. cat., Tate Gallery, London 1993. Summarises the information published in far greater detail in the author's papers in *Studies in Conservation*, cited below, but here with the benefit of coloured illustrations.

'The materials of J.M.W. Turner: pigments', *Studies in Conservation*, 38, 4, 1993, pp. 231–54.

'The materials and techniques of J.M.W. Turner: primings and supports', *Studies in Conservation*, 39, 3, 1994, pp. 145–53.

Turner's Painting Techniques in Context, 1995, ed. J.H. Townsend., London 1995. Proceedings of a one-day symposium held in June 1993.

M. Wyld and A. Roy, 'The Making of "The Fighting Temeraire"', in J. Egerton, *Making and Meaning: Turner, The Fighting Temeraire*, exh. cat., National Gallery, London 1995, pp. 121–3.

JOSEPH WRIGHT OF DERBY

R. Jones, 'Wright of Derby's Techniques of Painting', in J. Egerton, *Wright of Derby*, exh. cat., London, Paris and New York 1990, pp. 263–71. For further details see R. Jones, 'Notes for conservators on Wright of Derby's technique and studio practice', *The Conservator*, 15, 1991, pp. 13–21.

M. Wyld and D. Thomas, 'Wright of Derby's "Mr and Mrs Coltman": An Unlined English Painting', *National Gallery Technical Bulletin*, 10, 1986, pp. 28–32. Condition report and account of conservation treatment.

JOHANN ZOFFANY

A. Massing, 'Johann Zoffany, Group Portrait of the Woodley Family', *The Bulletin of the Hamilton Kerr Institute*, 1, 1988, pp. 123–4. Technical examination limited to the ground; condition report; account of restoration.

Chronological Index of Acquisitions

1824	**111**	Reynolds, purchased
	113	Hogarth, purchased
	114	Hogarth, purchased
	115	Hogarth, purchased
	116	Hogarth, purchased
	117	Hogarth, purchased
	118	Hogarth, purchased
1827	**109**	Gainsborough, presented
1830	**80**	Gainsborough, presented
1831	**124**	Jackson, bequeathed
1836	**129**	Lawrence, presented
1837	**130**	Constable, presented
1849	**677**	Shee, bequeathed (entered the NG in 1863)
1856	**472**	Turner, bequeathed
	479	Turner Bequest
	498	Turner Bequest
	508	Turner, bequeathed
	521	Turner, bequeathed
	524	Turner, bequeathed
	538	Turner, bequeathed
	1984	Turner, bequeathed
	1991	Turner, bequeathed
1862	**683**	Gainsborough, purchased
	684	Gainsborough, purchased
1863	**681**	Reynolds, purchased
	725	Wright, presented
1875	**925**	Gainsborough, purchased
1878	**2239**	Sievier, presented
1884	**1162**	Hogarth, purchased
1886	**1207**	Constable, presented
1888	**1259**	Reynolds, purchased
	1272	Constable, bequeathed
1900	**1811**	Gainsborough, bequeathed
1906	**2077**	Reynolds, bequeathed
1910	**2651**	Constable, bequeathed
	2652	Constable, bequeathed
1911	**2786**	Chantrey, presented
1915	**3044**	Sargent, presented
1920	**3529**	Stubbs, bequeathed
1923	**3812**	Gainsborough, purchased
1926	**4142**	Linnell, purchased
1927	**4257**	Lawrence, purchased
1934	**4756**	Hogarth, presented
1938	**4931**	Zoffany, purchased
1943	**5449**	Wood, presented
1950	**6022**	Jackson, presented
1951	**5984**	Gainsborough, bequeathed
	5985	Reynolds, bequeathed
1953	**6196**	Wilson, purchased
	6197	Wilson, purchased
1954	**6209**	Gainsborough, purchased
1956	**4998**	Inness, transferred from the Tate Gallery (see Appendix)
1958	**6280**	Johnson, bequeathed (see Appendix)
1960	**6301**	Gainsborough, purchased
1962	**6333**	Hoppner, bequeathed
1963	**6370**	Lawrence, bequeathed
1975	**6429**	Stubbs, purchased
1983	**6482**	Boxall, presented
1984	**6496**	Wright, purchased
1987	**6510**	Constable, acquired (through the Acceptance-in-lieu procedure)
1993	**6544**	Jones, purchased
1994	**6547**	Gainsborough, acquired (through the Acceptance-in-lieu procedure)
1997	**6569**	Stubbs, purchased

Index by Inventory Number

Photographic Credits

All National Gallery works have been photographed by the Gallery's own Photographic Department.

ABERDEEN, City of Aberdeen Art Gallery and Museums Collections: p. 318 Fig. 1

ARCHANGEL'SKOE, Archangel'skoe Museum, Russia: p. 342 Fig. 10

BISHOPSBOURNE, Reproduced by permission of the Trustees of the Rt. Hon. Olive, Countess Fitzwilliam's Chattels Settlement and Lady Juliet Tadgell: p. 243 Fig. 1; p. 244 Fig. 2; p. 245 Fig. 3

BEDFORD, The Trustees, The Cecil Higgins Art Gallery, Bedford, England: p. 311 Fig. 4

BELFAST, photograph © Ulster Museum Belfast, photograph reproduced with the kind permission of the Trustees of the Ulster Museum Belfast: p. 105 Fig. 1

BIRMINGHAM Museums and Art Gallery: p. 52 Fig. 2; p. 328 Fig. 1

BURY Art Gallery and Museum: p. 292 Fig. 1

CAMBRIDGE, Reproduction by permission of the Syndics of the Fitzwilliam Museum, Cambridge: p. 38 Fig. 1

CARDIFF, The National Museum of Wales: p. 188 Fig. 1

CHICAGO, photograph © 1997, The Art Institute of Chicago. All Rights Reserved: p. 175 Fig. 19

CLEVELAND, © The Cleveland Museum of Art, 1997, John L. Severance Fund, 1976.6: p. 116 Fig. 1

DERBY Museums and Art Gallery: p. 337 Fig. 6

EDINBURGH, National Gallery of Scotland: p. 118 Fig. 3; p. 214 Fig. 5

FLORENCE, Museo Stefano Bardini: p. 212 Fig. 1

FLORENCE, Uffizi: p. 165 Fig. 12; p. 209 Fig. 2

FORT WORTH, Kimbell Art Museum, Fort Worth, Texas: p. 380 Fig. 3

HAMBURG, Hamburger Kunsthalle, Co Elke Walford, Hamburg: p. 212. Fig. 2

INDIANAPOLIS, The Clowes Fund Collection, photograph © 1997 Indianapolis Museum of Art: p. 52 Fig. 1

IPSWICH Borough Council Museums and Galleries, Acquired with the assistance of the National Art Collections Fund, the Museums and Galleries Commission (via the Victoria and Albert Museum Grant-in-Aid Fund), Pilgrim Trust and the National Heritage Memorial Fund: p. 76 Fig. 3

KNUTSFORD, University of Manchester (Tabley House Collection): p. 269 Fig. 2

LONDON, Copyright © The British Museum, Reproduced by Courtesy of The Trustees of The British Museum: p. 138 Fig. 2; p. 139 Fig. 4; p. 142 Fig. 8; p. 191 Fig. 3; p. 204 Fig. 2; p. 209 Fig. 3; p. 224 Fig. 6; p. 225 Fig. 7; p. 299 Fig. 4; p. 394 Fig. 2; p. 408 Fig. 1, p. 412 Fig. 1

LONDON, Christie's Images: p. 130 Fig. 1; p. 137 Fig. 1; p. 232 Fig. 3

LONDON, The Courtauld Gallery: p. 69 Fig. 4; p. 298 Fig. 2

LONDON, Courtauld Institute Witt Library (photograph only): p. 408 Fig. 1

LONDON, The Garrick Club, (photograph: ET Archive): p. 117 Fig. 2

LONDON, Institute of Directors, (photograph: The Bridgeman Art Library): p. 310 Fig. 3

LONDON, National Gallery Archives: p. 48 Fig. 5; p. 60 Fig. 3; p. 319 Fig. 3; p. 363 Fig. 3; p. 393 Fig. 1

LONDON, National Maritime Museum: p. 106 Fig. 3; p. 203 Fig. 1; p. 230 Fig. 1; p. 309 Fig. 2

LONDON, by courtesy of The National Portrait Gallery: p. 220 Fig. 1; p. 236 Fig. 1; p. 238 Fig. 3; p. 368 Fig. 1; p. 378 Fig. 1; p. 402 Fig. 1; p. 409 Fig. 3; p. 426 Fig. 1; p. 430 Fig. 3

LONDON, from the archives of the Noortman Gallery, London and Maastricht: p. 437 Fig. 1

LONDON, Royal Academy of Arts: p. 69 Fig. 3; p. 223 Fig. 4; p. 422 Fig. 1; p. 423 Fig. 2

LONDON, © Science Museum/Science & Society Picture Library: p. 319 Fig. 2

LONDON, photographs courtesy of Sotheby's: p. 90 Fig. 1; p. 299 Fig. 3

LONDON, © Tate Gallery: p. 53 Fig. 3; p. 112 Fig. 3; p. 237 Fig. 2; p. 246 Fig. 4; p. 262 Fig. 1; p. 263 Fig. 2; p. 268 Fig. 1; p. 276 Fig. 3; p. 284 Fig. 1; p. 285 Fig. 3; p. 295 Fig. 1; p. 298 Fig. 1; p. 300 Fig. 5; p. 379 Fig. 2; p. 408 Fig. 2

LONDON, V & A Picture Library: p. 28 Fig. 1; p. 44 Fig. 1; p. 45 Fig. 3; p. 46 Fig. 4; p. 61 Fig. 2; p. 74 Fig. 1; p. 94 Fig. 1; p. 308 Fig. 1

MAINE, Colby College Art Museum: p. 185 Fig. 3

NEW HAVEN, Yale Center for British Art, Paul Mellon Collection & Fund: p. 33 Fig. 2; p. 45 Fig. 2; p. 67 Fig. 2; p. 83 Fig. 3; p. 259 Fig. 2; p. 329 Fig. 2; p. 334 Fig. 2; p. 353 Fig. 2

NEW YORK, Brooklyn Museum of Art, 13.75 Special Subscription Funds: p. 437 Fig. 2

NEW YORK, Pierpont Morgan Library, III, 63B: p. 123 Fig. 1

NORTHAMPTON, Smith College Museum of Art, Northampton, Massachusetts, Gift of the children of Mrs. Thomas W. Lamont (Florence Corliss, class of 1893), 1953: p. 131 Fig. 2

OXFORD, Ashmolean Museum: p. 95 Fig. 2; p. 160 Fig. 7; p. 189 Fig. 2; p. 212 Fig. 3; p. 215 Fig. 6; p. 336 Fig. 5 (photograph only); p. 380 Fig. 3 (photograph only)

PARIS, Musée des Arts décoratifs, photograph: Laurent-Sully Jaulmes, All Rights Reserved: p. 161 Fig. 9

PARIS, © Photo RMN: p. 29 Fig. 2; p. 222 Fig. 3; p. 360 Fig. 1

PITTSBURGH, © The Collection at Clayton, Pittsburgh, Pennsylvania: p. 373 Fig. 1

RICHMOND, photograph: Katherine Wetzel, ©1997 Virginia Museum of Fine Arts: p. 100 Fig. 2

ST PETERSBURG, The Hermitage Museum: p. 91 Fig. 3

SAN MARINO, Courtesy of the Huntington Library, Art Collections, and Botanical Gardens, San Marino, California: p. 106 Fig. 2

SPANISH TOWN, Jamaica, The Jamaica Archives, Inventory Volume 1B/11/3/19 f. 80: p. 352 Fig. 1

SUDBURY, Gainsborough's House, Sudbury, Suffolk: p. 77 Fig. 4; p. 82 Fig. 1; p. 90 Fig. 2; p. 100 Fig. 1; p. 110 Fig. 1

TORONTO, Art Gallery of Ontario, Gift of Reuben Wells Leonard Estate, 1936: p. 55 Fig. 4

TYNE & WEAR, Shipley Art Gallery, Gateshead (Tyne and Wear Museums): p. 224 Fig. 5

WASHINGTON DC, © 1997 Board of Trustees, National Gallery of Art, Washington: p. 250 Fig. 1; © 1996 Board of Trustees, National Gallery of Art, Washington: p. 334 Fig. 1

WINDSOR, The Royal Collection © Her Majesty The Queen: p. 181 Fig. 20; p. 251 Fig. 2

WORCESTER Art Museum, Worcester, Massachusetts, Museum Purchase: p. 96 Fig. 3

OPPOSITE: John Constable, *The Hay Wain* (detail)

PAGE 438: Richard Wilson, *The Valley of the Dee, with Chester in the Distance* (detail)

General Index